S0-AXM-731

LIBRARY MEDIA CENTER
DARTMOUTH HIGH SCHOOL

Observer's Directory of
Military Aircraft

William Green

—

Gordon Swanborough

Arco Publishing, Inc.
New York

Published by Arco Publishing, Inc.
215 Park Avenue South, New York, N.Y. 10003

© William Green and Gordon Swanborough, 1982

Library of Congress Catalog Card Number: 82–71835
ISBN 0–668–05649–5

Printed in Great Britain

CONTENTS

	Pages
Fighter/attack	7– 61
Bomber/strike	62– 72
Maritime reconnaissance/ASW	73– 87
Reconnaissance/FAC	88– 95
AEW/Special electronics	96–103
Transport	104–147
Tanker and tanker/transport	148–152
Light transport/utility	153–174
Trainer/light strike	175/194
Trainer	195–219
Prototype/Experimental	220–224
Helicopters	225–251
Index	252–256

INTRODUCTION

This *Military Aircraft Directory* is, in effect, a completely revised and updated edition of the volume published in 1974 under the title of *The Observer's Basic Military Aircraft Directory*. Not only has the content been completely brought up to date, however, but the format has been enlarged so that more information and more illustrations can be included, and a greater number of aircraft types be represented.

As before, the primary purpose of this edition is to provide a comprehensive guide to the characteristics of the aircraft in service with air forces and naval air arms throughout the world. This is done by means of three-view silhouette drawings, selected photographs and concentrated data presented in a consistent form. It is indicative of the continuing rapid pace of military aircraft development and production, that no fewer than 301 types are described in these pages, compared with 229 in the previous edition. Even this increase is not sufficient, however, to cover *every* type that is still to be found operating in military service; a few of the more elderly types that fly in small numbers have had to be excluded, as have several types that are primarily for civil or commercial use but some examples of which fly in military guise for VIP transport or communications duty.

Every effort has been made, within the limits set by the size of the book, to include all the newest types of military aircraft that have taken to the air up to the first quarter of 1982, including a few prototypes and experimental designs that have an uncertain future, and those types on which information is available that are expected to fly during the currency of this volume. At the other end of the spectrum, care has been taken to exclude those types known to be on the point of passing out of military service. Such is the nature of the aircraft business and defence affairs, however, that inevitably some of the aircraft described will no longer be in service within a few months of this book being published, while details of others, unknown at the time of going to press, will have emerged. The great majority of the types described are destined to serve for most of the present decade or beyond, giving this volume a long reference value.

As in the previous edition, the aircraft descriptions are grouped under a number of categories according to primary function. This serves to bring into close juxtaposition aircraft of generally similar characteristics and purpose, thus making direct comparison a simple matter. Readers should remember, however, that many of today's combat aircraft are either truly multi-rôle, or can be easily modified to suit any one of several rôles: one air force's air superiority fighter may be another's close support aircraft, while a transport for one service may serve elsewhere as an air-refuelling tanker, a maritime reconnaissance aircraft or for airborne early warning. The multiplicity of rôles fulfilled by some types has also made it necessary to include, in certain cases, entries for different variants in more than one functional group; in other cases, it has been possible to present data and illustrations for two or more variants within a single entry. In general, however, dimensions, weights and performance data are given for the principal service variant, while the "Status" paragraph summarises the total production history, including quantities built of all variants. Helicopters have been grouped in a single section at the end of the book, without differentiation according to rôle, since it is the nature of rotary-winged aircraft that they tend to serve in a multiplicity of rôles.

Further facilitating the use of this volume for reference purposes is a comprehensive index, cross-referencing the aircraft under all their various names and designations. All silhouettes used in this edition are the work of Dennis I Punnett and are the copyright of Pilot Press Ltd. Photographs have been selected from many sources, and the authors acknowledge the assistance given by the public relations staffs of many aircraft manufacturers and government agencies. The names of private individuals whose own copyright photographs have also been used, are listed separately on page 251.

(Top) An Aeritalia G.91Y of the 32nd Stormo of the Aeronautica Militare Italiana; (immediately above) a G.91R as serving with the Esquadra de Ataque 301 of the Força Aérea Portuguesa; (below) a G.91T advanced trainer. (Silhouette) Aeritalia G.91Y and extra side view of G.91R.

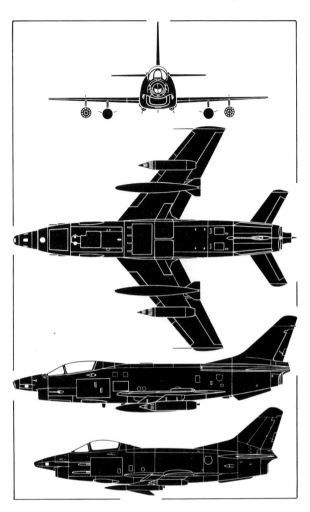

Country of Origin: Italy.

Type: Light fighter-bomber, reconnaissance aircraft and trainer.

Power Plant: (G.91R, T) One 5,000 lb st (2 268 kgp) Rolls-Royce Bristol Orpheus 803 or (G.91Y) two 2,725 lb st (1 236 kgp) dry and 4,080 lb st (1 850 kgp) with reheat General Electric J85-GE-13A turbojets.

Performance: (G.91R) Max speed, 668 mph (1 075 km/h) at sea level and 675 mph (1 086 km/h) at 5,000 ft (1 524 m); initial rate of climb, 6,000 ft/min (30·5 m/sec); service ceiling 43,000 ft (13 100 m); combat radius, 196 mls (315 km): ferry range, 1,150 mls (1 850 km).

Performance: (G.91Y) Max speed, 690 mph (1 110 km/h) at sea level and 670 mph (1 078 km/h) at 32,810 ft (10 000 m); initial rate of climb, 17,000 ft/min (86·36 m/sec); service ceiling, 41,000 ft (12 500 m); radius (LO-LO-LO with 2,910 lb (1 320 kg) load), 240 mls (385 km); ferry range, 2,110 mls (3 400 km).

Weights: (G.91R) Empty 6,835 lb (3 100 kg); normal take-off 11,995 lb (7 800 kg); max overload, 19,180 lb (8 700 kg).

Dimensions: Span (G.91R, T) 28 ft 1 in (8,56 m), (G.91Y) 29 ft 6½ in (9,01 m); length, (G.91R) 33 ft 9¼ in (10·30 m), (G.91T,Y) 38 ft 3½ in (1167 m); height (G.91R) 13 ft 1¼ in (4,00 m), (G.91T) 13 ft 11¼ in (4·25 m), (G.91Y) 14 ft 6¼ in (4·43 m); wing area (G.91R,T) 176·7 sq ft (16·4 m²), (G.91Y) 195·15 sq ft (18·13 m²).

Accommodation: Pilot only or (G.91T) two in tandem.

Armament: (G.91R/1) Four or (G.91T) two 0·50-in (12·7-mm) machine guns or (G.91R/3 and Y) two 30-mm DEFA cannon plus four underwing store stations for max of (G.91R) 2,000 lb (907 kg) or (G.91Y) 4,000 lb (1 814 kg) ordnance.

Status: Prototype first flown 9 August 1956; first pre-production flown 20 February 1958; first G.91R.3 (German assembly) flown 20 July 1965; first G.91T flown 31 May 1960; first G.91Y flown 27 December 1966. Production totals: prototypes, 3; G.91 pre-production, 27; G.91R/1, 98; G.91R/3 50 by Fiat and 282 by Dornier; G.91R/4, 50; G.91T/1, 76; G.91T/3, 66; G.91Y prototypes, 2; G.91Y pre-production, 20; G.91Y, 45, completed 1976.

Notes: The G.91 was originally designed for standardised NATO use as a strike fighter but was adopted only by Italy (single-seat G.91R/1, 1A and 1B with cameras in nose) and Germany (single-seat G.91R/3 and 4). Both countries used the two-seat G.91T, and the G.91Y was developed specially for Italy, which operates two *Stormi* (Wings) of this variant. From the *Luftwaffe*, the Portuguese Air Force acquired 40 G.91R/4s in 1966, and 23 R/3s plus six T/3s in 1976, these being still in service in 1982. The *Luftwaffe* retired its last remaining G.91s in 1982.

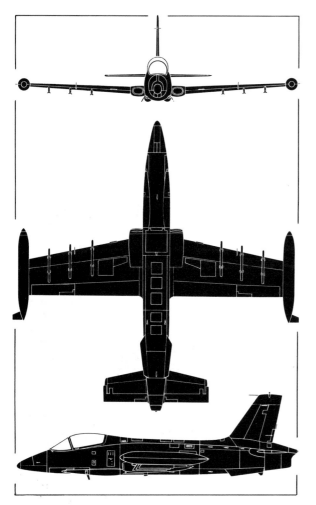

(Above) One of the South African Air Force's MB-326KC Impala 2s as used by Nos 4 and 8 Squadrons; (immediately below) the prototype MB-339K Veltro 2 in the air and (bottom) armed with six free-fall bombs. (Silhouette) Aermacchi MB-339K Veltro 2.

Country of Origin: Italy.

Type: Light strike aircraft.

Power Plant: One (326K) 4,000 lb st (1 815 kgp) Fiat-built Rolls-Royce Viper 632-42 or (Veltro) 4,320 lb st (1 960 kgp) Viper 632-43 turbojet.

Performance: (326K at max weight) Max speed (clean) 553 mph (890 km/h) at 5,000 ft (1 525 m) and 426 mph (686 km/h) at 30,000 ft (9 150 m); initial rate of climb, 6,500 ft/min (33,0 m/sec); time to 35,000 ft (10 670 m), 23 min 0 sec; combat radius with 2,822 lb (1 280 kg) weapons load, 167 mls (268 km) and with 4,000 lb (1 814 kg) weapon load, 81 mls (130 km); ferry range, 1,323 mls (2 130 km).

Performance: (Veltro, combat configuration) Max speed, 553 mph (890 km/h) at sea level; initial rate of climb, 7,500 ft/min (38 m/sec) service ceiling, 44,500 ft (13 565 m); time to 30,000 ft (9 145 m) from brakes release, 9·15 min; combat radius with 2,000-lb (908-kg) weapon load, LO-LO-LO, 234 mls (376 km) and HI-LO-HI, 403 mls (648 km).

Weights: (326K) Empty equipped, 6,885 lb (3 123 kg); take-off weights, clean, 10,240 lb (4 645 kg), patrol/visual reconnaissance, 11,130 lb (5 048 kg) and photo reconnaissance, 11,270 lb (5 111 kg); max permitted take-off weight, 13,000 lb (5 897 kg).

Weights: (Veltro) Operational empty, 6,997 lb (3 174 kg); loaded (clean), 10,974 lb (4 978 kg); max take-off, 13,558 lb (6 150 kg).

Dimensions: Span, over tip tanks, (326K), 35 ft 7 in (10,85 m), (Veltro), 36 ft 2⅜ in (11,05 m); length (326K) 35 ft 0¼ in (10,67 m), (Veltro) 36 ft 0 in (10,97 m); height (326K), 12 ft 2 in (3,72 m), (Veltro), 12 ft 9½ in (3,90 m); wing area 207,75 sq ft (19,30 m²).

Accommodation: Pilot only.

Armament: Fixed armament of two 30-mm DEFA cannon in lower front fuselage; six wing hardpoints, stressed to carry 750 lb (340 kg) each on outer positions and 1,000 lb (454 kg) each on mid and inboard positions.

Status: Prototype MB-326K flown 22 August 1970 with Viper 540; second prototype flown 1971 with Viper 632; prototype Veltro 2 flown 30 May 1980. Production/sales include (MB-326K): Dubai Defense Force/United Arab Emirates Air Force, 9; Ghana Air Force, 6; Tunisian Air Force, 8; Zaïre Air Force, 8; South African Air Force, 8 plus 100 MB-326KC Impala 2 produced by Atlas Aircraft Corp.

Notes: The MB-326K was developed in 1969/70 as a single-seat variant of the MB-326 family, which in its two-seat version was already serving in the light strike role with several air forces. The MB-339K Veltro 2 (Greyhound) is a variant of the MB-339.

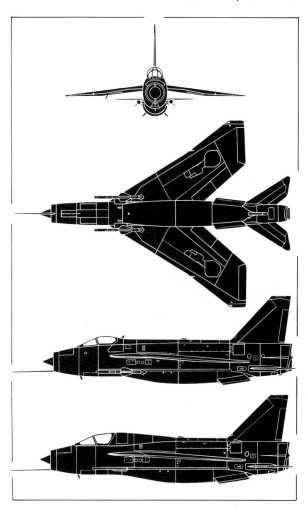

(Top) Lightning F Mk 6 of No 5 Squadron, one of two RAF operational Lightning squadrons in 1981; (immediately above) Lightning F Mk 53, Royal Saudi Air Force; (below) Lightning T Mk 5 two-seater of Lightning Training Flight. (Silhouette) Lightning F Mk 6 with additional side view of T Mk 55.

Country of Origin: United Kingdom.

Type: Interceptor, strike and reconnaissance fighter.

Power Plant: Two Rolls-Royce (F Mk 1, 1A, T Mk 4, 54) 11,250 lb st (5 103 kgp) dry and 14,430 lb st (6 545 kgp) with reheat Avon 201 or (F Mk 2, 2A, 52) Avon 210 or (F Mk 3, 6, T Mk 5, 55) 11,100 lb st (5 035 kgp) dry and 16,300 lb st (7 393 kgp) with reheat Avon 301 or (F Mk 53) Avon 302C turbojets.

Performance: (F Mk 6), Max speed, 808 mph (1 300 km/h) or Mach 1·06 at sea level and 1,386 mph (2 230 km/h) or Mach 2·1 at 36,000 ft (10 975 m); initial rate of climb, 50,000 ft/min (254 m/sec); max sustained altitude, 57,000 ft (17 375 m); max combat radius, 604 mls (972 km); ferry range, 1,554 mls (2 502 km).

Weights (approx): Normal take-off, 40,000 lb (18 144 kg); max with external loads, 41,700 lb (18 915 kg).

Dimensions: Span, 34 ft 10 in (10,61 m); length (over probe) 55 ft 3 in (16,84 m); height, 19 ft 7 in (5,97 m); wing area (F Mk 1, 1A, 2, 3, 52, T Mk 4), 458·52 sq ft (42,70 m²), (F Mk 2A, 6, 53, T Mk 5, 55) 474·5 sq ft (44,08 m²).

Accommodation: Pilot only or (T Mk 4, 54, 5, 55) pilot and instructor side-by-side.

Armament: (F Mk 1, 2, 53) Two 30-mm Aden guns internally with 130 rpg and two Firestreak AAMs on forward fuselage, (F Mk 3, 6, 53) two Red Top AAMs or air-to-air rocket packs and optional ventral pack containing two 30-mm Aden guns and (F Mk 53 only) two 1,000-lb (454-kg) capacity underwing pylons.

Status: Prototype (P.1B) first flown on 4 April 1957; first development batch F Mk 1 flown on 3 April 1958; first F Mk 1 flown on 29 October 1959; first F Mk 2 flown on 11 July 1961; first F Mk 3 flown on 16 June 1962; prototype T Mk 4 flown on 6 May 1959; prototype T Mk 5 flown 29 March 1962; F Mk 6 prototype flown on 17 April 1964; production F Mk 6 flown 16 June 1965; first F Mk 53 (Saudi Arabia) flown 1 November 1965; first T Mk 55 (for Saudi Arabia) flown 3 November 1966. Production totals: P.1B prototypes, 3; pre-production 20; F Mk 1 and 1A, 47; F Mk 2, 44 (of which 31 cvtd to F Mk 2A and five to F Mk 52); F Mk 3, 62; F Mk 6, 62; F Mk 53, 35 to Saudi Arabia (including one F Mk 6 cvtd) and 12 to Kuwait; T Mk 4, 21 (2 cvtd to T Mk 54); T Mk 5, 22; T Mk 55, six to Saudi Arabia and two to Kuwait. Production completed September 1972. Five ex-RAF Mk 2s and two Mk 4s sold to Saudi Arabia as F Mk 52 and T Mk 54.

Notes: The Lightning entered service with No. 74 Squadron, RAF, in June 1960. Two RAF squadrons remained operational in 1981.

(Above) Hawker Siddeley-built AV-8A of US Marine Corps Squadron VMA-231; (immediately below) a Harrier GR Mk 3 serving with the RAF in Germany; (bottom) Harrier T Mk 4 showing raised front fuselage and two-seat cockpit. (Silhouette) BAe Harrier GR Mk 3.

Country of Origin: United Kingdom.

Type: V/STOL strike and reconnaissance fighter.

Power Plant: One (GR 1, T 2) 19,000 lb st (8 620 kgp) Rolls-Royce Pegasus 101 or (GR 1A, T 2A) 20,000 lb st (9 071 kgp) Pegasus 102 or (GR 3, T 4, Mk 52A, AV-8A, TAV-8A) 21,500 lb st (9 752 kgp) Pegasus 103 (F402-RR-401) vectored-thrust turbofan.

Performance: (GR Mk 3) Max speed, over 720 mph (1 160 km/h) or Mach 0·95 at 1,000 ft (305 m), speed with typical external loads, 640–660 mph (1 030–1 060 km/h) or Mach 0·85–0·87 at 1,000 ft (305 m); cruising speed, 560 mph (900 km/h) or Mach 0·8 at 20,000 ft (6 096 m); operational ceiling, over 50,000 ft (15,240 m); tactical radius (HI-LO-HI), 260 mls (418 km) without external fuel and 400 mls (644 km) with two 100-Imp gal (454 l) external tanks; ferry range, 2,070 mls (3 330 km).

Weights: (GR Mk 3) Empty, 12,400 lb (5 624 kg); max take-off (VTO), 18,000 lb (8 165 kg); max take-off (STOL), over 23,000 lb (10 435 kg); max take-off, about 26,000 lb (11 793 kg).

Dimensions: Span, 25 ft 3 in (7,70 m); length, (single-seat) 45 ft 7¾ in (13,91 m); length (two-seat), 55 ft 9½ in (17,00 m); wing area, 201·1 sq ft (18,68 m²).

Accommodation: (GR 1, 1A, 3, AV-8A) Pilot only. (T2, 2A, 4, 52, TAV-8A) Two in tandem, full dual controls.

Armament: Provision for two 30-mm Aden gun pods under fuselage. Four wing hardpoints with combined capacity of 5,300 lb (2 400 kg) for bombs, Martel ASMs, (AV-8A) Sidewinders, etc.

Status: Prototype P. 1127 first hovered 21 October 1960; first Kestrel prototype flown on 7 March 1964; first development Harrier flown on 31 August 1966; first production GR Mk 1 flown on 28 December 1967; T Mk 2 prototype flown on 24 April 1969 and first production T Mk 2 on 3 October 1969. Mk 52 first flown on 16 September 1971. Production totals: development batch, 6; GR Mk 1/1A/3, 114; T Mk 2/2A/4, 23; AV-8A, 102; AV-8A (Spain), 11; TAV-8A, 8; TAV-8A (Spain) 2; Mk 52, 1.

Notes: As world's first V/STOL strike aircraft, the Harrier equips two RAF squadrons in Germany and one in UK; similar AV-8A is operated by US Marine Corps and (as the Matador) by the Spanish Navy. The two-seat operational trainer variants have longer fuselage; some RAF T Mk 4s have same laser target seeker as GR Mk 3s, but this is not carried by T Mk 4As, the Navy's T Mk 4(N)s or USMC TAV-8As, which have a taller fin. All the original RAF GR Mk 1s were converted to Mk 1A and then Mk 3 with engine changes. Starting in 1979, USMC is converting 61 AV-8As to AV-8C standard with improved systems and extended fatigue life.

(Top and immediately above) Two views of a Sea Harrier FRS Mk 1 in service with No 800 Squadron, the first FAA operational V/STOL squadron—note wing tanks and Sidewinder missiles; (below) Sea Harrier FRS Mk 1 in markings of No 801 Squadron. (Silhouette) Sea Harrier FRS Mk 1.

Country of Origin: United Kingdom.

Type: V/STOL shipboard multi-rôle fighter.

Power Plant: One 21,500 lb st (9 760 kgp) Rolls-Royce Pegasus 104 vectored-thrust turbofan.

Performance: Max speed, clean, approx 720 mph (1 160 km/h) at 1,000 ft (305 m) or Mach 0·95; max speed with two Martel ASMs and two Sidewinder AAMs, 640–660 mph (1 030–1 060 km/h) or Mach 0·85–0·87; operational ceiling, over 50,000 ft (15 240 m); tactical radius (intercept mission with two 100-Imp gal/455-l drop tanks, two 30-mm cannon and two Sidewinder AAMs), 450 mls (725 km); combat radius (strike mission, HI-LO-HI profile), 290 mls (467 km).

Weights: Empty, 12,500 lb (5 670 kg); max take-off weight (short take-off technique), 22,500 lb (10 206 kg); max overload take-off weight, 25,000 lb (11 339 kg).

Dimensions: Span, 25 ft 3 in (7,70 m); length, 47 ft 7 in (14,50 m); height, 12 ft 2 in (3,70 m); wing area, 201·1 sq ft (18,68 m²).

Accommodation: Pilot only.

Armament: Provision for two (flush fitting) podded 30-mm Aden cannon with 130 rpg beneath fuselage. Five external hardpoints (one fuselage and four wing) each stressed for 1,000 lb (454 kg), with max external ordnance load for STO (excluding cannon) of 5,000 lb (2 268 kg). Typical loads include two Martel or Harpoon ASMs on the inboard wing pylons and two Sidewinder AAMs on the outboard pylons.

Status: First Sea Harrier (built on production tooling) flown on 21 August 1978. First delivery, to RN, 18 June 1979. Production/order totals, FRS Mk 1 (RN), 34; FRS Mk 51 (India), 6; T Mk 60 (India), 2.

Notes: Sea Harrier was developed from RAF Harrier GR Mk 3 to meet RN requirements for a fighter/strike/reconnaissance aircraft to operate from *Invincible*-class through-deck cruisers, which have no catapults or arrester gear. Changes for naval rôle include a new front fuselage, with a raised cockpit and nose installation of "Blue Fox" intercept radar; new operational equipment, revised electrical and cabin environmental systems; modified Pegasus engine for maritime environment and modified armament provision for the primary intercept mission. Sea Harriers were issued to the RN trials squadron, No 700A, in 1979 and now equip Nos 899 (the HQ Squadron) and Nos 800 and 801 Squadrons for service aboard HMS *Hermes*, *Invincible* and *Illustrious*. For the Indian Navy, the Sea Harrier FRS Mk 51 is similar; the Indian T Mk 60 two-seater is equivalent to the Royal Navy's Harrier T Mk 4(N)s, which are in turn based on the RAF's T Mk 4As.

(Above) Convair F-106A serving with the 144th Fighter Interception Wing (194th Squadron), attached to the California Air National Guard; (immediately below) an F-106A in flight and (bottom) F-106A of the 87th Fighter Interception Squadron. (Silhouette) Convair F-106A.

Country of Origin: USA.

Type: All-weather interceptor and (F-106B) operational trainer.

Power Plant: One 16,100 lb st (7 303 kgp) dry or 24,500 lb st (11 115 kgp) with reheat Pratt & Whitney J75-P-17.turbojet.

Performance: Max speed, 1,326 mph (2 135 km/h) at 35,000 ft (10 670 m): service ceiling, 52,700 ft (16 063 m); combat radius (clean) 490 mls (790 km); ferry range, 1,800 mls (2 910 km).

Weights: Empty 24,038 lb (10 900 kg); normal take-off (clean), 31,480 lb (14 280 kg); max overload, 39,195 lb (17 780 kg).

Dimensions: Span, 38 ft 3½ in (11,67 m); length (over probe), 70 ft 8¾ in (21,55 m); height 20 ft 3½ in (6,18 m); wing area, 697·8 sq ft (64,80 m²).

Accommodation: Pilot only or (F-106B) pilot and instructor or observer in tandem.

Armament: Internal weapons bay for AAMs: typical load comprises one AIR-2A or AIR-2B Genie unguided rocket and four AIM-4F or AIM-4G Falcon AAMs. One 20-mm M-61 A1 multi-barrel rotary cannon introduced as standard from 1973.

Status: First prototype F-106A (YF-102B) flown on 26 December 1956; second prototype flown 26 February 1957: first F-106B flown on 9 April 1958. Deliveries began in July 1959. Production totals, F-106A, 275; F-106B, 63: YF-106C, two; completed in 1960.

Notes: The F-106 Delta Dart was an outgrowth of the F-102, based on the same delta wing but with a redesigned fuselage containing the uprated J75 engine and improved systems and equipment. The two production versions differed from each other only in the cockpit, the F-106B having a second seat, with some reduction in fuel capacity. The F-106As and Bs entered service with Air (later Aerospace) Defense Command of the USAF to operate within the Semi-Automatic Ground defense system over North America and subsequently underwent a number of modification programmes; one of these introduced under-wing drop tanks and flight refuelling equipment, and another, initiated in 1973, included installation of an M-61 multi-barrel cannon in the weapons bay in a semi-retractable installation for added dog-fight capability, in conjunction with a new SnapShoot gunsight. ADC was absorbed by TAC in 1979, and was redesignated as Air Defense Forces, TAC. In 1981, six squadrons of ADF still flew the F-106 but this strength was to decline from 1982 onwards as F-15 Eagles were progressively added to the TAC Air Defense Forces; the type also served in 1981 with five ANG units. The total USAF inventory of F-106 variants at the beginning of 982 was some 180 aircraft.

DASSAULT ETENDARD/SUPER ETENDARD

FIGHTER/ATTACK

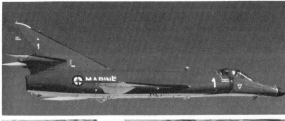

(Top) First production Super Etendard; (immediately above) first prototype Super Etendard undergoing deck-landing trials; (below) an Etendard IVP, with cameras in belly pod, leaves the catapult on the aircraft carrier "Clemenceau". (Silhouette) The Super Etendard.

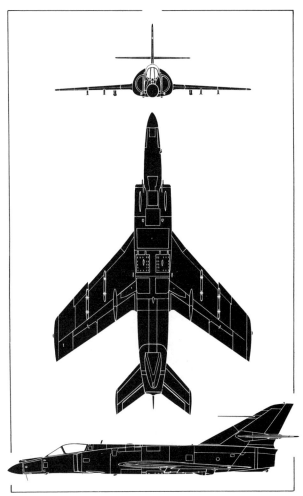

Country of Origin: France.

Type: Carrier-based fighter and tactical reconnaissance aircraft.

Power Plant: One (Etendard IVM) 9,700 lb st (4 400 kgp) SNECMA Atar 8B or (Super Etendard) 11,025 lb st (5 000 kgp) Atar 8 K-50 turbojet.

Performance: (Etendard IVM) Max speed, 673 mph (1,083 km/h) at 36,090 ft (11 000 m), 683 mph (1 099 km/h) at sea level; initial rate of climb, 19,685 ft/min (100 m/sec); service ceiling, 50,850 ft (15 500 m); tactical radius, 186 mls (300 km) at sea level and 435 mls (700 km) at 42,000 ft (12 800 m).

Performance: (Super Etendard): Max speed, 746 mph (1 200 km/h) at 985 ft (300 m) or Mach 0·97, 695 mph (1 118 km/h) at 36,000 ft (11 000 m) or Mach 1·05; radius of action (HI-LO-HI with 2,200-lb/998-kg bomb load), 225 mls (360 km), (LO-LO-LO), 160 mls (260 km), (anti-shipping mission with AM-39 Exocet ASM and 1,700-lb/771-kg bomb load), 225 mls (410 km); initial climb, 19,685 ft/min (100 m/sec).

Weights: (Etendard IVM) Empty, 12,786 lb (5 800 kg); max catapult weight, 19,840 lb (9 000 kg); max take-off, 22,486 lb (10 200 kg).

Weights: (Super Etendard): Empty, 14,220 lb (6 450 kg); max catapult weight 25,350 lb (11 500 kg); max take-off, 26,455 lb

(12 000 kg).

Dimensions: Span, 31 ft 6 in (9·60 m); length 47 ft 3 in (14·40 m); height, 14 ft 2 in (4,30 m); wing area, 312 sq ft (29·0 m²).

Accommodation: Pilot only.

Armament: Two 30-mm DEFA cannon with 122 rpg in fuselage. Four underwing pylons with max capacity of 3,000 lb (1 360 kg) plus (Super) one fuselage stores station.

Status: Prototype Etendard IV-01 first flown 24 July 1956; prototype (IVM-01) flown 21 May 1958; sixth and last pre-production (IVP-07) flown on 19 November 1960; first production IVM flown in July 1961; three Super Etendard prototypes flown on 28 October 1974, 9 March and 28 March 1975 respectively; first production Super Etendard flown 24 November 1977. Production totals, prototype, 1; pre-production, 6; IVM 69; IVP 21; Super Etendard, 71 for *Aéronavale* and 14 for Argentine Navy.

Notes: The Etendard evolved from a Dassault private venture submission for a NATO tactical strike fighter requirement but entered production to fulfil French *Aéronavale's* need for a carrier-based strike fighter (Entendard IVM) and an unarmed reconnaissance aircraft (Etendard IVP). In 1973 *Aéronavale* selected the Super Etendard, to replace the Etendard IVM in service with *Flottilles* 11F and 17F and the F-8E (FN) Crusader in *Flottille* 14F.

13

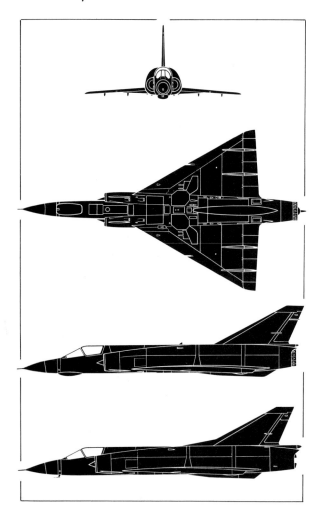

(Above) Dassault-Breguet Mirage IIIE in service with the Armée de l'Air; (immediately below) a Mirage IIIEP of the Pakistan Air Force; (bottom) a camera-equipped Mirage IIIR of the Armée de l'Air. (Silhouette) Dassault-Breguet Mirage IIIE, with additional side-view of the Mirage IIIC.

Country of Origin: France.

Type: Interceptor and close support fighter, (IIIR) recce and (IIIB, IIID) trainer.

Power Plant: One (IIIC,B) 9,370 lb st (4 250 kgp) dry and 13,225 lb st (6 000 kgp) with reheat SNECMA Atar 9B or (IIIE, O,R and S) 9,436 lb st (4 280 kgp) dry and 13,670 lb st (6 200 kgp) with reheat Atar 9C turbojet plus provision for one 3,307 lb st (1 500 kgp) SEPR 844 rocket engine or (IIID2Z and -R2Z) 15,873 lb st (7 000 kgp) with reheat Atar 9K-50 turbojet.

Performance: (IIIE) Max speed, 850 mph (1 370 km/h) at sea level and 1,460 mph (2 350 km/h) at 39,375 ft (12 000 m) or Mach 2·2; typical cruising speed at 36,090 ft (11 000 m), 593 mph (954 km/h) or Mach 0·9; time to reach 36,090 ft (11 000 m) 3 min; service ceiling at Mach 1·8, 55,775 ft (17 000 m); combat radius, ground attack mission, 745 mls (1 200 km).

Weights: Empty (IIIB) 13,820 lb (6,270 kg), (IIIE) 15,540 lb (7 050 kg), (III-R) 14,550 lb (6 600 kg); max take-off (IIIB) 26,455 lb (12 000 kg), (IIIE) 29,760 lb (13 000 kg).

Dimensions: Span, 27 ft 0 in (8·22 m); length (IIIE) 49 ft 3½ in (15 03 m), (IIIB) 50 ft 6¼ in (15·40 m), (IIIR) 50 ft 10¼ in (15·50 m); height, 14 ft 9 in (4 50 m); wing area 375 sq ft (34 85 m²).

Accommodation: Pilot only or (IIIB,D) two in tandem.

Armament: Two 30-mm DEFA cannon in fuselage. Fuselage centre-line pylon carries one AAM or two 1,000 lb (454 kg) bombs or one ASM; two underwing pylons each carry one 1,000 lb (454-kg) bomb or rocket pods, AAMs ASMs or fuel tanks.

Status: Prototype (III-001) first flown 17 November 1956; first IIIA flown on 12 May 1958; prototype IIIB flown on 20 October 1959; first production IIIB flown on 19 July 1962; first production IIIC flown on 9 October 1960; prototype IIIE flown on 5 April 1961; prototype IIIR flown on 31 October 1961; first Australian assembled IIIO flown 16 November 1963; first Swiss-assembled IIIS flown 28 October 1965. Three prototypes, 16 pre-production and 1,389 production models built by end of 1981 (including about 500 Mirage 5/50) of which 48 IIIOF, 50 IIIOA and 10 IIID built in Australia and 34 IIIS and 18 IIIRS in Switzerland.

Notes: Mirage IIIC is basic interceptor with Cyrano Ibis radar, IIIE is ground attack version, with Cyrano II radar, IIIB and IIID are two-seat operational trainers and IIIR and IIIRD are reconnaissance versions, all in service with *Armée de l'Air*. Export customers include: Brazil (IIIDBR, EBR); Israel (IIIBJ, CJ); Lebanon (IIIBL,EL); South Africa (IIIBZ,CZ,DZ,D2Z,EZ,RZ,R2Z); Argentina (IIIDA,EA); Pakistan (IIIDP,EP,RP); Spain (IIIDE,EE); Australia (IIID,O) Switzerland (IIIC,BS,RS and S) and Venezuela (IIIEV).

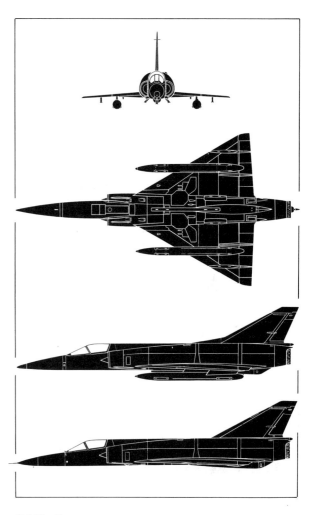

(Top) A Mirage 5V, operational with the Fuerza Aérea Venezolana; (immediately above) a two seat Mirage 5BD of the Force Aérienne Belge; (below) Mirage 50 prototype, with uprated Atar 9K-50 engine. (Silhouette) The Mirage 5, with additional side-view of Mirage 50.

Country of Origin: France.

Type: Ground-attack/multi-rôle fighter.

Power Plant: One (M5 and Nesher), 9,436 lb st (4 280 kgp) dry and 13,670 lb st (6 200 kgp) with reheat SNECMA Atar 9C or (50) 15,873 lb st (7 000 kgp) with reheat Atar 9K-50 turbojet.

Performance: (M5) Max speed 835 mph (1 335 km/h) or Mach 1·1 at sea level, 1,386 mph (2 230 km/h) or Mach 2·1 at 29,370 ft (12 000 m); time to climb to 49,210 ft (15 000 m) at Mach 1·8, 6 min 30 sec; combat radius with 2,000 lb (907 kg) bomb load (HI-LO-HI), 805 mls (1 300 km).

Performance: (50) Max speed 1,460 mph (2 350 km/h) or Mach 2·2 at 39,375 ft (12 000 m); initial rate of climb, 36,400 ft/min (185 m/sec); service ceiling at Mach 2·0, 59,055 ft (18 000 m); combat radius with 1,763 lb (800 kg) bombs (LO-LO-LO), 390 mls (630 km).

Weights: (M5) Empty equipped, 14,550 lb (6 600 kg); max loaded 29,760 lb (13 500 kg).

Weights: (50) Empty equipped, 15,765 lb (7 150 kg); normal take-off (clean), 21,825 lb (9 900 kg); max take-off, 30,200 lb (13 700 kg).

Dimensions: Span 26 ft 11½ in (8,22 m); length, 51 ft 0¼ in (15,55 m); height, 14 ft 9 in (4,50 m); wing area, 375·12 sq ft

(34·85 m²).

Accommodation: Pilot only or (5D) two in tandem, dual control.

Armament: Two 30-mm DEFA 5-52 cannon in base of intake fairings; seven external stations (three fuselage, four wing) with total capacity (weapons and/or fuel) of 9,260 lb (4 200 kg).

Status: Prototype first flown 19 May 1967; first production (5-BA) flown 6 March 1970; Milan S-01 flown 29 May 1970; prototype 50 flown 15 April 1979. Total sales, approx 500 by early 1982; customers include Belgium (27 BA, 63 BR, 16 BD); Pakistan (about 65 PA); Peru (22 P, 2 PD); Columbia (14 COA, COD, COR); Libya (58 D, 32 DE, 10 DR, 10 DD); Abu Dhabi (12 AD/AED, 3 DAD, 2 RAD); Venezuela (4 V, 2 DV); Gabon (4 G, 2 DG); Zaïre (9 M, 2 DM); Egypt (82 SDE, SDR, SDD and E2); France (50 F); Chile (14 50-C, 2 50-DC); Argentine (26 Nesher).

Notes: The Mirage 5 (and two-seat 5D) was developed as an export version of the Mirage IIIE, with simplified avionics for ground attack rôle; Milan S-01 was a single prototype with retractable foreplanes (*Moustaches*) to improve low-speed performance. Mirage 50 is improved multi-rôle version with provision for AI radar. The IAI Nesher (Eagle) was developed in Israel, with locally-produced Atar 9C engine; the export version is known as Dagger in Argentina.

(Above) A Dassault-Breguet Mirage F1 of the Armée de l'Air; (immediately below) Mirage F1AZ of the South African Air Force with Matra 550 Magic AAMs at the wing-tips and wing-mounted rocket pods; (bottom) Mirage F1B of the Kuwait Air Force. (Silhouette) Dassault-Breguet Mirage F1C.

Country of Origin: France.

Type: Multi-purpose fighter.

Power Plant: One 11,023 lb st (5 000 kgp) dry and 15,873 lb st (7 200 kgp) with reheat SNECMA Atar 9K-50 turbojet.

Performance: Max speed (clean), 915 mph (1 472 km/h) or Mach 1·2 at sea level, 1,450 mph (2 335 km/h) or Mach 2·2 at 39,370 ft (12 000 m); cruising speed for best range, 550 mph (885 km/h) at 29,530 ft (9 000 m); service ceiling, 65,600 ft (20 000 m); range with max external fuel, 2,050 mls (3 300 km), with max external combat load of 8,818 lb (4 000 kg), 560 mls (900 km), and with 4,410 lb (2 000 kg), 1,430 mls (2 300 km).

Weights: Empty, 16,314 lb (7 400 kg); loaded (clean), 24,030 lb (10 900 kg); max take-off, 32,850 lb (14 900 kg).

Dimensions: Span, 27 ft 6¾ in (8·40 m); length, 49 ft 2½ in (15,00 m); height, 14 ft 9 in (4·50 m); wing area, 269·098 sq ft (25 m²).

Accommodation: Pilot only.

Armament: Two 30-mm DEFA cannon in forward fuselage and (intercept rôle) two Matra 550 Magic or AIM-9 Sidewinder AAMs at wingtips and three 530 AAMs on hardpoints under fuselage centreline and wings or (ground attack rôle) up to 14 bombs or various combinations of rocket pods, fuel tanks, etc.

Status: First prototype flown 23 December 1966; first of three pre-production models flown 20 March 1969; first production F1C flown 15 February 1973; first F1B flown 26 May 1976; sole F1E (M53) flown 22 December 1974. Sales total 643 by early 1982: 236 for *Armée de l'Air* (200 F1C, 14 F1B, 22 F1R); foreign customers include Greece, (40 F1CG); Kuwait (18 F1CK, 2F1BK); Libya (32 F1ED, 6 F1BD); Iraq (56 F1EQ, 4 F1BQ); Jordan (17 F1EJ/BJ); Morocco (50 F1CH/BH); South Africa (16 F1CZ, 32 F1AZ); Spain (45 F1CE/CE-14A); Ecuador (18 F1C) and Qatar (12 F1CDA and 2 F1DDA).

Notes: The Mirage F1 was evolved as a replacement for the Mirage III in the interceptor rôle for the *Armée de l'Air*. It entered production in 1969 and deliveries began on 14 March 1973, the basic interceptor for France and export being designated the F1C. The F1A is a dedicated ground attack version with extra fuel and less avionics, F1B is an operational two-seat conversion trainer and F1R is a reconnaissance version ordered by *Armée de l'Air* with internal and external cameras. F1E is as F1A with more comprehensive avionics (but designation first used for single prototype with M53 engine). The French 5e *Escadre de Chasse* uses 24 F1-200s, which are modified F1Cs with provision for in-flight refuelling. Atlas Aircraft Corp assembled F1AZs for SAAF.

(Top) The Mirage 2000-1, the first of four single-seat prototypes; (immediately above) one of the Mirage 2000 prototypes carrying two Matra Magic and two Super 530D air-to-air missiles; (below) the two-seat Mirage 2000B-01 prototype. (Silhouette) Dassault-Breguet Mirage 2000.

Country of Origin: France.
Type: Single-seat milti-rôle fighter.
Power Plant: One 12,230 lb (5 600 kg) dry and 19,840 lb (9 000 kg) with reheat SNECMA M53-5 turbofan.
Performance: Max speed (clean) Mach 2·35 or 1,347 kts (2 495 km/h) above 36,090 ft (11 000 m); Mach 1·2 or 795 kts (1 472 km/h) at sea level; tactical radius (intercept mission with four AAMs and two 374-Imp gal/1 700-l drop tanks), 435 mls (700 km); max rate of climb, 49,000 ft/min (249 m/sec); time to Mach 2·0 at 49,200 ft (15 000 m) from brakes release, 4.0 min.
Weights: Combat, 19,840 lb (9 000 kg); max. take-off, 33,070 lb (15 000 kg).
Dimensions: Span, 29 ft 6$\frac{1}{2}$ in (9,00 m); length 50 ft 3$\frac{1}{2}$ in (15,33 m); wing area, 441·13 sq ft (41,00 m²).
Accommodation: Pilot only or (Mirage 2000B and 2000N) two in tandem.
Armament: Two 30-mm DEFA 554 cannon and (air superiority) two Matra 550 Magic and two Matra Super 530D AAMs, or (strike) up to 11,000 lb (5 000 kg) of ordnance on nine stations.
Status: Three official prototypes and one company-funded example of the single-seat Mirage 2000 first flown, respectively, on 10 March 1978, 18 September 1978, 26 April 1979 and 12 May

1980. Prototype two-seat Mirage 2000B flown on 11 October 1980. Production/sales: 63 for *Armée de l'Air* ordered by early 1982 (of total planned procurement of 127); 20 for Egyptian Air Force; 40 for Indian Air Force ordered May 1982.
Notes: The Mirage 2000 emerged in 1978 as the officially-favoured replacement for the Mirage III/5 series in *Armée de l'Air* service, and three major versions are now planned, as single-seat interceptor and attack aircraft and a two-seat tactical nuclear strike aircraft. A two-seat operational training version will also be available. Initial orders for 63 have been placed against expected total *Armée de l'Air* requirements for about 130. Initial deliveries will be of aircraft carrying Thomson-CSF/EMD RDM multi-rôle doppler radar with conversion of the first unit—one of the *escadrons* of the *2ᵉ Escadre Chasse* at Dijon—starting early in 1984. From 1985, the definitive Thomson CFS/EMD RDI pulse-doppler radar will be available, with RDM remaining available for export variants. Also in 1985, the more powerful M53-P2 engine will be introduced, with a military rating of 14,330 lb (6 500 kg) dry and 21,385 lb (9 700 kg) with maximum reheat. A two-seat low-level penetration version is being developed to carry the Aérospatiale ASMP (*air-sol moyenne portée*) stand-off nuclear missile. As Mirage 2000N, this is expected in service in 1986.

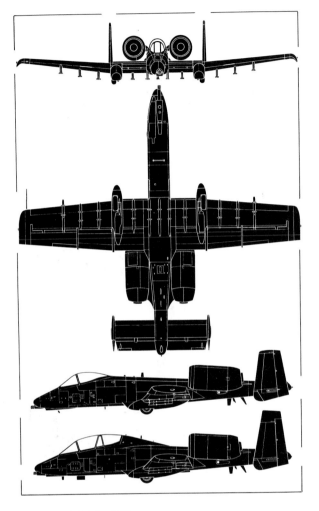

(Above) Fairchild A-10A Thunderbolt II in flight and (immediately below) in landing configuration with flaps and spoilers deployed; (bottom) the prototype two-seat A-10 showing the revised front fuselage. (Silhouette) Fairchild A-10A, with additional side view of the two-seat A-10B.

Country of Origin: USA.

Type: Close-support attack aircraft.

Power Plant: Two 9,065 lb st (4 112 kgp) General Electric TF34-GE-100 turbofans.

Performance: (At 38,136 lb/17 299 kg) Max speed, 433 mph (697 km/h) at sea level, 448 mph (721 km/h) at 10,000 ft (3 050 m); initial climb, 5,340 ft/min (27,12 m/sec); service ceiling, 34,700 ft (10 575 m); combat radius (with 9,540 lb/4 327 kg bomb load and 1,170 lb/531 kg of 30-mm ammunition, with allowance for 1·93 hr loiter at 5,000 ft/1 525 m), 288 mls (463 km) at (average) 329 mph (529 km/h) at 25,000–35,000 ft (7 620–10 670 m); ferry range, 2,487 mls (4 000 km).

Weights: Empty, 19,856 lb (9 006 kg); max take-off, 46,786 lb (22 221 kg).

Dimensions: Span 57 ft 6 in (17,53 m); length, 53 ft 4 in (16,25 m); height, 14 ft 8 in (4, 47 m); wing area, 506 sq ft (47,01 m²).

Armament: One seven-barrel 30-mm General Electric GAU-8/A Avenger rotary cannon. Eleven external stations for maximum of 9,540 lb (4 327 kg) ordnance (with full internal fuel and 1,170 lb/531 kg ammunition), or max of 16,000 lb (7 250 kg).

Status: First of two YA-10A prototypes flown 10 May 1972, first of six pre-production aircraft flown 15 February 1975; first production A-10A flown 21 October 1975; two-seat A-10 night/adverse weather prototype flown 4 May 1979. Production total of 825 A-10As planned for delivery to USAF, ANG and AFR by April 1986, of which some 600 delivered by early 1982.

Notes: The A-10A was one of two designs chosen by the USAF for full-scale evaluation to meet a requirement (known as A-X) for a specialised ground-attack aircraft. Two prototypes were built for a fly-off against the two Northrop A-9s, this involving about 125 hrs of flight testing (by each type) in a 60-day period commencing late October 1972, and the Fairchild design was declared the winning aircraft in January 1973. After the 356th Squadron of the 354th TFW had become the first A-10A unit to reach IOC on 15 October 1977, overseas deployment began at the beginning of 1979 to the 81st TFW in the UK, and in addition to the 23rd TFW in the USA, two squadrons of the Air Force Reserve and four units of the ANG also were equipping on the A-10A in 1981, this being the first time that National Guard units had received new aircraft off the production line. During 1979, Fairchild developed a two-seat prototype equipped for night/adverse weather operation and a similar variant was proposed by the USAF in 1981 as the A-10B combat-ready trainer.

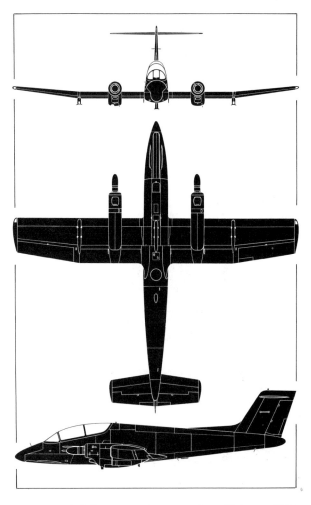

(Above and below) Air and ground views of the FMA IA 58A Pucara in operational service with the Fuerza Aérea Argentina. Note the various underwing loads, including bombs, air-to-ground rocket pods and long-range tanks. (Silhouette) IA 58A Pucara.

Country of Origin: Argentina.

Type: Counter-insurgency aircraft.

Power Plant: Two (IA 58A) 1,022 eshp Turboméca Astazou XVIG or (IA 66) 1,000 shp Garrett TPE 331-11-601W turboprops.

Performance: (IA 58A) Max speed 310 mph (500 km/h) at 9,840 ft (3 000 m); max cruising speed, 298 mph (480 km/h) at 19,685 ft (6 000 m); economical cruising speed, 267 mph (430 km/h); initial rate of climb, 3,543 ft/min (18,0 m/sec); service ceiling, 32,810 ft (10 000 m); range with two 66-Imp gal (300-l) auxiliary tanks, 1,890 mls (3 040 km) at 16,400 ft (5 000 m).

Weights: (IA 58A) Empty equipped, 8,900 lb (4,037 kg); max take-off, 14,990 lb (6 800 kg).

Dimensions: Span 47 ft 6¾ in (14,50 m); length 46 ft 9 in (14,25 m); height 17 ft 7 in (5,36 m); wing area, 326·1 sq ft (30·30 m²).

Accommodation: Pilot and observer in tandem.

Armament: Two 20-mm Hispano HS-2804 cannon and four 0·30-in (7,62-mm) FN machine guns in forward fuselage. One hardpoint on fuselage centre-line with 2,205-lb (1 000-kg) capacity and one under each wing with 1,100-lb (500-kg) capacity, for various ordnance loads including bombs, rockets or weapon pods.

Status: Aerodynamic prototype (unpowered) first flown on 26 December 1967; first powered prototype flown 20 August 1969; second prototype flown 6 September 1970; first production model flown 8 November 1974; first IA 58B flown 15 May 1979. In production for the Argentine Air Force (60 IA 58A and 40 IA 58B) and for Uruguayan Air Force (six).

Notes: The Pucara—originally known as the Delfin—was designed at the Fabrica Militar de Aviones at Cordoba to meet Argentine Air Force requirements for a light strike aircraft. The design was proved in flight testing of a glider version before construction of the prototypes began. Designated AX-01, the first prototype was powered by two AiResearch TPE 331-U-303 engines, being followed by the AX-02 with Astazou XVIG engines, as specified for production aircraft. Deliveries of the IA 58 against the initial Argentine Air Force order for 50 began in the first half of 1976. The IA 58B, flown (as a converted IA 58) in 1979, had a deepened front fuselage containing a pair of 30-mm DEFA 553 cannon and the IA 66 has TPE 331-11 engines in place of the Astazou turboprops. An IA 58 flew a short test programme with these engines in 1980, leading to a definitive IA 66 prototype in 1981 and a planned production batch of 59. A maritime surveillance version and a dual control trainer based on the Pucara were being projected in 1982.

(Above) F-16A Fighting Falcon of the 35th Tactical Fighter Squadron, 388th TFW, at Hill AFB, Utah; (immediately below) F-16A of the Force Aérienne Belge; (bottom) two seat F-16B of the Dutch Koninklijke Luchtmacht. (Silhouette) General Dynamics F-16C.

Country of Origin: USA.

Type: Air combat fighter.

Power Plant: One 14,800 lb st (6 713 kgp) dry and 23,830 lb st (10 809 kgp) with reheat Pratt & Whitney F100-PW-200 turbofan.

Performance: Max speed (with wing-tip AAMs), 1,333 mph (2 145 km/h) or Mach = 2·02 short endurance and 1,247 mph (2 007 km/h) or March 1·89 sustained, at 40,000 ft (12 190 m); tactical radius (interdiction mission HI-LO-HI on internal fuel with six MK 82 bombs, 360 mls (580 km).

Weights: Operational empty, 14,567 lb (6 613 kg); max take-off (wing-tip AAMs), 23,357 lb (10 594 kg); max take-off (interdiction), 35,400 lb (16 057 kg) or (F-16A-25 and subsequent), 37.500 lb (17 010 kg).

Dimensions: Span (over wing-tip AAMs), 32 ft 10 in (10,01 m); overall length (excluding nose pitot), 47 ft 7¾ in (14,52 m); height, 16 ft 5¼ in (5,01 m); wing area, 300 sq ft (17,87 m²).

Accommodation: Pilot only or (F-16B) two in tandem.

Armament: One 20-mm M61A-1 multi-barrel rotary cannon and external ordnance load of 12,000 lb (5 443 kg) distributed between nine stations, or 15,200 lb (6 894 kg) with reduced fuel.

Status: Two YF-16 prototypes flown on 20 January and 9 May 1974. First (of six) FSD F-16As flown 8 December 1976; first (of two) FSD F-16Bs flown 8 August 1977. First full production F-16A (USAF) flown 7 August and delivered 17 August 1978. USAF procurement plan totals 785 F-16A/Bs and 704 F-16C/Ds; export orders are 75 for Israel, 34 F-16A and 6 F-16B for Egypt, 30 F-16A and 6 F-16B for South Korea and 40 for Pakistan. In European licence-production programme, SABCA (Gosselies, Belgium) assembly line is building 116 for Belgium and 58 for Denmark (first flight 11 December 1978) and Fokker (Schiphol, Netherlands) is building 142 for Netherlands and 72 for Norway (first flight 3 May 1979). The F-16/J79 prototype for FX export version first flown 29 October 1980 and F-16/101 with F-101DFE alternative engine first flown 19 December 1980.

Notes: All customers listed above have ordered standard F-16As and F-16Bs; the alternative FX export variant is powered by 18,730 lb st (8 496 kgp) J79-GE-119 turbojet. Of the European users, the Royal Norwegian Air Force alone has specified a drag parachute, in an extended fairing at the base of the rudder; on Belgian Air Force aircraft, a similar fairing houses Loral Rapport III ESM. Single-seat F-16C and two-seat F-16D introduce a series of systems and airframe improvements, with deliveries starting 1982. Two F-16E prototypes with modified-delta wing and longer fuselage, were to fly mid-1982.

GENERAL DYNAMICS F-111

FIGHTER/ATTACK

(Top) General Dynamics F-111C of the Royal Australian Air Force; (immediately above) an F-111E serving with UK-based 20th Tactical Fighter Wing; (below) an F-111A at Nellis AFB. (Silhouette) General Dynamics F-111E, showing wings fully spread and fully swept.

Country of Origin: USA.

Type: Tactical strike fighter.

Power Plant: Two Pratt & Whitney (F-111A, C) 18,500 lb st (8 390 kgp) with reheat TF30-P-3 or (F-111D, E) 20,840 lb st (9 453 kgp) with reheat TF30-P-9 or (F-111F), 25,100 lb st (11 385 kgp) with reheat TF30-P-100 turbofans.

Performance: (F-111F) Max speed, 865 mph (1 390 km/h) or Mach 1·2 at sea level, 1,650 mph (2 655 km/h) or (five-min limit) Mach 2·5 above 40,000 ft (12 190 m); combat ceiling, 57,900 ft (17 650 m); combat radius with two drop tanks and 2,000-lb (908-kg) bomb, (HI-LO-HI), 920 mls (1 480 km); ferry range 3,375 mls (5 435 km).

Weights: (F-111F). Empty equipped, 47,500 lb (23 525 kg); normal take-off, 62,350 lb (28 280 kg); max overload 100,000 lb (45 360 kg).

Dimensions: Span (spread, except F-111C), 63 ft 0 in (19,20 m); (F-111C), 70 ft 0 in (21,34 m); span (swept.back except F-111C), 31 ft 11½ in (9,74 m); (F-111C), 33 ft 11 in (10,34 m); length, 75 ft 6½ in (23,02 m); height, 17 ft 1½ in (5,22 m); wing area, 525 sq ft (48,77 m²).

Accommodation: Pilot and observer side-by-side.

Armament: One 20-mm M-61A1 multi-barrel cannon internally,

optionally replaced with two 750-lb (340-kg) bombs. Four fixed and four pivoting underwing pylons have total capacity of 25,000 lb (11 340 kg) bombs, ASMs, rockets or fuel tanks.

Status: First development-batch F-111A flown on 21 December 1964; first development batch F-111B flown on 18 May 1965; first production F-111B flown on 29 June 1968; RF-111A prototype flown on 17 December 1967; F-111D prototype flown on 2 December 1968; first F-111E flown 20 August 1969; first F-111F flown August 1971. Production totals; F-111A development batch, 18 (including RF-111A prototypes); F-111A production 141; F-111B development batch 5, F-111B production 4; F-111C, 24; F-111D, 96; F-111E, 94; F-111F, 106; YF-111A (ex-TF-111K), 2. Production completed end-1973.

Notes: The world's first swing-wing aircraft to enter service, the F-111 in its fighter variants is in service with the 366th TFW (F-111A), 27th TFW (F-111D), 20th TFW (F-111E) and 48th TFW (F-111F), the last two based in the UK; model differences are concerned with intake design, engine thrust and avionics. During 1982, 42 F-111As were under conversion to EF-111A (see page 100). The F-111C for RAAF has larger wing of the FB-111 (see page 65); four of 24 were modified for tactical reconnaissance, first flight after conversion being made on 27 April 1979.

(Above) A TRAM-equipped A-6E Intruder of US Navy Squadron VA-65; (immediately below) an A-6E of VMA-224, one of the US Marine Corps attack squadron; (bottom) a KA-6D buddy refuelling tanker of VA-165 in landing configuration as it approaches the USS "Constellation". (Silhouette) Grumman A-6E Intruder with TRAM

Country of Origin: USA.

Type: Carrier-borne low-level strike aircraft.

Power Plant: Two 9,300 lb st (4 218 kgp) Pratt & Whitney J52-P-8A turbojets.

Performance: (A-6E) Max speed (clean, at 42,866 lb/19 460 kg), 654 mph (1 052 km/h) at sea level; initial rate of climb 8,600 ft/min (43.7 m/sec); time to 30,000 ft (9 150 m), 4·6 min; service ceiling, 44,600 ft (13 600 m); combat range, 2,320 mls (3 733 km) at 482 mph (776 km/h) average speed at 37,700–44,600 ft (11 500–13 600 m); combat radius (close support rôle with 28 Snakeye Mk 81 bombs), 370 mls (595 km) at 464 mph (747 km/h).

Weights: (A-6E) Empty, 25,980 lb (11 795 kg); typical combat take-off weight, 52,750 lb (23 928 kg); max take-off (catapult), 58,600 lb (26 605 kg); max take-off (field), 60,400 lb (27 420 kg).

Dimensions: Span, 53 ft 0 in (16,15 m); length, 54 ft 9 in (16,69 m); height, 16 ft 2 in (4,93 m); wing area, 529 sq ft (49,15 m²).

Accommodation: Pilot and observer side-by-side.

Armament: One 3,600 lb (1 633 kg) strongpoint on fuselage centreline and four underwing pylons; maximum combined capacity of 15,000 lb (6 804 kg).

Status: First of eight test and development aircraft (A2F-1)

flown on 19 April 1960. Entered US Navy service February 1963. Prototype KA-6D conversion flown on 23 May 1966 and first production conversion on 16 April 1970; first A-6E flown on 27 February 1970; A-6E/TRAM development aircraft flown 22 March 1974 and first full A-6E/TRAM conversion flown 29 October 1974. Total production, over 600 by 1982.

Notes: The Intruder (Grumman G-128) was chosen by the US Navy in 1957 to meet a requirement for a long-range strike aircraft operating at low level from carrier decks. Three of the development batch of A-6As were later converted to NA-6As as flight refuelling tankers for the F-14A flight test programme. An operational tanker for US Navy use was developed as the KA-6D and 62 A-6As were eventually converted to this standard. The A-6B (19 A-6A conversions) carried Standard ARM anti-radar missiles and the A-6C (12 A-6As converted) was fitted with FLIR and LLTV equipment for night target acquisition in Vietnam operations. The A-6E has an advanced IBM computer and a multi-mode radar; production totalled 159 plus 240 conversions from A-6A, B and C models to equip 12 USN and five USMC attack squadrons. Since 1980, A-6Es have been progressively modified to have TRAM (Target Recognition Attack Multisensors) with laser and IR equipment in an under-nose 'turret'.

(Top) F-14A Tomcat of the US Navy's Fighter Squadron Two, VF-2; (immediately above) an F-14A of VF-14, the "Top Hatters", showing maximum wing sweepback; (below) an F-14A of VF-14 making a touch-and-go landing aboard the USS "John F Kennedy". (Silhouette) Grumman F-14C Tomcat.

Country of Origin: USA.

Type: Ship-borne multi-purpose fighter.

Power Plant: Two 12,500 lb st (5 670 kgp) dry and 20,900 lb st (9 480 kgp) with reheat Pratt & Whitney TF30-P-412A or P-414 turbofans.

Performance: Max speed with four AIM-7 Sparrow missiles at 55,000 lb (24 948 kg) weight, 913 mph (1 470 km/h) or Mach 1·2 at sea level, 1,545 mph (2 485 km/h) or Mach 2·34 at 40,000 ft (12 190 m); service ceiling, over 50,000 ft (15 240 m); time to 60,000 ft (18,290 m), 2·1 min; tactical radius (internal fuel plus six AIM-7 and four AIM-9) 765 mls (1 232 km).

Weights: Empty, 39,762 lb (18 036 kg); normal take-off, 59,372 lb (26 931 kg). max take-off, 74,348 lb (33 724 kg).

Dimensions: Span (spread), 64 ft 1½ in (19,55 m); span (swept-back), 38 ft 2½ in (11,65 m); overall length, 62 ft 8 in (19,1 m); height, 16 ft 0 in (4,88 m).

Accommodation: Pilot and observer in tandem.

Armament: One 20-mm M-61A1 rotary cannon and (intercept mission) four AIM-7E Sparrow and four AIM-9G/H Sidewinder AAMs or six AIM-54A Phoenix and two AIM-9 AAMs.

Status: First of 12 research and development aircraft began flight trials on 21 December 1970, followed by second on 24 May 1971. Prototype F-14B (No 7 F-14A development airframe converted) first flown 12 September 1973. First F-14A (IIAF) flown 5 December 1975. Prototype (F-14B converted) with F101DFE engines flown 14 July 1981. Over 400 delivered to US Navy by end-1981. 80 delivered to Iran 1976/78.

Notes: The F-14A Tomcat was chosen by the US Navy in January 1969 as its new carrier-based fighter to take the place of the proposed F-111B programme. First Navy squadron to fly the Tomcat was VF-124, assigned the task of training crews for operational units the first two of which, VF-1 and VF-2, were operational aboard the USS *Enterprise* by the late summer of 1974. Eighteen USN squadrons were flying F-14As from seven aircraft carriers and shore stations by mid-1981. Two F-14As converted to YF-14Bs flew with YF401-P-400 engines but F-14B production was cancelled; one YF-14B was fitted with General Electric F101DFE engines for a short test programme in 1981 and this engine will power the projected F-14D, with other improvements. For 1983 introduction, the F-14C features improved TF30-P-414A engines and avionics. Starting in 1981, US Navy planned to introduce a total of 49 RF-14As to replace RF-8Gs in photo-reconnaissance rôle, carrying TARPS (Tactical Air Reconnaissance Pod System).

(Above) Hunter T Mk 8M two-seater in service as a radar system trainer for Fleet Air Arm Sea Harrier pilots; (immediately below) Hunter FGA Mk 9 serving with No 2 Tactical Weapons Unit, RAF; (bottom) Hunter F Mk 58, Swiss Flugwaffe. (Silhouette) Hunter FGA Mk 9, with additional side view of two-seat Hunter.

Country of Origin: United Kingdom.

Type: Interceptor, ground attack, reconnaissance fighter and trainer.

Power Plant: One (Mks 7, 8, 11, 12, 50, 51, 52, 53 and 62) 7,575 lb st (3 435 kgp) Rolls-Royce Avon 113, 115, 119, 121A or 122 or (Mks 6, 9, 10, 57, 58, 59, 66, 67, 69, 70–81) 10,150 lb st (4 600 kgp) Avon 203 or 207 turbojet.

Performance: (FGA Mk 9) Max speed, 710 mph (1 144 km/h) at sea level, 620 mph (978 km/h) at 36,000 ft (10 973 m); best range cruise, 460 mph (740 km/h); initial rate of climb, approx 8,000 ft/min (40·7 m/sec); service ceiling, about 50,000 ft (15 250 m); range (clean), 490 mls (789 km); range with four drop tanks, 1,840 mls (2 965 km).

Weights: (FGA Mk 9) Empty, 13,270 lb (6 020 kg); max take-off, 24,000 lb (10 885 kg).

Dimensions: Span, 33 ft 8 in (10,26 m); length, (single-seaters) 45 ft 10½ in (13,98 m), (two-seaters), 48 ft 10½ in (14,90 m); height, 13 ft 2 in (4,26 m); wing area, 349 sq ft (32,43 m²).

Accommodation: (Mks 6, 9, 10, 11, 50, 51, 52, 57, 58, 59, 70, 71, 73, 74, 76, 78) pilot only or (Mks 7, 8, 12, 53, 62, 66, 67, 69, 72, 75, 77, 79) two side-by-side, dual controls.

Armament: Four (single-seaters) or two (two-seaters) 30-mm

Aden cannon in front fuselage; two inner wing pylons with 1,000-lb (454-kg) capacity; two outer wing strongpoints for up to 24 3-in (7,6-cm) rockets.

Status: Hunter prototype first flown 20 July 1951; first production Mk 1 flown 16 May 1953; Mk 4 flown 20 October 1954; Mk 6 flown 25 March 1955; Mk 7 flown 11 October 1957. Production totals, 1,057 single-seaters plus 55 two-seaters for RAF/RN; 350 single-seaters plus 45 two-seaters for export; 189 single-seaters under licence by Fokker in Holland and 256 under licence by Fairey/Sabena in Belgium.

Notes: Hunter service in the RAF began in 1954 and a few examples were still operational in 1982, in both single-seat and two-seat versions. Mks 1 to 6 were RAF single-seaters, as were Mks 9, 10 and 11 as conversions; Mks 7 and 8 were two-seaters. Export variants from Mk 50 upwards included some production runs but also many refurbished examples, including all Mks from 70 to 81. Principal users of the Hunter in 1981 included Abu Dhabi (FGA/FR 76, T 77); Chile (FGA 71, T 72); India (F/FGA 56, T 66); Iraq (F/FGA 59A and 59B, T 69); Kuwait (T 67); Kenya (FGA 80, T 81); Lebanon (F/FGA 70, T 66C); Qatar (FGA 78, T 79); Singapore, FGA 74/74B, FR 74A, T 75); Switzerland (F 58/58A, T 68) and Zimbabwe (FGA 9).

(Top) The first of two prototypes of the HAL Ajeet in flight; (immediately above and below) ground views of the Ajeet prototype, modified from one of the last Gnats built in India. (Silhouette) HAL Ajeet.

Country of Origin: India (UK).

Type: Single-seat lightweight fighter.

Power Plant: One 4,500 lb st (2 043 kgp) HAL-built Rolls-Royce Bristol Orpheus 701-01 turbojet.

Performance: (Clean configuration), Max speed 634 mph (1 020 km/h) at 39,375 ft (12 000 m), or Mach 0·96, 685 mph (1 102 km/h) at sea level; tactical radius (LO-LO-LO with two 30-Imp gal/137-1 drop tanks and two Arrow rocket pods), 161 mls (259 km), (with two Arrow pods and two 500-lb/227-kg bombs), 127 mls (204 km); time to 39,375 ft (12 000 m) 6·05 min; service ceiling, 39,375 ft (12 000 m).

Weights: Basic empty weight, 5,074 lb (2 302 kg); loaded weight (clean), 7,803 lb (3 539 kg); max take-off, 9,195 lb (4 170 kg).

Dimensions: Span, 22 ft 1 in (6,73 m); length 29 ft 8 in (9,04 m); height, 8 ft 1 in (2,46 m); wing area 157·7 sq ft (14,65 m²).

Accommodation: Pilot only.

Armament: Two 30-mm Aden Mk 2 cannon with 90 rpg and four wing hardpoints each carrying one Arrow 122 pod containing 18 68-mm rockets, or Arrow pods on the two outboard hardpoints and one 500-lb (229-kg) bomb on each inboard hardpoint.

Status: Prototype Folland Gnat fighter flown (in UK) on 18 July 1955; first production aircraft flown 16 May 1956; first HAL-built

Gnat flown 18 November 1959; first T Mk 1 (UK) flown 31 August 1959; first Ajeet prototype (214th HAL-built Gnat modified) flown 6 March 1975, and second (215th HAL Gnat) on 5 November 1975. First production Ajeet flown 30 September 1976. Production totals (fighters), development batch 6; Finland 12; Yugoslavia 2; India 25 plus 15 for local assembly by HAL followed by 213 licence-built Gnat 1s and 79 Ajeets (ex-Gnat 2) with 10 Gnats converted to Ajeets; T Mk 1 (trainer) production (UK), 105.

Notes: The Ajeet (Unconquerable) is a derivative of the Hindustan Aeronautics licence-built Folland (Hawker Siddeley) Gnat from which it differs primarily in having integral wing fuel tankage, zero-level Martin Baker Mk GF4 (rather than Folland Type 2G) ejection seat, a Ferranti Isis F-195 (in place of GGS Mk 8) gunsight and upgraded avionics. Production of the Ajeet ended in 1981 and development of a tandem two-seat Ajeet trainer was continuing mid-1982, at which time the first of two prototypes was scheduled to fly. The Indian Air Force has a requirement for (approx) 40 Ajeet trainers. The type equips four squadrons in the IAF, replacing the locally-built Gnat. Apart from India, only Finland used the Gnat fighter operationally. The slightly larger Gnat T Mk 1 trainer, developed in the UK from Folland's original lightweight fighter design, was retired from RAF service in 1979.

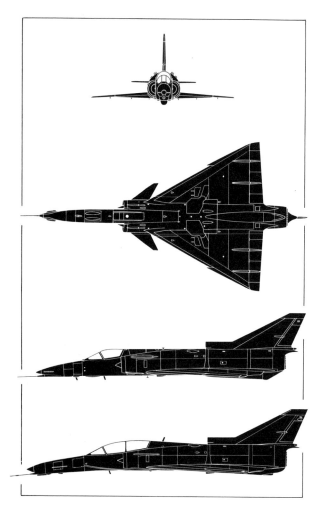

(Above) The Kfir C-2, showing the noseplanes of this definitive version of the fighter developed in Israel; (immediately below) a Kfir C-2 reveals its distinctive delta planform; (bottom) the Kfir two-seater. (Silhouette) IAI Kfir C-2 with extra side view of the two-seat variant.

Country of Origin: Israel.

Type: Multi-rôle fighter (and two-seat operational trainer).

Power Plant: One 11,870 lb st (5 385 kgp) dry and 17,900 lb st (8 120 kgp) with reheat Bet-Shemesh-built General Electric J79-GE-17 turbojet.

Performance: (C2) (Estimated) Max speed (50 per cent fuel and two Shafrir AAMs), 850 mph (1 368 km/h) at 1,000 ft (305 m) or Mach 1·12, 1,420 mph (2 285 km/h) above 36,000 ft (10 970 m) or Mach 2·3; max. low-level climb rate, 47,250 ft/min (240 m/sec); max ceiling, 59,050 ft (18 000 m); radius of action (air superiority mission with two 110 Imp gal/500 1l drop tanks), 323 mls (520 km); radius of action (ground attack mission HI-LO-HI profile), 745 mls (1 200 km).

Weights: (C2) Loaded (intercept with 50 per cent fuel and two AAMs), 20,700 lb (9 390 kg); max take-off, 32,190 lb (14 600 kg).

Dimensions: Span, 26 ft 11½ in (8,22 m); length, 51 ft 0¼ in (15,55 m); height, 13 ft 11½ in (4,25 m); wing area (excluding canard and dog-tooth), 375·12 sq ft (34,85 m²).

Accommodation: Pilot only.

Armament: Two 30-mm DEFA cannon with 125 rpg and (intercept) two or four Rafael Shafrir AAMs, or (ground attack) up to 8,820 lb (4 000 kg) of external ordnance.

Status: Prototype (J79 installation in French Mirage airframe) flown on 19 October 1970; prototype IAI-built airframe flown September 1971. Initial production version of Kfir delivered to Israeli air arm from April 1975 with improved Kfir-C2 from early in 1977; production rate at the beginning of 1982 reportedly 2·5 aircraft monthly. Twelve delivered to Colombia 1982.

Notes: The Kfir (Young Lion) was developed by IAI (under the code-name Black Curtain) after the company had earlier put into production a "pirated" copy of the Dassault-Breguet Mirage 5J as the Nesher (Eagle). Up to 100 Neshers are reported to have been built for IAI, about half being delivered in time to serve in the Yöm Kippur war in October 1973. The Kfir was evolved by fitting J79 engine—supplied from the US to support Israeli F-4 operations—in place of the Atar 9C and introducing airframe improvements. As first produced, the Kfir was optimised either for air superiority or air-to-ground operations. The Kfir-C2 differs from the initial production version in having modifications designed primarily to improve combat manoeuvrability, these comprising canard auxiliary surfaces which result in a close-coupled canard configuration, dog-tooth wing leading-edge extensions and nose strakes. A two-seat version of the Kfir differs in having a second cockpit in tandem with a slightly lengthened fuselage.

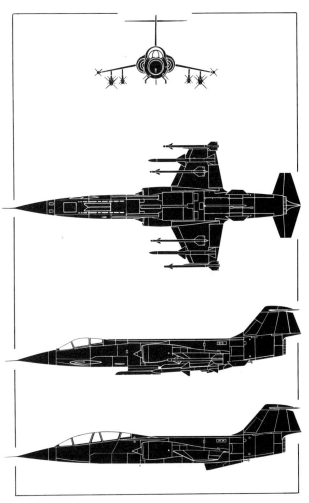

(Top) An Aeritalia-built F-104S of the 50th Stormo of the Italian Air Force; (immediately above) a European-built F-104G serving in the Luftwaffe and (below) an F-104G of the Hellenic Air Force. (Silhouette) Lockheed F-104S Starfighter and (lower sideview) the TF-104G.

Country of Origin: USA.

Type: Interceptor, fighter-bomber and reconnaissance fighter.

Power Plant: One General Electric (F-104A, B) 14,800 lb st (6 713 kgp) with reheat J79-GE-3B, (F-104C, D, F) 15,800 lb st (7 166 kgp) with reheat J79-GE-7 or (F-104G, J, DJ, CF-104) J79-GE-11A, or (F-104S) 17,900 lb st (8 120 kgp) with reheat J79-GE-19 turbojet.

Performance: (F-104G) Max speed, 1,320 mph (2 124 km/h) at 40,000 ft (12 192 m) and 915 mph (1 473 km/h) at 1,000 ft (305 m); initial rate of climb over 50,000 ft/min (254 m/sec); service ceiling, about 55,000 ft (16 764 m); tactical radius (with four drop tanks), 690 mls (1 110 km) at 610 mph (982 km/h).

Weights: (F-104G) Empty, 14,082 lb (6 390 kg); normal take-off (clean), 19,841 lb (9 000 kg); maximum overload, 28,780 lb (13 000 kg).

Dimensions: Span, 21 ft 11 in (6,68 m); length, 54 ft 9 in (16,69 m); height, 13 ft 6 in (4,11 m); wing area, 196·1 sq ft (18,22 m²).

Accommodation: Pilot only or (F-104B, D and F, TF-104G, CF-104D, F-104DJ) two in tandem, dual controls.

Armament: One M-61 rotary barrel cannon in forward fuselage and (according to rôle) one AAM at each wing-tip and/or four under-wing pylons with total load of 4,000 lb (1 815 kg).

Status: Prototype XF-104 flown on 7 February 1954; F-104A flown on 17 February 1956; F-104B flown on 7 February 1957; F-104G flown on 5 October 1960; CF-104 flown on 28 March 1961; CF-104D flown on 14 June 1961; F-104J flown on 30 June 1961; prototype F-104S flown in December 1966 and first production F-104S on 30 December 1968. Production totals, XF-104, 2; YF-104A, 15; F-104A, 153; F-104B, 26; F-104C, 77; F-104D, 21; F-104F, 30; F-104G, 1,266 (in USA, Germany, Belgium and Netherlands); TF-104G, 181; F-104J, 210 (by Mitsubishi); F-104DJ, 20 (by Mitsubishi); CF-104 and CF-104D, 200 (by Canadair); F-104S, 205 (by Aeritalia) completed 1978.

Notes: Production total of 2,406 makes Starfighter one of most successful fighters since World War II, as well as being one of the more controversial. By 1982, rather more than 1,000 single-seaters were still in service (plus about 200 two-seaters), the principal users then being the air forces of Canada (for its three NATO-assigned squadrons in Europe), Germany, Japan and Italy, the last-mentioned including the Italian-developed F-104S in its inventory. Other users, in smaller numbers, were the German Navy and the air forces of Belgium, Denmark, Greece, Jordan, the Netherlands, Norway and Turkey.

McDONNELL F-101 VOODOO

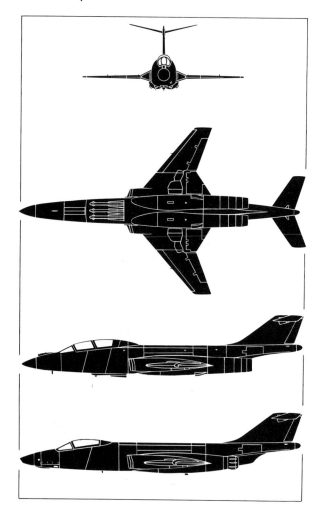

(Above) A camera-equipped RF-101C; (immediately below) a CF-101B in service with the Canadian Armed Forces; (bottom) a Canadian CF-101 with a temporary camouflage finish for participation in "Maple Flag" exercises at Cold Lake. (Silhouette) McDonnell F-101B, with additional side view of RF-101G.

Country of Origin: USA.

Type: All-weather interceptor.

Power Plant: Two (F-101B) 11,990 lb st (5 440 kgp) dry and 14,990 lb st (6 800 kgp) with reheat Pratt & Whitney J57-P-53 or 55 or (RF-101C) 10,100 lb st (4 580 kgp) and 14,880 lb st (6 750 kgp) with reheat J57-P-13 turbojets.

Performance: (F-101B) Max speed 1,093 mph (1 760 km/h) at 35,000 ft (10 668 m) or Mach 1·65, and 770 mph (1 240 km/h) at sea level; max rate of climb, 38,650 ft/min (196 m/sec); service ceiling, 52,000 ft (15 850 m); combat radius (area intercept), 694 mls (1 117 km); ferry range, 1,754 mls (2 823 km).

Weights: (F-101B) Empty, 28,492 lb (12 924 kg); normal take-off for intercept mission, 41,490 lb (18 820 kg); max loaded weight, 52,400 lb (23 768 kg).

Dimensions: Span, 39 ft 8 in (12,09 m); length (F-101B), 67 ft 4¾ in (20,55 m), (RF-101C) 69 ft 3 in (21,10 m); height 18 ft 0 in (5,49 m); wing area, 368 sq ft (34,2 m²).

Accommodation: (F-101B, CF-101B) Pilot and observer. (TF-101B, CF-101F) two pilots in tandem and (RF-101C) pilot only.

Armament: (F-101B, F-101F) Internal bay accommodating two AIM-4D Falcon AAMs and two AIR-2A Genie missiles under fuselage. (F-101C) Four 20 mm cannon in forward fuselage.

Status: Prototype (XF-88) flown 20 October 1948; first production F-101A flown on 29 September 1954; first of two YRF-101A prototypes flown on 10 May 1956; first RF-101C flown on 12 July 1957; first F-101B flown on 27 March 1957. Production quantities: F.101A, 77; F-101C, 47; YRF-101A, 2; RF-101A, 35; RF-101C, 166; F-101B, 480. Production completed 1961.

Notes: F-101A and improved F-101C served with Tactical Air Command; most were converted to RF-101G and RF-101H reconnaissance configuration for Air National Guard before being retired from service. RF-101A and RF-101C were camera-equipped production versions and some RF-101Cs served with the Chinese Nationalist Air Force. Two-seat F-101B interceptor was for long a mainstay of US continental air defence but by 1981 only 36 remained in USAF service with two ANG Fighter Interceptor Groups, plus about 60 equipping three Canadian squadrons. The latter originally received 56 F-101Fs and 10 TF-101Fs, which were redesignated CF-101B and CF-101F respectively after delivery. From 1970, the 58 surviving Canadian Voodoos were exchanged for 66 refurbished late-model USAF F-101Bs with more advanced MG-13 fire control and MB-5 autopilot and these were serving in 1982 with Nos 409, 416 and 425 Squadrons.

(Top) A McDonnell Douglas A-4L of the US Navy's Fleet Composite Squadron VC-2; (immediately above) an A-4M Skyhawk of the US Marine Corps; (below) an Israeli Air Force A-4E, with added avionics fairing. (Silhouette) McDonnell Douglas A-4M Skyhawk.

Country of Origin: USA.

Type: Carrier or land-based attack bomber.

Power Plant: One (A-4B,C,L,P,Q) 7,700 lb st (3 493 kgp) Wright J65-W-16A or (A-4E) 8,500 lb st (3 856 kgp) J52-P-6 or (A-4F,G,H,K) 9,300 lb st (4 218 kgp) J52-P-8A or (A-4M,N) 11,200 lb st (5 443 kgp) J52-P-408A turbojet.

Performance: (A-4M) Maximum speed, clean, 670 mph (1 078 km/h) at sea level, Mach 0·94 at 25,000 ft (7 620 m); initial rate of climb, 8,440 ft/min (43,0 m/sec); tactical radius, close support mission with 4,000 lb (1 814 kg) bomb load, 340 mls (538 km); ferry range 2,050 mls (3 307 km).

Weights: (A-4M) Empty, 10,465 lb (4 747 kg); basic operating, 12,250 lb (5 579 kg); max take-off 24,500 lb (11 113 kg).

Dimensions: Span, 27 ft 6 in (8,38 m); length overall (excluding refuelling probe) (A-4E,F,G,H,K), 40 ft 1½ in (12 22 m), (A-4M,N) 40 ft 3¾ in (12,17 m), (TA-4 versions), 42 ft 7¼ in (12,98 m); height overall (single-seaters), 15 ft 0 in (4,57 m), (two-seaters), 15 ft 3 in (4,66 m); wing area 260 sq ft (24,17 m²).

Accommodation: (A-4 series) Pilot only or (TA-4 series) two.

Armament: Two (all versions except H and N) 20-mm MK-12 cannon or (A-4H,TA-4H,A-4N) 30-mm DEFA cannon in wing roots. One centreline strong point and four wing pylons, combined

capacity 9,155 lb (4 153 kg).

Status: Prototype (XA4D-1) first flown on 22 June 1954; A-4B (A4D-2) flown 26 March 1956; A-4C (A4D-2N) flown 21 August 1958; A-4E (A4D-5) flown 12 July 1961; TA-4E (later TA-4F) flown 30 June 1965; A-4F flown 31 August 1966; TA-4J flown 21 November 1969; A-4H flown 27 October 1967; TA-4H flown 15 April 1969; A-4M Skyhawk II flown 10 April 1970; A-4N flown 8 June 1972; A-4L (conversion) flown August 1969; OA-4M (conversion) flown 23 May 1978; A-4S (conversion) flown 14 July 1973; TA-4S (conversion) flown 21 February 1975; Production totals include A-4A and prototypes, 166; A-4B, 542; A-4C, 638; A-4E, 500; A-4F, 146; TA-4F, 241; A-4G, 8 (plus 8 ex-USN); TA-4G, 2 (plus 2 ex-USN); A-4H, 90; TA-4H, 10; TA-4J, 292; A-4K, 10; TA-4K, 4; A-4M, 158; A-4N, 117; A4-KU, 30; TA-4KU, 6; total 2,960, completed February 1979.

Notes: In addition to new-build aircraft listed above, US Navy has 100 A-4L conversions of A-4Cs and USMC has 23 OA-4Ms from TA-4Fs for FAC duty. Argentine Air Force acquired 50 revised A-4Bs as A-4Ps and Argentine Navy, 16 as A-4Q. Israel received 60 A-4Es and 17 TA-4Js from US Navy stocks and Singapore acquired 40 A-4Bs modified to A-4S and three two-seat TA-4S. Indonesia purchased 14 A-4E and two TA-4H from Israel in 1980.

(Above) A McDonnell Douglas F-4J Phantom II of US Navy squadron VF-96 leaves the waist catapult of the USS "Constellation"; (immediately below) camera-equipped RF-4E of the Japanese Air Self-Defence Force; (bottom) Phantom FGR Mk 2 in RAF air defence finish adopted 1981. (Silhouette) F-4E Phantom, with additional side view of Phantom FG Mk 1.

Country of Origin: USA.

Type: Tactical strike fighter and reconnaissance aircraft.

Power Plant: Two (F-4B, N, RF-4B) 17,000 lb st (7 710 kgp) with reheat J79-GE-8 or (F-4C, D, RF-4C) J79-GE-15 or (F-4E, EJ, F, G, RF-4E) 17,900 lb st (8 120 kgp) J79-GE-17 or (F-4J) J79-GE-10 turbojets. (Phantom FG Mk 1, FGR Mk 2) 20,315 lb st (9,300 kgp) with reheat Rolls-Royce Spey 202 turbofans.

Performance: (F-4E) Max speed with external stores, 910 mph (1 464 km/h) or Mach 1·2 at 1,000 ft (305 m), 1,433 mph (2 304 km/h) or Mach 2·17 at 36,000 ft (10 793 m); initial rate of climb, 49,800 ft/min (253 m/sec); service ceiling (clean), 58,750 ft (17 907 m); combat radius (CAP with four AAMs and three drop tanks), 288 mls (463 km) and (HI-LO-HI with four AAMs, bombs and drop tanks), 505 mls (813 km); ferry range, 1,612 mls (2 595 km).

Weights: Empty equipped, 30,425 lb (13 800 kg); typical loaded, 51,810 lb (21 500 kg); fully-loaded (eight AAMs, one drop tank) 58,000 lb (26 308 kg); max overload 61,795 lb (28 055 kg).

Dimensions: Span, 39 ft 7½ in (11,77 m); length (F-4A, B, C, D, G, J, N), 58 ft 1½ in (17,76 m), (RF-4B, C, E, F-4E), 63 ft 0 in (19,20 m); (Phantom 1 and 2) 57 ft 7 in (17,55 m); height 16 ft 5½ in (5,02 m); wing area 530 sq ft (49,2 m²).

Accommodation: Two pilots or pilot and observer.

Armament: Semi-recessed installation of four AIM-7 Sparrow AAMs under fuselage and four wing pylons for four AIM-9 Sidewinders or up to 16,000 lb (7 257 kg) of external stores plus (F-4E, F-4EJ, F-4F) one 20-mm M-61A1 rotary cannon in nose.

Status: Prototype (XF4H-1) first flown 27 May 1958; F-4B flown 25 March 1961; RF-4B flown 12 March 1965; F-4C on 27 May 1963; YRF-4C on 8 August 1963; production RF-4C on 18 May 1964; F-4D on 8 December 1965; YF-4E on 7 August 1965 and production F-4E on 30 June 1967; F-4E (J) on 14 January 1971; RF-4E flown on 15 September 1970; F-4F on 18 May 1973; F-4G on 20 March 1963; YF-4J on 4 June 1965 and production F-4J on 27 May 1966; YF-4K on 27 June 1966 and Phantom FG Mk 1 on 2 November 1966; YF-4M on 17 February 1967 and Phantom FGR Mk 2 on 26 December 1967; F-4N on 4 June 1972. Production total 5,211 completed 20 May 1981 (in Japan), comprising F-4A (F4H-1F), 47; F-4B, 637; RF-4B, 46; F-4C, 583; RF-4C, 505; F-4D, 825; F-4E, 1,387; F-4E (J), 140; RF-4E, 162; F-4F, 175; F-4G, 12; F-4J, 522; Phantom 1, 52; Phantom 2, 118.

Notes: Conversion programmes produced 178 F-4N (from F-4B) and 302 F-4S (from F-4J) for USN and 116 F-4G (from F-4E) Wild Weasels for USAF; original USN F-4Gs were converted to F-4B.

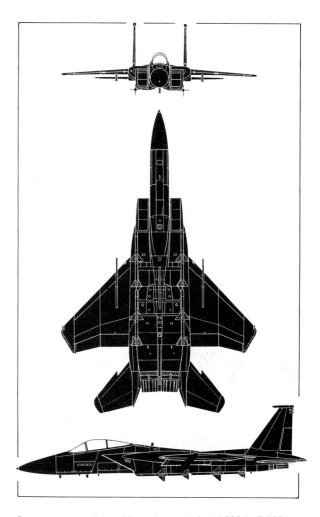

(Top) Air and (immediately above) ground views of a McDonnell Douglas F-15 Eagle of the 32nd Tactical Fighter Squadron based in the Netherlands; (below) the prototype two-seat "Strike Eagle" (F-15E) with FAST packs, bombs and AAMs. (Silhouette) McDonnell Douglas F-15C Eagle.

Country of Origin: USA.
Type: Air superiority fighter and two-seat operational trainer.
Power Plant: Two 23,904 lb (10 855 kgp) with reheat Pratt & Whitney F100-P-100 turbofans.
Performance: (F-15C) Max sustained speed (approx) 1,520 mph (2 446 km/h) or Mach 2·3 above 36,000 ft (10 975 m); max short-period dash speed, 1,650 mph (2 655 km/h) or Mach 2·5; max low altitude speed (approx) 915 mph (1 470 km/h) or Mach 1·2 at 1,000 ft (305 m); initial rate of climb, over 50,000 ft/min (254 m/sec); service ceiling, approx 65,000 ft (19 800 m); unre-fuelled ferry range, over 3,500 mls (5 630 km).
Weights: (F-15C) Normal take-off weight, interceptor with full internal fuel and four AIM-7 Sparrows, 44,500 lb (20 185 kg); normal take-off weight with three 600-US gal (2271-1) drop tanks, 57,400 lb (26 035 kg); max weight, 68,000 lb (30 845 kg).
Dimensions: Span, 42 ft 9½ in (13,04 m); length 63 ft 9½ in (19,44 m); height, 18 ft 5½ in (5,63 m); wing area, 608 sq ft (56,50 m²).
Accommodation: Pilot only or (F-15B, F-15D) two in tandem.
Armament: One 20-mm M-61A-1 rotary cannon. Provision in semi-recessed housings under fuselage for four Raytheon AIM-7F Sparrow plus four AIM-9L Sidewinder AAMs under wings and

five weapons stations with total capacity for 16,000 lb (7 257 kg).
Status: First of 20 development and test F-15As flown on 27 July 1972; second aircraft flown on 26 September 1972 and third aircraft on 4 November 1972. First F-15B (originally TF-15A) flown on 7 July 1973; first Fast Pack installation flown 27 July 1974; first F-15C on 27 February 1979; first F-15D on 19 June 1979; prototype Strike Eagle (F-15E) flown 8 July 1980. Produc-tion totals, YF-15A, 2; F-15A, 383; F-15B, 60; F-15C/D in production 1981 to meet total USAF requirement for 870. Exports to Israel (40 F-15A), Saudi Arabia (47 F-15C/15 F-15D) and Japan (16 F-15J/F-15DJ plus 84 licence-built by Mitsubishi).
Notes: The F-15A Eagle was developed to provide USAF's Tactical Air Command with an air superiority fighter for service in the period 1975-1985. Deliveries to TAC began 15 November 1974 and by mid-1981 the Eagle equipped the US-based 1st, 33rd and 49th TF Wings, the 18th TFW in Japan, the 36th TFW in Germany and the 32nd TFW in the Netherlands. F-15C and two-seat F-15D differ from original A and B models in having 2,000 lb (907 kg) more internal fuel, provision for Fast Pack conformal fuel/sensor packs and programmable radar signal processors. Prototype two-seat Strike Eagle (F-15E) was developed as an all-weather interdictor with revised radar and avionics.

McDONNELL DOUGLAS F-18A HORNET

(Above) An early production F-18A Hornet reveals its distinctive profile in flight; (immediately below) the twin fins and rudder are an unusual feature of the Hornet's configuration; (bottom) a bomb-carrying F-18 at touchdown. (Silhouette) F-18A and (lower sideview) TF-18A.

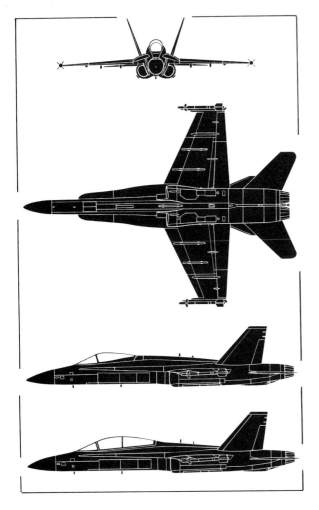

Country of Origin: USA.

Type: Single-seat shipboard fighter and attack aircraft and two-seat operational trainer.

Power Plant: Two 10,600 lb (4 810 kg) dry and 16,000 lb (7 260 kg) reheat General Electric F404-GE-400 turbofans.

Performance: Max speed (with two wingtip-mounted AIM-9s and two fuselage-mounted AIM-7s), 1,190 mph (1 915 km/h) above 36,000 ft (10 970 m) or Mach 1·8, 915 mph (1 472 km/h) at sea level or Mach 1·2; combat ceiling, about 50,000 ft (15 240 m); combat radius (fighter escort mission on internal fuel), 460 mls (740 km), (with three 315 US gal/1 1921 external tanks). 735 mls (1 180 km); ferry range, over 2,300 mls (3 700 km).

Weights: Loaded (air superiority mission with two AIM-9s, two AIM-7s and full cannon ammunition), 35,800 lb (16 240 kg); max take-off, 50,000 lb (22 680 kg).

Dimensions: Span, 37 ft 6 in (11,43 m); length 56 ft 0 in (17,07 m); height, 15 ft 4 in (4,67 m); wing area, 400 sq ft (37,16 m²).

Accommodation: Pilot only or (TF-18A, CF-18B), two in tandem.

Armament: One 20-mm multi-barrel M61A1 rotary cannon with 570 rounds and (air-air combat) two IR-homing AIM-9 Sidewinder and two radar-guided AIM-7 Sparrow missiles. Nine external stores stations for maximum of 17,000 lb (7 710 kg) ordnance.

Status: First of 11 (nine F-18As and two TF-18As) full-scale development (FSD) aircraft flown 18 November 1978, first TF-18A (FSD) flown 25 October 1979. First production F-18A flown April 1980. Total planned procurement of 1,366 (including 153 TF-18As) for US Navy and USMC. Canadian Armed Forces ordered 113 single-seat shore-based CF-18As and 24 two-seat CF-18Bs, for delivery starting October 1982; RAAF ordered 57 F-18As and 18 TF-18As (GAF-assembled) for delivery from 1985.

Notes: Chosen to replace the F-4 Phantom II in the US Navy and the US Marine Corps and the A-7 Corsair II in the US Navy, the Hornet is destined to become one of the principal Naval aircraft of the mid/late 'eighties. It was developed after the USN had comprehensively evaluated both the GD F-16 and Northrop YF-17 Lightweight Fighter prototypes and had selected, in January 1976, the latter to provide the basis for its new Naval fighter/attack aircraft. McDonnell Douglas became the prime contractor for the F-18, which is of similar configuration to the YF-17 but of slightly larger overall dimensions with more internal fuel capacity, Hughes APG-65 radar and more wing area. Separate F-18 fighter and A-18 attack variants were at first planned but both rôles were later combined in a single basic version.

McDONNELL DOUGLAS/BAe AV-8B HARRIER II

(Top) The first of a pilot production batch of AV-8Bs making its maiden flight at St Louis; (immediately above and below) ground views of the first AV-8B showing the larger wing of this development of the Harrier. (Silhouette) McDonnell Douglas AV-8B Harrier II.

Country of Origin: USA.

Type: V/STOL ground attack aircraft.

Power Plant: One 21,500 lb st (9 760 kgp) Rolls-Royce F402-RR-405 vectored-thrust turbofan.

Performance: (Estimated, FSD aircraft) Max speed (clean aircraft), 685 mph (1 100 km/h) at 1,000 ft (305 m) or Mach 0·9 (with high-drag external load), 530 mph (852 km/h) at 5,000 ft (1 525 m) or Mach 0·71; combat radius (with max external load and one gun), 213 mls (343 km), (with full internal fuel, seven 580 lb/259 kg bombs and one gun), 247 mls (398 km), (with two external tanks), 725 mls (1 167 km); ferry range (four drop tanks), 2,880 mls (4 635 km).

Weights: Operational empty, 12,750 lb (5 783 kg); max short take-off, 28,750 lb (13 041 kg); max take-off, 29,750 lb (13 495 kg).

Dimensions: Span 30 ft 4 in (9,24 m); length 46 ft 4 in (14,12 m); height, 11 ft 8 in (3,55 m); wing area, 230 sq ft (21,37 m²).

Accommodation: Pilot only.

Armament: Provision for two pod-mounted 30-mm cannon beneath fuselage. Six wing pylons and fuselage centreline pylon for up to 9,200 lb (4,173 kg), typical max load comprising 16 570-lb (259-kg) Mk 82 bombs.

Status: First of two YAV-8B prototypes (AV-8A conversions) flown on 9 November 1978. First of four AV-8B (FSD) aircraft flown 5 November 1981. First of 12 pilot production AV-8Bs, part of US Marine Corps planned procurement of 336, to fly mid-1982. First FSD Harrier GR Mk 5 to fly early 1984. First (of 60) production GR Mk 5s to fly early 1986.

Notes: Under collaborative agreements signed between Hawker Siddeley and the McDonnell Douglas Corporation, work proceeded on an improvement of the AV-8A/Harrier, to meet a specific US Marine Corps requirement for a new attack aircraft to replace the AV-8A and the A-4M. The new features of the AV-8B are a supercritical wing with two additional strong points, some lift-improvement devices, uprated engine with redesigned intakes and strengthened undercarriage for higher operating weights. Two AV-8As were converted (by McDonnell Douglas at St Louis) to YAV-8B prototypes and four full-scale development AV-8Bs were ordered, the latter featuring a raised cockpit similar to that of the Sea Harrier. The USMC has a requirement for 336 AV-8Bs and the RAF is to order 60 as Harrier GR Mk 5s, the latter to be assembled in the UK by British Aerospace. BAe also is responsible for production of major fuselage portions of all AV-8Bs for assembly at St Louis.

(Above) A MiG-17F Fresco-C with additional stores pylons outboard of the standard tank-carrying pylons. (Immediately below) A Polish-built MiG-17F (LIM-5) with additional wing pylon and landing chute and (bottom) an Egyptian MiG-17F. (Silhouette) MiG-17F Fresco-C.

Country of Origin: Soviet Union.

Type: Light air superiority and close air support fighter.

Power Plant: One 5,732 lb st (2 600 kgp) and 7,452 lb st reheat Klimov VK-1F turbojet.

Performance: (Fresco-C) Max speed (clean aircraft), 711 mph (1 145 km/h) or Mach 0·974 at 9,840 ft (3 000 m), 702 mph (1 130 km/h) or Mach 0·986 at 16,400 ft (5 000 m), 626 mph (1 071 km/h) or Mach 0·93 at 32,810 ft (10 000 m); max climb, 12,795 ft/min (65 m/sec); ceiling (without reheat), 49,540 ft (15 000 m), (with reheat), 54,460 ft (16 600 m); range (internal fuel), 422 mls (680 km) at 16,400 ft (5 000 m), 603 mls (970 km) at 32,810 ft (10 000 m), (with two 88 Imp gal/400 l drop tanks), 640 mls (1 030 km) at 16,400 ft (5 000 m), 913 mls (1 470 km) at 32,810 ft (10 000 m).

Weights: Loaded (clean), 11,733 lb (5 340 kg), with two 88 Imp gal/400 l drop tanks), 13,380 lb (6 069 kg).

Dimensions: Span, 31 ft 7⅛ in (9 63 m); length, 36 ft 4⅝ in (11,09 m); height, 12 ft 5⅝ in (3,80 m); wing area, 243·26 sq ft (22,60 m²).

Armament: Three 23-mm NR-23 cannon and (close air support) four 551-lb (250-kg) bombs or UV-16-57 pods each containing 16 × 55-mm S-5 rockets, or combination of the two.

Accommodation: Pilot only (see also two-seat trainer FT-5, page 216).

Status: The first prototype of the MiG-17, the SI, was first flown in December 1949, entering Soviet service (Fresco-A) in 1952. The first genuinely transonic Soviet production aircraft, the MiG-17 was an extrapolation of the MiG-15 retaining only the fuselage of the earlier fighter forward of the rear frame of the engine plenum chamber. Numerous variants were produced, the principal being the MiG-17F (Fresco-C) improved day fighter, the MiG-17P and PF (Fresco-B and D) limited all-weather fighters, and the MiG-17PFU (Fresco-E) armed with AA-1 Alkali AAMs. Licence production was undertaken in Poland and Czechoslovkia from late 1955, and in China in 1956 (as the F-5). The MiG-17 was phased out of production in the Soviet Union in the late 'fifties, and in Poland and Czechoslovakia in the early 'sixties, but continued in China (in two-seat conversion trainer form) into the 'seventies.

Notes: Although obsolete and withdrawn from the first-line inventories of all WarPac air arms, the MiG-17F (Fresco-C) still fulfils the close air support role in some numbers with the air forces of Afghanistan, China, Cuba, Egypt, Sudan, Syria, Uganda and Vietnam.

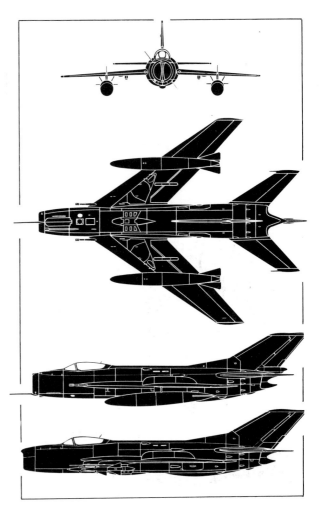

(Above top) F-6 Farmers of No 15 Sqdn, Pakistan Air Force, and (immediately above) an F-6 of No 14 Sqdn with (now standard) tail braking chute housing. (Below) F-6s of No 25 Sqdn, PAF. (Silhouette) Farmer-C with additional sideview of Farmer-E (F-6yi).

Country of Origin: Soviet Union (and China).

Type: Clear-weather day (Farmer-C and F-6bin) and limited all-weather (Farmer-D and E, and F-6jia and yi) air superiority and interceptor fighter.

Power Plant: Two 4,732 lb st (2 600 kgp) and 7,165 lb st (3 250 kgp) reheat Tumansky RD-9B-811 or (F-6) Wopen WP-6 turbojets.

Performance: (Farmer-C and F-6bin) Max speed (clean), 902 mph (1 450 km/h) or Mach 1·35 at 32,800 ft (10 000 m), (with two drop tanks), 715 mph (1 150 km/h) or Mach 1·12; initial climb (at max take-off weight), 22,640 ft/min (115 m/sec); time to 32,810 ft (10 000 m), 1·85 min; max range (clean), 863 mls (1 390 km) at 45,920 ft (14 000 m), (with drop tanks), 1,366 mls (2 200 km).

Weights: Empty equipped, 11,399 lb (5 172 kg); loaded, 16,314 lb (7 400 kg); max take-off, 19,621 lb (8 900 kg).

Dimensions: Span, 29 ft 6⅓ in (9,00 m); length (excluding probe), 41 ft 4 in (12,60 m); height, 12 ft 9½ in (3,90 m); wing area, 269·1 sq ft (25,00 m²).

Armament: (MiG-19S) Three 30-mm NR-30 cannon and (F-6bin) two K-13A (Atoll) or (Pakistan F-6) AIM-9 Sidewinder AAMs and two 32 × 57-mm rocket pods, or (MiG-19SW) two 37-mm cannon

and two 551-lb (250-kg) bombs, or (MiG-19SF and PF Farmer-D) two 30-mm cannon, or (MiG-19PM Farmer-E) four AA-1 Alkali semi-active radar homing AAMs.

Accommodation: Pilot only (see also FT-6 page 216).

Status: First genuine prototype (SM-2) flown 27 May 1952, with production prototype (SM-9) following on 5 January 1954, large-scale manufacture being ordered on 31 August 1955 as MiG-19S (Farmer-C). Production of MiG-19S and limited all-weather derivatives (MiG-19PF and PM) phased out in Soviet Union late 1957, but MiG-19S manufacture continued in Czechoslovakia until 1961. Production undertaken in China from 1958 at Shenyang and, subsequently, at Tientsin as F-6 and F-6bin (MiG-19S), F-6jia (MiG-19PF) and F-6yi (MiG-19PM), and continuing at latter facility at beginning of 1982, with production reducing from 200 to 100 annually.

Notes: Although all versions of the Soviet-and Czech-built MiG-19 have been phased out of first-line WarPac service, the Chinese-built derivatives serve in large numbers, being the principal fighter equipment of the Chinese Air Force and having been exported to Albania (36), · Bangladesh (36), Egypt (80), Pakistan (150), Tanzania (12), Vietnam and Zambia (12). Several thousand F-6s have been built in China.

FIGHTER/ATTACK

MIKOYAN-GUREVICH MIG-21 (FISHBED)

(Above) A MiG-21PFMA Fishbed-J of the Cuban Air Force. (Immediately below) A MiG-21M of the Indian Air Force, and (bottom) a MiG-21bis Fishbed-N of the Soviet Air Force. (Silhouette) The upper three views depict the MiG-21bis with (sideviews) MiG-21SMT and MiG-21PF.

Country of Origin: Soviet Union.

Type: Single-seat (Fishbed-C and E) clear-weather day, (Fishbed-D, F, J and K) limited all-weather and (Fishbed-L and N) multi-role fighter, (Fishbed-H) tactical reconnaissance aircraft and (Mongol) two-seat conversion trainer.

Power Plant: (Fishbed-N) One 16,535 lb st (7 500 kgp) reheat Tumansky R-25 turbojet.

Performance: Max speed (clean aircraft with half fuel), 808 mph (1 300 km/h) or Mach 1·06 at 1,000 ft (305 m), 1,386 mph (2 230 km/h) or Mach 2·1 above 36,090 ft (11 000 m); initial climb, 58,000 ft/min (295 m/sec); combat radius (air superiority mission with centreline drop tank and four AAMs), 340 mls (547 km), (with three drop tanks and two AAMs), 500 mls (805 km).

Weights: Empty, 11,465 lb (5 200 kg); combat (centreline drop tank and four AAMs), 17,550 lb (7960 kg); max take-off, 19,280 lb (8 745 kg).

Dimensions: Span, 23 ft 5½ in (7,15 m); length (including probe), 51 ft 8½ in (15,76 m), (without probe), 44 ft 2 in (13,46 m); wing area, 247·57 sq ft (23,00 m²).

Armament: (Fishbed-C) One 30-mm NR-30 cannon and two AA-2-2 Atoll AAMs, (Fishbed-D, E and F) two Atoll AAMs and provision for GP-9 gun pack with twin-barrel 23-mm GSh-23 cannon, or (Fishbed-J, K, L and N) four AA-2-2 Atoll AAMs (mix of IR- and radar-homing), or two Atolls and two IR-homing AA-8 Aphids with provision for centreline GP-9 pack.

Accommodation: Pilot only, or (Mongol) instructor and pupil in tandem.

Status: Aerodynamic prototype (Ye-4) flown 14 June 1956, the first series version (Ye-6T) entering production in 1959 as the MiG-21F (Fishbed-C) clear-weather day fighter. Succeeded by limited all-weather version (Ye-7) which entered service as MiG-21PF (Fishbed-D) and in progressively improved versions, including MiG-21PFS and MiG-21PFM (Fishbed-F) and PFMA (Fishbed-J). Second generation version, the MiG-21MF with lighter R-13-300 engine (offering 30 per cent greater dry thrust than R-11F2S-300 of preceding models) entered service from 1970, followed from mid 'seventies by multi-role MiG-21bis (Fishbed-L) and MiG-21Mbis (Fishbed-N), the latter having an R-25 engine offering 13·6 per cent more power with reheat. Over 6,000 MiG-21s manufactured since 1959, with production (for export) continuing at some 200 annually at the beginning of 1982, when some 1,300 remained in Soviet service. Licence production of MiG-21Mbis is continuing in India. A version built in China is designated F-7.

MIKOYAN-GUREVICH MIG-23 (FLOGGER)

(Above, top) A MiG-23 Flogger-E of Libyan AF, (immediately above) a MiG-23MF Flogger-B with Apex and Aphid AAMs, and (below) MiG-23BN Flogger-Hs of the Czechoslovak Air Force. (Silhouette) The upper three views depict Flogger-B with (bottom) Flogger-H.

Country of Origin: Soviet Union.

Type: Single-seat (Flogger-B, E and G) all-weather air superiority and interceptor fighter, (Flogger-F and H) close air support and counterair fighter, and (Flogger-C) two-seat conversion trainer.

Power Plant: One 17,635 lb st (8 000 kgp) and 25,350 lb st (11 500 kgp) reheat Tumansky R-29B turbofan.

Performance: (Flogger-B) Max speed (clean aircraft with half fuel), 838 mph (1 350 km/h) at 1,000 ft (305 m) or Mach 1·1, 1,520 mph (2 446 km/h) or Mach 2·3 above 36,090 ft (11 000 m); combat radius (high-altitude air superiority mission on internal fuel with four AAMs), 530 mls (850 km), with centreline combat tank), 700 mls (1 126 km); ferry range (max external fuel), 2,100 mls (3 380 km) at 495 mph (795 km/h) or Mach 0·75; service ceiling, 59,050 ft (18 000 m).

Weights: Normal loaded (clean), 34,170 lb (15 500 kg); max take-off, 44,312 lb (20 100 kg).

Dimensions: (Estimated) Span (spread), 46 ft 9 in (14,25 m), (sweptback), 27 ft 6 in (8,38 m); length (including probe), 55 ft 1½ in (16,80 m); wing area, 293·4 sq ft (27,26 m²).

Armament: One 23-mm twin-barrel GSh-23L cannon and (Flogger-B and G) two AA-7 Apex semi-active radar-guided and two AA-8 Aphid IR-homing AAMs, or (Flogger-E) four AA-2-2 (two IR-

homing and two radar-guided) AAMs, or (Flogger-F and H) up to 9,920 lb (4 500 kg) of bombs and/or ASMs on five stations.

Accommodation: Pilot only or (Flogger-C) instructor and pupil in tandem.

Status: An aerodynamic prototype (Ye-231) entered flight test in the winter of 1966–67, and initial series model optimised for air-to-air tasks entered service as the MiG-23 (Flogger-B) in 1971. An export equivalent of the Flogger-B is the Flogger-E; an improved air-to-air version is the Flogger-G which began to enter service in 1978, and Flogger-F and H are air-to-ground versions with a redesigned forward fuselage which entered service 1975–76. Production rate of all versions of Flogger (including MiG-27, see page 39) was approximately 50 monthly at the beginning of 1982, when 2,300–2,500 (all variants) were in Soviet service.

Notes: As a combat aircraft family, Flogger is now numerically the most important basic type in Soviet service. Flogger-B and E (MiG-23MF) and Flogger-F and H (MiG-23BN) have been widely exported, and India is assembling the latter under licence, current orders calling for the Indian Air Force to receive 70 single-seat Flogger-Fs and 15 two-seat Flogger-Cs. The forward fuselage of the Flogger-F and H is essentially similar to that of the MiG-27, the Flogger-H having upgraded avionics equipment.

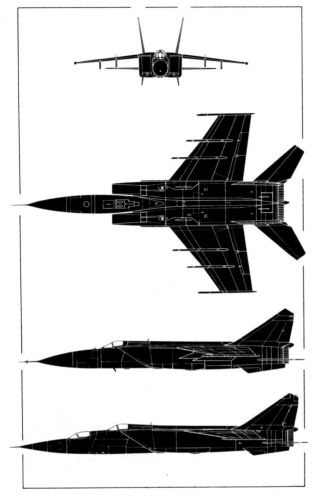

(Above) A MiG-25 Foxbat-A with four Acrid AAMs, (immediately below) a reconnaissance Foxbat-B and (bottom) the optimised ELINT Foxbat-D. (Silhouette) The upper three views depict the standard Foxbat-A and the additional sideview illustrates the Foxbat-C.

Country of Origin: Soviet Union.

Type: Single-seat (Foxbat-A) interceptor fighter, (Foxbat-B and D) reconnaissance aircraft and (Foxbat-C) two-seat conversion trainer.

Power Plant: Two 20,500 lb st (9 300 kgp) and 27,120 lb st (12 300 kgp) reheat Tumansky R-31 turbojets.

Performance: (Foxbat-A) Max speed (short-period dash with four AAMs), 1,850 mph (2 980 km/h) or Mach 2·8 above 36,000 ft (10 970 m); max. speed at sea level, 650 mph (1 045 km/h) or Mach 0·85; initial climb, 40,950 ft/min (208 m/sec); service ceiling, 80,000 ft (24 385 m); combat radius (including allowance for Mach 2·5 intercept), 250 mls (400 km), (range-optimised profile at econ power), 400 mls (645 km).

Weights: (Foxbat-A) Empty equipped, 44,100 lb (20 000 kg); max. take-off, 77,160 lb (35 000 kg).

Dimensions: Span, 45 ft 9 in (13,94 m); length (including probe), 73 ft 2 in (22,30 m); height, 18 ft 4½ in (5,60 m); wing area, 602·8 sq ft (56,00 m²).

Armament: Four AA-6 Acrid AAMs (two semi-active radar homing and two IR homing).

Accommodation: Pilot only, or (Foxbat-C) tandem seating for instructor and pupil.

Status: The MiG-25 entered service (in Foxbat-A form) in 1970, reconnaissance (Foxbat-B) and conversion trainer versions following in 1971 and 1973 respectively, with an optimised ELINT (electronic intelligence) model achieving service status in 1974. The Foxbat-A and C versions of the MiG-25 have been exported to Algeria, Syria and Libya, the last-mentioned country having received some 60 aircraft, and the Foxbat-B (eight aircraft) and C versions have been exported to India.

Notes: Foxbat-A is currently employed by the Soviet air defence forces, and Foxbat-B and D by the tactical air arm. Foxbat-B and D are reportedly capable of Mach 3·2 in clean condition, the former possessing both photographic and ELINT capabilities, and the latter being an optimised ELINT version. An advanced interceptor version of the MiG-25 was reportedly under development at the beginning of 1982, when it was expected to be deployed operationally within two–three years. A two-seater armed with up to eight AA-9 long-range radar-guided AAMs, a new radar with full lookdown-shootdown capability and a 165-mile (270-km) tracking range, the new version is believed to have uprated R-31F turbojets, and an improved automatic flight control system and data link. The designation MiG-25MP has been reported for this advanced Foxbat.

Both the photographs above and below and the silhouette (right) depict the Flogger-D, the initial series production version of the MiG-27 for Soviet Frontal Aviation. The MiG-27s below belong to a regiment assigned to the Trans-Baikal Military District.

Country of Origin: Soviet Union.
Type: Tactical strike and close air support fighter.
Power Plant: One 14,330 lb st (6 500 kgp) and 17,920 lb st (8 130 kgp) reheat Tumansky R-29-300 turbofan.
Performance: Max speed (clean aircraft with half fuel), 685 mph (1 102 km/h) or Mach 0·95 at 1,000 ft (305 m), 1,056 mph (1 700 km/h) or Mach 1·6 at 36,090 ft (11 000 m); combat radius (HI-LO-HI mission profile on internal fuel with 4,410 lb/2 000 kg external ordnance), 310 mls (500 km), (with centreline fuel tank), 360 mls (580 km); service ceiling, 52,500 ft (16 000 m).
Weights: (Estimated) Normal loaded (clean), 35,000 lb (15 875 kg); max take-off, 45,000 lb (20 410 kg).
Dimensions: (Estimated) Span (spread), 46 ft 9 in (14,25 m), (sweptback), 27 ft 6 in (8,38 m); length (including probe), 54 ft 0 in (16,46 m); wing area, 293·4 sq ft (27,26 m²).
Armament: One 23-mm six-barrel rotary cannon and up to 7,716 lb (3 500 kg) or external ordnance on five stores stations. Typical external load comprises centreline drop tank and four 1,102-lb (500-kg) bombs, plus two AA-2-2 Atoll IR-homing missiles for self defence. A mix of AS-7 Kerry, AS-9, AS-11 and AS-12 ASMs may be carried.
Accommodation: Pilot only.

Status: The MiG-27 is a dedicated air-to-ground derivative of the basic MiG-23 (see page 37) and is believed to have first entered Soviet service in 1975–76 (Flogger-D), with production continuing (Flogger-J) at the beginning of 1982
Notes: Whereas the MiG-23 Flogger-F and H (see page 37) were minimum change air-to-ground members of the basic MiG-23 family by Soviet standards of evolutionary design, the MiG-27 was tailored closely for ground attack. The forward fuselage is essentially similar to that of Flogger-F and H, apart from some augmentation of the side armour, but a modified undercarriage for enhanced rough field operation has necessitated bulging the fuselage adjacent to the main wheel bays, and in optimising the MiG-27 for the low-level role (with some sacrifice in speed and high-altitude capability), a modified turbofan is installed, this having a larger LP compressor, shorter, simplified two-position exhaust nozzle and larger-area fixed air intakes (as opposed to the variable intakes of the MiG-23). The current Flogger-J model is characterised by a longer nose embodying two optical flats and small fillets above the intake box to increase lift and enhance turning performance. At the beginning of 1982, the MiG-27 was believed used exclusively by Soviet Frontal Aviation and had not been exported, but is to be licence-built in India.

(Above) A Mitsubishi F-1 serving with the 3rd Air Squadron of the JASDF's 3rd Air Wing at Misawa Air Base; (immediately below and bottom) ground views of F-1s in service at Misawa, the first JASDF base to receive the F-1. (Silhouette) Mitsubishi F-1.

Country of Origin: Japan.

Type: Single-seat close air support fighter.

Power Plant: Two 4,710 lb st (2 136kgp) dry and 7,070 lb st (3 207 kgp) with reheat Ishikawajima-Harima TF40-IHI-801A (Rolls-Royce/Turboméca Adour) turbofans.

Performance: Max speed, 1,056 mph (1 700 km/h) at 40,000 ft (12 190 m), or Mach 1·6; initial rate of climb, 35,000 ft/min (177,8 m/sec); time to climb to 36,000 ft (11 000 m), 2 min; combat radius (internal fuel only plus four Sidewinder AAMs), 173 mls (278 km), LO-LO-LO (with eight 500-lb/226,8-kg bombs and two 180-Imp gal/820-1 drop tanks), 218 mls (351 km), HI-LO-HI (with ASM-1 anti-shipping missiles and one 180 Imp gal/820 1 drop tank), 346 mls (556 km).

Weights: Operational empty, 14,017 lb (6 358 kg); max take-off, 30,146 lb (13 674 kg).

Dimensions: Span, 25 ft 10¼ in (7,88 m); length 58 ft 7 in (17,86 m); height, 14 ft 4¾ in (4,39 m); wing area, 228 sq ft (21,18 m²).

Accommodation: Pilot.

Armament: One 20-mm Vulcan JM-61 multi-barrel cannon. Five external stores stations for up to 8,000 lb (3 629 kg) of ordnance. Detachable multiple ejector racks may be fitted for up to twelve 500-lb (227-kg) bombs. Wingtip attachment points for two or four Sidewinder or Mitsubishi AAM-1 air-to-air missiles. Two Mitsubishi ASM-1 anti-shipping missiles may be carried. The fuselage and two wing hardpoints are 'wet' to allow up to 540 Imp gal (2 463 l) of additional fuel to be carried in three 180-gal (820-l) drop tanks.

Status: Two prototypes (adapted from the second and third production T-2 airframes) flown on 3 June and 7 June 1975, with first production F-1 following on 16 June 1977. Seventy (of planned total procurement of 77) ordered by March 1982, with approximately 65 delivered to the ASDF by that time. First delivery 26 September 1977.

Notes: The F-1 has been developed—as Japan's first indigenous combat aircraft since World War II—to replace the F-86F Sabre in the Air Self Defence Force. The prototypes were T-2 conversions and retained the two cockpits of the trainer, with weapons system equipment and test instrumentation in the rear cockpit. The production aircraft retain the contours of the T-1 fuselage for manufacturing convenience but the rear cockpit is fully faired. The F-1 equips two squadrons of the 3rd Air Wing, starting with the 3rd Squadron at Misawa in 1980, and one squadron of the 8th Air Wing.

(NANCHENG) KIANG 5 (FANTAN-A)

FIGHTER/ATTACK

(Top, immediately above and below) Three illustrations of the A-5 Kiang in service with the Chinese People's Republic Air Force, showing the carriage of rocket pods on wing pylons and bombs on racks on each side of the centre fuselage. (Silhouette) Nancheng A-5 Kiang

Country of Origin: Chinese Republic.
Type: Tactical strike fighter.
Power Plant: Two 5,730 lb st (2 600 kgp) dry and 7,165 lb st (3 250 kgp) reheat Wopen 6A (modified Tumansky RD-9B-811) turbojets.
Performance: (Estimated) max speed, 900 mph (1 450 km/h) at 32,800 ft (10 000 m) or Mach 1·35, 686 mph (1 100 km/h) or Mach 0·95 at sea level; range cruise, 590 mph (950 km/h) or Mach 0·83; tactical radius (LO-LO-LO mission profile with two 157-Imp gal/760-1 drop tanks and full internal ordnance), 230 mls (370 km), (HI-LO-HI), 405 mls (650 km); ferry range (max external fuel), 1,270 mls (2 050 km).
Weights: (Estimated) Empty, 13,000 lb (5 900 kg); normal loaded, 17,000 lb (7 700 kg); max take-off 19,000 lb (8 620 kg).
Dimensions: (Estimated) Span, 29 ft 6 in (9,00 m); length (without probe), 47 ft 0 in (14,30 m); height, 13 ft 0 in (3,95 m).
Accommodation: Pilot only.
Armament: Two 30-mm cannon in wing roots. Typical internal ordnance load, four 551-lb (250-kg) bombs, plus two 551-lb (250-kg) bombs on fuselage hardpoints and two or four pods each containing eight 57-mm rockets on wing stations, two of which can alternatively carry fuel tanks.

Status: Prototype development in the late 'sixties with production deliveries commencing 1972-73 and continuing from Nancheng factory during 1982.
Notes: The Kiang 5 (A-5) interdictor and counterair aircraft is a derivative of the Chinese-built MiG-19S (F-6) day fighter, which was itself first put into production in Shenyang in the early 'sixties and some thousands of which have been built in China. The Kiang 5 or A-5, which was at first known as the F-6bis, differs from its predecessor primarily in having a redesigned forward fuselage with lateral air intakes, a revised centre fuselage incorporating a weapons bay, a revised verical tail and extended flaps. The internal weapons bay, although having only a modest capacity, is an interesting feature in a single-seat attack aircraft, and appears to have been the primary reason for the redesign of the MiG-19's "straight through" air flow arrangement. The Kiang 5 is one of the most important types in the front-line inventory of the Air Force of the People's Liberation Army and several hundred were believed to be in service in 1982. The A-5 is also reported to be in service in an air defence rôle with the Aviation of the People's Navy, probably carrying air-to-air missiles on two of the wing pylons in place of the bombs or rocket pods carried for the close-support rôle.

41

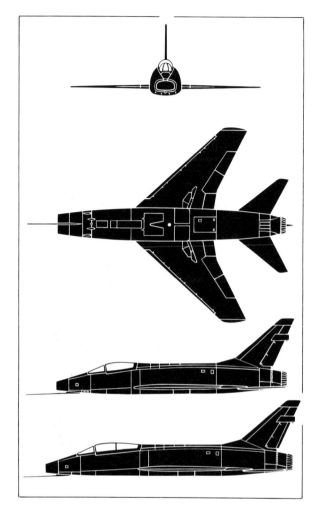

(Above and immediately below) Air and ground views of F-100D Super Sabres of the Kongelige Dansk Flyvevabnet (Danish Air Force); (bottom) an F-100D serving with the Turkish Air Force. (Silhouette) North American F-100D, with additional side view of two seat F-100F.

Country of Origin: USA.

Type: Tactical fighter-bomber (and operational trainer).

Power Plant: One (F-100A) 9,700 lb st (4 000 kgp) Pratt & Whitney J57-P-7 or (F-100C or F-100D) 10,200 lb st (4 627 kgp) dry and 16,000 lb st (7 258 kgp) with reheat J57-P-21 or -21A turbojet.

Performance: (F-100D) Max speed, 920 mph (1480 km/h) at 35,000 ft (10 670 m) or Mach 1·4; typical cruising speed, 565 mph (910 km/h) at 36,000 ft (10 970 m); initial rate of climb, 18,800 ft/min (95,5 m/sec); combat radius with six Snakeye bombs (total 3,360 lb/1 524 kg), 280 mls (450 km); ferry range with four external tanks, 1,970 mls (3 170 km).

Weights: Empty (F-100D), 21,000 lb (9 525 kg), (F-100F) 22,300 lb (10 115 kg); normal loaded (F-100D), 29,762 lb (13 500 kg), (F-100F) 30,700 lb (13 925 kg); max take-off (F-100D), 38,048 lb (17 260 kg).

Dimensions: Span, 38 ft 9½ in (11,81 m); length (F-100D), 49 ft 6 in (15,09 m), (F-100F), 52 ft 6 in (16,00 m); height, 16 ft 2⅔ in (4,95 m); wing area, 385·2 sq ft (35,77 m²).

Accommodation: (F-100C and D) Pilot only; (F-100F) Two in tandem, full dual controls.

Armament: (F-100C and F-100D) Four or (F-100F) two 20-mm M-39E cannon and (F-100D) 7,500 lb (3 400 kg) or (F-100F) 6,000 lb (2 720 kg) of external ordnance on underwing pylons.

Status: Prototypes (YF-100A) first flown on 25 May and 14 October 1953 respectively; first production F-100A flown on 29 October 1953; first production F-100C (Los Angeles) flown on 17 January 1955 and first F-100C (Columbus) on 8 September 1955; first F-100D (Los Angeles) flown on 24 January 1956 and first F-100D (Columbus) flown on 12 June 1956; prototype two-seat TF-100C flown on 6 August 1956; first production F-100F flown on 7 March 1957. Production totals, YF-100A, 2; F-100A, 203; F-100C, 451 at Los Angeles and 25 at Columbus; F-100D, 940 at Los Angeles and 334 at Columbus; F-100F, 339.

Notes: F-100 was world's first operational fighter with a true supersonic performance in level flight. Through MAP, several European nations received F-100s; of these, Denmark and Turkey were the last two to have the type in service, with F-16s replacing the final F-100s in the RDAF in 1981/82 but three squadrons of F-100s still surviving in Turkey, including both single-seat F-100Ds and two-seat F-100Fs. The Chinese Nationalist Air Force in Taiwan was another large-scale user of the F-100, with a few still in service. During 1981, Sperry Flight Systems began delivery of QF-100 target drone conversion of F-100Ds to the USAF.

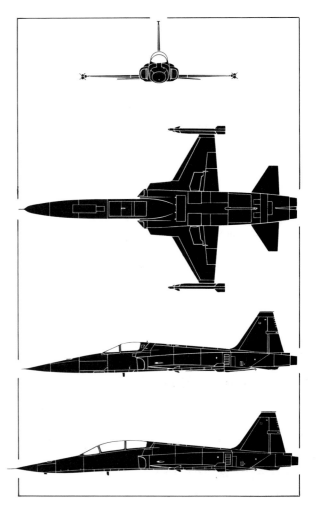

A Northrop F-5E reveals its distinctive wing planform, with tip-mounted AAM launching rails; (immediately above) a two-seat F-5F of the Iranian Islamic Air Force; (below) an F-5E of the Hellenic Air Force (Silhouette) Northrop F-5E and (lower sideview) F-5F.

Country of Origin: USA.

Type: Single-seat air superiority and (RF-5) tactical reconnaissance fighter and (F-5B/F) two-seat combat trainer.

Power Plant: Two (F-5A, B) 2,720 lb st (1 233 kgp) dry and 4,080 lb st (1 850 kgp) with reheat General Electric J85-GE-13 or (F-5E, F) 3,500 lb st (1 588 kgp) dry and 5,000 lb st (2 268 kgp) with reheat J85-GE-21 turbojets or (F-5G) one 10,000 lb st (4 540 kgp) dry and 16,000 lb st (7 258 kgp) with reheat F404-GE-F1G1 turbofan.

Performance: (F-5E) max speed, 1,075 mph (1 730 km/h) or Mach 1·63 at 36,090 ft (11 000 m) and 760 mph (1 223 km/h) or Mach 1·0 at sea level; initial rate of climb, 34,500 ft/min (175 m/sec); service ceiling, 51,800 ft (15 790 m); combat radius, max fuel and two AAMs, 656 mls (1 056 km); combat radius, two AAMs and 5,200 lb (2 358 kg) ordnance (LO-LO-LO), 138 mls (222 km); ferry range, 1,350 mls (2 176 km).

Weights: Empty (F-5E), 9,683 lb (4 392 kg), (F-5F), 10,567 lb (4 793 kg); normal take-off (F-5E, clean), 15,400 lb (6 985 kg); max take-off (F-5E), 24,676 lb (11 193 kg); max take-off (F-5F), 25,225 lb (11 442 kg).

Dimensions: Span (F-5A), 25 ft 3 in (7,70 m), (F-5E), 26 ft 8 in (8,13 m); length (F-5A), 47 ft 2 in (14,38 m), (F-5B), 46 ft 4 in (14,12 m), (F-5E), 48 ft 2 in (14,68 m), F-5F, 51 ft 7 in (15,72 m); height (F-5A), 13 ft 2 in (4,01 m), (F-5E), 13 ft 4½ in (4,08 m), (F-5F), 13 ft 1¾ in (4,01 m); wing area (F-5A), 170 sq ft (15,79 m²), (F-5E), 186 sq ft (17,30 m²).

Accommodation: (F-5A, F-5E) Pilot only. (F-5B, F-5F) Two in tandem, dual controls.

Armament: Two 20-mm M-39 cannon in forward fuselage; provision for AAM at each wing tip and five external strong points for maximum of (F-5A), 6,200 lb (2 812 kg) or (F-5E) 7,000 lb (3 175 kg) of ordnance.

Status: First prototype (N-156) flown 30 July 1959; first production F-5A flown 19 May 1964; first F-5B flown 24 February 1964; YF-5-21 development aircraft flown 28 March 1969; first F-5E flown 11 August 1972; first F-5F flown 25 September 1974; first RF-5E flown 29 January 1979. Production quantities: N-156F prototypes, 3; F-5A/F-5B, 879 by Northrop, 250 by Canadair and 70 by CASA; 1,200 F-5E/F-5F built by mid-1982 and continuing.

Notes: F-5A (and two-seat F-5B) were derived from company-funded N-156 lightweight fighter prototype, and exported to, or used by, some 18 air forces as well as USAF. Improved F-5E also exported to nine other nations not already using original model. Single-engined F-5G is separately described.

(Above) An impression of the F-5G Tigershark as it might appear in USAF Aggressor unit camouflage; (immediately below and bottom) two views of a full scale mock-up of the F-5G. (Silhouette) Northrop F-5G Tigershark.

Country of Origin: USA.

Type: Air defence fighter.

Power Plant: One 10,000 lb st (4 810 kgp) dry and 16,000 lb st (7 260 kgp) with reheat General Electric F404-GE-F1G1 turbofan.

Performance: Max speed, 1,321 mph (2 124 km/h) at 40,000 ft (12 200 m) or Mach 2·0 and 740 mph (1 190 km/h) at sea level or Mach 1·05; initial rate of climb, 50,300 ft/min (255,5 m/sec); time to 40,000 ft (12 200 m), 2·3 min; acceleration, Mach 0·9 to Mach 1·2 at 30,000 ft (9 150 m), 30 sec; max sustained turn rate, 11 deg/sec at Mach 0·8 at 15,000 ft (4 575 m); ferry range, 1,716 mls (2 760 km) with max external fuel.

Weights: Empty, 11,220 lb (5 089 kg); take-off weight clean, 17,240 lb (7 820 kg); max take-off, 26,140 lb (11 857 kg).

Dimensions: Span, 26 ft 8 in (8,13 m) to centreline of wing-tip missiles; length, 46 ft 6¾ in (14,19 m); height, 13 ft 10¼ in (4,22 m); wing area, 186 sq ft (17,28 m²).

Armament: Two 20-mm M39A2 cannon in front fuselage. Four wing pylons and fuselage centreline strongpoint have combined capacity for up to 7,000 lb (3 175 kg) of ordnance. Two AIM-9 Sidewinder AAMs at wing-tips.

Accommodation: Pilot only.

Status: Initial batch of six F-5G Tigersharks put in hand November 1980; first flight scheduled for September 1982.

Notes: The F-5G was developed from the F-5E (separately described) on the basis of design and project studies in the late 'seventies and construction of a pre-production batch was put in hand when the US government drew up its FX programme to encourage the production (on a company-funded basis) of a new lightweight international fighter. The new features of the F-5G—for which Northrop adopted the name Tigershark during 1981—compared with the F-5E Tiger II include using a single engine that offers some 60 per cent more power than the two J85s in the earlier model. Structural changes associated with the new engine and small airframe improvements increase the empty weight by less than 20 per cent. Other changes in the F-5G include a wider nose radome to permit installation (from 1984 onwards, in the F-5G-2 variant) of a new General Electric coherent multi-mode pulse Doppler radar; a panoramic cockpit canopy for better all-round vision; enlarged wing-root leading-edge extensions; shorter vertical tail surfaces with a cooling air intake in the base of the fin and splitter plates associated with enlarged intakes. Production deliveries of the F-5G-1, with avionics and weapons system similar to those of the F-5E, were set to begin in July 1983. A two-seat version of the Tigershark will also be available.

PANAVIA TORNADO F MK 2 (ADV)

(Top and immediately above) Air and ground views of the first of three prototypes of the Tornado F Mk 2, showing semi-recessed stowage for Sky Flash missiles; (below) the third F Mk 2 prototype in RAF air defence colours. (Silhouette) Panavia Tornado F Mk 2.

Country of Origin: United Kingdom.

Type: Air defence fighter.

Power Plant: Two 9,000 lb st (4 082 kgp) dry and 16,000 lb st (7 258 kgp) with reheat Turbo-Union RB.199-34R-04 Mk 101 turbofans, or uprated later variants.

Performance: Max speed, $M = 2 \cdot 2$ at high altitude (over 800 kts/1 480 km/h IAS); take-off run, normal load, 2,500 ft (762 m); landing run, with reverse thrust, 1,200 ft (366 m); radius of action for CAP, approx 400 naut mls (740 km) with 2-hr loiter and fuel for 10-min combat; ferry range, internal and external fuel, more than 1,750 naut mls (3 220 km).

Weights: Max take-off, full mission load, about 52,000 lb (23 587 kg).

Dimensions: Span, spread, 45 ft $7\frac{1}{4}$ in (13,90 m); span, fully swept, 28 ft $2\frac{1}{2}$ in (8,59 m); overall length (excluding nose pitot), 59 ft 3 in (18,06 m).

Accommodation: Pilot and navigator in tandem cockpits.

Armament: One fixed forward-firing 27-mm Mauser cannon in front fuselage. Four BAe Sky Flash AAMs in semi-recessed housings under fuselage. Two AIM-9L Sidewinder AAMs on inboard sides of underwing pylons.

Status: First prototype flown on 27 October 1979; second

prototype flown on 18 July 1980; third and final prototype first flown on 18 November 1980 and, with Marconi Avionics Foxhunter AI radar first fitted, on 17 June 1981. Planned production total, 185 for RAF with first to fly in 1983, destined to re-equip seven squadrons of Phantoms and two squadrons of Lightnings in air defence rôle in UK and Germany.

Notes: A derivative of the basic IDS Tornado (separately described), the Tornado F Mk 2 has been developed exclusively to meet British requirements, in a programme authorised to proceed on 4 March 1976. Production is shared between the three nations involved in the basic Tornado, with final assembly of all F Mk 2s taking place at the British Aerospace Warton facility. Also known as the ADV (Air Defence Variant), the Tornado F Mk 2 differs in a number of important respects from the GR Mk 1. The fuselage is lengthened by 4 ft $5\frac{1}{2}$ in (1,36 m), partly behind the cockpit to provide sufficient space for the semi-recessed and staggered stowage of four Sky Flash AAMs and partly ahead of the cockpit to lengthen the nose and radome for the Marconi Avionics Foxhunter track-while-scan pulse-Doppler AI radar. The wing leading edge "nib" fairings are extended forwards and Krueger flaps are deleted from these nibs. A permanently-installed, retractable air-refuelling probe replaces one of the Mauser cannon.

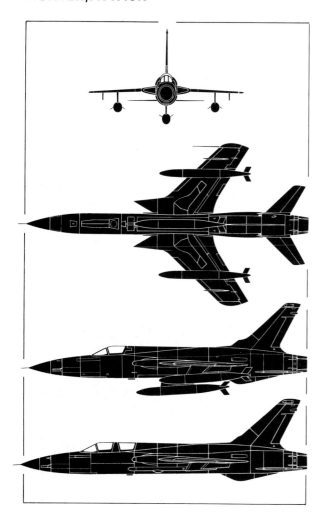

(Above) A two seat Republic F-105F Thunderchief; (immediately below) an F-105G, the "Wild Weasel" variant equipped to counter surface-to-air missiles; (bottom) a single-seat F-105D with three drop tanks. (Silhouette) Republic F-105D, with additional side view of the F-105G.

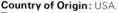

Country of Origin: USA.

Type: Long-range fighter bomber, (F-105G) tactical ECM aircraft or (F-105F) operational two-seat conversion trainer.

Power Plant: One (F-105B) 23,500 lb st (10 660 kgp) with reheat Pratt & Whitney J75-P-5 or (late F-105B) 16,100 lb st (7 303 kgp) dry and 24,500 lb st (11 113 kgp) with reheat J75-P-19 or (F-105D, F and G) J75-P-19W with 26,500 lb st (12 020 kgp) take-off rating for 2·5 min with water injection.

Performance: (F-105D) Max speed, 836 mph (1 344 km/h) at sea level, 1,372 mph (2 208 km/h) or Mach 2·08 above 36,090 ft (11 000 m); initial rate of climb, 34,500 ft/min (175,2 m/sec); service ceiling, 42,000 ft (12 800 m); combat radius (with eight M117 bombs, total 6,392 lb/2 900 kg), 716 mls (1 152 km); ferry range, 2,206 mls (3 550 km).

Weights: Empty, 27,500 lb (12 474 kg); normal loaded (F-105D) 38,034 lb (17 250 kg), (F-105F) 40,073 lb (18 175 kg); maximum overload (F-105D), 52,546 lb (23 834 kg), (F-105F), 54,027 lb (24 500 kg).

Dimensions: Span, 34 ft 11¼ in (10,65 m); length (F-105D), 64 ft 3 in (19,58 m), (F-105F), 69 ft 7½ in (21,21 m); height (F-105D), 19 ft 8 in (5,99 m), (F-105F), 20 ft 2 in (6,15 m); wing area, 385 sq ft (35,76 m²).

Accommodation: (F-105D) Pilot only; (F-105F) two in tandem, dual controls; (F-105G) pilot and observer in tandem.

Armament: One 20-mm M-61 multi-barrel cannon. Internal weapons bay with capacity for up to 8,000 lb (3 628 kg) of bombs plus 6,000 lb (2 722 kg) externally on fuselage and wing points.

Status: First of two YF-105A prototypes flown on 22 October 1955; first F-105B development aircraft flown on 24 May 1957; first F-105D flown on 9 June 1959; first F-105F flown on 11 June 1963; prototype T-Stick II conversion flown on 9 August 1969. Production totals: YF-105A, 2; JF-105B, 3; F-105B, 75; F-105D, 600; F-105F, 143, completed 1964.

Notes: In addition to the single-seat F-105B and F-105D, the two-seat F-105F was used operationally in Vietnam, with an observer in the rear seat, and a total of 54 were converted to F-105G with "Wild Weasel" radar homing and warning system plus provision for AGM-45 Shrike and AGM-78 Standard ARMs. Thirty F-105Ds were modified to T-Stick II configuration with improved all-weather bombing capability, and had saddle-back fairing from cockpit to fin. After withdrawal from Vietnam, F-105Bs, Ds and Gs were issued to four Tactical Fighter Wings of the ANG, with which they were still operational in 1982, while two squadrons of the AF Reserve flew F-105Ds and Fs.

(Top) One of the Saab 35BS Drakens supplied to Finland's Ilmavoimat; (immediately above) a Saab 35E reconnaissance Draken of Sweden's Flygvapen; (below) a two-seat TF-35 of the Royal Danish Air Force. (Silhouette) The Saab J 35F Draken with additional side views of the SK 35C and the 35E.

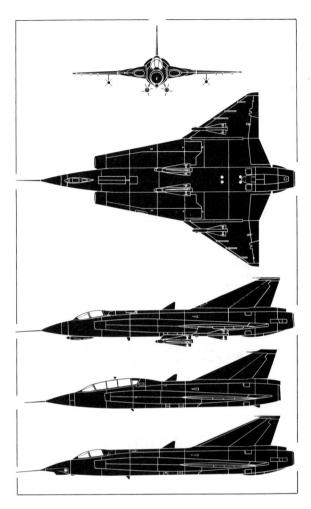

Country of Origin: Sweden.

Type: All-weather fighter, reconnaissance and attack aircraft and two-seat operational trainer.

Power Plant: One (J 35A, J 35B and SK 35C) 15,000 lb st (6 803 kgp) with reheat Volvo Flygmotor RM6B (Avon 200) or (J 35D, S 35E, J 35F and Saab 35X) 12,790 lb st (5 800 kgp) dry and 17,635 lb st (8 000 kgp) with reheat RM6C (Avon 300).

Performance: (Saab 35X) Max speed, 924 mph (1 487 km/h) or Mach 1·4 at 36,090 ft (11 000 m); initial rate of climb, 22,650 ft/min (11,5 m/sec); radius of action (clean), HI-LO-HI profile, 395 mls (635 km); radius of action (two drop tanks and two 1,000 lb/454 kg bombs) HI-LO-HI profile, 621 mls (1 000 km); ferry range, 2,020 mls (3 250 km).

Weights: Take-off clean, 25,132 lb (11 400 kg); take-off (two 1,000 lb/454 kg bombs and two drop tanks), 32,165 lb (14 590 kg); max take-off, 33,070 lb (15 000 kg); max overload, 35,275 lb (16 000 kg).

Dimensions: Span, 30 ft 10 in (9,40 m); length (including nose probe), 50 ft 4 in (15,4 m); height, 12 ft 9 in (3,9 m); wing area, 529·6 sq ft (49,2 m²).

Accommodation: Pilot or (SK 35C) two with dual controls.

Armament: (J 35F) One or (Saab 35X) two 30-mm Aden cannon in wings (optional in place of extra fuel); nine external stores stations (three beneath fuselage and three under each wing) with capacity of 1,000 lb (454 kg) each. Primary air-to-air armament comprises two or four RB 24 Sidewinders.

Status: First of three prototypes flown on 25 October 1955; second in March 1956, third in June 1956. First production J 35A flown on 15 February 1958; first J 35B flown on 29 November 1959; first SK 35C flown on 30 December 1959; first J 35D flown on 27 December 1960; first S 35E flown on 27 June 1963; first Saab 35XD flown on 29 January 1970. Total production over 600 completed 1972, including 20 F-35, 20 RF-35 and 11 TF-35 for R. Danish Air Force, and 6 J35BS, 6 J35F, 12 J35XS (assembled by Valmet) and three SK 35C for Finnish Air Force.

Notes: The delta-winged Saab 35 Draken was the primary front-line fighter equipment of the Swedish Air Force until the introduction of the Viggen, the JA 37 version of which was progressively replacing the J 35D and J 35F interceptors in 1981/82. S 35 Draken is reconnaissance variant and Sk 35 is tandem two-seat trainer. Denmark acquired Model 35XD export Drakens in 1970 in fighter-bomber (F-35), tactical recce (RF-35) and training (TF-35) variants. Finland's total of 27 Drakens includes 12 assembled by Valmet OY.

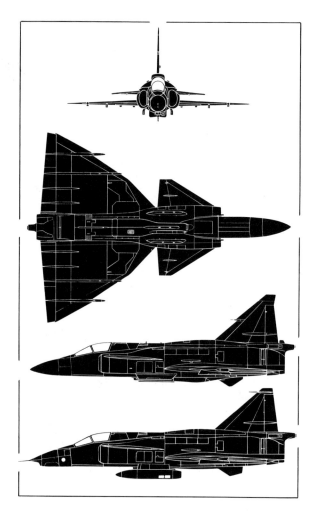

(Top) A Saab AJ 37, the attack version of the Viggen, carrying two Rb 75 Maverick ASMs and two ECM pods; (immediately above) a camera-equipped SF 37 Viggen; (below) the JA 37 all-weather fighter carrying six AAMs. (Silhouette) The JA 37, with additional side view of AJ 37.

Country of Origin: Sweden.

Type: Multi-purpose fighter, reconnaissance aircraft and two-seat operational trainer.

Power Plant: One (AJ, SF, SH, SK) 14,700 lb st (6 667 kgp) dry and 26,450 lb st (12 000 kgp) with reheat Volvo Flygmotor RM 8A (Pratt & Whitney JT8D-22) or (JA) 16,200 lb st (7 350 kgp) dry and 28,110 lb st (12 750 kgp) with reheat RM 8B turbofan.

Performance: (JA 37) Max speed (with two RB 24 Sidewinder and two RB 71 Sky Flash AAMs), 1,255–1,365 mph (2 020–2 195 km/h) or Mach = 1·9–2·1 above 36,000 ft (11 000 m), 838 mph (1 350 km/h) or Mach = 1·1, at 1,000 ft (305 m); patrol endurance, 1·5–2·0 hrs; tactical radius (HI-LO-HI), over 620 mls (1 000 km); time to 32,810 ft (10 000 m), 1·5 min.

Weights: (JA 37) Normal loaded (two RB 24s and two RB 71s), (approx) 37,480 lb (17 000 kg).

Dimensions: Span, 34 ft 9¼ in (10,60 m); length (excluding probe), 50 ft 8¼ in (15,45 m), (including probe), 53 ft 9½ in (16,40 m); height, 19 ft 4¼ in (5,90 m), wing area (including foreplanes), 561·88 sq ft (52,20 m²).

Armament: One (JA 37) 30-mm Oerlikon KCA revolver-type cannon with 150 rounds, two RB 71 Sky Flash radar-homing AAMs and two or four RB 24 Sidewinder infrared-homing AAMs.

(AJ 37) Seven external stores stations (four beneath wings and three under fuselage); primary armament comprises RB 04E or RB 05A ASMs plus provision for RB 24 AAMs.

Status: First of six single-seat Viggen prototypes flown 8 February 1967 and the sixth by April 1969. Two-seat SK 37 prototype flown 2 July 1970. First production AJ 37 flown 23 February 1971, deliveries to Swedish Air Force began 21 June 1971. First SF 37 flown 21 May 1973, deliveries began April 1977. Prototype SH 37 flown 10 December 1973 and first production delivery on 19 June 1975. Prototype SK 37 flown 2 July 1970. Four JA 37 prototypes (AJ 37 conversions) flown on 4 June, 27 September, 22 November 1974 and 30 May 1975 respectively. Pre-production JA 37 flown on 15 December 1975 and first full production JA 37 on 4 November 1977. Production orders placed for 180 AJ, SK, SF and SH 37 Viggens and 149 JA37s.

Notes: Initial production version of the double-delta Viggen was the AJ 37, a single-seat all-weather attack version with secondary interceptor capability. Deliveries began in 1971. Generally similar to the AJ 37, the SH 37 is equipped for overland tactical reconnaissance, the SF 37 for sea surveillance and the SK 37 as a two-seat operational conversion trainer. The JA 37 Jakt Viggen replaced earlier variants on production line in 1979.

SEPECAT JAGUAR

FIGHTER/ATTACK

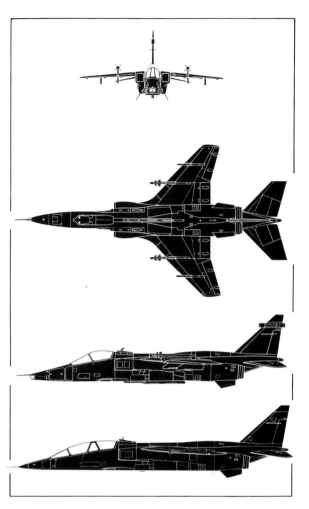

(Top) Jaguar GR Mk 1 of RAF No 2 Squadron with reconnaissance pod under fuselage; (immediately above) Jaguar 1 of the Indian Air Force's No 14 Squadron; (below) Jaguar International B two-seat operational trainer of the Sultan of Oman's Air Force. (Silhouette) Jaguar International with additional side view of Jaguar T Mk 2.

Country of Origin: France/United Kingdom.

Type: Tactical strike fighter and advanced trainer.

Power Plant: Two (GR Mk 1, T Mk 2, A, E) 4,620 lb st (2 100 kgp) dry and 7,140 lb st (3 240 kgp) with reheat Rolls-Royce/Turboméca RT172 Adour 102 or (GR Mk 1, T Mk 2, International) 5,320 lb st (2 410 kgp) dry and 8,040 lb st (3 645 kgp) with reheat, or RT172-26 Adour 104/804 or (international) 5,520 lb st (2 504 kgp) dry and 8,400 lb st (3 811 kgp) with reheat Adour 811 turbofans.

Performance: (GR Mk 1, International, at typical weights for representative tactical missions). Max speed 840 mph (1 350 km/h) or Mach 1·1 at low level, 1,055 mph (1 698 km/h) or Mach 1·6 at high altitude; combat radius (with external fuel) (LO-LO-LO-), 282 mls (454 km), (HI-LO-HI), 440 mls (708 km); ferry range (without in-flight refuelling), 2,190 mls (3 524 km).

Weights: (GR Mk 1, International) Typical empty weight, 15,432 lb (7 000 kg); normal take-off, 24,000 lb (11 000 kg); max take-off, 34,000 lb (15 500 kg).

Dimensions: Span 28 ft 6 in (8,69 m); length (including nose probe), 55 ft 2½ in (16,83 m); length overall (two-seat variants, 57 ft 6¼ in (17,53 m); height overall, 16 ft 0½ in (4,89 m); gross wing area, 260·3 sq ft (24,18 m²).

Accommodation: Pilot only or (T Mk 2, E) two in tandem.

Armament: Two (GR Mk 1) 30-mm Aden or (International, A, E) DEFA 553 or (T Mk 2) one 30-mm Aden cannon in lower front fuselage. One external stores attachment point on fuselage centreline and four underwing attachment points, to carry up to 10,000 lb (4 534 kg) combined external load. Overwing pylons (International only) carry dogfight AAMs.

Status: First of eight prototypes (Jaguar E) flown 8 September 1968; first Jaguar A, 29 March 1969; Jaguar M, 14 November 1969; Jaguar S (GR Mk 1) 12 October 1969; Jaguar B (T Mk 2) 30 August 1971. First production Jaguar E flown 2 November 1971; first production Jaguar A flown 20 April 1972; first GR Mk 1 flown 11 October 1972, first T Mk 2 flown 22 March 1973; first flown with Adour 104, 2 September 1975; first flown with Adour 811, 14 August 1978. Production: Prototypes 8: GR Mk 1, 165; T Mk 2, 38; Jaguar A, 160; Jaguar E, 40; Jaguar International, 76 (Ecuador 10 plus two two-seaters; Oman 20 plus four two-seaters, India 35 plus five two-seaters plus approximately 60 assembled in India by HAL.

Notes: RAF Jaguars equip nine squadrons in Germany and UK. *Armée de l'Air* Jaguars (some with Adour 101 lacking PTR) equip nine squadrons, including two equipped to launch ASMs.

49

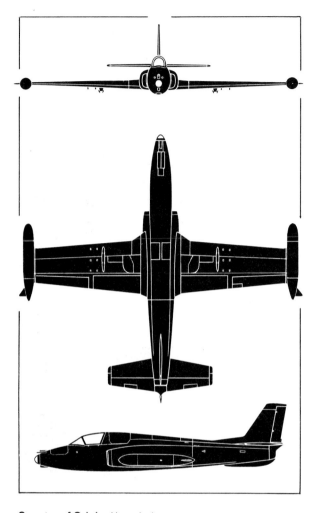

(Above) One of the prototypes of the Soko Jastreb, showing fuselage access panels; (immediately below) a service model of the Jastreb; (bottom) the first Jastreb prototype with a selection of possible underwing stores. (Silhouette) The Soko Jastreb.

Country of Origin: Yugoslavia.

Type: Light strike aircraft.

Power Plant: One 3,000 lb st (1 361 kgp) Rolls-Royce Viper 531 turbojet.

Performance: Max speed, 510 mph (820 km/h) at 19,680 ft (6 000 m) at mid-mission weight; max cruising speed, 460 mph (740 km/h) at 16,400 ft (5 000 m); initial rate of climb, 4,135 ft/min (21 m/sec); service ceiling, 39,375 ft (12 000 m); max range, 945 mls (1 520 km); typical mission radius, strike configuration, 300 mls (480 km).

Weight: Empty equipped, 6,217 lb (2 820 kg); max bomb/rocket load, 1,100 lb (500 kg); take-off, basic strike mission, 8,750 lb (3 970 kg); take-off, armed reconnaissance mission, 8,805 lb (3 994 kg); take-off, strike mission, max ordnance load, 9,620 lb (4 364 kg); max take-off (with two JATO bottles) 10,000 lb (4 541 kg).

Dimensions: Span (without tip tanks), 34 ft 7¾ in (10,56 m); span over tip tanks, 38 ft 4 in (11,68 m); length, 35 ft 1½ in (10,71 m); height, 11 ft 11½ in (3,64 m); wing area, 204·5 sq ft (19 m²).

Accommodation: Pilot only or (TJ-1 Jastreb Trainer) two in tandem with dual controls.

Armament: Three 0·50-in (12,7-mm) Colt-Browning machine guns in nose of fuselage. Two wing hard points each to carry one bomb of up to 550 lb (250 kg) or cluster-bombs or photo flares, plus provision for six air-to-air rockets of 127-mm or 57-mm diameter attached directly to wing supports. Armed reconnaissance version has provision to carry four 100-lb (45,5-kg) flash bombs under wings for night photography in lieu of rockets.

Status: Two prototypes flown 1967/1968; production deliveries began 1970. Production totals, at least 100 J-1 basic strike aircraft and 20 RJ-1 armed reconnaissance aircraft for Yugoslav Air Force plus four J-1s exported to Zambian Air Force 1971. Approximately 25 TJ-1 two-seat training Jastrebs built for Yugoslav Air Force.

Notes: The Jastreb (Hawk) was developed from the Galeb basic jet trainer (separately described) with which it shares a common configuration and basic structure, but has only a single-seat cockpit in its J-1 strike and RJ-1 tactical reconnaissance versions. A two-seat training variant, known as the TJ-1 and also in service with the Yugoslav Air Force, is even more closely akin to the Galeb, from which it differs primarily in having the uprated Viper 531 engine; a prototype two-seater with this engine was also known as the Galeb 3. The J-1E and RJ-1E export versions were supplied to Zambia.

(Top) A prototype IAR-93 Orao under test in Rumania; (immediately above) one of the first Oraos undergoing flight testing in Yugoslavia, where the project is managed by Soko; (below) the first prototype of the two-seat Orao. (Silhouette) Soko/IAR Orao.

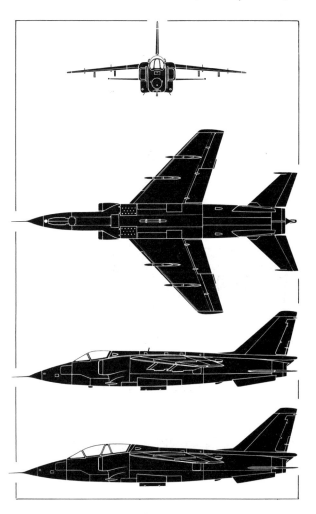

Country of Origin: Jugoslavia and Romania.

Type: Tactical fighter (and two-seat operational trainer).

Power Plant: Two (prototypes) 4,000 lb st (1 814 kgp) Rolls-Royce Viper 632-41 and (production) 5,101 lb st (2 270 kgp) with reheat Viper turbojets.

Performance: (Production version, with reheat) Max speed, 700 mph (1 126 km/h) or Mach 0·92 at sea level and 665 mph (1 070 km/h) or Mach 0·95 at 25,000 ft (7 620 m); initial rate of climb, 14,882 ft/min (76 m/sec); service ceiling, 42,650 ft (13 000 m); combat radius with 4,410 lb (2 000 kg) ordnance load (LO-LO-LO), 186 mls (300 km); (HI-LO-HI), 224 mls (360 km).

Weights (Prototype): Empty equipped, 13,450 lb (6 100 kg); take-off weight, clean, 19,577 lb (8 880 kg); max take-off, 23,150 lb (10 500 kg).

Weights (Production version, with reheat): Empty equipped, 12,570 lb (5 700 kg); take-off weight, clean, 18,960 lb (8 600 kg); max take-off, 23,130 lb (10 500 kg).

Dimensions: Span, 31 ft 7 in (9,63 m); length, 42 ft 10 in (14,88 m); height, 14 ft 7¼ in (4,45 m); wing area, 279·86 sq ft (26,00 m²).

Accommodation: Pilot only or (operational trainer) two in tandem.

Armament: Two 23-mm cannon and up to 5,510 lb (2 500 kg) of ordnance on one fuselage centreline and four wing hardpoints.

Status: First two prototypes (one in Jugoslavia, one in Romania) flown on 31 October 1974; two two-seat prototypes flown subsequently, followed by a batch of pre-production aircraft in 1977/78.

Notes: The Orao (Eagle) was developed jointly by the Yugoslav (SOKO) and Romanian (CIAR) industries (thus being known initially by the achronym JuRom); the Romanian industry designation is IAR-93 (for Industriei Aeronautice Romăne). The Jugoslav SOKO organisation is airframe team leader and is responsible for final assembly of Jugoslav- and Romanian-manufactured components. The Jugoslav and Romanian air forces are reported each to have a requirement for about 200 of these fighters, deliveries of which began in 1980/81, some two years behind the originally-planned schedule. Although the prototypes have standard British-built Viper engines, the production model of the Orao is designed to make use of a new and uprated version of the Viper with afterburning—a development undertaken specifically for this aircraft, with manufacture of the necessary components under licence in the two countries. The two-seat version of the Orao incorporates a second cockpit in a fuselage of the same length.

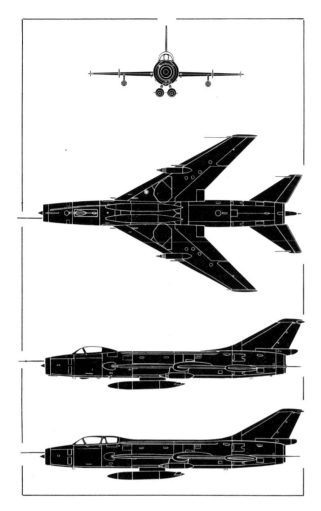

(Above) The two-seat Su-7UM Moujik. (Immediately below) An Su-7BM, of
the Egyptian Air Force and (bottom) an Su-7BM of the Indian Air Force.
(Silhouette) The upper three views illustrate the Su-7BMK Fitter-A and the
lower sideview depicts the Su-7UMK Moujik.

Country of Origin: Soviet Union.
Type: Single-seat (Fitter-A) close air support and interdiction
aircraft, and two-seat (Moujik) conversion trainer.
Power Plant: One 14,990 lb st (6 800 kgp) dry and 21,164 lb st
(9 600 kgp) reheat Lyulka AL-7F-1 turbojet.
Performance: Max speed (clean with max dry thrust), 540 mph
(870 km/h) or Mach 0·72 at 1,000 ft (305 m), (max reheat),
720 mph (1 160 km/h) or Mach 0·95 at 1,000 ft (305 m),
1,055 mph (1 700 km/h) or Mach 1·6 at 36,090 ft (11 000 m); max
climb rate, 29,500 ft/min (149,8 m/sec); service ceiling, 49,200 ft
(15 000 m); tactical radius (HI-LO-HI mission profile with two 132
Imp gal/600 l drop tanks and two 1,635-lb/750-kg bombs),
285 mls (460 km); max range (max external fuel), 900 mls
(1 450 km).
Weights: Empty equipped, 19,000 lb (8 616 kg); normal loaded,
26,455 lb (12 000 kg); max take-off, 29,750 lb (13 500 kg).
Dimensions: Span, 28 ft 9¼ in (8,77 m); length (including pitot),
55 ft 1½ in (16,80 m); height, 15 ft 0 in (4,57 m).
Accommodation: Pilot only, or (Moujik) tandem seating for
instructor and pupil.
Armament: Two 30-mm NR-30 cannon with 70 rpg. Four
underwing stores stations for two 1,102-lb (500-kg) and two

1,635-lb (750-kg) bombs or equivalent loads of rocket pods, air-
to-surface missiles, etc.
Status: An aerodynamic prototype (the S-1) was flown in 1955,
and in productionised (S-22) form was ordered into large-scale
manufacture in 1958 as the Su-7B. Progressively improved series
versions comprised the Su-7BM, Su-7BKL and Su-7BMK, parallel
two-seat transitional training aircraft being the Su-7U, Su-7UM
and Su-7UMK. Quantity production continued until late 'sixties
when replaced by variable-geometry derivative of the basic design
(see page 55).
Notes: Although suffering an embarrassingly limited external
stores flexibility owing to its use of 60 deg of wing sweep and
possessing an overly modest radius of action with a worthwhile
ordnance load, the Su-7 provided the bulk of the Soviet Air Force's
tactical air-to-ground capability for more than a decade. Only
some 200 remained in WarPac first-line service at the beginning
of 1982, at which time it was being phased out of Indian service
in favour of the Jaguar, but it is retained in the inventories of the
air forces of Algeria, Egypt, Iraq, South Yemen and Syria. The Su-
7BKL and BMK feature a unique wheel-skid (*kolo lizhni*) arrangement permitting rough field operation without recourse to low-
pressure mainwheel tyres.

(Top) The definitive version of the Sukhoi single-engined interceptor, the Fishpot-C, and (immediately above and below) its production predecessor, the Fishpot-B. (Silhouette) Su-11 Fishpot-C with two AA-3 Anab air-to-air missiles on the wing pylons.

Country of Origin: Soviet Union.

Type: Single-seat (Fishpot-C) limited all-weather interceptor and two-seat (Maiden) conversion trainer.

Power Plant: One 14,990 lb st (6 800 kgp) dry and 21,164 lb st (9 600 kgp) reheat Lyulka AL-7F-1 turbojet.

Performance: (Estimated) Max speed (clean with half fuel), 720 mph (1 160 km/h) or Mach 0·95 at 1,000 ft (305 m), 1,190 mph (1 915 km/h) or Mach 1·8 at 36,090 ft (11 000 m), (high drag configuration: e.g., two AAMs and two drop tanks), 790 mph or Mach 1·2 at 36,090 ft (11 000 m); initial climb, 27,000 ft/min (137 m/sec); service ceiling, 55,000 ft (16 765 m); tactical radius (supersonic intercept mission on internal fuel), 280 mls (450 km); max range (with two 132 Imp gal/600 l drop tanks), 1,100 mls (1 770 km).

Weights: (Estimated) Combat, 27,000 lb (12 247 kg); max take-off, 30,000 lb (13 608 kg).

Dimensions: (Estimated) Span, 27 ft 0 in (8,23 m); length (including pitot), 60 ft 0 in (18,30 m); height, 16 ft 0 in (4,88 m); wing area, 425 sq ft (39,48 m²).

Accommodation: Pilot only, or (Maiden) tandem seating for instructor and pupil.

Armament: Two AA-3 Anab (one IR-homing and one semi-active radar-homing) AAMs, plus one cannon pack carried on the fuselage centreline (as option to drop tanks).

Status: An aerodynamic prototype of the basic design, the T-3, was flown in 1953–54, the initial production derivative, the Su-9 (Fishpot-B) entering Soviet service in the early 'sixties. A progressive development with uprated engine, larger, longer-ranging Uragan 5B (Skip Spin) radar, more effective armament, and a lengthened and recontoured forward fuselage, the Su-11 (Fishpot-C) entered service during 1966–67, production terminating in the early 'seventies and some 300–400 remaining in service at the beginning of 1982.

Notes: The Su-11 stemmed from early 'fifties parallel development of two combat aircraft types employing extensive component commonality but each possessing certain critical features to suit widely differing roles. One of these emerged in production form as the Su-7 Fitter-A (see page 52) optimised for ground attack and featuring a 60 deg swept wing, and the other evolved as the Su-9 Fishpot-B with a 60 deg delta wing and intended as a pure interceptor. Further development of the latter resulted in the Su-11 Fishpot-C which differed externally primarily in having a lengthened fuselage nose with an enlarged air intake. The Su-11 is being progressively phased out of first-line service.

(Above) An Su-15VD Flagon-D with two Anab AAMs and (below) the definitive production Su-15 Flagon-F. (Silhouette) The upper three views illustrate the Flagon-F interceptor and the lower sideview depicts the two-seat Flagon-C conversion trainer.

Country of Origin: Soviet Union.

Type: Single-seat (Flagon-D, E and F) all-weather interceptor and (Flagon-C) two-seat conversion trainer.

Power Plant: Two 11,600 lb st (5 260 kgp) and 15,875 lb st (7 200 kgp) Tumansky R-13F2-300 turbojets.

Performance: (Estimated) Max speed (short-period dash, clean aircraft), 1,520 mph (2 455 km/h) or Mach 2·3 above 36,000 ft (10 970 m), (sustained with two Anab AAMs), 1,380 mph (2 220 km/h) or Mach 2·1 above 36,000 ft (10 970 m); time to 36,000 ft (10 975 m) from brakes release (half fuel and two AAMs), 2·5 min; service ceiling, 60,000–65,000 ft (18 290–19 810 m); tactical radius (internal fuel), 450 mls (725 km), (with two drop tanks), 620 mls (997 km).

Weights: (Estimated) Combat, 36,000 lb (16 326 kg); max, 40,000 lb (18 144 kg).

Dimensions: (Estimated) 34 ft 6 in (10,50 m); length (excluding pitot), 72 ft 0 in (22,00 m); height, 16 ft 6 in (5,00 m).

Accommodation: Pilot only (Flagon-D, E and F), or (Flagon-C) tandem seating for instructor and pupil.

Armament: Four AA-3 Anab (two IR-homing and two radar-homing) AAMs. Provision for two additional IR-homing AAMs on fuselage pylons as alternatives to drop tanks. Centreline Cannon pack (containing either one or two 23-mm weapons) frequently carried.

Status: The first prototype of the Su-15 is believed to have flown in 1965, the initial version utilising essentially the same wing as the Su-11 (a simple 60 deg delta), pre-series aircraft only (Flagon-A) retaining this planform. The first service version (Flagon-D) introduced a longer-span, compound-sweep wing (the outer panels having 45 deg leading edge sweep), attaining initial operational capability 1969–70. Production of Su-15 series fighters terminated in the mid 'seventies, but about 700 remained in service with the Soviet air defence forces at the beginning of 1982.

Notes: The current service versions of the Su-15 are the Flagon-E and F single-seaters and the Flagon-C two-seater. By comparison with the initial service Flagon-D, the later models have martinally larger air intakes and revised intake trunking, and the Flagon-F has a rather larger ogival (as opposed to the Flagon-E's conical) radome. The systems of the Su-15 have been progressively upgraded during its service life, but it is being steadily replaced by the all-weather interceptor version of the MiG-23 (see page 37) and its importance may be expected to have diminished considerably by the mid 'eighties.

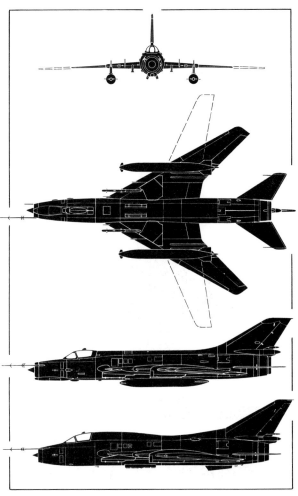

(Top) The Tumansky-engined Su-22 Fitter-J in Libyan Service; (immediately above) the two-seat Su-17 Fitter-G and (below) the Su-17 Fitter-H. (Silhouette) Three upper views depict the Su-17 Fitter-D, the lower sideview illustrating the Su-22 Fitter-J.

Country of Origin: Soviet Union.

Type: Single-seat (Fitter-C, D and H) attack and counterair, and (Fitter-F and J) multi-role fighter, and two-seat (Fitter-E and G) conversion trainer.

Power Plant: One 17,195 lb st (7 800 kgp) and 24,700 lb st (11 200 kgp) reheat Lyulka AL-21F turbojet or (Fitter-F and J) 17,635 lb st (8 000 kgp) and 25,350 lb st (11 500 kgp) Tumansky R-29B turbofan.

Performance: (Fitter-H estimated in clean condition) Max speed (short endurance dash), 1,430 mph (2 300 km/h) or Mach 2·17 at 39,370 ft (12 000 m), (sustained), 808 mph (1 300 km/h) or Mach 1·06 at sea level, 1,190 mph (1 915 km/h) or Mach 1·8 at 39,370 ft (12 000 m); combat radius (drop tanks on outboard wing pylons and 4,410-lb/2 000-kg external ordnance), 320 mls (515 km) LO-LO-LO, 530 mls (853 km) HI-LO-HI.

Weights: Max take-off, 39,022 lb (17 700 kg).

Dimensions: (Estimated) Span (spread), 45 ft 0 in (13,70 m), (sweptback), 32 ft 6 in (9,90 m); length (including probe), 58 ft 3 in (17,75 m); height, 15 ft 5 in (4,70 m); wing area (spread), 410 sq ft (38,00 m²).

Armament: One (Fitter-E and G) or two 30-mm NR-30 cannon and max external ordnance load or 7,716 lb (3 500 kg). Provision

(Fitter-F and J) for two AA-2 Atoll AAMs.

Accommodation: Pilot only or (Fitter E and G) two in tandem.

Status: Variable-geometry derivative of fixed-geometry Su-7 (see page 52) and flown as technology demonstration prototype in 1966 as S-22I (alias Su-7IG). Initial series Su-17 (Fitter-C) entered Soviet service in 1971, with upgraded model (Fitter-D) following 1976, and extensively revised version (Fitter-H) in 1979.

Notes: A dedicated interdiction and counterair aircraft, the Su-17 Fitter-H has evolved as the result of an extraordinary incremental development of the fixed-geometry Su-7 ground attack fighter, the first aerodynamic prototype of which (the S-1) was flown in 1955. The current production models (Fitter-G, H and J) feature a new and deeper forward fuselage with raised aft decking, taller vertical tail surfaces, a ventral fin and (Fitter-F and J) bulged rear-fuselage. Export versions of the Su-17 are designated Su-20 and -22, the latter being re-engined export variants of the Fitter-D and H with the Tumansky engine being known under the ASCC designation system as Fitter-F and J, these having multi-role capability with provision for two IR-homing missiles. Recipients of export versions have included Algeria, Egypt, Iraq, Libya and Poland. The two-seat Fitter-E and G retain full operational capability, but the port 30-mm cannon is discarded.

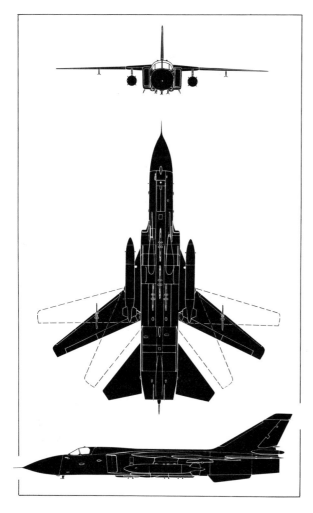

(Above) An Su-24 Fencer with ventral speed brakes partly deployed and (below) with auxiliary fuel tanks on wing glove pylons. (Silhouette) The planview depicts the Su-24 Fencer with wings at mid sweep, the minimum and maximum sweep angles being dotted.

Country of Origin: Soviet Union.
Type: Deep penetration interdiction and strike aircraft.
Power Plant: Two 17,635 lb st (8 000 kgp) and 25,350 lb st (11 500 kgp) reheat Tumansky R-29 turbofans.
Performance: (Estimated) Max speed (clean), 915 mph (1 470 km/h) or Mach 1·2 at sea level, 1,520 mph or Mach 2·3 above 36,000 ft (11 000 m), (with two combat tanks and full internal fuel), 685 mph (1 102 km/h) or Mach 0·95 at sea level, 1,254 mph (2 018 km/h) or Mach 1·9 above 36,000 ft (11 000 m); combat radius (HI-LO-HI mission profile with Mach 0·9 cruise at 36,000 ft/11 000 m and allowance for low-altitude dash with 4,400 lb/2 000 kg ordnance and combat tanks), 1,050 mls (1 690 km), (LO-LO-LO mission profile with Mach 0·85 cruise and Mach 0·95 dash with same external stores), 345 mls (555 km); max climb rate (clean with half fuel), 35,000 ft/min (178 m/sec); service ceiling, 57,415 ft (17 500 m).
Weights: (Estimated) Empty equipped, 41,890 lb (19 000 kg); max take-off, 87,080 lb (39 500 kg).
Dimensions: (Estimated) Span (spread), 56 ft 6 in (17,25 m), (sweptback), 33 ft 9 in (10,30 m); length (excluding pitot), 65 ft 6 in (20,00 m); height, 18 ft 0 in (5,50 m); wing area (spread), 452 sq ft (42,00 m²).

Accommodation: Pilot and weapon systems operator.
Armament: One 23-mm six-barrel Gatling-type rotary cannon, one 30-mm cannon and (short-range interdiction mission) up to 22 220-lb (100-kg) or 551-lb (250-kg) bombs, or 16 1,102-lb (500-kg) bombs distributed between eight stores stations (including two swivelling pylons on movable wing panels). Alternative loads include AS-7 Kerry ASMs, AS-9, AS-11 or AS-12 anti-radiation ASMs and AS-10 electro-optical ASMs, plus AA-2-2 Atoll or AA-8 Aphid AAMs for self defence.
Status: Prototype of Su-24 believed to have flown in 1970, with initial service from late 1974, and 400–450 in Soviet service by beginning of 1982.
Notes: The first Soviet combat aircraft dedicated to interdiction and counterair missions to be designed for such from the outset, the Su-24 is the counterpart of the General Dynamics F-111, but is somewhat less sophisticated, is lighter, dimensionally smaller and possesses a higher thrust-to-weight ratio. Greater emphasis is placed on short-field operation and air-to-air missiles may be mounted on the swivelling pylons to provide some self-defence capability. Su-24s are deployed within the Baltic, Carpathian and Far Eastern Military Districts, with production running at 8–9 monthly.

(Top and immediately above) Tu-128 Fiddler-B long-range patrol fighters of the Soviet air defence organisation, and (below) Fiddler-B interceptors at their base in the Soviet Union. (Silhouette) The standard Fiddler-B with quartet of Ash missiles.

Country of Origin: Soviet Union.

Type: Long-range interceptor fighter.

Power Plant: Two unidentified turbojets each possessing a max rating of approx. 26,000–27,000 lb st (11 795–12 245 kgp).

Performance: (Estimated) Max speed (clean), 1,085 mph (1 745 km/h) at 39,370 ft (12 000 m) or Mach 1·65, (high drag configuration, eg, four AA-5 Ash AAMs), 925 mph (1 490 km/h); tactical radius (high-altitude patrol mission with four AAMs and allowance for supersonic intercept), 780 mls (1 255 km); max fuel range, 3,105 mls (5 000 km); service ceiling, 65,615 ft (20 000 m).

Weights: (Estimated) Normal combat, 78,000 lb (35 380 kg); max take-off, 96,000 lb (43 545 kg).

Dimensions: Span, 59 ft 0 in (18,00 m); length 91 ft 10 in (28,00 m).

Armament: Four AA-5 Ash (two infra-red and two semi-active radar homing) AAMs.

Accommodation: Crew of two in tandem.

Status: The Tu-128 is believed to have entered flight test in 1957–58, and to have entered service with the Soviet air defence forces (Fiddler-B) in the early 'sixties. At the beginning of 1982, the Tu-128 was in process of phasing out with 100–120 remaining in service.

Notes: The largest and heaviest interceptor fighter to have achieved service status, the Tu-128 was biased in design towards economical high-altitude operation and appears to have been intended to patrol sections of the Soviet periphery unprotected by SAM screens. An early version (displayed at Tushino in 1961) carried only two Ash missiles (Fiddler-A), a ventral pack (presumably housing early warning radar) being accompanied by twin ventral fins, but there is no evidence that this version achieved service status. Fiddler-B has an extremely large radar known to NATO as "Big Nose" and is believed to fly normal patrol missions of 3·5 to 4·0 hours endurance. It has been alleged that Fiddler and Backfire have a common design origin in the experimental Tu-98 (Backfin) *circa* 1955, Backfire stemming from a low-risk programme involving the scaling-up of Fiddler, variable geometry only being applied to the former after the successful demonstration of this feature by the Sukhoi Su-7IG (Fitter-B) in 1966. The Fiddler-B reportedly now equips only four–five air regiments in the Soviet air defence forces and is being progressively phased out in favour of such types as the MiG-23 Flogger-B and G. It is likely to have been withdrawn from service with the air defence organisation by late 1983 or early 1984, and may now be considered as obsolescent.

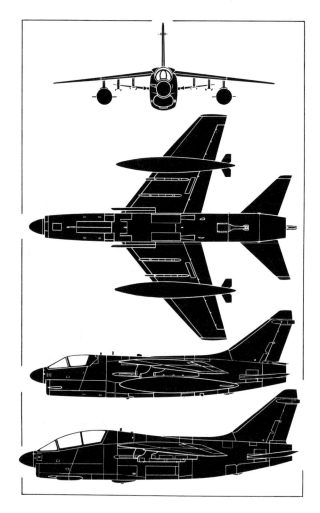

(Above) Vought A-7E Corsair II in service with US Navy attack squadron VA-27 on the USS "Enterprise"; (immediately below) Vought A-7H of the Hellenic Air Force; (bottom) a two-seat A-7K for the Air National Guard. (Silhouette) Three-view drawing of the Vought A-7E with additional side view of the A-7K.

Country of Origin: USA.

Type: Tactical attack aircraft and (TA-7C,TA-7H,A-7K) two-seat operational trainer.

Power Plant: One (A-7A) 11,350 lb st (5 150 kgp) Pratt & Whitney TF30-P-6 or (A-7B and A-7C) 12,200 lb st (5 534 kgp) TF30-P-8 or (A-7P)-P-408 or (A-7D, A-7K), 14,250 lb st Allison (Rolls Royce RB. 168 Spey) TF41-A-1 or (A-7E and A-7H) 15,000 lb st (6 800 kgp) TF41-A-2 or (TA-7H) TF41-A-400.

Performance: (A-7D) Max speed (clean), 663 mph (1,067 km/h) at 7,000 ft (2 133 m); initial rate of climb, 10,900 ft/min (55,4 m/sec); service ceiling, 38,800 ft (11 826 m); tactical radius with internal fuel and 3,600 lb (1 623 kg) external weapon load, 700 mls (1 127 km); ferry range, over 3,000 mls (4 900 km).

Weights: (A-7D) Empty, 19,490 lb (8 840 kg); max take-off 42,000 lb (19 050 kg).

Dimensions: Span, 38 ft 8½ in (11,79 m); length, 46 ft 1½ in (14,05 m); length (two-seaters), 48 ft 8 in (14,80 m); height, 16 ft 0 in (4,88 m); wing area, 375 sq ft (34,84 m²).

Accommodation: Pilot only or (TA-7C,TA-7H,A-7K) two pilots in tandem.

Armament: One 20-mm M61-A-1 multi-barrel gun in fuselage. Two external weapon stations on fuselage and six underwing pylons carry a maximum combined load of 15,000 lb (6 804 kg) including bombs, ASMs, AAMs, rockets, gun pods or fuel tanks.

Status: First of seven development A-7As flown on 27 September 1965; first A-7B flown on 6 February 1968; first A-7C (redesignated A-7E) flown on 25 November 1968; first A-7D (TF30 engine) flown on 5 April 1968; first A-7D (TF41 engine) flown on 26 September 1968; YA-7H (prototype two-seat A-7E conversion) flown on 29 August 1972; first TA-7C (A-7B conversion) flown 17 December 1976; first A-7H flown 6 May 1975; first TA-7H flown 4 March 1980; first A-7K flown 29 October 1980; first A-7P flown 20 July 1981. Production totals, A-7A, 199; A-7B, 196; A-7D, 459; A-7C, 67; A-7E, 596; A-7H, 59; TA-7H, six; A-7K, 30 (ordered as of mid-1982).

Notes: The first 67 A-7Es for US Navy retained the TF30-P-8 powerplant and were later redesignated A-7C. The first A-7E with TF41 engine was converted to YA-7H (later YA-7E) two-seat trainer and US Navy subsequently ordered conversion of 40 A-7B and 41 A-7C to TA-7C trainers. One of 60 A-7Hs built for Greece was converted to TA-7H, plus five built as new; one A-7D was converted to TA-7D as prototype for ANG A-7K two-seat operational proficiency trainers in production in 1982. Twenty A-7Ps are refurbished A-7As for Portugal.

(Top) Vought RF-8G of US Navy VFP-63 reconnaissance squadron; (immediately above) an ex-US Navy F-8H serving with the Philippine Air Force; (below) Vought F-8E (N) of Aéronavale with Matra 530 AAM on the fuselage pylon. (Silhouette) Three-view of the F-8J Crusader with additional side-view of the RF-8G.

Country of Origin: USA.

Type: Carrier-borne fighter and reconnaissance aircraft.

Power Plant: One (F-8L) 16,200 lb st (7 327 kgp) Pratt & Whitney J57-P-12 or (F-8K) 16,900 lb st (7 665 kgp) J57-P-16 or (F-8E (FN), F-8H and F-8J) 18,000 lb st (8 165 kgp) J57-P-20 or -20A turbojet.

Performance: (F-8J) Max speed, 1,120 mph (1 800 km/h) at 40,000 ft (12 190 m); cruising speed for best range, 560 mph (900 km/h) at 36,000 ft (10 970 m); time to climb to 57,000 ft (17 373 m), 6·5 min; service ceiling, 58,000 ft (17 680 m); combat radius, 600 mls (966 km); max range (clean) 1,400 mls (2 253 km).

Weights: Empty, 19,751 lb (8 960 kg); normal loaded, approx 29,000 lb (13 155 kg); max take-off, 34,000 lb (15 420 kg).

Dimensions: Span, 35 ft 8 in (10,87 m); length (F-8H, K and L), 54 ft 3 in (16,54 m); length (F-8E (FN) and F-8J), 54 ft 6 in (16,61 m); height, 15 ft 9 in (4,80 m); wing area, 375 sq ft (34,84 m²).

Accommodation: Pilot only.

Armament: Four 20-mm Mk 12 cannon in fuselage. Four fuselage stations and two wing pylons. (RF-8G) No guns or ordnance.

Status: Two XF-8A prototypes (originally XF8U-1) flown on 25 March and 30 September 1955 respectively. Deliveries of produc-

tion F-8A began March 1957. YTF-8A (two-seat trainer) prototype flown on 6 February 1962. RF-8A first flown on 17 December 1956; F-8B first flown on 3 September 1958; F-8C first flown December 1957 and first production example 20 August 1958; first F-8D flown 16 February 1960; first F-8E flown on 30 June 1961; prototype F-8E (FN) flown 27 February 1964 and first production 26 June 1964; first F-8H flown 17 July 1967; first F-8J flown 31 January 1968. Production totals: XF-8A prototypes, 2; F-8A, 318; F-8B, 130; F-8C, 187; F-8D, 152; F-8E, 286; F-8E (FN), 42; RF-8A, 144, making grand total of 1,261.

Notes: One-third of all Crusaders built, or 446 aircraft, were cycled through conversion/updating programmes between 1967 and 1970 to extend their useful life with US Navy reserve units. Through these programmes, 73 RF-8As became RF-8Gs, 61 F-8Bs became F-8Ls, 87 F-8Cs, became F-8Ks, 136 F-8Es became F-8Js and 89 F-8Ds became F-8Hs. By 1982, only the RF-8G remained in USN service, equipping one active squadron (VFP-63) and two Reserve units. France acquired the F-8F (FN) version in 1964/65, with blown flaps and improved low speed control. They have been modernised to F-8J standard and served in 1982 with *Flottille* 12F. In 1979, the Philippine Air Force acquired 35 surplus US Navy F-8Hs of which 25 have been refurbished for service.

(Above) A Yak-28P Firebar with four wing missile pylons; (immediately below) fitted with two Anab AAM test rounds and (bottom) with standard paired Anab armament and original short radome. (Silhouette) The standard service Firebar with the definitive radome.

Country of Origin: Soviet Union.

Type: All-weather interceptor fighter.

Power Plant: Two 10,140 lb st (4 600 kgp) and 13,670 lb st (6 200 kgp) reheat Tumansky R-11 turbojets.

Performance: Max speed (short-period dash with half fuel and two AA-3 Anab AAMs), 1,240 mph (1 995 km/h) or Mach 1·88 at 36,090 ft (11 000 m), (sustained), 760 mph (1 225 km/h) or Mach 1·15 at 36,090 ft (11 000 m); max continuous cruise, 560 mph (900 km/h) or Mach 0·9; tactical radius (high-altitude intercept mission), 560 mls (900 km); max range (with pinion tanks), 1,495 mls (2 405 km); service ceiling, 55,000 ft (16 765 m).

Weights: (Estimated) Normal loaded, 37,480 lb (17 000 kg); max take-off, 40,785 lb (18 500 kg).

Dimensions: (Estimated) Span, 41 ft 0 in (12,50 m); length, 72 ft 0 in (21,95 m); height, 13 ft 0 in (3,96 m).

Armament: Two AA-3 Anab (one IR-homing and one semi-active radar-homing) AAMs. It may be assumed that the Firebars remaining in service have been adapted for later AAMs (e.g., AA-7 Apex).

Accommodation: Crew of two in tandem.

Status: Evolved in parallel with the Yak-28 (Brewer-A) tactical strike aircraft, the Yak-28P is believed to have flown in prototype form in 1960, with production deliveries to the Soviet air defence squadrons commencing some three–four years later. Although progressively modernised, only some 200 Yak-28P interceptors remained in service at the beginning of 1982 when it was anticipated that this type would be phased out of the air defence system in 1983–84.

Notes: The Yak-28P is one of a family of aircraft evolved simultaneously for differing roles. The tactical attack versions of the Yak-28 (Brewer-A, B and C) featured a single cockpit for the pilot with the navigator/bomb aimer occupying a position in a glazed nose. The Brewer-D was a tactical photo-reconnaissance model and Brewer-E was an electronic countermeasures escort aircraft (the first such to enter Soviet service), the Maestro being a conversion trainer version of the Firebar with individual single-seat cockpits in tandem. Small numbers of the various versions of the Brewer remained in service at the beginning of 1982 but were not believed to be included in the first-line inventory. Current service Firebars include examples with both short and long nose radomes, the latter having presumably been adopted to lessen drag and reduce rain erosion, but not indicating any increase in radar capability. Missiles cannot be carried when pinion tanks (for ferrying) are fitted.

YAKOVLEV YAK-36MP (FORGER)

(Top) The Yak-36 Forger-B tandem two-seater hovering with lift engine doors open, and (immediately above and below) Yak-36MP fighters aboard the carrier Kiev. (Silhouette) The Yak-36MP Forger-A. Note stores racks on non-folding portion of the wing.

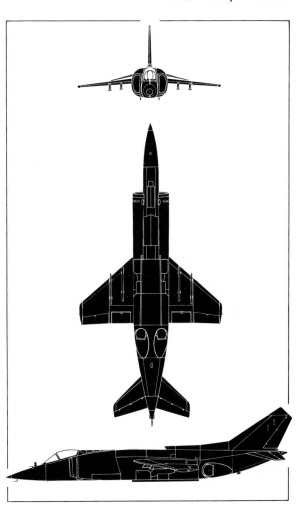

Country of Origin: Soviet Union.

Type: Shipboard vertical take-off and landing air defence and strike fighter, and (Forger-B) two-seat conversion trainer.

Power Plant: One (estimated) 17,640 lb st (8 000 kgp) lift/cruise turbojet plus two (estimated) 7,935 lb st (3 600 kgp) lift turbojets.

Performance: (Estimated) Max speed, 695 mph (1 120 km/h) or Mach 1·05 above 36,000 ft (10 970 m), 725 mph (1 167 km/h) or Mach 0·95 at sea level; high-speed cruise, 595 mph (958 km/h) or Mach 0·85 at 20,000 ft (6 095 m); tactical radius (internal fuel and 2,000 lb/900 kg mix of bombs and rockets), 230 mls (370 km) HI-LO-HI, 150 mls (240 km) LO-LO-LO, (reconnaissance mission with recce pod, two drop tanks and two air to air missiles), 340 mls (547 km).

Weights: (Estimated) Empty 12,125 lb (5 500 kg); max take-off, 22,000 lb (9 980 kg).

Dimensions: (Estimated) Span, 24 ft 7 in (7,50 m); length, 52 ft 6 in (16,00 m); height, 11 ft 0 in (3,35 m); wing area, 167 sq ft (15,50 m²).

Armament: Four underwing pylons with total capacity (estimated) of 2,205 lb (1 000 kg) for bombs, gun or rocket pods, or IR-homing AAMs.

Accommodation: Pilot only, or (Forger-B) instructor and pupil in tandem.

Status: The Yak-36MP (Forger-A) is believed to have flown in prototype form in 1971, and to have first attained service evaluation status in 1976. At the beginning of 1982, this type was deployed aboard the carriers, Kiev, Minsk and Novorossiisk.

Notes: The Yak-36 is unique among current service combat aircraft in that it possesses vertical take-off and landing capability, but is incapable of performing a rolling take-off. Utilising a vectored-thrust engine for cruise and, in combination with fore- and aft-disposed vertically-mounted lift, engines, VTOL, the Yak-36 possesses only radar ranging and an infra-red sensor, and thus has strictly limited usefulness. Each of the three Kiev-class vessels includes in its aircraft complement a squadron of 12–15 Yak-36s for the primary operational roles of fleet defence against shadowing maritime aircraft, reconnaissance and anti-shipping strike. No internal armament is provided. The tandem two-seat conversion trainer version, the Yak-36UV (Forger-B), has an extended forward fuselage to accommodate the second seat, the nose being drooped to provide a measure of vertical stagger. It may be assumed that the Yak-36MP is considered interim fighter equipment.

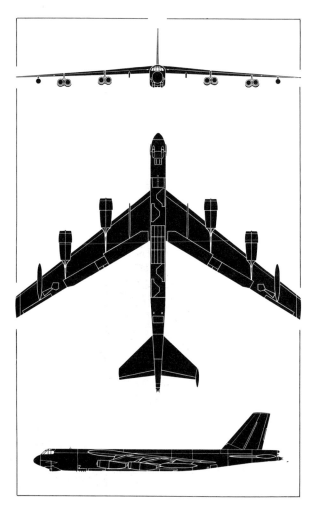

(Above) Boeing B-52G of Strategic Air Command in flight and (immediately below) a similar aircraft coming in to land at one of the UK bases; (bottom) a ground view of B-52G showing the outrigger wheels near the wing tips. (Silhouette) Boeing B-52H Stratofortress.

Country of Origin: USA.

Type: Long-range strategic bomber.

Power Plant: Eight (B-52C, D, and E) 10,500 lb st (4 763 kgp) dry or 12,100 lb st (5 488 kgp) with water injection Pratt & Whitney J57-P-19W or 29WA turbojets or (B-52F,G) 11,200 lb st (5 080 kgp) dry or 13,750 lb st (6 242 kgp) with water injection J57-P-43W, WA, or WB turbojets or (B-52H) 16,500 lb st (7 484 kgp) dry or 17,000 lb st (7 718 kgp) with water injection TF33-P-3 turbofans.

Performance: (B-52H) Max speed, 630 mph (1 013 km/h) at 23,800 ft (7 254 m); average cruising speed, 521 mph (839 km/h) at 40,000 ft (12 200 m); initial rate of climb, 3,000 ft/min (15,12 m/sec); service ceiling, 47,700 ft (14 540 m); combat radius with max bomb-load, 4,350 mls (7 000 km).

Weights: (B-52H) Empty, 172,740 lb (78 355 kg); max take-off, 488,000 lb (221 350 kg).

Dimensions: Span, 185 ft 0 in (56,42 m); length, 157 ft 7 in (48,03 m); height, 40 ft 8 in (12,39 m); wing area, 4,000 sq ft (371,6 m²).

Accommodation: Two pilots, gunner and ECM operator on flight deck upper level and navigator and bombardier below.

Armament: Internal weapons bay with provision for up to 36,000 lb (16 330 kg) of conventional or nuclear free fall bombs; or eight AGM-69A SRAMs. Underwing provision (B-52C,D,E and F) for up to 12 750-lb (340-kg) bombs on each of two pylons or (B-52G and H) six AGM-69A SRAMs each side, plus ALE-25 diversionary rocket pods; or (initially) 12 and (eventually) 20 Boeing AGM-86B ALCMs internally and externally. Tail armament of four 0·50-in (12,7 mm) guns in MD-9 remotely controlled turret or (B-52H only) one 20-mm ASG-21 multi-barrel cannon.

Status: First and second prototypes (XB-52 and YB-52) first flown on 2 October 1952 and 15 April 1952; B-52D flown on 4 June 1956; B-52E on 3 October 1957; B-52F on 6 May 1958; B-52G on 26 September 1958 and B-52H on 6 March 1961. First B-52G/AGM-86B launch, 3 August 1979; first B-52G (OAS) flown 3 September 1980. Production totals: B-52A, 3; RB-52B, 27; B-52B, 23; B-52C, 35; B-52D, 170; B-52E, 100; B-52F, 89; B-52G, 193; B-52H, 102; total 743, completed October 1962.

Notes: Since 1971, 281 B-52G and H have been through updating programmes, providing for carriage of 20 Short-Range Attack Missiles and fitting Electro-optical Viewing System, Forward-Looking Infra-Red and Low-Light-Level TV and improved avionics. New programmes introduce air Offensive Avionic System (OAS) and 173 B-52Gs are being adapted to carry AGM-86B ALCMs.

DASSAULT MIRAGE IVA

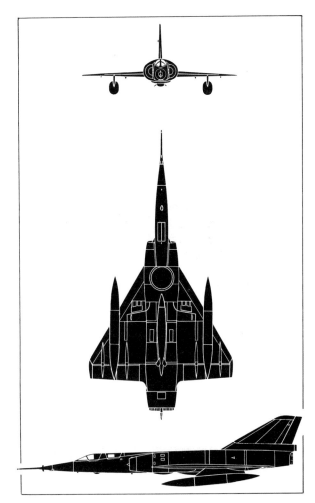

(Above and below) Air and ground views of Dassault Mirage IVAs as camouflaged for the low-altitude nuclear strike rôle performed by the 91e and 94e Escadres de Bombardement of the Armée de l'Air. (Silhouette) Dassault Mirage IVA.

Country of Origin: France.

Type: Medium-range strategic bomber.

Power Plant: Two 10,360 lb st (4 700 kgp) dry and 15 430 lb (7 000 kgp) with reheat SNECMA Atar 09K turbojets.

Performance: Max speed, 1,454 mph (2 340 km/h) at 40,000 ft (13 125 m); max stabilised speed, 1,222 mph (1 966 km/h) at 60,000 ft (19 685 m); time to climb to 36,090 ft (11 000 m), 4 min 15 sec; service ceiling, 65,600 ft (20 000 m); tactical radius (supersonic to target, return at 595 mph/958 km/h at 40,000 ft/13 125 m), 770 mls (1 240 km); max range with drop tanks, 1,485 mls (4 000 km).

Weights: Empty, 31,967 lb (14 500 kg); normal loaded 69,666 lb (31 600 kg); max take-off 73,800 lb (33 475 kg).

Dimensions: Span, 38 ft 10½ in (11,85 m); length, 77 ft 1 in (23,49 m); height, 17 ft 8½ in (5,40 m); wing area, 839·6 sq ft (78,00 m²).

Accommodation: Pilot and navigator in tandem.

Armament: (Strategic mission) One 60 KT free-falling bomb, semi-recessed in fuselage. (Tactical strike mission) up to 16 1,000-lb (454-kg) bombs externally under wings (six each side) and fuselage (four), or four AS.37 Martel anti-radar missiles.

Status: Prototype first flown on 17 June 1959; three pre-production models flown on 12 October 1961, 1 June 1962 and 23 January 1963 respectively. First production Mirage IVA flown on 7 December 1963. Production totals, one prototype, three pre-production, 62 full production, completed 1967.

Notes: The Mirage IVA was developed to provide France with a nuclear deterrent force, capable of striking at targets in the Soviet Bloc territory with French-produced nuclear bombs. In this rôle, it achieved full operational status in March 1968 when the 62nd and last example was delivered to complete the 'Force de Frappe' which originally operated nine four-aircraft squadrons in three Escadres. Subsequently, the Mirage IVs were given a more specific low-level tactical strike rôle with the HE or tactical nuclear bombs, and were re-organised into six escadrons divided between the 91e and 94e Escadres de Bombardement. Four Mirage IVAs also operate with the Centre de Instruction de FAS 328 at Bordeaux in the strategic reconnaissance rôle, with a special equipment pod under the fuselage. Of 47 Mirage IVAs in Armée de l'Air inventory in 1982, 15 were to be modified to carry the French ASMP (air-sol moyenne portee, air-launched stand-off missile) for service from 1985 onwards, when the remainder of the force was to be retired. The Mirage IVA force is supported by 11 (of 12 originally delivered) Boeing C-135F tankers.

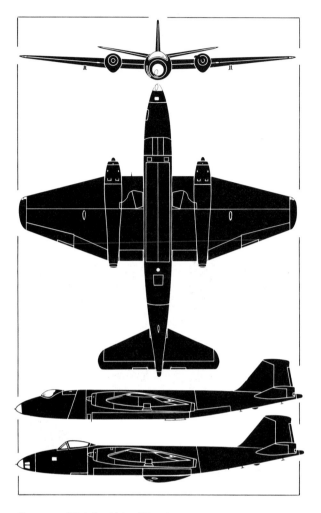

(Top) A Canberra Mk 52 in service with the Ethiopian Air Force; (immediately above) a Canberra B Mk 62 of the Fuerza Aerea Argentina; (below) a Canberra PR Mk 9 serving with the RAF's No 39 Squadron. (Silhouette) Three-view drawing of the Canberra B Mk 6 with extra side view of the B(I) Mk 8

Country of Origin: United Kingdom.

Type: Tactical bomber, reconnaissance, trainer and target tug.

Power Plant: Two (B Mk 6) 7,400 lb st (3 357 kgp) Rolls-Royce Avon 109 or (PR Mk 9) 10,050 lb st (4 560 kgp) Avon 206.

Performance: (B(I) Mk 6) Max speed 518 mph (834 km/h) at sea level and 580 mph (933 km/h) at 35,000 ft (10 668 m); typical cruising speed, 402 mph (647 km/h) at 20,000 ft (6 096 m); initial rate of climb, 3,400 ft/min (17,2 m/sec); max operational altitude 48,000 ft (14 630 m); max range, interdictor rôle, 800 mls (1 287 km); max ferry range, 3,630 mls (5 842 km).

Weights: (B(I) Mk 6) Normal take-off (clean), 51,448 lb (23 336 kg); normal take-off (with tip tanks), 55,590 lb (25 215 kg); max take-off, 56,250 lb (25 514 kg).

Dimensions: Span, 63 ft 11½ in (19,50 m); span over tip tanks, 65 ft 6 in (19,96 m); span (PR Mk 9), 67 ft 10 in (20,67 m); length, 65 ft 6 in (19,96 m); length (PR Mk 9), 66 ft 8 in (20,32 m); height, 15 ft 8 in (4,77 m); wing area, 960 sq ft (89,19 m²); wing area (PR Mk 9), 1,045 sq ft (97,08 m²).

Accommodation: Pilot and navigator; (and bomb-aimer).

Armament: Internal bomb bay with capacity for 6,000 lb (2 722 kg) or (interdictor versions) 3,000 lb (1 360 kg) of bombs plus four 20-mm cannon in a ventral pack. Provision under wings for two pylons carrying up to 1,000 lb (454 kg) of ordnance (bombs or rocket pods) each.

Status: Prototype first flown 13 May 1949; first B Mk 2 flown on 23 April 1950; PR Mk 3 on 19 March 1950; T Mk 4 on 6 June 1952; B Mk 6 on 26 January 1954; PR Mk 7 on 28 October 1953; B(I) Mk 8 on 23 July 1954; PR Mk 9 on 8 July 1955. Production totals: prototypes, 4; B Mk 2, 418; PR Mk 3, 36; T Mk 4, 58; B Mk 5, 1; B Mk 6, 99; B (I) Mk 6, 22; PR Mk 7, 74; B(I) Mk 8, 57; PR Mk 9, 23; B(I) Mk 12, 16; T Mk 13, 1; PR Mk 57, 10; B(I) Mk 58, 71. Other marks by conversion. Total UK production 902, plus 56 B Mk 20 and T Mk 21 built in Australia and 403 B-57 variants built in USA.

Notes: Dwindling force of RAF Canberras, concentrated at RAF Wyton, includes T Mk 4, B Mk 6, E Mk 15, T Mk 17, TT Mk 18 and T Mk 19 variants; T Mk 22 serves in the RN FRADU together with some TT Mk 18s. Overseas, the Canberra remains operational with several air forces, including Argentina (B Mk 62, T Mk 64), Ethiopia, (B Mk 52), Ecuador (B Mk 6), India, (PR Mk 57, B(I) Mk 58, B Mk 66, T Mk 67 and B(I) Mk 12), Peru (B Mk 72, T Mk 74, B(I) Mk 78), South Africa (T Mk 4, B(I) Mk 12), Venezuela (B Mk 82, PR Mk 83, T Mk 84 and B(I) Mk 88) and Zimbabwe (formerly Rhodesia) (B Mk 2, T Mk 4).

(Above and immediately below) Two aerial views of General Dynamics FB-111A bombers in service with Strategic Air Command; (bottom) a ground view of an FB-111A with wings fully forward. (Silhouette) General Dynamics FB-111A with six drop tanks.

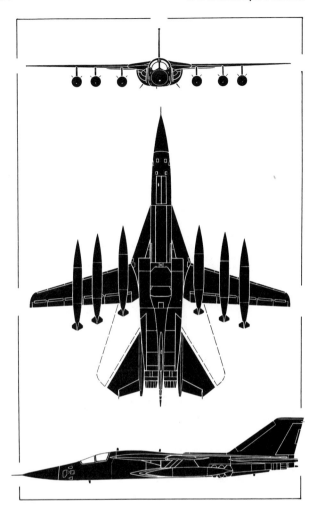

Country of Origin: USA.

Type: Supersonic strategic bomber.

Power Plant: Two 12,500 lb st (5 670 kgp) dry and 20,350 lb st (9 230 kgp) with reheat Pratt & Whitney TF30-P-7 turbofans.

Performance: Max speed, 1,450 mph (2 334 km/h) or Mach 2·5 at 50,000 ft (15 240 m); max speed at sea level, about 910 mph (1 470 km/h), equivalent to Mach 1·2; initial rate of climb at max weight, 2,874 ft/min (14,6 m/sec); rate of climb at combat weight, 23,418 ft/min (7 138 m/sec); service ceiling at combat weight, 50,263 ft (15 320 m); total mission range, HI-LO-LO-HI with one refuelling, 6,150 mls (9 900 km) at average 511 mph (822 km/h); ferry range, unrefuelled, 4,800 mls (7 725 km).

Weights: Empty, approximately 47,500 lb (21 545 kg); normal take-off, 114,000 lb (51 710 kg); max overload, 119,000 lb (53 908 kg).

Dimensions: Span (spread), 70 ft 0 in (21,34 m); span (fully swept-back), 33 ft 11 in (10,34 m); height, 17 ft 1½ in (5,22 m); wing area, 550 sq ft (51,1 m²).

Accommodation: Pilot and navigator side-by-side in pressurised escape capsule.

Armament: Internal weapon bay can accommodate two 750-lb (340-kg) bombs, two Boeing AGM-69A SRAM ASMs or other weapons of similar weight. Eight under-wing pylons can carry up to 48 750-lb (340-kg) bombs or a maximum load of 37,500 lb (17 000 kg) of assorted weapons or four Boeing AGM-69A SRAM missiles (subject to limitation on external loads when wings are fully swept).

Status: Prototype (F-111A conversion) first flown on 30 July 1967; first production FB-111A flown on 13 July 1968. Deliveries began October 1969; production of 76 completed 1971.

Notes: The FB-111A was developed from the F-111A fighter (separately described) to provide Strategic Air Command with a supersonic bomber to replace the B-58 Hustler and early versions of the long-range subsonic B-52 Stratofortress. A programme to acquire 210 examples was announced but this was later cut to 76, to equip two Wings with two squadrons each—the 50th Bomb Wing at Pease AFB, NH and the 380th Strategic Aerospace Wing at Plattsburgh, NY. The FB-111A differs from the F-111 in having the larger span wing originally developed for the US Navy F-111B, beefed-up structure and undercarriage to permit higher operating weights, plus uprated engines and revised avionics for its strategic rôle. Like the F-111, the FB-111A has terrain-following radar and can fly at supersonic speed at about 200 ft (60 m) for "under-the-radar" approach to its target.

(Above) A Hawker Siddeley Buccaneer S Mk 2 of No 16 Squadron, RAF and (immediately below) a similar aircraft carrying a Westinghouse Pave Spike target designator on the inboard wing pylon and a laser-guided bomb outboard; (bottom) Buccaneer S Mk 50 of the S.A.A.F. (Silhouette) Buccaneer S Mk 2B.

Country of Origin: United Kingdom.

Type: Tactical strike and anti-shipping aircraft.

Power Plant: Two (S Mk 2 and 50) 11,100 lb st (5 035 kgp) Rolls-Royce Spey RB.168-1A Mk 101 turbofans plus (S Mk 50) 8,000 lb st (3 630 kgp) Bristol Siddeley BS.605 rocket engine.

Performance: (S Mk 2, estimated): Max speed, 645 mph (1 040 km/h) or Mach 0·85 at 250 ft (75 m), 620 mph (998 km/h) or Mach 0·92 at 30,000 ft (9 145 m); typical low-level cruise, 570 mph (917 km/h) at 3,000 ft (915 m); tactical radius (HI-LO-LO-HI) with standard fuel, 500–600 mls (805–966 km).

Weights: Typical loaded 46,000 lb (20 865 kg); max take-off, 62,000 lb (28 123 kg).

Dimensions: Span, 44 ft 0 in (13,41 m); length, 63 ft 5 in (19,33 m); height, 16 ft 3 in (4,95 m); wing area, 514·7 sq ft (47·82 m²).

Accommodation: Pilot and observer in tandem.

Armament: Internal weapons bay (with rotary bomb door), capacity up to 4,000 lb (1 814 kg) and four wing stations each with 3,000 lb (1 360 kg) capacity, carrying Bullpup, Martel or Sea Eagle ASMs, laser-guided "smart" bombs or rocket pods.

Status: First of 20 development batch aircraft flown on 30 April 1958; first production S Mk 1 flown on 23 January 1962;

prototype S Mk 2 flown on 17 May 1963; first production S Mk 2 flown on 5 June 1964; first RAF S Mk 2B flown on 8 January 1970. Operational use of S Mk 1 began July 1962, S Mk 2 in October 1965 (RN) and July 1970 (RAF). Production quantities, development batch, 20; S Mk 1, 40; S Mk 2, 84; S Mk 2B, 42; S Mk 50, 16.

Notes: Buccaneer S Mk 1 and original S Mk 2s were delivered to RN, the S Mk 2B being ordered new for the RAF. Most S Mk 2s were transferred to RAF when relinquished by RN, becoming, with RAF equipment, S Mk 2A and S Mk 2B respectively without and with provision for Martel ASMs; unmodified aircraft without and with Martel provision became S Mk 2C and 2D for continuing service with RN until final retirement of HMS *Ark Royal*. RAF force eventually comprised five squadrons, Nos 15 and 16 in RAF Germany and Nos 12, 208 and 216 for maritime strike duties in the UK. The German-based aircraft could carry *Pave Spike* laser designators in wing pods to guide *Pave Way* "smart" bombs, and are fitted to carry one Sidewinder AAM under the starboard wing, for self-defence. The SAAF has 13 rocket-boosted S Mk 50s in service with No 24 Squadron. These are essentially similar to the S Mk 2 but are fitted with a retractable Rolls-Royce Bristol BS.605 twin-chamber rocket engine to boost take-off.

ILYUSHIN IL-28 (BEAGLE)

(Top) A standard Il-28 Beagle in DDR service; (immediately above) a Polish Il-28 serving in the maritime role with ECM equipment in the wingtip pods, and (below) an Egyptian Il-28. (Silhouette) The standard Il-28 with Il-28U depicted by upper sideview.

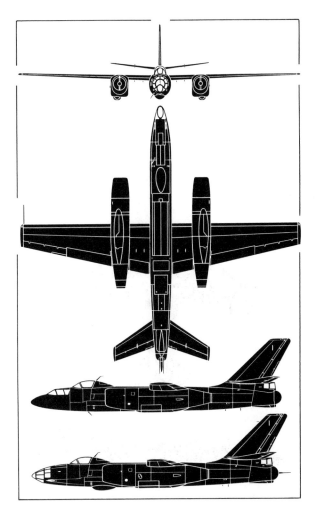

Country of Origin: Soviet Union (China).

Type: Light tactical bomber, torpedo and reconnaissance aircraft, and (Il-28U) conversion trainer.

Power Plant: Two 5,952 lb st (2 700 kgp) Klimov VK-1 turbojets.

Performance: (At normal loaded weight) Max speed, 497 mph (800 km/h) at sea level, 559 mph (900 km/h) at 14,765 ft (4 000 m); initial climb, 2,953 ft/min (15 m/sec); time to 16,405 ft (5 000 m), 6·5 min, to 32,810 ft (10 000 m), 18 min; service ceiling, 40,355 ft (12 300 m); range (max fuel), 1,355 mls (2 180 km) at 478 mph (770 km/h) at 32,810 ft (10 000 m), 1,490 mls (2 400 km) at 267 mph (430 km/h).

Weights: Empty equipped, 28,417 lb (12 890 kg); normal loaded, 40,565 lb (18 400 kg); max take-off, 46,297 lb (21 000 kg).

Dimensions: Span (excluding tip tanks), 70 ft 4¾ in (21,45 m); length, 57 ft 10¾ in (17,65 m); height, 21 ft 11¾ in (6,70 m); wing area, 654·44 sq ft (60,80 m²).

Armament: Two 23-mm NR-23 cannon in lower forward fuselage and two similar weapons in Il-K6 tail turret, and provision for normal and maximum bomb loads of 2,205 lb (1 000 kg) and 6,614 lb (3 000 kg) respectively in weapons bay, typical loads including four 1,102-lb (500-kg) or eight 551-lb (250-kg) bombs, plus (B-5) four air-to-surface missiles on inboard wing racks.

Accommodation: Pilot, navigator/bombardier and rear gunner.

Status: First of three prototypes flown on 8 August 1948, with initial deliveries to Soviet Air Force commencing late 1950. Several thousand Il-28s were built in the Soviet Union before production phase-out in 1959, variants including the Il-28R reconnaissance aircraft, the Il-28T torpedo-dropping and mine-laying aircraft, and the Il-28U (Mascot) pilot and operational trainer. A substantial number of Il-28s were exported to China where licence manufacture was initiated at Pinkiang as the B-5. Deliveries of Chinese-built aircraft commenced 1964–65, and production was continuing in small numbers at the beginning of 1982 primarily to make up attrition.

Notes: Although now totally obsolete and retained by WarPac air forces only for second-line duties (e.g., weather reconnaissance, target towing, etc.), the Il-28 alias B-5 remains the primary light tactical bomber of the Chinese air arm. This service currently possesses some 400 bombers of this type and an additional quantity of approximately 100 is included in the inventory of the Chinese naval air arm. A small number of Chinese-built IL-28 bombers have been exported to Albania, and a Chinese-developed dual-control trainer variant is in limited service. A half-dozen Soviet-built examples remain in Egyptian service.

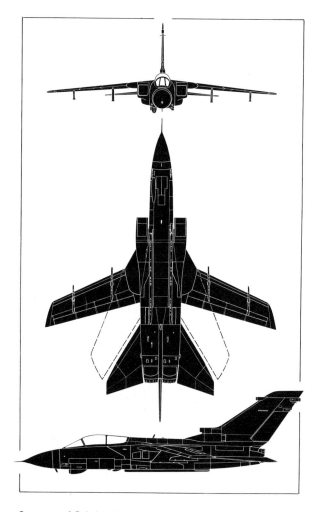

(Above) The first production Panavia Tornado GR Mk 1 in RAF strike colours; (immediately below) an early production IDS Tornadao from the German production line serving at the TTTE, Cottesmore; (bottom) pre-production Tornado P-16 in German Navy markings. (Silhouette) Panavia Tornado GR Mk 1.

Country of Origin: United Kingdom/Federal Germany/Italy.
Type: Multi-rôle strike aircraft.
Power Plant: Two 9,000 lb st (4 082 kgp) dry and 16,000 lb st (7 258 kgp) with reheat (approx) Turbo-Union RB.199-34R-04 Mk 101 turbofans.
Performance: (Prototype aircraft, demonstrated); Max speed, clean, 1,452 mph (2 337 km/h) or Mach 2·2 above 36,000 ft (11,000 m); max speed, with external stores, 691 mph (1 112 km/h) or Mach 0·92; max speed over 720 mph (1 160 km/h) or Mach 0·95 at sea level; time to climb to 30,000 ft (9 150 m), less than 2 mins; combat radius, (HI-LO-LO-HI), 860 mls (1 385 km); fery range, about 2,420 mls (3 890 km).
Weights: (Prototypes) Empty equipped, 22,000-23,000 lb (9 980-10 430 kg); max weapon load 16,000 lb (7 257 kg); take-off weight, clean, 45,000 lb (20 411 kg); max take-off, 58,400 lb (26 490 kg).
Dimensions: Span 45 ft 7¼ in (13,90 m); span, fully-swept, 28 ft 2½ in (8,60 m); length, 54 ft 9½ in (16,70 m); height, 18 ft 8½ in (5,70 m).
Accommodation: Pilot and navigator/observer in tandem.
Armament: Two 27-mm IWKA-Mauser cannon in lower front fuselage; three under-fuselage and four swivelling wing strong

points for bombs, AAMs, ASMs such as Martel, Sea Eagle, Kormoran, AS 30 etc., rocket pods, scatter-bomb weapons, reconnaissance pods, ECM pods, fuel tanks etc.
Status: First of nine prototypes (P-01) flown 14 August 1974 in Germany; first in UK (P-02) on 30 October 1974; first in Italy (P-05) on 5 December 1975. First of six pre-production aircraft (P-11) flown 5 February 1977 in Germany; first in UK (P-12) on 14 March 1977; first in Italy (P-14) on 8 January 1979. First production aircraft (BT-001) flown on 10 July 1979 (in UK); first German production (GT-001) on 27 July 1979; first strike configuration (BS-001) on 14 March 1980 in UK; first German strike aircraft (GS-001) on 31 March 1980; first Italian production aircraft (IT-001) on 25 September. Production programme calls for 640 aircraft (plus four pre-production) comprising 220 for RAF (GR Mk 1), 212 for *Luftwaffe*, 112 for *Marineflieger* and 100 for AMI.
Notes: Tornado (originally known as MRCA—Multi-Role Combat Aircraft) is the product of a multi-national European design and production effort embracing British Aerospace, MBB and Aeritalia. The IDS (interdictor/strike) version described, including some as dual control trainers (RAF GR Mk 1T), entered service at the Trinational Tornado Training Establishment, in January 1981.

(Top and immediately above) Two in-flight photographs of one of the Rockwell B-1 prototypes, respectively with wings forward and swept back; (below) a B-1 prototype on test at Edwards AFB. (Silhouette) Rockwell B-1B, showing wings fully forward and fully swept back.

Country of Origin: USA.
Type: Long-range strategic bomber.
Power Plant: Four 17,000 lb st (7 711 kgp) dry and 30,000 lb st (13 608 kgp) with reheat General Electric F101-GE-100 turbofans.
Performance: (Prototype B-1, estimated) Max speed, 1,450 mph (2 334 km/h) at 40,000 ft (12 190 m) or Mach 2·2, and 900 mph (1 450 km/h) at 1,500 ft (460 m) or Mach 1·2 and 648 mph (1 042 km/h) at sea level or Mach 0·85; max range without refuelling, 6,100 mls (9 820 km).
Weights: (Prototype B-1) Max take-off (design), 395,000 lb (179 172 kg).
Dimensions: Span, wings spread, 136 ft 8½ in (41,66 m); span, wings swept, 78 ft 2½ in (23,83 m); length (over nose probe), 150 ft 2½ in (45,80 m); height, 33 ft 7¼ in (10,24 m); approximate wing area 1,950 sq ft (181,2 m²).
Armament: Three internal weapons bays contain (prototypes) 24 Boeing AGM-69 SRAM short-range attack missiles, or 75,000 lb (34 020 kg) of free-fall bombs; four fuselage hardpoints provide for carriage of eight more SRAMs or 40,000 lb (18 145 kg) of free-fall weapons.
Accommodation: Two pilots and two system operators.

Status: Four prototypes built, flown respectively 23 December 1974, 1 April 1976, 14 June 1976 and 14 February 1979.
Notes: The B-1 was designed in response to the USAF Advanced Manned Strategic Aircraft (AMSA) requirement in 1969, initial contracts being placed with North American Rockwell's Los Angeles Division on 5 June 1970. Plans for procurement of 244 B-1As to replace SAC B-52s were abandoned in 1979 and the four prototypes were dedicated to completion of a flight test programme, with particular emphasis upon the No 4 aircraft which carried representative offensive and defensive avionics systems. The test programme ended with flights by Nos 3 and 4 on 15 April and 30 April 1981 respectively, by which time the four aircraft had totalled 1,985·2 hrs in 247 flights. A derivative of the B-1 was prepared in March 1981 to meet the revised USAF requirement for a Long-Range Combat Aircraft (LRCA), with the ability to carry Boeing AGM-86B air-launched cruise missiles internally (16) and externally (14), and in October 1981 President Reagan announced that procurement of 100 of these modified B-1s was to go ahead. The B-1B is expected to have a gross weight of 477,000 lb (213 367 kg), with increased fuel capacity, and 30,750 lb st (13 948 kgp) F101-GE-102 turbofans. Introduction into service will begin in 1986.

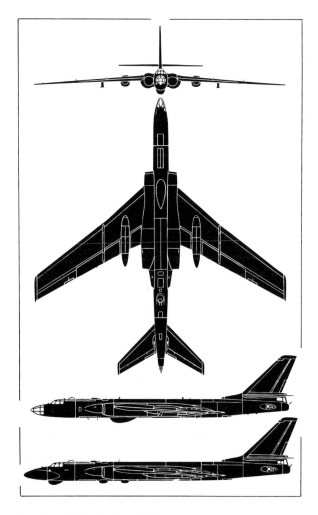

(Above) A Tu-16 Badger-C of the Soviet Naval Air Force with a Kingfish missile under the port wing. (Immediately below) A standard anti-shipping Badger-C and (bottom) a Navy Badger-G. (Silhouette) Badger-G (modified) with sideview of Badger-D.

Country of Origin: Soviet Union.

Type: (Badger-A) Medium-range strategic bomber, (Badger-C and G) anti-shipping, (Badger-E) photographic, (Badger-D) maritime and (Badger-K) electronic reconnaissance, and (Badger-H and J) electronic countermeasures aircraft.

Power Plant: Two 19,290 lb st (8 750 kgp) Mikulin AM-3M turbojets.

Performance: (Badger-A) Max speed, 575 mph (925 km/h) or Mach 0·87 at 36,090 ft (11 000 m); tactical radius with max payload, 1,800 mls (2 895 km); range (with 8,377-lb/3 800-kg ordnance), 3,200 mls (5 150 km), (with max fuel), 3 570 mls (5 750 km); service ceiling, 40,025 ft (12 200 m).

Weights: (Badger-A) Empty, 88,185 lb (40 000 kg); normal loaded, 115,742 lb (52 500 kg); max take-off, 169,756 lb (77 000 kg).

Dimensions: Span, 108 ft 0½ in (32,93 m); length, 114 ft 2 in (34,80 m); height, 35 ft 6 in (10,80 m); wing area, 1,772·28 sq ft (164,65 m²).

Armament: (Badger-A) Forward dorsal, rear ventral and tail barbettes each housing two 23-mm NR-23 cannon, plus one fixed forward-firing 23-mm cannon. Maximum internal bomb load, 8,377 lb (3 800 kg); (Badger-C) One AS-2 Kipper stand-off missile,

or (Badger-G) two AS-5 Kelt or AS-6 Kingfish stand-off missiles.

Accommodation: Crew complement varying from six to nine members according to version.

Status: The Tu-16 was flown in prototype form (Tu-88) in 1952, entering Soviet service in strategic bombing form (Badger-A) in 1955, production variants including the AS-1 Kennel missile-launching Badger-B and AS-2 Kipper missile-launching Badger-C anti-shipping versions. Total of approximately 2,000 built when production was phased out in 1964. Licence manufacture initiated in China as the B-6, but first deliveries (from Xian) did not commence until 1969, limited production of the B-6 continuing at the beginning of 1982. Apart from 350–400 retained by the Soviet strategic bombing force, some 70 are equipped as convertible flight-refuelling tankers and 90–100 have been converted for electronic countermeasures (Badger-H and J), reconnaissance (Badger-K) and intelligence (Badger-F). In addition, the inventory of the Soviet Naval Air Force includes 270–280 Tu-16s (Badger-C and G) for maritime strike and 80–90 for electronic (Badger-D) and photographic (Badger-E) reconnaissance and electronic intelligence missions. A small number of Tu-16s remained in service with the Egyptian Air Force at the beginning of 1982, equipping one air brigade.

(Top) A Tu-22 Blinder-C of the Soviet Naval Air Force and (immediately above and below) the Blinder-A operating with the Soviet Long-range Aviation component. (Silhouette) The Blinder-C with camera windows in the weapons bay doors.

Country of Origin: Soviet Union.
Type: Medium-range reconnaissance-bomber (Blinder-A), missile carrier (Blinder-B), maritime reconnaissance-strike aircraft (Blinder-C) and operational conversion trainer (Blinder-D).
Power Plant: Two (estimated) 27,000 lb st (12 250 kgp) reheat turbojets.
Performance: (Estimated) Max speed, 720 mph (1 160 km/h) or Mach 0·95 at 1,000 ft (305 m), (short-period dash), 930 mph (1 496 km/h) or Mach 1·4 at 40,000 ft (12 150 m); normal range cruise, 560 mph (900 km/h) or Mach 0·85 at 40,000 ft (12 150 m); combat radius, 1,925 mls (3 100 km); service ceiling, 54,000 ft (16 455 m).
Weights: (Estimated) Max take-off, 185,000 lb (83 915 kg).
Dimensions: (Estimated) Span, 91 ft 0 in (27,74 m); length, 133 ft 0 in (40,50 m); height, 17 ft 0 in (5,18 m); wing area, 2,030 sq ft (188,60 m²).
Armament: Single 23-mm NR-23 cannon in remotely-controlled tail barbette and (Blinder-A) 4,410 lb (2 000 kg) of free-fall weapons in internal bay, or (Blinder-B) one AS-4 Kitchen missile semi-recessed beneath fuselage.
Accommodation: Flight crew of three or (Blinder-D) four (with instructor accommodated in a raised cockpit aft of the standard

flight deck).
Status: Flown in prototype form (as the Tu-105) in 1959–60, the Tu-22 achieved initial operational capability with the Soviet Air Force in 1966–67, but production was apparently limited to some 250 aircraft of which about 25 per cent were delivered to the Soviet Naval Air Force for maritime recce and strike missions. Production was phased out in 1971–72, but some 120 remain with the Long-range Aviation component and approximately 40 with the Naval Air Force. Twelve (Blinder-A) were supplied to Iraq and 20 (Blinder-C) to Libya.
Notes: The first Soviet bomber possessing supersonic dash capability, the Tu-22 was apparently considered to possess an inadequate tactical radius with the result that it enjoyed what was, by Soviet standards, a comparatively short production run. Apart from certain unsatisfactory aspects of the performance of the Tu-22, a motivation for production phase-out may well have been provided by prototype development of a variable-geometry bomber (which was to emerge as Backfire) intended to meet an essentially similar requirement to that for which the Tu-22 was conceived. It is possible that this fact engendered use of 'Tu-22M' in reference to Backfire during SALT II talks but as a class appellative rather than as a designation for the later warplane.

(Above) A Backfire-B with an AS-4 Kitchen missile semi-recessed beneath the fuselage, and (below) Backfire-Bs with stores racks beneath the engine air intake trunking. (Silhouette) Backfire-B with wings at minimum sweep, maximum sweep being shown dotted.

Country of Origin: Soviet Union.

Type: Medium-range strategic bomber and maritime strike and reconnaissance aircraft.

Power Plant: Two (estimated) 33,070 lb st (15 000 kgp) and 46,300 lb st (21 000 kgp) reheat Kuznetsov turbofans.

Performance: (Estimated) Max speed (short-period dash), 1,265 mph (2 036 km/h) or Mach 1·91 at 39,370 ft (12 000 m), (sustained), 1,056 mph (1 700 km/h) or Mach 1·6 at 39,370 ft (12 000 m), 685 mph (1 100 km/h) or Mach 0·9 at sea level; combat radius (unrefuelled with single AS-4 Kitchen ASM and high-altitude subsonic mission profile), 2,610 mls (4 200 km), max unrefuelled combat range (with 12,345-lb/5 600-kg internal ordnance load), 5,560 mls (8 950 km).

Weights: (Estimated) Max take-off, 260,000 lb (118 000 kg).

Dimensions: (Estimated) Span (spread) 115 ft 0 in (35,00 m), (sweptback), 92 ft 0 in (28,00 m); length, 134 ft 0 in (40,80 m); height, 29 ft 6 in (9,00 m); wing area, 1,830 sq ft (170,00 m²).

Armament: Remotely-controlled tail barbette containing twin 23-mm NR-23 cannon. Internal load of free-falling weapons up to 12,345 lb (5 600 kg) or one AS-4 Kitchen inertially-guided stand-off missile.

Accommodation: Pilot and co-pilot side-by-side on flight deck

and two–three additional crew members further aft.

Status: Flight testing of initial prototype commenced late 1969, with pre-production series of up to 12 aircraft following in 1972–73. Initial version (Backfire-A) was built in only small numbers, differing from the major production model (Backfire-B) primarily in undercarriage geometry. Initial operational capability attained with Backfire-B 1975–76, production rate of 30 annually being attained in 1977, and remaining constant at beginning of 1982, when 75–80 Backfires were believed in service with each of Soviet Long-range Aviation and the Soviet Naval Air Force.

Notes: An exceptionally versatile multi-purpose aircraft capable of performing nuclear strike, conventional attack, and anti-shipping and reconnaissance missions, the Backfire is capable of both peripheral and inter-continental sorties, the latter by means of inflight refuelling. It is considered likely by western intelligence analysts that Backfire will be mated with the new 745-mile (1 200-km) range cruise missile expected to be deployed by Soviet Long-range Aviation from 1983–84. When the current AS-4 Kitchen is carried by Backfire no gravity bombs can be housed by the internal weapons bay. The type designation of Backfire remained uncertain at the beginning of 1982, although US sources have given this as Tu-26

(Above) A formation of three Shackleton MR Mk 3s, operated by No 35 Squadron of the South African Air Force; (immediately below) a ground view of one of the SAAF Shackleton MR Mk 3s; (bottom) a Shackleton AEW Mk 2 of No 8 Squadron, RAF. (Silhouette) Avro Shackleton MR Mk 3 with extra side view of the AEW Mk 2.

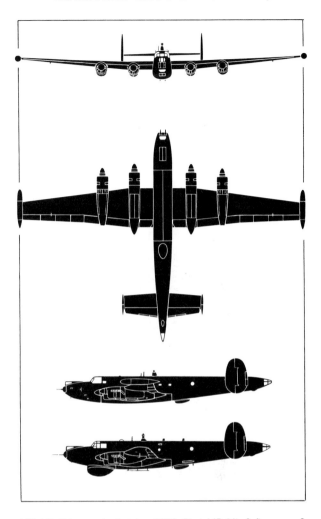

Country of Origin: United Kingdom.

Type: Airborne early warning and maritime patrol aircraft.

Power Plant: Four 2,450 hp Rolls-Royce Griffon 57A 12-cylinder liquid-cooled engines, plus (Mk 3 only) two 2,500 lb st (1 134 kgp) Rolls-Royce Bristol Viper 203 turbojets.

Performance: (MR Mk 3) Max speed, 302 mph (486 km/h) at 12,000 ft (3 658 m); max cruising speed, 253 mph (407 km/h) at 10,000 ft (3 050 m); long-range cruising speed, 200 mph (322 km/h); initial rate of climb, 850 ft/min (4,3 m/sec); service ceiling, 19,200 ft (5 852 m); range, 3,660–4,215 mls (5 890–6 780 km).

Weights: (MR Mk 3) Empty, 57,800 lb (26 218 kg); normal loaded, 85,000 lb (38 555 kg); max take-off, 100,000 lb (45 360 kg).

Dimensions: (MR Mk 3) Span, 119 ft 10 in (36,53 m); length, 92 ft 6 in (28,19 m); height, 23 ft 4 in (7,11 m); wing area, 1,458 sq ft (135,45 m²).

Accommodation: Flight crew of three plus eight in tactical compartment in fuselage.

Armament: Two 20-mm cannon in nose.

Status: First of three prototypes flown on 9 March 1949. Deliveries of MR Mk 1 began on 28 September 1950; deliveries of MR Mk 2 began in October 1952. First MR Mk 3 flown on 2 September 1955; deliveries began 1957; first AEW Mk 2 (conversion) flown 30 September 1971; deliveries began in January 1972. Production quantities: Prototypes, 3; MR Mk 1, 77; MR Mk 2, 69 (12 converted to AEW Mk 2); MR Mk 3, 42 (including 8 for SAAF).

Notes: The Shackleton was derived indirectly from the famous Lancaster bomber by way of the Lincoln, having the latter's wing, tail unit and undercarriage with a new fuselage. Production passed through three variants, of which the Mk 1 and Mk 2 had tailwheel undercarriages and, respectively, short and long fuselages, and the Mk 3 had a nosewheel undercarriage and (through a later modification programme) jet boost engines in the inboard nacelles. After Nimrods replaced Shackletons in the maritime reconnaissance role, No 8 Squadron, RAF, continued to operate AEW Mk 2s for airborne early warning. Twelve of these aircraft were modified MR Mk 2s with APS-20 search radar under the nose, in place of the retractable radome farther aft, Orange Harvest wide-band passive ECM, Doppler navigation equipment and other special sensors. Replacement of the Shackleton AEW Mk 2s by Nimrod AEW Mk 3s was to begin in 1982, but the South African Air Force continues to operate seven of the eight MR Mk 3s supplied in 1957 and equipping No 35 Squadron based at Cape Town.

(Top) The first Nimrod MR Mk 2, in the original Coastal Command finish; (immediately below) an MR Mk 2 in the revised finish with tactical aircraft markings, current in 1982; (bottom) one of the three Nimrod R Mk 1s used for special reconnaissance duties. (Silhouette) British Aerospace Nimrod MR Mk 2.

Country of Origin: United Kingdom.

Type: Long-range maritime patrol aircraft.

Power Plant: Four 12,160 lb st (5 515 kgp) Rolls-Royce Spey RB. 168 Mk 250 turbofans.

Performance: Max speed, 575 mph (926 km/h); max transit speed, 547 mph (880 km/h); economical transit speed, 490 mph (787 km/h); typical ferry range, 5,180–5,755 mls (8 340–9 265 km); typical endurance, 12 hrs.

Weights: (MR Mk 2); Normal take-off, 184,000 lb (83 460 kg); max overload, 192,000 lb (87 090 kg).

Dimensions: Span, 114 ft 10 in (35,00 m); length, 126 ft 9 in (38,63 m); height, 29 ft 8½ in (9,08 m); wing area, 2,121 sq ft (197,05 m²).

Accommodation: Normal flight crew of three (two pilots and a flight engineer) plus a nine-man team in the tactical compartment including two navigators, five sensor operators and two observers/stores loaders.

Armament: Internal weapons bay, approximately 49 ft (14,8 m) long, can accommodate homing torpedoes, mines, depth charges, bombs, etc.

Status: Prototypes (converted Comet 4C airframes) first flown on 23 May and 31 July 1967, respectively. First production MR Mk 1 flown on 28 June 1968, deliveries of 46 ordered by RAF began on 2 October 1969. Three R Mk 1 delivered to RAF 1972. First MR Mk 2 production-conversion flown 13 February 1979, delivered to RAF 23 August 1979.

Notes: Designed as a replacement for the Shackleton, the Nimrod was derived from the Comet commercial airliner, using substantially the same wing and tail unit, with the same basic fuselage cross section but with the addition of an unpressurised pannier under the fuselage to accommodate the weapons bay and operational equipment. The fuselage was shortened by 6 ft 6 in (1,98 m) and Spey turbofans substituted for the original Avons. The total Nimrod MR Mk 1 force in Strike Command comprised five squadrons, of which one (Malta-based) has been disbanded, leaving Nos 42, 120, 201 and 206 operational from the UK in 1981. In addition three Nimrods for electronic reconnaissance duties, and designated R Mk 1s, serve with No 51 Squadron; these aircraft can be distinguished by the lack of MAD 'sting' fairing. Of the total of 46 aircraft built as MR Mk 1s, 11 are allocated for conversion to AEW Mk 3 configuration, separately described, and the other 35 are progressively being upgraded to MR Mk 2 standard with greatly improved detection capabilities; these also feature wing-tip ESM pods.

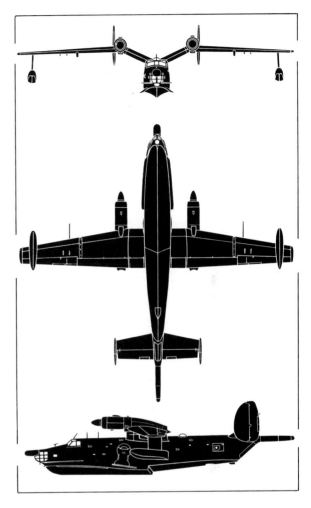

(Top) A Be-12 Mail seen in Egyptian markings prior to the 1976 abrogation of the Egyptian-Soviet Friendship Treaty, and (immediately above and below) Be-12s in service with the Soviet Naval Air Force. (Silhouette) The standard Be-12 Mail.

Country of Origin: Soviet Union.

Type: Medium-range maritime reconnaissance and anti-submarine warfare amphibian.

Power Plant: Two 4,000 ehp Ivchenko AI-20D turboprops.

Performance: Max speed, 380 mph (610 km/h) at 10,000 ft (3 050 m); typical patrol speed, 200 mph (320 km/h) at 985–1,970 ft (300–600 m); initial climb rate, 3,000 ft/min (15,2 m/sec); service ceiling, 37,000 ft (11 280 m); max endurance, 8 hrs; max range, 2,485 mls (4 000 km).

Weights: Max take-off, 65,035 lb (29 500 kg).

Dimensions: Span, 97 ft 6 in (29,70 m); length, 101 ft 11 in (32,90 m); height, 22 ft 11½ in (7,00 m); wing area, 1,030 sq ft (95,69 m²).

Armament: Internal weapons bay for homing torpedoes, depth bombs, mines, etc., and pylon beneath each wing for additional ordnance, with rail launchers for air-to-surface missiles.

Accommodation: Flight crew of five comprising two pilots, a navigator, a radar operator and a MAD (Magnetic Anomaly Detection) gear operator.

Status: Believed to have been flown in prototype form in 1960, the Be-6 entered service with the Soviet Naval Air Force during 1965–66, production of 100–120 being completed in the early

seventies, and 70–80 of these remaining in service with the Northern and Baltic Fleet Air Forces at the beginning of 1982.

Notes: Marginally smaller than the Shin Meiwa US-1 air-sea rescue amphibian (see page 86), the Be-12, known unofficially as the Tchaika (Gull) in the Soviet Union, is the only amphibious flying boat remaining in service for maritime reconnaissance and anti-submarine warfare tasks. This aircraft has established a large number of officially-recognised international records for Class C3 Group II turboprop-powered amphibious aircraft, these including altitudes with and without payloads, and closed-circuit speed records, the most recent record being established in November 1978. In fact, the Be-12 holds all 21 FAI records for its class, albeit an exceedingly *small* class. Possessing a high length-to-beam ratio, the Be-12 has a tailwheel-type undercarriage consisting of single-wheel main units retracting upward through 180 deg to lie flush within the sides of the hull and an aft-retracting tailwheel. For a period in the 'seventies, a small number of Be-12s were based in Egypt for operation over the Mediterranean, and although these displayed Egyptian insignia they were crewed by Soviet naval personnel. There has been no indication that the Soviet Union is pursuing waterborne aircraft development, and the Be-12 may be expected to be replaced by land-based aircraft.

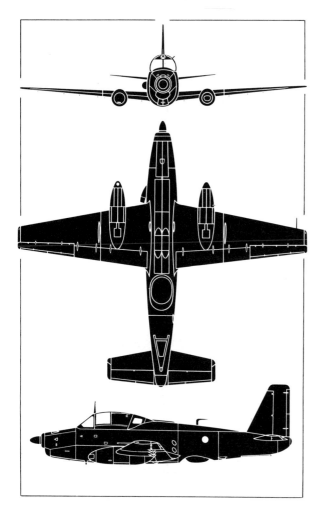

(Above) An air view of the Alizé; (immediately below) one of the modified Alizés as in continuing service with two Flottilles of the French Aéronavales; (bottom) An Alizé in Indian Navy service, as operated from the aircraft carrier Vikrant. (Silhouette) Breguet Alizé.

Country of Origin: France.

Type: Carrier-borne anti-submarine attack aircraft.

Power Plant: One 2,100 eshp Rolls-Royce Dart R.Da. 21 turboprop.

Performance: Max speed, 285 mph (460 km/h) at sea level, 292 mph (470 km/h) at 10,000 ft (3 048 m); normal patrol speed, 144 mph (232 km/h) at 1,500 ft (457 m); initial rate of climb, 1,380 ft/min (7,0 m/sec); service ceiling, 20,500 ft (6 248 m); endurance (search configuration at 1,500 ft/457 m), 5 hr 12 min; ferry range, 1,785 mls (2 870 km).

Weights: Empty equipped, 12,566 lb (5 700 kg); max take-off, 18,100 lb (8 200 kg).

Dimensions: Span, 51 ft 2 in (15,6 m); length, 45 ft 6 in (13,86 m); height, 16 ft 5 in (5,0 m); wing area, 387·5 sq ft (36 m²).

Accommodation: Pilot and radar operator side-by-side in cockpit, with second radar operator in sideways-facing seat to rear.

Armament: Internal weapon bay can accommodate one torpedo or three depth bombs of 353-lb (160-kg) weight or similar loads. Underwing provision for two 353-lb (160-kg) or 385-lb (175-kg) depth bombs and six 5-in (12,7-cm) rockets or two ASMs.

Status: First of two Br 960 prototypes flown on 3 August 1951;

aerodynamic prototype of Br 1050 flown on 26 March 1955; prototype Alizé flown on 6 October 1956. Delivery of production aircraft began March 1959. Production totals, two prototypes, three pre-production aircraft, 87 production aircraft; deliveries completed 1962.

Notes: The Alize was developed in 1954 from the Br 960 Vultur, which had an Armstrong Siddeley Mamba turboprop in the nose and a Hispano-Suiza Nene turbojet in the rear fuselage. This dual power plant configuration was abandoned for the Alizé, a large retractable radome taking the space that the turbojet had occupied. *Aéronavale* acquired a production batch of 75, and three squadrons were equipped with the type to serve aboard the aircraft carriers *Foch* and *Clémenceau*, and to train crews for these units. The Alizé inventory was down to 37 by 1979, and of these, 28 were being updated 1980–1983 to have Thomson-CSF Iguane radar, improved radio/navaids, VLF Omega INS and ESM, for continued service with *Flottilles* 4F and 6F until the early 'nineties, some 15 years later than at one time expected. The first squadron of fully modified Alizés became operational late in 1981. In 1961, 12 Alizés were acquired by the Indian Navy and are used (with up to a dozen more subsequently purchased from *Aéronavale*) to equip No 310 Squadron, 'The Cobras', at INS Garuda.

DASSAULT-BREGUET ATLANTIC

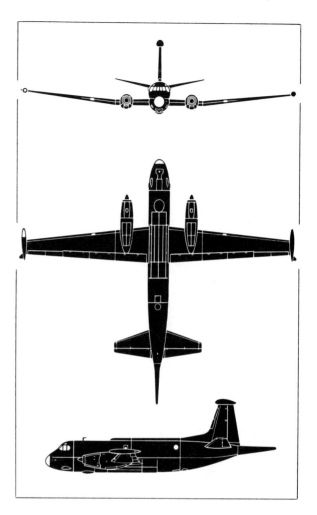

(Top and immediately above) Two views of the first prototype of the Atlantic Nouvelle Generation, converted from an Atlantic 1; (below) One of the Atlantic 1s serving with the Dutch MLD. (Silhouette) Dassault-Breguet Atlantic 1.

Country of Origin: France.

Type: Long-range maritime patrol aircraft.

Power Plant: Two 5,750 shp Rolls-Royce (Snecma-built) Tyne RTy 20 Mk 21 turboprops.

Performance: (Atlantic 1) Max speed, 409 mph (658 km/h) at high altitudes; cruising speeds, 363 mph (584 km/h) at 19,685 ft (6 000 m), 342 mph (550 km/h) at 26,250 ft (8 000 m); cruising speed for maximum endurance, 195 mph (320 km/h); initial rate of climb, 2,450 ft/min (12,44 m/sec); service ceiling 32,800 ft (10 000 m); patrol endurance at range of 620 mls (1 000 km) from base, 12 hrs; max endurance 18 hrs.

Weights: Empty, 52,900 lb (24 000 kg); max take-off (Atlantic 1) 95,900 lb (43 500 kg); max take-off (Atlantic NG) 101,850 lb (46 200 kg).

Dimensions: (Atlantic 1) Span, 119 ft 1¼ in (36,30 m); length 104 ft 1¼ in (31,75 m); height 37 ft 1¼ in (11,33 m); wing area, 1,295·3 sq ft (120,34 m²).

Dimensions: (ANG) Span, 122 ft 4½ in (37,30 m); length, 107 ft 0¼ in (32,62 m); height, 36 ft 1¾ in (11,02 m).

Accommodation: Crew of 12 comprising two pilots, flight engineer, three observers and, in the central tactical compartment, a tactical co-ordinator, radar/navigator, two sono-buoy operators, radio operator, and ECM/MAD operator.

Armament: Internal weapons bay can accommodate four homing torpedoes or nine acoustic torpedoes or depth charges, mines, or (ANG only) up to two AM-39 Exocet ASMs. Four underwing pylons can each carry one AS.12 or similar ASM.

Status: Two prototypes flown on 21 October 1961 and 23 February 1962; two pre-production aircraft (with lengthened, production-standard fuselage) flown on 25 February 1963 and 10 September 1964; first production examples delivered to Aéronavale and Marineflieger on 10 December 1965; first second-batch aircraft (Netherlands), delivered 30 January 1971. Production totals, 40 for France, 20 for Germany, 9 for Netherlands and 18 for Italy; production of 87 completed 1973. Atlantic NG programme launched 23 February 1978; first of two prototypes (converted Atlantic 1s) flown 8 May 1981; delivery of 42 to Aéronavale to begin 1986.

Notes: The Atlantic 1 equips four Aéronavale Flottilles, Nos 21F, 22F, 23F and 24F, two Staffeln of MG 3 of the West German Marineflieger (including five aircraft modified for ECM duties), No 321 Squadron of the Dutch Marine Luchtvaartdienst and the 86° and 88° Gruppi of Italy's Marinavia. Pakistan's Naval Aviation force operates three Atlantic 1s acquired 1975 from Aéronavale.

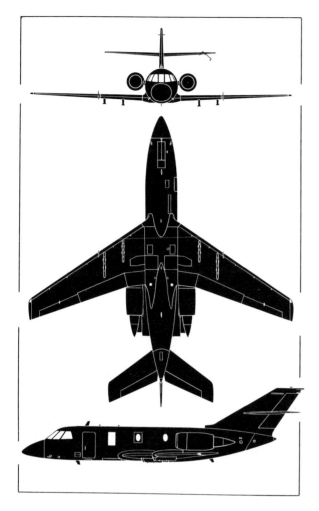

(Above) The first of five Mystère 20G Gardians for French Aéronavale service; (immediately below) a Mystère/Falcon 20 used for VIP transport by the RAAF; (bottom) Mystère TS trainer with Cyrano radar. (Silhouette) Dassault-Breguet Mystère 20G Gardian.

Country of Origin: France.

Type: Search and rescue, maritime surveillance and VIP transport.

Power Plant: Two 5,440 lb st (2 468 kgp) Garrett AiResearch ATF3-6-2C turbofans.

Performance: (HU-25A) Max cruising speed, 531 mph (855 km/h) at 40,000 ft (12 200 m) or Mach 0·80; economical cruising speed, M = 0·72; max range with crew of five, 5 per cent fuel reserve plus 30 min, 2,590 mls (4 170 km).

Weights: (HU-25A) Empty, 19,000 lb (8 620 kg); equipped empty, with five crew and complete avionics, 20,890 lb (9 475 kg); max take-off weight, 32,000 lb (14 515 kg).

Dimensions: Span, 53 ft 6 in (16,30 m); length, 56 ft 3 in (17,15 m); height, 17 ft 5 in (5,32 m); wing area, 450 sq ft (41,80 m²).

Accommodation: Crew of five for US Coast Guard MRS mission, comprising two pilots, surveillance system operator and two visual observers. Three passenger seats on port side of the cabin.

Status: Mystère 20 prototype first flown 4 May 1963; Falcon 20G prototype first flown 28 November 1977; first HU-25A development aircraft (with CF700 engines) flown 4 August 1978; prototype Falcon 20H flown 30 April 1980; first Gardian flown 15 April 1981. Production: 477 Mystère/Falcon 20 sold by February 1982, including 41 HU-25A Guardian for US Coast Guard, five Mystère 20H Gardian for *Aéronavale* and about 50 for military or quasi-military use.

Notes: US Coast Guard in January 1977 adopted the Dassault-Breguet Mystère 20G to meet its Medium Range Surveillance (MRS) requirement for a replacement for its Grumman HU-16 amphibians and interim Convair HC-131s. The variant chosen differed from the basic Mystère/Falcon 20 biz-jet in having new turbofan engines, strong points under the wings and fuselage to carry a variety of sensor pods (including SLAR, IR and ultra violet) and survival packs, a completely revised avionics fit and special interior arrangements. Generally similar to the Guardian is the Mystère 20H Gardian, adopted by *Aéronavale* for maritime surveillance duty in the Pacific. These aircraft have a larger fuselage fuel tank, four wing hardpoints with increased capacity, primarily French avionics and gross weight increased to 33,510 lb (15 200 kg). Mystère/Falcon 20s are in military service with the RAAF (three VIP transports, No 34 Squadron), the CAF (eight CC-117, VIP transports and EW trainers), *Armée de l'Air* (eight VIP transports, two Cyrano radar trainers, four test-beds for CEV) and the air arms of Belgium (2), Iran (9), Jordan (1), Libya (1), Norway (2), Pakistan (1) and South Africa (1).

EMBRAER EMB-111

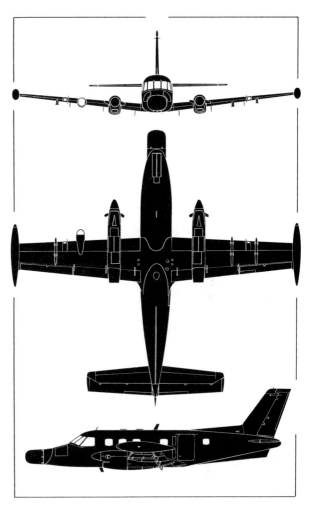

(Top and immediately above) Two views of the EMBRAER EMB-111 in service with the Força Aérea Brasileira. (below) An EMB-111 of the Forces Aeriennes Gabonaises, lacking the wing-mounted searchlight and armament of the Brazilian aircraft. (Silhouette) EMBRAER EMB-111.

Country of Origin: Brazil.

Type: Maritime patrol and coastal surveillance aircraft.

Power Plant: Two 750 shp Pratt & Whitney (Canada) PT6A-34 turboprops.

Performance: Max cruising speed, 239 mph (385 km/h) at 9,840 ft (3 000 m); economical cruise, 219 mph (352 km/h) at 10,000 ft (3 050 m); average patrol speed, 198 mph (318 km/h) at 2,000 ft (610 m); initial rate of climb, 1,190 ft/min (6,04 m/sec); service ceiling (at 11,684 lb/5 300 kg), 25,500 ft (7 770 m); range (max fuel and 45 min reserves), 1,830 mls (2 945 km) at 10,000 ft (3 050 m).

Weights: Empty equipped, 8,289 lb (3 760 kg); max take-off, 15,432 lb (7 000 kg).

Dimensions: Span, 52 ft 4⅜ in (15,95m); length, 48 ft 11 in (14,91 m); height, 16 ft 2 in (4,92 m); wing area, 313·21 sq ft (29,10 m²).

Armament: Four underwing pylons for eight 5-in (12,7-cm) air-to-surface rockets (two per pylon), or four launchers with seven 2·75-in (7-cm) FFAR rockets, or three pylons plus a leading-edge mounted 50-million candlepower searchlight.

Accommodation: Pilot and co-pilot side-by-side, and navigator, observer and radio/radar operator in main cabin.

Status: First development aircraft flown 15 August 1972. Production of 12 for Brazilian Air Force complete. Six (EMB-111N) delivered to Chilean Navy in 1979. One delivered to Gabon Air Force in 1981.

Notes: The EMB-111 is a derivative of the EMB-110 Bandeirante (separately described) the principal external differences being a nose radome, wingtip fuel tanks, and wing strong points for four pylons to carry air-to-surface rockets which form the principal armament. The EMB-111, which carries the designation P-95 in the FAB but is not known as the Bandeirante, also has a central chute for the launching of smoke marker buoys or smoke grenades for target marking, and flares of 200,000 candlepower are available for night illumination. The nose radome contains the AIL AN/APS-128 (SPAR-1) sea patrol radar, and the EMB-111 carries a full complement of navigation and communication equipment. The wing-tip tanks, which are a new feature of the EMB-111 variant, are permanently attached. Deliveries to the *Força Aérea Brasileira* began on 11 April 1978 and these aircraft serve with the 7° *Grupo de Aviação* at Salvador AFB, Bahia. The Chilean Navy has acquired six similar EMB-111Ns and the *Forces Aériennes Gabonaises* (Gabon) acquired one in 1981, although this aircraft lacks the wing-mounted search light.

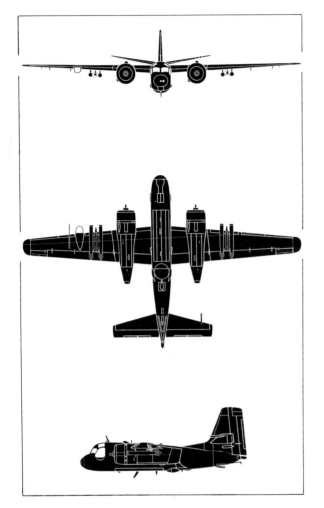

(Above) A de Havilland-built CP-121 Tracker serving with the CAF; (Immediately below) One of the Royal Australian Navy's S-2E Trackers; (bottom) A Grumman C-1A carrier on-board delivery version of the S-2. (Silhouette) Grumman S-2E Tracker.

Country of Origin: USA.

Type: Carrier or land-based anti-submarine aircraft (and COD transport).

Power Plant: Two (XS2F-1) 1,425 hp Wright R-1820-76 or (S-2A, -2B, -2C) 1,525 hp R-1820-82 or (S-2D, -2E, -2G) 1,525 hp R-1820-82WA piston radials.

Performance: (S-2E) Max speed, 265 mph (426 km/h); cruising speed, 150 mph (241 km/h) at 1,500 ft (450 m); initial rate of climb, 1,390 ft/min (7,0 m/sec); service ceiling, 21,000 ft (6 400 m); range, 1,300 mls (2 095 km); endurance with max fuel, 10 per cent reserves, 9 hrs.

Weights: Empty, 18,750 lb (8 505 kg); max take-off 29,150 lb (13 222 kg).

Dimensions: Span (S-2A, -2B, -2C) 69 ft 8 in (21,23 m), (S-2D, -2E, -2F, -2G) 72 ft 7 in (22,13 m); length (S-2A, -2B, -2C) 42 ft 3 in (12,88 m), (S-2D, -2E, -2F, -2G) 43 ft 6 in (13,26 m); height (S-2A, -2B, -2C), 16 ft 3½ in (4,96 m), (S-2D, -2E, -2F, -2G), 16 ft 7½ in (5,06 m); wing area (S-2A, -2B, -2C), 485 sq ft (45,06 m²), (S-2D, -2E, -2F, -2G) 496 sq ft (46,08 m²).

Accommodation: Crew of four comprising pilot, co-pilot/navigator/radio operator, radar operator and MAD operator.

Armament: Internal weapons bay accommodates two homing torpedoes, two MK 101 depth bombs, four 385 lb (1 75 kg) depth charges or similar loads. Provision under wings for six pylons to carry torpedoes (ferry only), rockets or bombs.

Status: First of two prototypes (XSF-1) flown on 3 July 1953; first S2F-1 (S-2A) flown on 30 April 1953; first S2F-2 (S-2C) flown on 12 July 1954; first S2F-3 (S-2D) flown on 25 July 1962; first S2F-3S (S-2E) flown in September 1960; first S-2G flown in 1972. Production totals: XSF-1, 2; S-2A, 755; S-2C, 77; S-2D, 100; S-2E, 252; grand total 1,186, completed 1968. In addition, 100 built by de Havilland Canada as CS2F-1 (CP-121).

Notes: Production versions of the Tracker for US Navy and export were S-2A (originally S2F-1) with smaller wing and fuselage; S-2C with enlarged bomb-bay and S-2D/S-2E with increased dimensions, more fuel and updated equipment. Conversions were S-2B and S-2F, S-2As with equipment updates, and S-2G, modified S-2Es introduced in 1972 for operation until 1976. Based on the Tracker, the C-1A (originally TF-1) had a new 9-seat fuselage; 87 were built, of which about 30 still in USN service 1981/82, with all S-2s retired. Many Trackers were exported new or ex-US Navy and users in 1982 included Argentina, Australia, Brazil, Nationalist China, Japan, South Korea, Peru, Thailand, Turkey, Uruguay and Venezuela. CAF uses CP-121s.

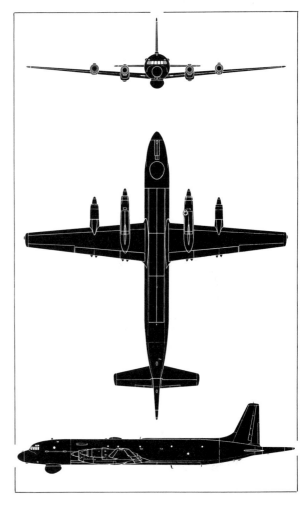

(Top and immediately above) The Il-38 in service with the Soviet Naval Air Force, and (below) one of three Il-38s serving with No 315 Squadron of Indian Naval Aviation at Dabolim. (Silhouette) The standard service version of the Il-38 May.

Country of Origin: Soviet Union.

Type: Open-ocean maritime surveillance aircraft.

Power Plant: Four 4,250 ehp Ivchenko AI-20M turboprops.

Performance: (Estimated) Max continuous cruise, 400 mph (645 km/h) at 15,000 ft (4 570 m); normal cruise, 370 mph (595 km/h) at 26,250 ft (8 000 m); patrol speed, 250 mph (400 km/h) at 2,000 ft (610 m); loiter endurance, 12 hrs at 2,000 ft (610 m); max range, 4,500 mls (7 240 km).

Weights: (Estimated) Empty equipped, 80,000 lb (36 287 kg); max take-off, 140,000 lb (63 500 kg).

Dimensions: Span, 122 ft 9 in (37,40 m); length, 131 ft 0 in (39,92 m); height, 33 ft 4 in (10,17 m); wing area, 1,507 sq ft (140,00 m²).

Armament: Three internal bays for homing torpedoes, depth bombs, etc.

Accommodation: Normal operating crew of 12 of which four including two pilots, are accommodated on the flight deck and the remainder operate the sensors from the tactical compartment above the weapons bays.

Status: A derivative of the Il-18 commercial transport, the Il-38 is believed to have first flown as a prototype during 1967–68, entering service with the Soviet Naval Air Force early in 1970.

Production of the Il-38 was apparently phased out in 1976–77, fewer than 100 having been built of which 60–70 were being operated by the air components of the four Soviet Fleets at the beginning of 1982. Three refurbished ex-Soviet Navy Il-38s were supplied to the Indian Navy in 1977–78.

Notes: The standard open-ocean surveillance aircraft operated by all four Soviet Naval Air Forces, the Il-38 was derived from the Il-18 in a similar manner to that of the US Navy's equivalent P-3 Orion from the Electra commercial transport. Apart from the re-engineering necessitated to adapt the basic design for the nautical role, the fuselage of the Il-38 was lengthened and the wing was positioned further forward on the fuselage. Another military variant of the commercial Il-18 with which the Il-38 may be confused is the electronic countermeasures and intelligence (ECM and ELINT) Coot-A. The airframe of Coot-A appears basically unchanged from that of its commercial progenitor, but it features a long ventral pod housing side-looking radar, further containers on each side of the forward fuselage and numerous antennae and blisters. The Coot-A first appeared in service in 1978. Prior to 1976 and the abrogation of the Egyptian-Soviet Friendship Treaty, some Il-38s operated by Soviet crews were flown in Egyptian markings.

KAWASAKI P-2J (& LOCKHEED P-2)

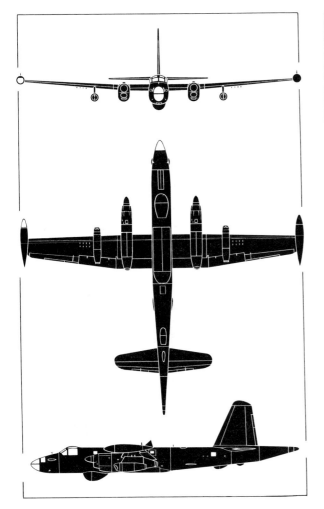

(Above) A Lockheed SP-2H of the Dutch MLD, which still had a few of the original Neptunes in service in 1982; (immediately below and bottom) Air and ground views of the Kawasaki P-2J serving with the JMSDF. (Silhouette) Kawasaki P-2J.

Country of Origin: Japan (and USA).

Type: Maritime patrol and anti-submarine patrol aircraft.

Power Plant: Two 2,850 ehp General Electric T64-IHI-10 turboprops and two 3,085 lb st (1 400 kgp) Ishikawajima J3-IHI-7C turbojets.

Performance: Max permissible speed (dive) 403 mph (649 km/h); max cruising speed, 250 mph (402 km/h); economical cruising speed, 230 mph (370 km/h); initial rate of climb, 1,800 ft/min (9,2 m/sec); service ceiling, 30,000 ft (9 150 m); range with max fuel, 2,765 mls (4 450 km).

Weights: Empty, 42,500 lb (19 277 kg); max take-off weight, 75,000 lb (34 019 kg).

Dimensions: Span (over tip-tanks), 97 ft 8½ in (29,78 m); length, 95 ft 10¾ in (29,23 m); height, 29 ft 3½ in (8,93 m); wing area, 1,000 sq ft (92,9 m²).

Accommodation: Crew of 12, comprising two pilots on flight deck and ten-man tactical team in fuselage.

Armament: Internal stowage for up to 8,000 lb (3 629 kg) of weapons which can include homing torpedoes, mines, bombs, etc. Provision for up to 16 5-in (12,7-cm) rockets under wings.

Status: Prototype (converted P-2H) first flown on 21 July 1966. First production P-2J flown on 8 August 1969. Deliveries to

JMSDF began in October 1969 with first squadron equipped by February 1971. Production of 83 completed February 1979.

Notes: After the Kawasaki company had built 46 P-2H Neptunes under licence for the JMSDF, it undertook development of the P-2J to provide a successor with improved operational capability. The P-2J has a lengthened fuselage which allows it to accommodate a more modern search and control system, as well as an additional crew member to serve as the combat co-ordinator. Fuel capacity is increased and a change of power plant, to Japanese-built versions of the T64 turboprop, results in a major reduction in empty weight with no significant loss of performance. Like the final production series of Neptunes, the P-2J has underwing jet engines to boost the combat speed. The original Lockheed P-2 Neptune had been evolved during World War II, the prototype flying (as the XP2V-1) on 17 May 1945. The Neptune enjoyed a 15-year production life, with 838 being delivered to the US Navy in several versions and about 200 built by Lockheed for export. When Kawasaki delivered the last P-2J, a total of 1,182 Neptunes of all varieties had been built; apart from those serving in Japan. Neptunes were still in operational service in 1982 with the French *Aéronavale* and the Dutch *Marine Luchtvaartdienst* with replacement due 1983/84, and Argentina's *Comando de Aviacion Naval*.

LOCKHEED P-3 ORION (& CP-140 AURORA)   MARITIME RECONNAISSANCE/ASW

(Top) The first of 13 Lockheed P-3C Orions for the Dutch MLD; (immediately above) P-3C of the US Navy Patrol Squadron VP-45; (below) A CP-140 Aurora, the CAF version of the Orion, at CFB Greenwood, Nova Scotia. (Silhouette) Lockheed P-3C Orion.

Country of Origin: USA.

Type: Long-range maritime patrol aircraft.

Power Plant: Four (P-3A) 4,500 eshp Allison T56-A-10W or (P-3B, C, D, E, F) 4,910 eshp T56-A-14 turboprops.

Performance: (P-3B, 3C) Max speed, 473 mph (761 km/h) at 15,000 ft (4 570 m); economical cruise, 378 mph (608 km/h) at 25,000 ft (7 620 m); typical patrol speed, 237 mph (381 km/h) at 1,500 ft (450 m); initial rate of climb, 1,950 ft/min (9,9 m/sec); service ceiling, 28,300 ft (8 625 m); mission radius with 3-hr search, 1,550 mls (2 494 km); max range, 4,766 mls (7 670 km).

Weights: (P-3B, 3C) Empty, 61,491 lb (27 890 kg); max warload, 20,000 lb (9 071 kg); normal take-off, 135,000 lb (61 235 kg); max loaded, 142,000 lb (64 410 kg).

Dimensions: Span, 99 ft 8 in (30,37 m); length, 116 ft 10 in (35,61 m); height, 33 ft 8½ in (10,29 m); wing area, 1,300 sq ft (120,77 m²).

Accommodation: Flight crew of five and five-man tactical team.

Armament: Weapons bay in fuselage can house one 2,000 lb (908 kg) mine, three 1,000 lb (454 kg) mines, two Mk 101 nuclear depth bombs with four Mk 43, 44 or 46 torpedoes or eight Mk 54 depth bombs or similar loads. Total of ten underwing pylons which can carry mines or rockets; max underwing load is 12,000 lb

(5 443 kg) with 7,252 lb (3 290 kg) internal ordnance.

Status: Aerodynamic prototype (modified Electra) first flown on 19 August 1958; full prototype (YP3V-1/YP-3A) flown on 25 November 1959; first P-3A flown on 15 April 1961; first P-3C flown on 18 September 1968; first CP-140 Aurora flown 22 March 1979. Production totals: YP3V-1, 1; P-3A, 157; P-3B, 125, P-3C, over 200 delivered against planned USN procurement of 316 by 1989; WP-3D, 2; RP-3D, 1, all for US Navy or government agencies; plus new-build for export; P-3B (RAAF), 11; P-3B (RNZAF), 5; P-3B (Norway), 7; P-3C (RAAF), 10; P-3C (Japan), 3 plus 42 assembled/built by Kawasaki; P-3C Update II, (MLD), 13; P-3F (IIAF), 6; CP-140, 18.

Notes: First Orion variant entered US Navy service August 1962; newer P-3C is destined to equip 24 USN and 13 USNR patrol squadrons. Successive improvements to avionics/weapons systems identified as P-3C Update (starting January 1975), Update II (starting August 1977) and Update III (starting 1983). Three P-3As were supplied to Spain; four converted to WP-3A for weather reconnaissance of which three later became VP-3A executive transports. Two P-3Bs became EP-3Bs for electronic recce, later EP-3E plus 10 more P-3Bs converted. CP-140 for Canada incorporates electronic systems based on S-3A Viking.

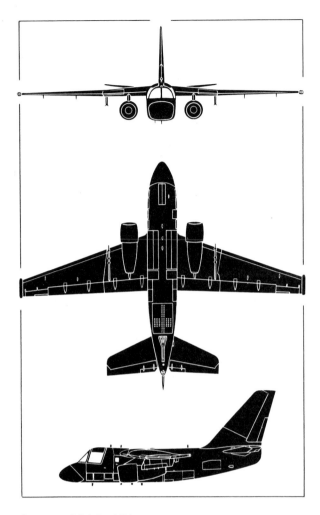

(Above) Lockheed S-3A Viking in service with US Navy anti-submarine squadron VS-21 and (immediately below) an S-3A from VS-22 with MAD boom extended; (bottom) A VS-21 Viking makes a touch-and-go landing on the USS John F Kennedy. (Silhouette) Lockheed S-3A.

Country of Origin: USA.

Type: Carrier-borne anti-submarine aircraft.

Power Plant: Two 9,275 lb st (4 207 kgp) General Electric TF34-GE-400A turbofans.

Performance: Max speed, 518 mph (834 km/h) max cruising speed, 426 mph (686 km/h); typical loiter speed, 184 mph (257 km/h) at sea level; initial rate of climb, over 4,200 ft/min (21,3 m/sec); service ceiling, over 35,000 ft (10 670 m); combat range, 2,300 mls (3 705 km); ferry range, 3,450 mls (5 560 km).

Weights: Empty, 26,650 lb (12 088 kg); normal loaded, 42,500 lb (19 277 kg); max take-off, 52,540 lb (23 832 kg).

Dimensions: Span, 68 ft 8 in (20,93 m); length, 53 ft 4 in (16,26 m); height, 22 ft 9 in (6,93 m); wing area, 598 sq ft (55,56 m²).

Accommodation: Crew of four comprising two pilots side-by-side on flight deck and tactical co-ordinator and sensor operator in cabin.

Armament: Internal weapons bays accommodate four MK 46 torpedoes, four MK 82 bombs, four MK 57 or 54 depth charges or MK 53 mines. Additional weapon stowage on two wing pylons, for bombs, depth charges, rockets, etc.

Status: First of eight development and evaluation S-3As flown

on 21 January 1972, second aircraft flown 19 May 1972, third aircraft (first with full avionics fit), flown 17 July 1972; first deck-landing (by first production S-3A), 26 November 1973; first delivery to US Navy VS-41 Squadron, 20 February 1974. First US-3A (No 7 FSD S-3A conversion) flown 2 July 1976. Production: 187 (including 8 FSD), completed June 1978.

Notes: Development of an anti-submarine aircraft to replace the Grumman S-2 Tracker began in 1967 when the US Navy issued a Request for Proposals, with the contract award to Lockheed announced in August 1969. A key design feature of the S-3A was a high speed capability for transit between carrier and search area, and contributing to this objective is the use of retractable MAD and FLIR radomes and a retractable in-flight refuelling probe. Drop tanks can be carried on the wing pylons to extend the ferry range, and the fifth aircraft in the development batch was completed as a flight refuelling tanker for trials. The S-3A is now the standard US Navy anti-submarine aircraft, equipping 11 operational and one training squadrons. A single US-3A operated COD in the Indian Ocean and in 1981 two more aircraft were under conversion to this standard, which was also a candidate for further conversion or production, together with the ES-3A for TASES (replacing the EA-3B) and the KS-3A tanker.

MYASISHCHEV M-4 (BISON)

(Top) The M-4 Bison-A which was still included in the first line inventory of Soviet Long-range Aviation at the beginning of 1982. (Immediately above and below) The Bison-B maritime equivalent of the Bison-A. (Silhouette) The Bison-A strategic bomber.

Country of Origin: Soviet Union.
Type: Maritime reconnaissance, long-range heavy strategic bomber and flight-refuelling tanker.
Power Plant: Four 19,180 lb st (8 700 kgp) Mikulin AM-3D turbojets.
Performance: Max speed (at normal combat weight), 620 mph (998 km/h) or Mach 0·94 at 39,370–42,650 ft (12 000–13 000 m); long-range cruise (with 10,000-lb/4 500-kg payload), 520 mph (835 km/h) or Mach 0·787; unrefuelled combat radius, 3,480 mls (5 600 km).
Weights: Max take-off, 363,760 lb (165 000 kg).
Dimensions: Span, 165 ft 7⅜ in (50,48 m); length, 154 ft 10¼ in (47,20 m).
Armament: Two 23-mm NR-23 cannon in each of four remotely-controlled gun barbettes (two above and two below the fuselage fore and aft of the wing). Provision for up to 10,000 lb (4 500 kg) of free-fall weapons internally.
Accommodation: Flight crew of six.
Status: The M-4 first flown as a prototype on 20 January 1953, operational capability being attained in 1955–56. Production was subsequently limited owing to the inability of the M-4 to fully meet the range requirements of the specification to which it had

been designed, the more economical engines with which it had been planned to replace the AM-3 and thus fulfil range demands failing to materialise before the aircraft reached obsolescence as a strategic bomber. Fewer than 200 M-4s were built, a proportion of which were assigned to the Soviet Naval Air Force (Bison-B and C) for maritime reconnaissance, these having now been phased out of service. However, Soviet Long-range Aviation retained in service about 75 M-4s at the beginning of 1982, some 45 of these still being configured as bombers and the remainder having been modified as flight refuelling tankers for use with M-4 and Tu-95 bombers.
Notes: A comparatively small number of the Bison-B version of the M-4, a minimum-change maritime reconnaissance derivative of the strategic bombing Bison-A, were delivered to the Soviet Navy, the Bison-C being a more extensively revised maritime version with 28,660 lb st (13 000 kg) Dobrynin turbofans, a modest increase in wing span, a new wing section and a redesigned fuselage nose. Despite the one-third improvement in range and endurance offered by the Bison-C (believed designated M-6), the maritime capability of this aircraft was apparently inferior to that of the Tu-142 (Bear), and both Bison-B and C appear to have been phased out of naval service during 1979–80.

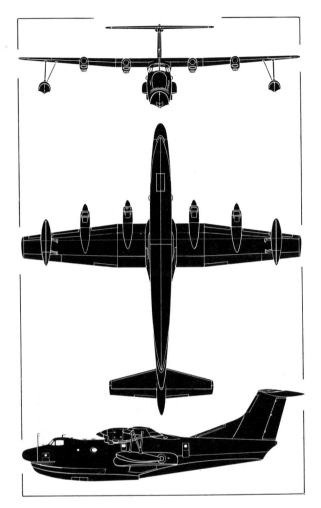

(Above) A flying view of a Shin Meiwa PS-1 flying-boat operated by the 31st Koku-tai; (immediately below) a PS-1 under test at Kobe; (bottom) a US-1 amphibian serving with the 71st Koku-tai. (Silhouette) Shin Meiwa US-1.

Country of Origin: Japan.

Type: Long-range maritime patrol flying boat and (US-1) search and rescue amphibian.

Power Plant: Four 3,060 ehp Ishikawajima-built General Electric T64-IHI-10 turboprops.

Performance: (PS-1) Max speed, 340 mph (547 km/h) at 5,000 ft (1 525 m); normal cruise, 265 mph (426 km/h) at 5,000 ft (1 525 m); initial rate of climb, 2,264 ft/min (6,9 m/sec); service ceiling 29,530 ft (9 000 m); normal range, 1,347 mls (2 168 km); ferry range 2,948 mls (4 744 km); max endurance, 15 hrs.

Performance: (US-1) Max speed, 299 mph (481 km/h); cruising speed, 265 mph (426 km/h); initial rate of climb, 1,510 ft/min (7,7 m/sec); service ceiling, 21,400 ft (6 520 m); radius of search mission, 1,035 mls (1 665 km) with 2·3-hr search.

Weights: (PS-1) Empty equipped, 58,000 lb (26 300 kg); normal take-off, 79,366 lb (36 000 kg); max t-o, 99,208 lb (45 000 kg).

Weights: (US-1) Empty equipped, 56,218 lb (25 500 kg); max take-off weight, water, 94,800 lb (43 000 kg); max take-off weight, land, 99,200 lb (45 000 kg).

Dimensions: Span, 108 ft 8¾ in (33,14 m); length, 109 ft 11 in (33,50 m); height, 31 ft 10½ in (9,71 m); wing area, 1,462 sq ft (135,8 m²).

Accommodation: (PS-1) Flight crew of three, comprising two pilots and a flight engineer. Tactical team of seven, comprising co-ordinator, two sonar operators, MAD operator, radar operator, radio operator and navigator, in upper deck compartment.

Accommodation: (US-1) Crew of nine and provision for 20 seated survivors or 12 stretchers; or up to 69 passengers.

Armament: (PS-1) Weapons compartment in upper deck, aft of tactical compartment, accommodates four 330-lb (150-kg) anti-submarine bombs. One weapons pod beneath each wing between the engine nacelles, each containing two homing torpedoes. Pylon beneath each wing tip can carry three 5-in (12,7-cm) rockets.

Status: Two prototypes (PX-S) first flown, respectively, on 5 October 1967 and 14 June 1968 and delivered to JMSDF on 31 July and 30 November 1968. Two pre-production models (PS-1) delivered in 1972. Initial production deliveries in 1973 with total procurement of 23 by JMSDF. First US-1 flown 16 October 1974 and first land take-off on 3 December 1974; first delivery 5 March 1975. Production of eight funded by 1982.

Notes: The initial unit formed to operate the PS-1 was the 31st Koku-tai (Air Group) at Iwakuni. Design of an amphibian version, the US-1, was begun in June 1970, and examples of this version entered service with the 71st *Koku-tai* of the JMSDF in 1976.

TUPOLEV TU-142 (BEAR)

MARITIME RECONNAISSANCE/ASW

(Top) A Soviet Naval Air Force Bear-C with wide undernose radome, and (immediately above and below) the Bear-D featuring a large ventral radome housing surface-to-surface misslie guidance radar. (Silhouette) Bear-D with sideview (lower) of Bear-C.

Country of Origin: Soviet Union.

Type: Long-range maritime patrol, reconnaissance, electronic intelligence and anti-shipping missile guidance aircraft.

Power Plant: Four 14,795 eph Kuznetsov NK-12MV turboprops.

Performance: (Bear-F estimated) Max speed, 510 mph (820 km/h) at 41,000 ft (12 500 m), 530 mph (853 km/h) at 29,530 ft (9 000); max continuous cruise, 440 mph (708 km/h) at 36,090 ft (11,000 m); econ. cruise, 370 mph (595 km/h); max range (with 25,000 lb/11 340 kg payload), 7,200 mls (11 585 km); service ceiling, 44,290 ft (13 500 m).

Weights: (Bear-F) Normal loaded, 380,000 lb (172 370 kg); max take-off, 414,460 lb (188 000 kg).

Dimensions: Span, 167 ft 6 in (51,05 m); length, 162 ft 6 in (49,53 m); height, 40 ft 0 in (12,15 m); wing area, 3,150 sq ft (292,60 m²).

Armament: (Optional) Paired 23-mm NR-23 cannon in manned tail position.

Accommodation: Normal operating crew of 11–13, with two pilots and flight engineer on flight deck, navigator in extreme nose and sensor operators in tactical compartments.

Status: The Tu-142 is a maritime-optimised derivative of the Tu-95 strategic bomber. The Tu-95 was first flown in the summer of

1954, and began to enter service in the strategic bombing role (Bear-A) during the second half of 1956, being joined by a variant (Bear-B) serving as a launch aircraft for the AS-3 Kangaroo 400-mile (650-km) range Mach 1·8 stand-off missile. Approximately 100 of these versions of the Tu-95 remained in service with Soviet Long-range Aviation at the beginning of 1982. A number of Bear-B missile carriers were adapted for maritime reconnaissance use by Soviet Naval Aviation and a version built for this role from the outset (Bear-C) entered Soviet naval service in the early 'sixties. Further development of the basic design optimised for naval requirements and catering for increased all-up weights appeared as the Tu-142 in the mid 'sixties, and the beginning of 1982, production was continuing at a rate of about six annually, primarily to make up attrition.

Notes: Versions of the Tu-142 currently serving with the Northern, Baltic and Pacific Fleet Air Forces include Bear-D which fulfils a support function in operations involving air-to-surface and surface-to-surface missiles, the Bear-E, which is a straight maritime reconnaissance version, and the Bear-F which appeared in the early 'seventies as a much refined anti-submarine version. The last-mentioned version features aft-extended inboard engine nacelles. The Bear-G is similar but has a stretched forward fuselage.

AERITALIA-AERMACCHI AM.3C BOSBOK

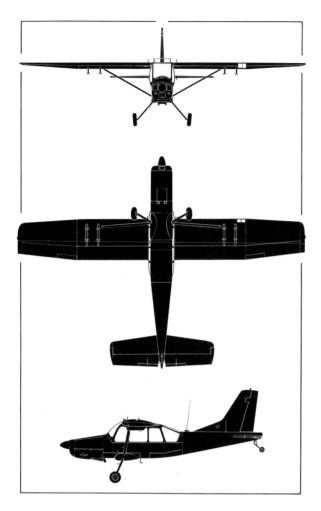

(Above) Flying and (immediately below) ground views of Aermacchi AM-3Cs as first delivered to the South African Air Force; (bottom) a later photograph of an SAAF AM-3C Bosbok in camouflage, as serving with Nos 41 and 42 Squadrons. (Silhouette) Aermacchi AM-3C Bosbok.

Country of Origin: Italy.

Type: Battlefield surveillance and forward air control aircraft.

Power Plant: One 340 hp Piaggio-Lycoming GSO-480-B1B6 six-cylinder horizontally-opposed engine.

Performance: (At normal loaded weight) Max speed 162 mph (260 km/h) at sea level and 173 mph (278 km/h) at 8,000 ft (2 440 m); max cruise 153 mph (246 km/h) at 8,000 ft (2 440 m); initial rate of climb, 1,378 ft/min (7·0 m/sec); service ceiling, 27,560 ft (8 400 m); max range, 615 mls (990 km) with 30-min fuel reserve; max endurance 5 hrs 45 mins.

Weights: Empty equipped, 2,548 lb (1 156 kg); normal loaded (2 crew) 3,307 lb (1 500 kg); max take-off (with underwing stores) 3,750 lb (1 700 kg).

Dimensions: Span, 41 ft 5½ in (12,64 m); length, 29 ft 3½ in (8,93 m); height 8 ft 11 in (2,72 m); wing area 219·15 sq ft (20,36 m²).

Accommodation: Standard arrangement is two in tandem with dual controls and rear seat removable to allow stores to be carried.

Armament: Two underwing stores stations stressed for 375 lb (170 kg) each. Armament options include four LAU-32A or MATRA 181 rocket launchers, 12 90-mm SURA rockets, two Nord AS 11 missiles, two 7·62-mm Minigun pods, two Matra 7·62-mm

twin machine gun pods or bombs in various combinations. A ventral pack can be carried on the fuselage containing cameras, or cameras can be mounted in the fuselage.

Status: First and second AM.3 prototypes (with Continental GTSIO-520-C engines) first flown on 12 May 1967 and 22 August 1968. Both re-engined with Lycoming GSO-480 and flown as AM.3C during 1969. First production AM.3C flown late 1972. Production total, approximately 45, completed 1974.

Notes: Original design was Aermacchi MB.335, developed jointly by Aermacchi and Aerfer as AM.3 and based on the wing of the original Aermacchi-Lockheed AL.60. Production was launched in response to two contracts placed by the South African Air Force in May and September 1970, and was handled by Aeritalia, which had meanwhile acquired the Aerfer company. In South Africa, the AM.3C was named Bosbok; a total of 40 was supplied, with deliveries completed by December 1975, and the Bosbok was in service in time to be used operationally when South Africa intervened briefly in the Angolan war. It was continuing in service in 1982, operated by Nos 41 and 42 Squadrons, principally from Potchefstroom. Three AM.3Cs delivered to the Rwanda Air Force are no longer in service. The Aermacchi-Lockheed AL-60 and related Atlas Kudu are separately described.

(Top) A Boeing RC-135U equipped with side-looking radar and other electronic sensors; (immediately above) a similarly-equipped RC-135V reconnaissance aircraft; (below) an EC-135H airborne command post. (Silhouette) Boeing RC-135U.

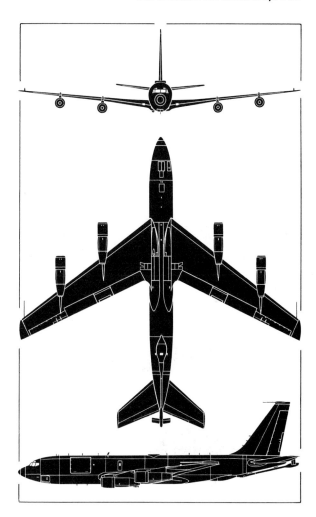

Country of Origin: USA.

Type: Airborne command post, electronic and weather reconnaissance aircraft.

Power Plant: Four 13,750 lb st (6 237 kgp) Pratt & Whitney J57-P-59W turbojets or 18,000 lb st (8 165 kgp) TF33-P-9 turbofans.

Performance: (EC-135C at 301,600 lb/136 895 kg take-off weight). Max speed, 607 mph (976 km/h) at 25,000 ft (7 620 m); initial rate of climb, 2,480 ft/min (12,6 m/sec); time to 20,000 ft (6 100 m), 10·5 min; service ceiling 33,750 ft (10 287 m); ferry range, 7,472 mls (12 025 km) at average 513 mph (826 km/h) cruising speed at 29,200 ft (8 900 m); maximum endurance 15·9 hrs at 448 mph (721 km/h).

Weights: (EC-135C) Basic equipped, 127,560 lb (57 860 kg); max take-off, 301,600 lb (136 805 kg).

Dimensions: (EC-135C) Span, 130 ft 10 in (39,88 m); length, 136 ft 2 in (41,50 m); height, 41 ft 8 in (12,69 m); wing area, 2,433 sq ft (226,03 m²).

Accommodation: (EC-135C) Flight crew of four (two pilots, navigator, boom operator) and command post crew of 15.

Status: First EC-135C flown 28 February 1964. Production totals, KC-135B/EC-135C, 17; RC-135B/RC-135C, 10; RC-135A,

4, delivery completed 1966; all other models by conversion.

Notes: As production variants of the basic KC-135A tankers (separately described), the USAF acquired 17 boom-equipped KC-135Bs (redesignated after delivery as EC-135Cs) to be used by SAC as airborne command posts; 10 RC-135Bs equipped (by Martin) for optical and electronic reconnaissance and redesignated after further modification as RC-135Cs; and four RC-135As equipped for photo-mapping and geodetic surveying by MATS. The RC-135Cs eventually became RC-135Us (3) and RC-135Vs, (7, plus one U also further converted) with large side-looking airborne radar (SLAR) checks each side of the front fuselage, chin or nose radomes and many aerials. Other reconnaissance versions were the four RC-135Ds (from KC-135As), single RC-135E (from C-135B), six RC-135Ms (from C-135Bs), two RC-135Ss (from C-135Bs), single RC-135T (from KC-135A) and four KC-135Rs (from KC-135As). Operated by SAC as command posts and airborne relay links, the EC variants converted from KC-135As included six EC-135As, four EC-135Gs, five EC-135Hs, three EC-135Ks, eight EC-135Ls and five EC-135Ps; three KC-135Bs and one EC-135C were converted to EC-135Js. For weather reconnaissance duty with MAC, 10 C-135Bs were modified into WC-135Bs, of which six remain in service in 1982.

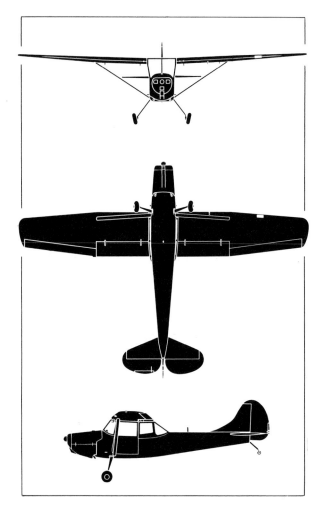

(Above) A Cessna O-1 (L-19A) of the JGSDF and (immediately below) a similar aircraft of the Royal Thai Air Force; (bottom) An Italian Army Siai Marchetti SM 1019, derived from the Cessna O-1. (Silhouette) Cessna O-1 Bird Dog.

Country of Origin: USA (SM 1019: Italy).

Type: Observation and forward control aircraft.

Power Plant: One 213 hp Continental O-470-11 piston engine or (SM 1019) 317 shp Allison 250-B15G turboprop.

Performance: (O-1E) Max speed, 115 mph (184 km/h); economical cruise (29 per cent power) 104 mph (166·5 km/h) at 5,000 ft (1 525 m); initial rate of climb, 1,150 ft/min (5·8 m/sec); service ceiling, 18,500 ft (5 640 m); range, 530 mls (848 km).

Performance: (SM 1019) Max cruising speed, 177 mph (285 km/h) at 5,000 ft (1 525 m); economical cruise, 135 mph (217 km/h) at 10,000 ft (3 050 m); initial rate of climb, 1,625 ft/min (8,25 m/sec); range with external stores, 320 mls (515 km); range with max fuel (10 min reserve) 765 mls (1 230 km).

Weights: Empty (O-1), 1,614 lb (680 kg); max take-off (O-1E), 2,400 lb (1 090 kg), (O-1F) 2,800 lb (1 270 kg).

Weights: (SM 1019) Empty equipped, 1,520 lb (690 kg); max payload, 1,300 lb (590 kg); max take-off, 3,196 lb (1 450 kg).

Dimensions: Span 36 ft 0 in (10,9 m); length (O-1) 25 ft 10 in (7,89 m); length (SM 1019) 27ft 11½ in (8,52 m); height (O-1) 7 ft 4 in (2,23 m); height (SM 1019), 7 ft 9¾ in (2,38 m); wing area, 174 sq ft (16,16 m²).

Accommodation: Two seats in tandem for pilot and observer or co-pilot, with optional dual controls.

Armament: (SM 1019) Two stores stations under wings capable of carrying minigun pods, rockets, etc., up to a maximum external load of 500 lb (227 kg).

Status: Prototype (Model 305) first flown December 1949; first production L-19A (O-1A) rolled out November 1950. First deliveries of TL-19D (TO-1D), second half of 1956. First deliveries of L-19E (O-1E), November 1956. Production totals, O-1A, 2,499; L-19A-IT, 66; O-1B, 62; XL-19B, one; XL-19C, two; TO-1D, 307; O-1E, 494, grand total, 3,431. Approximately 100 also built by Fuji in Japan. SM 1019 first and second prototypes flown 24 May 1969 and 18 February 1971. Production total, 80 for Italian Army.

Notes: The Cessna Model 305, built as a private venture, won a competition in 1950 to become the new standard liaison and observation monoplane for the US Army. Originally designated L-19 the series was redesignated O-1 in 1962. Other major users of the Bird Dog include Japan (where it was built under licence), France, Canada, Italy and Pakistan. In Italy, Siai-Marchetti fitted turboprop engines in two re-manufactured Bird Dogs to meet the requirements of the *Aviazione Leggera dell' Esercito* (Italian Army Aviation), and a batch of 80 of these SM 1019E1s was acquired for battlefield surveillance and FAC duty.

(Top) Cessna O-2A, as used in the forward air control rôle by units of the US Air National Guard; (immediately above) a Cessna O-2B and (below) an O-2A as supplied in 1970 to the Imperial Iranian Air Force. (Silhouette) Cessna O-2A.

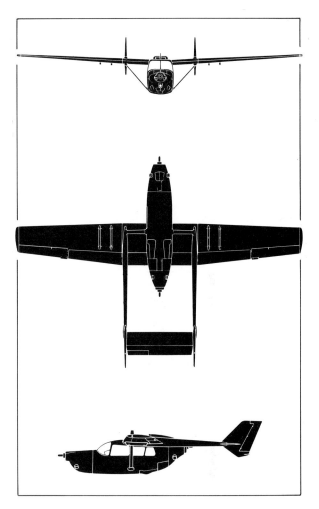

Country of Origin: USA.

Type: Forward air control and observation aircraft.

Power Plant: Two 210 hp Continental IO-360-C/D six-cylinder horizontally-opposed engines.

Performance: (O-2A) Max speed 178 mph (287 km/h) at sea level; cruising speed, 129 mph (207 km/h) at 5,000 ft (1 525 m); initial rate of climb, 935 ft/min (4,75 m/sec); service ceiling 15,100 ft (4 600 m); combat radius, 60 mls (97 km/h) with 4·5 hr loiter.

Weights: Empty, 3,350 lb (1 475 kg); normal take-off 4,850 lb (2 200 kg); max overload, 5,400 lb (2 450 kg).

Dimensions: Span, 38 ft 2 in (11,63 m); length, 29 ft 9 in (9,07 m); height, 9 ft 4 in (2,84 m); wing area, 202·5 sq ft (18,81 m²).

Accommodation: Pilot and observer, side-by-side; two passengers optional in cabin.

Armament: (O-2A only). Four wing strong points permit carriage of 7·62-mm minigun pods, rockets, flares and similar loads.

Status: Cessna 337 commercial prototype flown 28 February 1961. First O-2A flown January 1967, deliveries began April 1967. First O-2B delivered 31 March 1967. First Reims FTMA Milirole flown 26 May 1970. Production totals: O-2A, 501; O-2B, 31; O-2

(Iran), 12.

Notes: This military version of the distinctive "push-pull" Cessna Skymaster was first ordered by the USAF in December 1966. The O-2A variant introduced wing strong points to carry marker flares, rockets or gunpods and a special electronic installation, and had a higher gross weight than the commercial Skymaster. The O-2Bs were purchased off-the-shelf and modified for psychological warfare in Vietnam, and 12 O-2As were acquired by the Iranian Imperial Air Force in 1970 for training, liaison and observation duties. A military version of the Skymaster developed in France by Reims Aviation, known as the FTMA Milirole, has four wing strongpoints plus new high-lift trailing edge flaps which give a 40 per cent improvement in field performance, and can carry four passengers or two stretchers or cargo. Among operators of the Milirole is the Zimbabwe (previously Rhodesian) Air Force, which acquired 20 and adopted the name Lynx for this type. A military version of the commercial T337 with 225 hp TSIO-360 engines is marketed by Summit Aviation as the Sentry O2-337 and has four wing strongpoints like the O-2A. The Royal Thai Navy ordered six of these, and other military users of the Sentry or commercial Super Skymaster include the Venezuelan Navy and the air forces of Haiti, Ecuador, Honduras and Nicaragua.

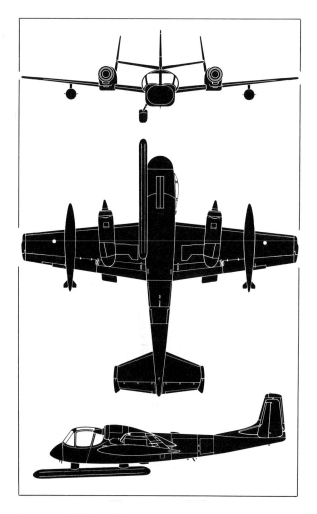

(Above and below) Three views of the Grumman OV-1D as operated in the electronic and visual battlefield reconnaissance rôle by the US Army. The long pod under the front fuselage contains side-looking radar. (Silhouette) Grumman OV-1D Mohawk.

Country of Origin: USA.

Type: STOL observation aircraft.

Power Plant: Two 1,150 shp Lycoming (OV-1A, -1B, -1C) T53-L-7 or L-15 or (OV-1D) 1,400 shp T53-L-701 turboprops.

Performance: (OV-1A) Max level speed, 308 mph (496 km/h) at 5,000 ft (1 520 m); max cruising speed, 304 mph (489 km/h); economical cruising speed, 207 mph (334 km/h); initial rate of climb, 2,950 ft/min (150 m/sec); max range, 1,410 mls (2 270 km).

Performance: (OV-1D) Max level speed, 305 mph (491 km/h) at 10,000 ft (3 050 m); economical cruising speed, 207 mph (334 km/h); initial rate of climb, 3,618 ft/min (18,3 m/sec); service ceiling, 25,000 ft (7,620 m); max range, 1,011 mls (1 627 km).

Weights: (OV-1A) Empty equipped, 9,937 lb (4 507 kg); normal take-off, 12,672 lb (5 748 kg); maximum loaded, 15,031 lb (6 818 kg).

Weights: (OV-1D) Empty equipped, 12,054 lb (5 467 kg); normal take-off, 15,544 lb (7 051 kg); max loaded, 18,109 lb (8 214 kg).

Dimensions: Span (OV-1A, -1C), 42 ft 0 in (12,80 m); span (OV-1B, -1D), 48 ft 0 in (14,63 m); length, 41 ft 0 in (12,50 m); height, 12 ft 8 in (3,86 m); wing area (OV-1A, -1C), 330 sq ft (30,65 m²); wing area (OV-1B, -1D), 360 sq ft (33,45 m²).

Accommodation: Crew of two side-by-side, optional dual control.

Status: Prototype (YOV-1A) first flown 14 April 1959. First deliveries (OV-1A) 1961. Production completed December 1970. Production Quantities: YOV-1A, 9; OV-1A, 64; OV-1B, 101; OV-1C, 133; OV-1D, 37.

Notes: As the Grumman G-134, the Mohawk design won joint Army and Marine Corps backing for development as a battlefield surveillance aircraft with STOL capability and able to operate from unprepared fields. Nine test examples were completed in 1959 and the first production orders were placed. Three versions were built in parallel, designated according to rôle equipment carried—OV-1A with cameras, OV-1B with side-looking airborne radar and OV-1C with cameras and infra-red sensors. Final production version was the OV-1D, with an improved camera installation plus provision for carrying SLAR or IR equipment; conversion of 108 OV-1Bs and -1Cs to OV-1D standard began in 1974 and 32 RV-1Cs and RV-1Ds are conversions for electronic reconnaissance. Israel received two Mohawks, in 1976, equipped for electronic surveillance and known as EV-1s, and the Philippines, Thailand and Australia were among the countries interested in procuring refurbished Army OV-1s in 1982.

(Top and immediately above) Two aspects of Lockheed SR-71 "Blackbird" strategic reconnaissance aircraft, as operated exclusively by the 9th SRW of Strategic Air Command; (below) two-seat SR-71B used for training. (Silhouette) Lockheed SR-71A.

Country of Origin: USA.

Type: Long-range strategic reconnaissance aircraft.

Power Plant: Two 32,500 lb st (14 740 kgp) with afterburning Pratt & Whitney J58 (JT11D-20B) turbojets.

Performance: (Estimated) Max speed, over Mach 3, equivalent to approximately 2,000 mph (3 218 km/h) at high altitudes; operating ceiling, above 80,000 ft (24 384 m); range, about 3,000 mls (4 828 km) at Mach 3 at 79,000 ft (24 080 m); max endurance, 1½ hrs at Mach 3.

Weights: (Estimated): Empty, 60,000 lb (27 216 kg); max take-off, 170,000 lb (77 110 kg).

Dimensions: Span, 55 ft 7 in (16,95 m); length, 107 ft 5 in (37,74 m); height, 18 ft 6 in (5,64 m).

Accommodation: Crew of two in tandem, comprising pilot and reconnaissance systems officer.

Status: First A-11 prototype flown on 26 April 1962; first SR-71A flown on 22 December 1964. Production batches of 18 A-11 (including three YF-12A) and 31 SR-71A built.

Notes: Design of the Lockheed A-11 began in 1959, to produce an aircraft of such high performance that it could penetrate enemy airspace without fear of being intercepted. Responsibility for the design and prototype construction was entrusted to the well-known Lockheed 'Skunk Works", the secret experimental department run by C L Johnson, and the first flight was made from a secret base in Nevada known as "Kelly Johnson's ranch". Some A-11s were used operationally in the reconnaissance rôle, and three were converted to YF-12As to evaluate the design's potential as an interceptor, with an armament of four AAMs and firecontrol radar. For recce duty, A-11s also launched Lockheed GTD-21 pilotless drones. The later SR-71A, of similar configuration to the A-11, has a longer fuselage and is optimized for reconnaissance. Delivery of production SR-71As equipped for this rôle began in January 1966, the aircraft being used to equip a unit of the 9th Strategic Reconnaissance Wing of SAC at Beale AFB, where they soon became known as Black Birds because of their all-black finish. For training purposes, the Wing had two SR-71Bs with a raised rear cockpit containing a second set of controls, and one of these was later replaced by a similarly modified SR-71C. The SR-71 uses special fuel, designated JP-7, and a special version of the KC-135 refuelling tanker therefore had to be assigned to the SR-71 force, being designated KC-135Q. The SR-71's internal equipment ranges from multiple-sensor high-performance systems interdiction reconnaissance to strategic systems capable of extreme-altitude specialised surveillance.

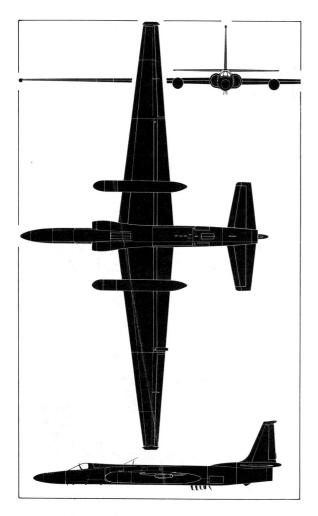

(Above and immediately below) Air and ground views of the Lockheed U-2R, the latest operational version of the reconnaissance aircraft used by SAC; (bottom) the first Lockheed TR-1A, completed during 1981. (Silhouette) Lockheed TR-1A.

Country of Origin: USA.

Type: High altitude and special purpose reconnaissance aircraft.

Power Plant: One (U-2A) 11,200 lb st (5 080 kgp) J57-P-13A or (U-2B, C, D, R and TR-1) 17,000 lb st (7 711 kgp) Pratt & Whitney J75-P-13B turbojet.

Performance: Max speed, 528 mph (850 km/h) at 40,000 ft (12 192 m); cruising speed, 460 mph (740 km/h); service ceiling, approx 80,000 ft (24 384 m); range, up to 4,000 mls (6 440 km); max endurance, over 8 hrs.

Performance: (TR-1, estimated) Max speed, 430 mph (692 km/h) at 60,000 ft (18 290 m); ceiling, 90,000 ft (27 430 m); max range, over 3,000 mls (4 830 km); max endurance, 12 hr.

Weights: Normal take-off, 15,850 lb (7 190 kg); max, 17,270 lb (7 835 kg) with slipper tanks on wings, max take-off (U-2R, TR-1) 29,000 lb (13 154 kg).

Dimensions: Span (U-2A, D) 80 ft 0 in (24,38 m), (U-2R, TR, ER), 103 ft 0 in (31,39 m); length (U-2A, D), 49 ft 7 in (15,11 m), (U-2R, TR, ER), 63 ft 0 in (19,20 m); height (U-2A, D), 13 ft 0 in (3,96 m), (U-2R, TR, ER), 16 ft 0 in (4,88 m); wing area (U-2A, D), 565 sq ft (52,5 m²).

Accommodation: Pilot only or (U-2D, U-2CT and TR-1B) two pilots or pilot and observer.

Status: Prototype first flown 1 August 1955; production completed by 1958. Production totals, 48 U-2A/B/C and five U-2D. New production batch launched 1979, comprising 23 TR-1A, two TR-1B and one ER-2 (for NASA); first TR-1A delivered August 1981 and ER-2 delivered 10 June 1981.

Notes: Single-seat models of this clandestine reconnaissance aircraft were designated U-2A, -2B or -2C according to equipment and power plant, some also having been redesignated WU-2A for operation by SAC on fall-out sampling missions, later taken over by RB-57Fs. The two-seat U-2Ds were used for training and other special tasks and as WU-2Ds for high altitude research. In USAF service, U-2s were first operated by the 4080th Strategic Wing at Laughlin AFB, later by 100th SR Wing at Davis-Monthan AFB and finally by 9th SRW at Beale AFB, alongside SR-71s. The 9th operated U-2Rs from a batch of 25 built 1968/69 using components of earlier U-2Bs, with lengthened fuselages and greater wing span, plus large equipment-carrying pods on wings. The TR-1A, of similar configuration to U-2R, was put into production in 1979 to meet USAF requirement for a tactical battlefield reconnaissance aircraft which will be operated primarily in Europe (by SAC on behalf on TAC) and will carry sensors enabling it to "see" some 35 mls (55 km) into hostile territory without overflying.

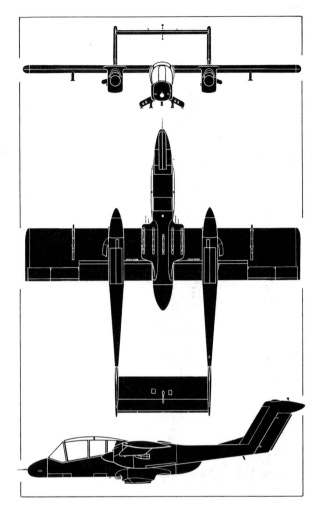

(Top) An OV-10D Bronco in the NOS (Night Observation System) configuration for the US Marine Corps; (immediately above) a USAF OV-10A operating in the FAC rôle in Europe; (below) a Royal Thai Air Force OV-10C. (Silhouette) Rockwell OV-10A Bronco.

Country of Origin: USA.

Type: Forward air control, target tug and utility aircraft.

Power Plant: Two 715 shp Garrett AiResearch T76-G-10 or 10A (left) and -12 or 12A (right) turboprops.

Performance: (OV-10A) Max speed, 280 mph (452 km/h) at sea level; cruising speed, 203 mph (328 km/h) at 5,000 ft (1 525 m); initial rate of climb, 2,380 ft/min (12,1 m/sec); service ceiling, 26,000 ft (7 925 m); mission radius, 58 mls (93 km) with 3-hr loiter; ferry range, 1,428 mls (2 300 km).

Weights: Empty, 7,190 lb (3 260 kg); normal loaded, 12,500 lb (5 670 kg); max take-off, 14,444 lb (6 550 kg).

Dimensions: Span, 40 ft (12,19 m); length (excluding nose probe) 39 ft 9 in (12,12 m); length (OV-10D), 42 ft 3 in (12,88 m); overall height, 15 ft 1 in (4,62 m); wing area, 291 sq ft (27,03 m²).

Accommodation: Two in tandem.

Armament: Four 7·62-mm M60 C machine guns in sponsons.

Status: First of seven YOV-10A prototypes flown on 16 July 1965; first flight in production configuration, March 1967; first production OV-10A flown on 6 August 1967; first OV-10B flown 3 April 1970; OV-10B(Z) flown 3 September 1970; first OV-10C flown 9 December 1970; first YOV-10D flown on 9 June 1970. Production totals YOV-10A, 7; OV-10A (USAF), 157; OV-10A

(USMC), 114; OV-10B, 18; OV-10C, 32; OV-10E, 16; OV-10F, 16; OV-10G, 24.

Notes: The OV-10 was built to joint USAF/USMC/USN requirements for an armed forward air control and light armed reconnaissance aircraft and was deployed to Vietnam in 1968 for use by all three services. Export models are the OV-10B target tug for Germany, OV-10C for Thailand, OV-10E for Venezuela, OV-10F for Indonesia and OV-10G for South Korea. Morocco has six OV-10As released by the USAF and delivery of 16 OV-10As to the Philippine Air Force and eight more for Thailand was arranged during 1981. The German OV-10B(Z) version had an additional J85 turbojet above the fuselage but only one was temporarily converted. Two YOV-10Ds were Night Observation Gun-Ships converted from OV-10As for Marine Corps evaluation, having a three-barrel 20-mm gun in a remotely-controlled ventral turret and IR sensor in the nose. Subsequently the Marines acquired 18 OV-10D conversions for the Night Observation Surveillance (NOS) rôle; they have 1,040 shp T76-G-420/421 engines, FLIR and laser target designator in a nose turret and additional stores capability on the wing pylons. OV-10As and OV-10Ds are operational with Marine Squadrons VMO-1 and VMO-2; the USAF has two Tactical Air Support Squadrons flying OV-10As in the USA and Europe.

(Above) The first Nimrod AEW Mk 3, of 11 aircraft assigned for conversion from MR Mk 1 standard; (immediately below) the same aircraft on its first take-off and (bottom) the second development aircraft, in revised finish and markings. (Silhouette) BAe Nimrod AEW Mk 3.

Country of Origin: United Kingdom.

Type: Airborne early warning and control system aircraft.

Power Plant: Four 12,160 lb st (5 515 kgp Rolls-Royce RB 168-20 Spey Mk 250 turbofans.

Performance: No details have been released for publication but maximum and transit speeds are likely to be generally similar to those of the M.R. Mk 2 and maximum endurance is in excess of 10 hours Mission requirement calls for 6-7 hours on station at 29,000-35,000 ft (8 840-10 670 m) at approximately 350 mph (563 km/h) at 750-1,100 mls (1 120-1 600 km) from base.

Weights: Max take-off weight, approximately 190,000 lb (85 185 kg).

Dimensions: Span, 115 ft 1 in (35,08 m); length 137 ft 8½ in (41,97 m); height 35 ft 0 in (10,67 m); wing area, 2,121 sq ft (197,05 m²).

Accommodation: Flight crew of four and tactical team of six. Tactical team comprises tactical air control officer, communications control officer, EWSM (Electronic Warfare Support Measures) operator and three air direction officers located in the tactical area of the cabin.

Armament: None.

Status: First of three development aircraft flown on 16 July 1980

and second aircraft on 23 January 1984. Full RAF programme calls for conversion of 11 Nimrod MR Mk 1, to AEW standard, including the development aircraft, for service starting 1982.

Notes: The Nimrod AEW Mk 3 airborne warning and control system aircraft is equipped with Marconi mission system avionics with identical radar aerials mounted in nose and tail, these being synchronised and each sequentially sweeping through 180 deg in azimuth in order to provide uninterrupted coverage throughout the 360 deg of combined sweep. Pods are located at the wingtips (containing aerials for the Loral 1017A ESM equipment) and weather radar is installed in the front of the starboard wing pinion tank in place of the searchlight fitted in this position in the MR Nimrod. Additional fuel tanks are located in the weapons bay, and to meet the need for cooling air for the extra electronic equipment carried, an additional air conditioning pack is mounted in the rear fuselage, as indicated by a small air intake on the starboard side. Prior to the first flight of the first AEW Mk 3 conversion, a Comet 4C was fitted with the nose radome and one half of the radar system to permit testing to begin, and first flew in this form on 16 July 1980. The Nimrod AEW Mk 3s were to replace Shackletons in No 8 Squadron, RAF, from 1982 onwards, and will be based at RAF Waddington.

(Top) A Boeing E-3A Sentry as used by three squadrons of the 552nd Airborne Warning & Control Wing of the USAF: (below) the first of 18 E-3As procured for operation by air forces of the North Atlantic Treaty Organization. (Silhouette) Boeing E-3A Sentry.

Country of Origin: USA.

Type: Airborne warning and control system aircraft.

Power Plant: Four 21,000 lb st (9 525 kgp) Pratt & Whitney TF33-P-100A turbofans.

Performance: (At max weight) Average cruising speed, 479 mph (771 km/h) at 28,900–40,100 ft (8 810–12 220 m); average loiter speed, 376 mph (605 km/h) at 29,000 ft (8 840 m); initial rate of climb, 2,640 ft/min (13,4 m/sec); service ceiling, 33,100 ft (10 090 m); time on station (unrefuelled) at 1,150 mls (1 850 km) from base, 6 hrs, (with one refuelling), 14·4 hrs; ferry range (crew reduced to four members), 5,034 mls (8 100 km) at 475 mph (764 km/h).

Weights: Empty, 170,277 lb (77 238 kg); normal loaded, 214,300 lb (97 206 kg); max take-off, 325,000 lb (147,420 kg).

Dimensions: Span, 145 ft 9 in (44,42 m); length, 152 ft 11 in (46,61 m); height 41 ft 4 in (12,60 m); wing area, 2,892 sq ft (268,67 m²).

Armament: None.

Accommodation: Operational crew of 17 comprising flight crew of four, a systems maintenance team of four, a battle commander and an air defence operations team of eight.

Status: First of two (EC-137D) development aircraft (with Westinghome and Hughes competitive radars respectively) flown 9 February 1972; second EC-137D became E-3A (T/S) Test System aircraft when fitted with winning Westinghouse radar and resumed testing February 1975; first of two YE-3A (T/S) pre-production aircraft flew 25 July 1975 and, with production configured avionics, on 31 October 1975. First E-3A delivered 24 March 1977. First NATO E-3A flown (as bare airframe) 18 December 1980 and delivered to Dornier, West Germany, early 1981 for equipment installation. Deliveries of 18 for NATO (excluding UK) operation commenced January 1982, with full deployment following in 1984.

Notes: The AWACS system includes extensive sensors, communications and navigation equipment plus a very large capacity airborne computer. The production E-3A is intended to meet the requirements of both Tactical Air Command and Aerospace Defence Command, with no change of equipment. Its capabilities include surveillance, detecting, tracking and weapons selection and direction. The USAF programme covers 31 new E-3As plus one EC-137D and two YE-3As converted to production configuration. NATO ordered 18 E-3As in 1980 for joint force (except UK/USA/France) and in 1981 the US Congress finally approved the sale of five E-3As to Saudi Arabia.

(Above and immediately below) Two views of the first Boeing E-4B advanced airborne command post for operation by the USAF; (bottom) one of the 12 commercial Boeing 747s purchased for service with the Imperial Iranian Air Force. (Silhouette) Boeing E-4B.

Country of Origin: USA.

Type: Airborne command post aircraft.

Power Plant: Four 52,500 lb st (23 814 kgp) General Electric F103-GE-100 turbofans.

Performance: (Typical Boeing 747-200 with CF6-50E engines): Max speed, 602 mph (969 km/h); operating ceiling, over 45,000 ft (13 715 m); range, 6,500 mls (10,562 km) with full mission load; unrefuelled endurance, 12 hrs. With air refuelling, E-4B can remain airborne for up to 72 hrs.

Weights: Max take-off, over 800,000 lb (362 880 kg); (max commercial 747-200 take-off weight, 833,000 lb 377 840 kg).

Dimensions: Span, 195 ft 8 in (59,64 m); length, 231 ft 4 in (70,51 m); height, 63 ft 5 in (19,33 m); wing area, 5,685 sq ft (528,14 m²).

Accommodation: The E-4B accommodates two complete flight crews with rest area on upper deck and an operating crew of some 50 personnel on the main deck.

Status: First E-4A flown 13 June 1973, delivered December 1974 and second E-4A delivered May 1975; third E-4A (first with F103 engines) flown 6 June 1974, delivered September 1975. First E-4B flown (in test-bed configuration) 1975 and (fully-equipped) 10 June 1978; delivered to USAF 21 December 1979.

Production: E-4A, 3; E-4B, 1 plus 2 planned for future procurement; 747 military transport, 12 (second-hand purchase by IIAF).

Notes: Since 3 February 1961, at least one Airborne Command Post operated by SAC has been continuously airborne in the *Project Looking Glass* programme to provide and maintain facilities for a command communications structure in the event of a national emergency or a war situation. In February 1973, the Boeing 747 was selected to replace the smaller EC-135s used to perform this task and an initial order was placed for two as Advanced Airborne Command Posts (AABNCP). The first two aircraft were delivered with Pratt & Whitney F105-PW-100 (JT9D) engines and an avionics system transferred from the EC-137s, entering service as the National Emergency Airborne Command Post (NEACP) in 1975. The third E-4A introduced the definitive General Electric F103 (CF6-50E) engines, later retro-fitted in the early aircraft, and the E-4B, which flew its first operational NEACP mission in March 1980, has a very much more advanced avionics system, carries a larger battle staff and has provision for in-flight refuelling. The E-4s are operated by the 1st Airborne Command & Control Squadron as part of the 55th Strategic Reconnaissance Wing operating from Offutt AFB, Nebraska.

DOUGLAS A-3 SKYWARRIOR

(Top) A Douglas EA-3B of Fleet Air Reconnaissance Squadron VQ-2, refuelling from a tanker aircraft; (immediately above) an EA-3B at take off, and (bottom) an ERA-3B serving with VAQ-33 in 1981. (Silhouette) Douglas EKA-3B Skywarrior.

Country of Origin: USA.

Type: Electronic countermeasures and flight refuelling tanker.

Power Plant: Two 10,500 lb st (4 763 kgp) dry and 12,400 lb st (5 625 kgp) with water injection Pratt & Whitney J57-P-10 turbojets.

Performance: (A-3B) Max speed 640 mph (1 029 km/h) at sea level, 610 mph (982 km/h) at 10,000 ft (3 050 m) and 560 mph (901 km/h) at 36,000 ft (10 973 m); service ceiling 41,300 ft (12 600 m); tactical radius, 1,050 mls (1 690 km); max range, 2,900 mls (4 667 km).

Weights: (EA-3B) Empty, 41,192 lb (18 685 kg); normal loaded, 61,593 lb (27 940 kg); max take-off, 78,000 lb (35 380 kg).

Dimensions: Span, 72 ft 6 in (22,10 m); length, 76 ft 4 in (23,27 m); height, 22 ft 9½ in (6,94 m); height (EA-3B) 23 ft 6 in (7,16 m); wing area, 812 sq ft (75,44 m²).

Accommodation: (EA-3B) Flight crew of three and four electronics operators in pressurized fuselage.

Armament: Bomber versions had internal provision for up to 12,000 lb (5 443 kg) and two 20-mm cannon in remotely controlled tail barbette; recce and tanker versions unarmed.

Status: Prototype (XA3D-1) first flown on 28 October 1952; YA3D-1 first flown on 16 September 1953; YRA-3B first flown on 22 July 1958; EA-3B first flown on 10 December 1958; TA-3B first flown on 29 August 1959. Production quantities: A-3A, 50; A-3B, 164; EA-3B, 24; RA-3B, 30; TA-3B, 12. Other variants by conversion. Production completed 1961.

Notes: Development of the Skywarrior was started in parallel with work on the super-carriers of the USS Forrestal type that were evolved soon after World War II, and at the time of first flight the XA3D-1 prototype was the largest carrier-based aircraft in the world. The A-3A and A-3B bomber versions, the latter with more powerful engines and provision for flight refuelling, equipped US Navy bomber squadrons until the mid-sixties but were retired after the Navy relinquished its strategic bombing rôle and the Skywarrior squadrons re-equipped with RA-5Cs. Many A-3Bs were then converted to KA-3B refuelling tankers, becoming the only carrier-based tankers in the Fleet inventory, with a capacity of 1,300 US gal (4 925 l), and the addition of ECM equipment then produced 30 examples of the EKA-3B version. In 1982, two US Navy squadrons were flying EA-3Bs in the TASES (Tactical Signal Exploitation System) rôle, expected to continue until 1985, and one squadron used ERA-3Bs (RA-3Bs with cameras removed and new EW equipment) for fleet EW training. Two USNR squadrons fly EKA-3B tankers.

(Above and immediately below) Two flying views of the prototype Grumman/GD EF-111A tactical jamming aircraft for the USAF; (bottom) the EF-111A undergoing USAF testing prior to service in 1982. (Silhouette) Grumman/GD EF-111A.

Country of Origin: USA.

Type: Electronic countermeasures aircraft.

Power Plant: Two 10,750 lb st (4 876 kgp) dry and 18,500 lb st (8 392 kgp) with reheat Pratt & Whitney TF30-P-3 turbofans.

Performance: Max speed, 1,450 mph (2 338 km/h) at 47,000 ft (14 326 m) or Mach 2·2; typical combat speed, 1,160 mph (1 865 km/h) at 17,000 ft (5 182 m) or Mach 1·6; initial rate of climb, 21,430 ft/min (109 m/sec); service ceiling, 35,800 ft (10 912 m) at combat weight; time to 28,000 ft (8 534 m) at max take-off weight, 31 mins; combat radius, 288 mls (463 km) with 4 hr loiter over combat area and 1,032 mls (1 662 km) with 1 hr loiter over combat area; ferry range 2,483 mls (3 995 km); internal fuel only.

Weights: Empty weight, 53,418 lb (24 230 kg); design take-off weight, 72,750 lb (33 000 kg); max take-off weight, 87,478 lb (39 680 kg).

Dimensions: Span (spread), 63 ft 0 in (19,20 m); span (swept-back), 31 ft 11½ in (9,74 m); height, 20 ft 0 in (6,10 m); wing area, 525 sq ft (48,77 m²).

Armament: None.

Accommodation: Pilot and electronic warfare officer (EWO) side-by-side in emergency escape module.

Status: First flight of prototype (partial aerodynamic configuration) 15 December 1975; first flight with full aerodynamic configuration, 10 March 1977; fully-equipped second prototype first flown 17 May 1977; initial production conversion flown 26 June 1981.

Notes: The USAF decided in principal to adopt a variant of the General Dynamics F-111 as a Tactical Jamming System in November 1971, to perform the missions of screening air activity over friendly territory from observation by enemy ground radars, of jamming enemy ground radars while escorting formations of attack fighters into enemy airspace and of providing electronic countermeasures protection for fighter-bombers on interdiction missions. For this purpose, up to 10 high-powered electronic jammers are carried by the EF-111A, controlled by a computer and operating in conjunction with sensitive directional receivers that intercept the ground radar signals. The jamming transmitters are carried in the weapons bay with a 16 ft (4,9 m) long "canoe" radome fairing projecting beneath the fuselage. Receiving antennae are carried in a large fairing at the top of the fin. The USAF plans to acquire 42 EF-111As (including the prototype), which Grumman is converting from F-111As. The F-111A is separately described in the Fighter/Attack section.

GRUMMAN E-2 HAWKEYE

AEW/SPECIAL ELECTRONICS

(Top) A Grumman E-2C on a pre-delivery test flight and (immediately above) a similar aircraft with Navy Squadron VAW-126 on the USS "John F Kennedy"; (below) one of the four E-2Cs supplied to the Heyl Ha'avir in Israel. (Silhouette) The Grumman E-2C Hawkeye.

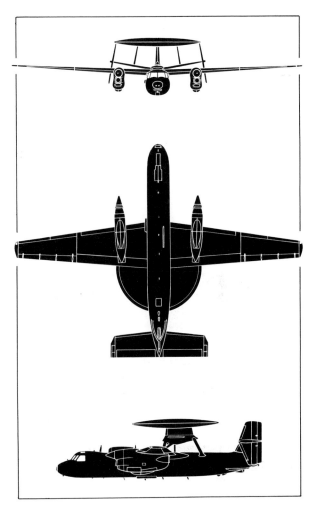

Country of Origin: USA.

Type: Airborne early warning aircraft.

Power Plant: Two (E-2A, B) 4,050 shp Allison T56-A-8/8B or (E-2C) 4,910 shp Allison T56-A-425 turboprops.

Performance: (E-2C) Max speed, 374 mph (602 km/h) at max take-off weight; cruising speed, 310 mph (499 km/h) for best range; initial rate of climb, 2,515 ft/min (12,8 m/sec); service ceiling, 30,800 ft (9 390 m); time on station, 4 hrs at 200 mls (320 km) from base; endurance with max fuel, 6 hr 6 min; ferry range, 1,604 mls (2 580 km).

Weights: (E-2C) Empty, 38,009 lb (17 241 kg); max internal fuel load, 12,400 lb (5 624 kg); max take-off 51,900 lb (23 541 kg) with standard fuel, 59,880 lb (27 161 kg) with auxiliary fuel in outer wings.

Dimensions: Span, 80 ft 7 in (24,56 m); length, 57 ft 7 in (17,55 m); height, 18 ft 4 in (5,59 m); wing area, 700 sq ft (65,03 m²).

Armament: None.

Accommodation: Flight crew of two and team of three for ATDS (Airborne Tactical Data System) operation.

Status: Prototype (W2F-1) first flown 21 October 1960; first fully-equipped prototype flown on 19 April 1961; development

E-2A with AN/APS-111 flown on 17 August 1965; prototype E-2B flown on 20 February 1969; prototype YE-2C flown on 20 January 1971; first production E-2C flown 23 September 1972. First delivery to US Navy, December 1972. Production totals: W2F-1 prototype, 3; E-2A, 59; E-2C, 85 funded by USN up to FY82 (plus two YE-2C conversions from E-2A) and four delivered to Israel and eight ordered by JASDF, delivery starting 1983.

Notes: The E-2A, B and C differ primarily in radar and avionics, the E-2A and E-2B having an AN/APS-96 long-range radar, while the E-2C introduced the AN/APS-120 and later standard aircraft have the AN/APS-125; the E-2B and C have Litton L-304 multi-purpose computer. The E-2B was produced only by conversion of 52 E-2As; two others became TE-2As for use as conversion trainers, later replaced by TE-2Cs for use by the two readiness training squadrons, RVAW-110 and RVAW-120. The USN Hawkeyes are operated by 12 VAW squadrons, each with four aircraft attached to one of the carrier air wings. Since December 1976, all E-2Cs have been delivered with AN/APS-125 radar in place of the earlier AN/APS-120, and continued procurement is planned until this type is standard throughout the USN squadrons. A Carrier On-board Delivery (COD) variant of the E-2 was developed as the C-2 Greyhound, separately described.

(Above) A Grumman EA-6B Prowler carrying three jamming pods and two fuel tanks; (immediately below) EA-6B of Navy Squadron VAQ-129 and (bottom) a ground view of one of the EA-6Bs of VAQ-138 serving on the USS "Dwight D Eisenhower". (Silhouette) Grumman EA-6B Prowler.

Country of Origin: USA.

Type: Carrier-borne electronic warfare aircraft.

Power Plant: Two 9.300 lb st (4 218 kgp) Pratt & Whitney J52-P-8A (first 22 aircraft) or 11,200 lb st J52-P-408 turbojets.

Performance: Max speed, 613 mph (987 km/h) at sea level; average cruising speed, at optimum altitude, 483 mph (777 km/h); initial rate of climb, 10,030 ft/min (50,1 m/sec); service ceiling, 41,000 ft; combat range with max external fuel, 2,400 mls (3 863 km); range with five ECM pods, 1,100 mls (1 770 kg).

Weights: Empty, 32,162 lb (14 588 kg); internal fuel, 15,422 lb (6 995 kg); max external fuel, 10,025 lb (4 547 kg); take-off weight, ECM mission, 54,461 lb (24 703 kg); take-off weight, ferry mission, 60,610 lb (27 492 kg); max permitted take-off weight, 65,000 lb (29 483 kg).

Dimensions: Span, 53 ft 0 in (16,15 m); length, 59 ft 10 in (18,14 m); height, 16 ft 3 in (4,95 m); wing area, 529 sq ft (49,15 m²).

Accommodation: Pilot and electronic countermeasures operator side-by-side in forward cockpit; two operators side-by-side in rear cockpit.

Status: Prototype EA-6B flown on 25 May 1968. Production deliveries for US Navy began January 1971 and operational deployment began mid-1972. Total deliveries, 90 up to 1982 with additional procurement planned by USN.

Notes: The first electronic countermeasures version of the Grumman A-6 Intruder was the EA-6A, first flown on 26 April 1963 and originally developed under the designation A2F-1Q. This was a two-seater, like the A-6A, but had the bombing/navigation system equipment deleted to make room for more than 30 antennae required to detect, locate, classify, record and jam enemy transmissions. Production totalled 27 for US Marine Corps use. The EA-6B is a more extensive revision of the same basic design but the front fuselage is lengthened by 40 in (1,02 m) to allow two extra seats to be inserted aft of the pilots, the additional crew being needed to handle extra electronics equipment. The EA-6B was renamed Prowler, and procurement began in FY 1969 with the objective of providing one four-aircraft squadron for each carrier air wing. Marine Squadron VMAQ-2 also flies the Prowler. An expanded capability (EXCAP) version entered service in 1973 and the first improved capability (ICAP) example flew in July 1975, with further improvements in jamming efficiency. The early-production EA-6Bs were modified to ICAP standard, and an ICAP-2 configuration was then developed for future introduction, the first flight of this variant being made on 24 June 1980.

TUPOLEV TU-126 (MOSS)

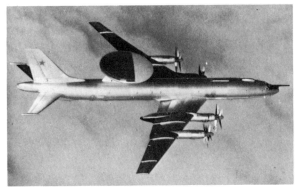

The photographs above and below, and the silhouette, depict the standard service version of the Tu-126 Moss airborne warning and control system aircraft which has been operational with the Soviet Air Force since the latter half of the 'sixties.

Country of Origin: Soviet Union.

Type: Airborne warning and control system aircraft.

Power Plant: Four 14,795 eph Kuznetsov NK-12MV turboprops.

Performance: (Estimated) Max speed, 528 mph (850 km/h); max continuous cruise, 460 mph (740 km/h) at 25,000 ft (7 620 m); normal operating speed, 404 mph (650 km/h); service ceiling, 40,000 ft (12 190 m); max unrefuelled range, 7,800 mls (12 550 km).

Weights: (Estimated) Max take-off, 374,785 lb (170 000 kg).

Dimensions: Span, 168 ft 0 in (51,20 m); length (including refuelling probe), 188 ft 0 in (57,30 m); height, 51 ft 0 in (15,50 m); wing area, 3,349 sq ft (311,10 m²).

Accommodation: The Tu-126 is believed to possess a flight crew of four-five, plus a complement of 10–12 systems operators in tactical compartments, with provision for the accommodation of relief crews.

Status: A derivative of the Tu-114 commercial transport, the Tu-126 airborne warning and control system aircraft first became known to western intelligence agencies in the mid 'sixties, and approximately a dozen aircraft of this type were in Soviet service at the beginning of 1982. It is believed that production of this type was restricted to 14–15 aircraft.

Notes: Retaining the wings, tail surfaces, power plant and undercarriage of the Tu-114 (Cleat) airliner, which was phased out of service by Aeroflot in the 'seventies, and mating these components with a new fuselage of similar cross section surmounted by a saucer-shaped rotating early warning radar scanner housing of approximately 37 ft 6 in (11,40 m) diameter, the Tu-126 is primarily intended to locate low-flying intruders and to vector interceptors towards them. Apart from its fighter control task, it may be assumed to be intended to assist strike aircraft in eluding enemy interception. The Tu-126 is equipped for in-flight refuelling, the fuel line being carried externally from the nose probe along the starboard side of the fuselage to the wing leading edge and thus to the integral wing tanks. Some scepticism has been expressed by western experts concerning the overland detection capability of the Tu-126, and it is anticipated that this type will be phased out of service in the mid 'eighties in favour of an AWACS aircraft derivative of the Il-76 (Candid) which will markedly extend Soviet overwater and overland detection and interceptor control capability. The Tu-126 has been used extensively in overwater exercises around the Soviet periphery and its most important task is apparently the patrol of sections unprotected by surface-to-air missile screens.

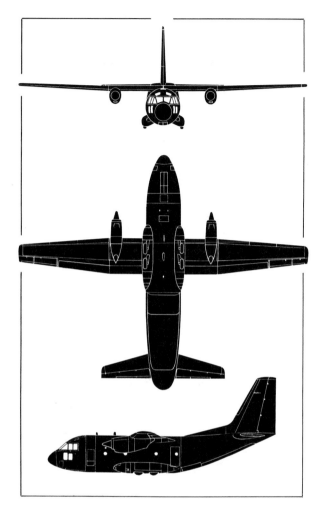

(Top) An Aeritalia G 222 of the AMI's 46ᵃ Aerobrigata, the first service unit to use this transport; (immediately below) one of the Somali Air Force G 222s; (bottom) G 222VS with ECM equipment under nose and atop the fin. (Silhouette) Aeritalia G 222T.

Country of Origin: Italy.

Type: General-purpose military transport.

Power Plant: Two 3,400 shp General Electric T64-GE-P4D or (G.222T) 4,860 shp Rolls-Royce Tyne RTy 20 Mk 801 turboprops.

Performance: Max level speed, 336 mph (540 km/h) at 15,000 ft (4 575 m); cruising speed, 273 mph (440 km/h) at 19,685 ft (6 000 m); initial rate of climb, 1,705 ft/min (8,67 m/sec); service ceiling, 25,000 ft (7 620 m); mission range, 1,380 mls (2 220 km) with 44 troops; range with max fuel, 3,075 mls (4 950 km).

Weights: Empty equipped, 33,950 lb (15 400 kg); max payload, 19,841 lb (9 000 kg); mission take-off weight, 54,013 lb (24 500 kg); max take-off weight, 61,730 lb (28 000 kg).

Dimensions: Span, 94 ft 2 in (28,70 m); length, 74 ft 5½ in (22,70 m); height, 32 ft 1¾ in (9,80 m); wing area, 882.64 sq ft (82,00 m²).

Accommodation: Flight crew of three (two pilots and radio operator/flight engineer) and seats for up to 44 equipped troops or 32 paratroops, or 36 stretchers plus eight seats or assorted military stores and supplies up to max payload limit.

Status: First and second prototypes flown on 18 July 1970 and 22 July 1971 respectively. First production G.222 flown 23 December 1975. G.222VS prototype flown 9 March 1978. First

G.222T flown 13 May 1980. Production orders: Italian Air Force (AMI), 44; Argentine Army, 3; United Arab Emirates Air Force, 2; Somali Air Force, 4; Libyan Arab Republic Air Force (G.222T), 20.

Notes: Ordered by the Italian Air Force as a replacement for Fairchild C-119s, the G.222 originated with the Fiat company, which was awarded a research project contract in 1963 to cover preliminary work on a V/STOL military transport. The basic design was to use a combination of cruise turboprops and lift jets for V/STOL capability, but only the alternative conventional configuration, without the lift jets, was accepted for development. Fiat built two prototypes and a static test specimen at their Turin plant, with 2,970shp CT64-820 engines and unpressurised; the production model, with uprated engines, has provision for pressurisation. Manufacture of the G.222 is distributed throughout the Italian aerospace industry with final assembly at a new plant set up by the state-owned Aeritalia in the South of Italy. The AMI has six G.222RMs equipped for radio and radar calibration and two G.222VS variants for ECM duty, in addition to basic transport variant. The G.222T, developed primarily to meet an order from Libya, differs in having Tyne engines which bestow an improved performance including max cruise speed of 350mph (563 km/h); the overload weight of this variant is 63,933 lb (29 000 kg).

AEROSPATIALE (NORD) N262 FREGATE

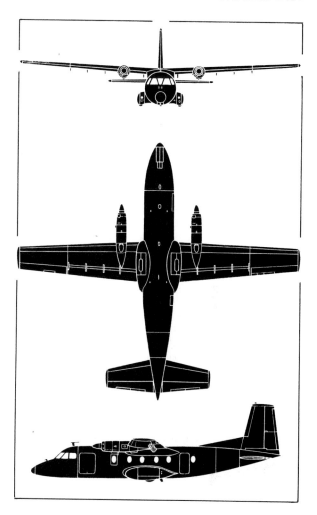

(Top and immediately above) Flying and landing views of an Aérospatiale N.262A serving with the French Aéronavale as a navigation trainer; (below) one of the N.262D Frégates of Armée de l'Air. (Silhouette) N.262D Frégate.

Country of Origin: France.

Type: Light transport and aircrew trainer.

Power Plant: Two (Srs A) 1,065 eshp Turboméca Bastan VIC or (Srs D) 1,130 ehp Bastan VIIA turboprops.

Performance: (Srs D) Max speed, 260 mph (418 km/h); typical high cruising speed, 254 mph (408 km/h); initial rate of climb, 1,496 ft/min (7,6 m/sec); service ceiling, 26,250 ft (8 000m); range with max fuel 1,135 mls (1 825 km); range with max (29 passengers) payload, 405 mls (650 km).

Weights: Basic empty weight, 13,613 lb (6 175 kg); basic operating weight, 15,873 lb (7 200 kg); max payload, 6,834 lb (3 100 kg); max take-off weight, 23,370 lb (10,600 kg).

Dimensions: Span, 71 ft 10 in (21,90 m); length, 63 ft 3 in (19,28 m); height, 20 ft 4 in (6,21 m); wing area, 592 sq ft (55,0 m²).

Accommodation: Two pilots on flight deck; up to 29 passenger or troop seats in cabin, or 18 paratroops, or 12 stretchers with two attendants.

Status: Prototype Nord 262 first flown 24 December 1962; first production Nord 262B flown 8 June 1964; first Nord 262A flown early 1965; prototype Nord 262C/D Frégate flown July 1968; first delivery to *Armée de l'Air*, 8 January 1969. Production totals:

prototype, one; pre-production, three; Nord 262A, 70; Nord 262B, four; Nord 262C, 9; Nord 262D, 24; production was completed in 1978.

Notes: This light transport originated as a design by Avions Max Holste, which had initially produced the MH-250 Super Broussard with piston engines and then derived from it the turboprop-powered MH-260. Holste built 10 MH-260s while Nord (later to merge with Sud to form *Aérospatiale*) developed the basic design to have a new circular-section pressurised fuselage. The first four production aircraft were designated Nord 262B, while the main production variant was the Nord 262A. After Aérospatiale was formed, the Nord 262C and 262D Frégate were introduced, respectively for commercial and military use, with more powerful engines and higher weights. The *Armée de l'Air* was the only customer for the Nord 262D, acquiring a total of 24 to supplement six Nord 262As purchased earlier to serve in the light transport, liaison and multi-engine training rôle. Five of the Nord 262As were later transferred to *Aéronavale*, which also ordered 15 on its own account during 1967, similarly to be used as transports or trainers. Other military users of the Nord 262 included the Congo Air Force, which had one, and the governments of Upper Volta (two) and the Gabon (three).

(Above) An An-12 Cub-B electronic intelligence aircraft. Note additional blister fairings and antennae. (Immediately below) An An-12BP Cub-A of Soviet Transport Aviation and (bottom) an Iraqi An-12BP Cub-A. (Silhouette) The An-12BP Cub-A.

Country of Origin: Soviet Union.
Type: Heavy-duty freighter and troop transport, and (Cub-B and C) electronic intelligence aircraft.
Power Plant: Four 4,000 ehp Ivchenko AI-20K turboprops.
Performance: Max speed, 444 mph (715 km/h); max cruise, 373 mph (600 km/h); range cruise, 342 mph (550 km/h) at 25,000 ft (7 500 m); initial climb, 1,970 ft/min (10,0 m/sec); service ceiling, 33,500 ft (10 200 m); range (max payload), 2,236 mls (3 600 km), (max fuel), 3,540 mls (5 700 km).
Weights: Empty, 61,730 lb (28 000 kg); normal loaded, 121,475 lb (55 100 kg); max take-off, 134,480 lb (61 000 kg).
Dimensions: Span, 124 ft 8 in (38,00 m); length, 121 ft 4½ in (37,00 m); height, 32 ft 3 in (9,83 m); wing area, 1,286 sq ft (119,50 m²).
Armament: Two 23-mm NR-23 cannon in tail position.
Accommodation: Crew of five comprising two pilots, navigator, radio operator and flight engineer and up to 90 fully-equipped troops or 60 paratroops. Up to 44,090 lb (20 000 kg) of freight, or various wheeled or tracked vehicles, including the PT-76 chassis-mounted ZSU-23-4 SP anti-aircraft gun system with its Gun Dish tracking radar, the PT-76 light amphibious tank, the ASU-57 or ASU-85 self-propelled assault guns, the BRDM-1 reconnaissance

car, and the BTR-60 or BTR-152 armoured personnel carrier.
Status: Evolved from the commercial An-10A, the An-12 began to enter Soviet Air Force service in 1959, approximately 850 having been built for military and commercial use by the time production phased out in 1973. The An-12BP (Cub-A) currently remains the mainstay of the Soviet military air transport fleet with some 420–430 in service. The An-12BP was also supplied to the air forces of Egypt, India, Indonesia, Iraq, Algeria, Poland, Bangladesh, Sudan, Syria and Yugoslavia, and remains in service with these countries (apart from Egypt and Indonesia) at the beginning of 1982.
Notes: A number of An-12 transports have been adapted for the electronic intelligence (Cub-B) and countermeasures (Cub-C) tasks. The former features a series of blister fairings under the forward and centre fuselage, and various antennae, and the latter has pods containing stand-off jamming equipment faired into the forward fuselage and electronic equipment replacing the tail gun position. The An-12BP (Cub-A) is being progressively replaced in Soviet Air Force service by the Il-76 (Candid), but is unlikely to be phased out of service until the late 'eighties. Chinese sources have indicated that a copy of the An-12 is being built by the Chinese aircraft industry at Zian as the C-8.

ANTONOV AN-22 (COCK)

(Top) The third of five An-22 prototypes and (immediately above) an early production example delivered to the transport component of the Soviet Air Force. (Below) The definitive nose radome arrangement of the An-22, also illustrated by the silhouette.

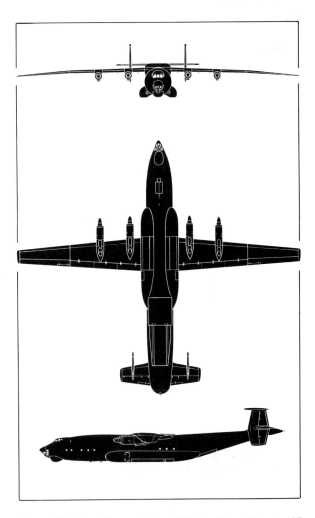

Country of Origin: Soviet Union.
Type: Long-range heavy-duty freight and troop transport.
Power Plant: Four 15,000 shp Kuznetsov NK-12MA single-shaft turboprops.
Performance: Max speed, 460 mph (740 km/h); max cruise, 422 mph (679/h); range (with max payload of 176,350 lb/ 80 000 kg), 3,107 mls (5 000 m), (with max fuel and payload of 99,200 lb/45 000 kg), 6,800 mls (10 950 km); cruising altitude, 26,250–32,800 ft (8 000–10 000 m).
Weights: Empty equipped, 251,327 lb (114 000 kg); max take-off, 551,156 lb (250 000 kg).
Dimensions: Span, 211 ft 3½ in (64,40 m); length, 189 ft 8 in (57,80 m); height, 41 ft 4 in (12,53 m); wing area, 3,713·6 sq ft (345,00 m²).
Accommodation: Crew of five or six with cabin aft of flight deck for 28–29 passengers. Loads can include various wheeled or tracked vehicles including all tanks in the Soviet Army inventory up to and including the T-62 battle tank, vehicle-mounted surface-to-air missiles systems (e.g., SA-4 Ganif, SA-8 Gecko and SA-9 Gaskin), self-propelled guns, armoured personnel carriers, or up to 175 fully-equipped troops or paratroops. The maximum freight load is 176,350 lb (80 000 kg).

Status: The first of five prototypes of the An-22 was flown on 27 February 1965, production deliveries to the Soviet Air Force commencing in the spring of 1967, a number of similar aircraft being supplied to Aeroflot. Production was completed in 1974 after manufacture of some 60 transports of this type, about 50 of these remaining in Soviet Air Force service at the beginning of 1982.
Notes: A small number of An-22 transports are currently utilised by Aeroflot, primarily in the undeveloped areas of the northern Soviet Union, but these effectively form a reserve for the transport component of the Soviet Air Force and are assigned to military tasks (although retaining Aeroflot insignia and commercial registrations) during large-scale exercises or such operations as that involving the occupation of Afghanistan when An-22s in Aeroflot markings flew in troops and armoured vehicles during the opening phase of the occupation. Until the appearance of the Lockheed C-5A Galaxy, the An-22 was the world's largest aircraft, and it has been responsible for establishing 27 FAI-homologated records for payload-to-height and speed with payload which still stand. The An-22-equipped transport units are all concentrated in the western Soviet Union opposite NATO with the airborne divisions they support.

(Above) An early production An-26 Curl freighter, and (immediately below) An-26s of the Soviet Air Force and (bottom) the Yugoslav Air Force. (Silhouette) The An-26 Curl. The An-32 Cline is essentially similar apart from overwing engine nacelles.

Country of Origin: Soviet Union.

Type: Short- to medium-range general-purpose transport.

Power Plant: Two 2,820 ehp Ivchenko AI-24T turboprops and one 1,984 lb st (900 kgp) Tumansky RU-19-300 auxiliary turbojet (in starboard nacelle).

Performance: Max speed, 335 mph (540 km/h) at 19,685 ft (6 000 m); long-range cruise, 273 mph (440 km/h) at 22,965 ft (7 000 m); initial climb, 1,575 ft/min (8,0 m/sec); service ceiling, 24,935 ft (7 600 m); range (with max payload, 12,125 lb/ 5 500 kg), 683 mls (1 100 km), (max fuel), 1,584 mls (2 550 km).

Weights: Empty, 33,113 lb (15 020 kg); normal loaded 50,706 lb (23 000 kg); max take-off, 52,911 lb (24 000 kg).

Dimensions: Span, 95 ft 9½ in (29,20 m); length, 78 ft 1 in (23,80 m); height, 28 ft 1½ in (8,57 m); wing area, 807·1 sq ft (74,98 m²).

Accommodation: Basic crew of five comprising two pilots, navigator, flight engineer and radio operator. Tip-up seats to accommodate up to 40 troops or 34 paratroops, or, for aeromedical role, 24 casualty stretchers and a medical attendant. The hold can accommodate a variety of motor vehicles, including the GAZ-69 and UAZ-469.

Status: The An-26 is one member of a family of transport aircraft stemming from the An-24 feederliner flown for the first time in April 1960, approximately 1,100 of which had been built when production phased out in 1978. Small numbers of An-24s were supplied to some 20 air forces for military transportation tasks. The An-26 was flown in 1968, with deliveries commencing in the following year. The An-26 serves with the logistic support units attached to the various Soviet Frontal Aviation divisions and has been supplied to the air forces of Afghanistan, Angola, Benin, Bulgaria, Cuba, Czechoslovakia, East Germany, Hungary, Iraq, Peru, Poland, Rumania, Somalia and Yugoslavia. A further derivative, the An-32 (Cline) intended for hot-and-high conditions was flown in 1976, and has been selected by the Indian Air Force to fulfil its medium tactical transport aircraft requirement.

Notes: The An-26 (Curl) differs from the An-24 (Coke) primarily in having a redesigned rear fuselage of 'beaver-tail' configuration, uprated engines (offered as options on the An-24V Seriiny II) and the auxiliary turbojet (of the An-24RT freighter) as standard. The An-32 (Cline) has 4,190 ehp AI-20M turboprops in overwing installations but possesses an essentially similar airframe to that of the An-26. Licence manufacture on behalf of the Indian Air Force is expected to be undertaken by Hindustan Aeronautics. A derivative of the An-24/26 is being manufactured in China.

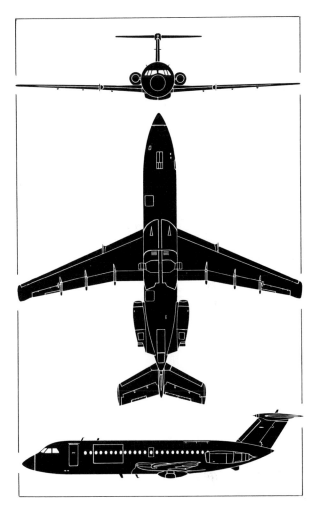

(Top) A BAC One-Eleven 475 belonging to the Air Force of the Sultanate of Oman and (immediately above) a view showing the freight loading door of this variant; (below) the BAC One-Eleven 200 used for research flying at the R.A.E. Bedford. (Silhouette) BAC One-Eleven 475.

Country of Origin: United Kingdom.

Type: Personnel and cargo transport.

Power Plant: Two (Srs 200) 10,330 lb st (4 686 kgp) Rolls-Royce Spey 506 or (Srs 475) 12,550 lb st (5 693 kgp) Spey 512DW turbofans.

Performance: (Srs 200) Max cruising speed, 541 mph (871 km/h) at 21,000 ft (6 400 m); economical cruising speed, 461 mph (742 km/h) at 25,000 ft (7 620 m); initial rate of climb, 2,500 ft/min (12,17 m/sec); operational ceiling, 35,000 ft (10 670 m); range with typical payload, 875 mls (1 410 km); range with max fuel, 2,130 mls (3 430 km).

Performance: (Srs 475) Max cruising speed, 541 mph (871 km/h) at 21,000 ft (6 400 m); economical cruising speed, 461 mph (742 km/h) at 25,000 ft (7 620 m); initial rate of climb, 2,480 ft/min (12,6 m/sec); operational ceiling, 35,000 ft (10 670 m); range with typical payload, 1,865 mls (3 000 km); range with max fuel, 2,300 mls (3 700 km).

Weights: (Srs 200) Operating weight empty, 46,405 lb (21 049 kg); max payload, 19,095 lb (8 661 kg); max take-off weight, 79,000 lb (35 833 kg).

Weights: (Srs 475) Operating weight empty, 51,473 lb (23 348 kg); max payload, 21,527 lb (9 764 kg); max take-off weight, 98,500 lb (44 678 kg).

Dimensions: Span (Srs 200), 88 ft 6 in (26,97 m); span (Srs 475), 93 ft 6 in (28,50 m); length, 93 ft 6 in (28,50 m); height, 24 ft 6 in (7,47 m); wing area (Srs 200), 1,003 sq ft (93,18 m²); wing area (Srs 475), 1,031 sq ft (95,78 m²).

Accommodation: Two pilots and (Srs 200, Srs 475) up to 89 passengers in cabin.

Status: First BAC One-Eleven (Srs 200) flown 20 August 1963; first production model (Srs 201) flown on 19 December 1963. Srs 475 prototype flown on 27 August 1970 and first production 475 flown on 5 April 1971. Production total 230 in the UK, plus components for 22 to be assembled in Romania by CIAR.

Notes: Evolved from an original project design of the Hunting Aircraft company, the BAC One-Eleven was produced by British Aircraft Corporation (now part of British Aerospace) as a potential jet successor to the Viscount. The Royal Australian Air Force has two Srs 200s in service with No 34 (VIP) Squadron at Fairbairn, Canberra. The Srs 475 combines the uprated engines and extended wing span of the Srs 500 with the Srs 200 fuselage, and the Sultan of Oman's Air Force acquired three examples fitted with large freight-loading doors in the forward fuselage side and a quickly-removable freight floor overlay and cargo handling system.

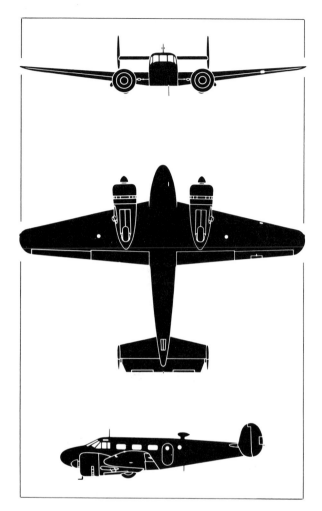

(Above) A Beechcraft C-45 of the Argentine Army (Ejercito Argentino); (immediately below) Beechcraft C-45 of the Uruguayan Aviacion Naval; (bottom) Super Beech 18 operated by the Japanese Maritime Safety Board. (Silhouette) Beechcraft Model 18.

Country of Origin: USA.

Type: Light transport and multi-engine crew trainer.

Power Plant: Two 450 hp Pratt & Whitney R-985-AN-1 Wasp Junior seven-cylinder radial engines.

Performance: Max speed, 230 mph (368 km/h); cruising speed, 211 mph (340 km/h); initial rate of climb, 1,280 ft/min (6,5 m/sec); service ceiling, 22,000 ft (6 710 m); range, 1,300 mls (2 585 km).

Weights: Typical empty weight, 5,610 lb (2 546 kg); normal take-off, 8,500 lb (3 860 kg); max loaded, 9,000 lb (4 082 kg).

Dimensions: Span, 47 ft 7 in (14,5 m); length, 31 ft 11½ in (10,4 m); height 9 ft 2½ in (2,8 m); wing area, 349 sq ft (32,4 m²).

Accommodation: Two crew with dual controls. Up to seven passenger seats in cabin.

Status: Prototype (commercial model) first flown on 15 January 1937. Production deliveries (military and civil) began 1938. Total production, 7,091, including 5,204 in military versions, final delivery 26 November 1969.

Notes: The Beech 18 enjoyed an uninterrupted production life of 32 years, from 1937 to 1969, which set a world record for longevity of a single type of aircraft. In this period, it evolved through many versions, for both military and civil use, but all but the final Super 18 model retained essentially the same characteristics.

Large numbers were used by the USAF for communications (C-45 variant) and for training (AT-7 and AT-11 versions) but these are no longer in service; similar models were operated by the US Navy (RC-45J and TC-45J), and by numerous foreign air forces, particularly in South America. One of the largest post-war users of the Beech 18 was the RCAF, which at one time had nearly 400 on strength under the wartime name of Expeditor. The Japanese armed forces were also at one time among the largest users of Beech 18s, but by 1982 it was serving only in limited numbers anywhere, and principally with the air forces of South or Central American nations including Argentina, Columbia, Dominica, Ecuador, Mexico, Paraguay and Uruguay. Elsewhere, a few examples lingered on in Indonesia, Turkey and Zaïre. As well as earlier models, a few Super 18s were also still in use, notably with the Japanese Maritime Safety Board, an agency comparable to the US Coast Guard. Introduced in 1954 as a refined version of the D18S, the Super 18 embodied a number of design refinements, the G18 of 1959 introducing an enlarged windshield, the 1961 model embodying further refinement in the form of enlarged so-called panoramic windows, this version being supplanted by the H18 in 1962. Several schemes were later devised to give the Beech 18 a longer fuselage and/or a tricycle undercarriage.

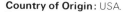

(Top) Beechcraft UC-12B logistics support aircraft in US Navy service, (immediately above) the US Army's RU-21J electronic surveillance variant of the Super King Air 200; (below) the C-12A Huron US Army transport. (Silhouette) Beechcraft C-12A Huron as used by the USAF and US Army.

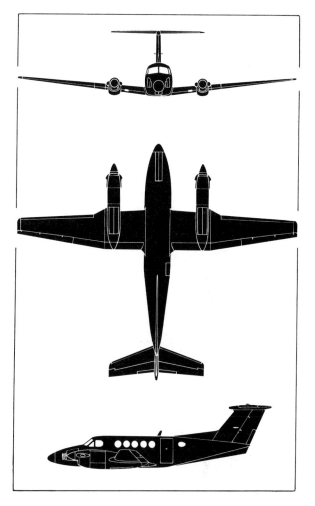

Country of Origin: USA.

Type: Personnel and cargo transport and (200T) maritime reconnaissance aircraft.

Power Plant: Two (C-12A) 750 shp Pratt & Whitney Canada PT6A-38 or (C-12B, C, D, SKA 200) 850 shp PT6A-41 turboprops.

Performance: (SKA 200) Max speed, 333 mph (536 km/h) at 15,000 ft (4 570 m); max cruising speed, 320 mph (515 km/h) at 25,000 ft (7 620 m); economical cruise, 313 mph (503 km/h); initial rate of climb, 2,450 ft/min (12,5 m/sec); service ceiling, over 35,000 ft (10 668 m); range, 1,370–2,572 mls (2 204–3 495 km).

Weights: Empty (SKA 200), 1,437 lb (3 373 kg); max cargo capacity, 2,963 lb (1 345 kg); max take-off (SKA 200), 12,500 lb (5 670 kg), (200 T), 14,000 lb (6 350 kg).

Dimensions: Span (standard aircraft) 54 ft 6 in (16,61 m), (200 T with tip tanks), 56 ft 7 in (17,25 m), (200 T without tip tanks), 55 ft 6½ in (16,93 m); length, 43 ft 9 in (13,34 m); height, 14 ft 10 in (4,52 m); wing area, 303 sq ft (28,15 m²).

Accommodation: Two pilots and up to 13 passenger seats in cabin; (200 T) two observers and radar/tactical navigator in cabin.

Status: Two prototypes of Super King Air 200 (Beech Model 101) flown 27 October and 15 December 1972. First commercial customer deliveries early 1974. Prototype 200T flown 9 April 1979.

Production/Sales: RU-21J, 3 delivered 1974; C-12A, 111, deliveries commenced 1975; UC-12B, 66, deliveries began September 1979, continuing through 1983; C-12C, 14; C-12D, 21; 200T, 13 for Japanese Maritime Safety Agency, delivered 1979–1981; one 200T for Uruguayan Navy, delivered January 1981; Super King Air 200, three for Irish Army Air Corps, delivered 1977–80; eight for Argentine Air Force; two for Algerian Air Force; one each for Bolivian Air Force, Greek Army, Guyana Defence Force and Ivory Coast Air Force.

Notes: The Super King Air 200 is used as a staff or VIP transport. The 200T maritime patrol version carries AIL or Litton search radar with 360-deg scan in ventral radome, additional fuel in wing-tip tanks and other rôle equipment. First Super King Air 200s for US Army were three RU-21Js with extensive electronic surveillance equipment for *Cefly Lancer* programme. As a utility personnel/staff transport the Super King Air 200 was adopted by all four US armed forces: C-12A is used by USAF (30) and US Army (81) and UC-12B by US Navy/Coast Guard. The Army also uses the C-12C which has more powerful engines than the C-12A, and the C-12D, like the UC-12B, has an enlarged cargo-loading door and high-flotation landing gear.

(Above) One of the USAF's 19 Boeing T-43A navigation trainers; (immediately below) a Boeing 737 used as a VIP transport by the Fôrça Aérea Brasileira, designated VC-96; (bottom) an impression of the Boeing 737 for maritime surveillance. (Silhouette) Boeing T-43A.

Country of Origin: USA.

Type: Navigation trainer, maritime surveillance and VIP transport.

Power Plant: Two 14,500 lb st (6 577 kgp) Pratt & Whitney JT8D-9 turbofans.

Performance: (T-43) Max operating speed, 576 mph (927 km/h) at 23,000 ft (7 010 m); max range, 3,225 mls (5 190 km) with standard fuel; training mission endurance, 1 hr 30 min at low altitude, 4 hr 40 min using long-range cruise at 35,000 ft (10 668 m) or 5 hr 30 min using max endurance cruise at 30,000 ft (9 150 m).

Performance: (737-200) Max level speed, 586 mph (943 km/h) at 23,500 ft (7 165 m); max cruise, 576 mph (927 km/h) at 22,600 ft (6 890 m); range, from 2,130 mls (3 423 km) in airline configuration with 115 seats or up to 4,300 mls (6 920 km) in executive configuration with 30 seats.

Weights: Operating weight empty (737-200), 60,550 lb (27 470 kg); max take-off, (737-200), 115,500 lb (52 390 kg) up to 128,100 lb (58 110 kg) for high gross weight option; design mission gross weight (T-43A), 106, 167 lb (48 157 kg).

Dimensions: Span, 93 ft 0 in (28,53 m); length, 100 ft 0 in (30,48 m); height, 37 ft 0 in (11,28 m); wing area, 980 sq ft (91,05 m²).

Accommodation: Flight crew of two; accommodation for up to 130 passengers in airline configuration; typical executive/VIP interior for 30 passengers. (T-43A, three instructor stations, 12 student stations and four navigator proficiency stations in cabin.

Status: Prototype 737-100 first flown 9 April 1967; first 737-200 flown 8 August 1967; first T-43A flown 10 April 1973, deliveries completed July 1974. 737MR (Indonesia) for delivery May 1982-September 1983. Production/sales total, 978 Boeing 737s of all types by beginning of 1982, including 19 T-43A, three 737MR for Indonesia, two 737-200s to Brazilian Air Force and one each for Niger and Venezuelan governments.

Notes: The USAF selected the Boeing 737-200 as the basic airframe for its Undergraduate Navigation Training System introduced in 1974 at Mather AFB, where the T-43As remain in service with the 323rd Flying Training Wing. In addition to Brazil, Niger and Venezuela, which purchased new 737s from Boeing, the Mexican Air Force and Egyptian Air Force have acquired one each second-hand. Ordered by the Indonesian Armed Forces-Air Force (TNI-AU) in 1981, the 737MR has 16,000 lb st (7 257 kgp) JT8D-17 engines and supplementary fuel in the fuselage to give a single-mission range of 3,000 mls (4 828 km). Principal sensor is Motorola side-looking multi-mission radar, carried in the rear fuselage.

BRITISH AEROSPACE (HSA) HS.748 & ANDOVER   TRANSPORT

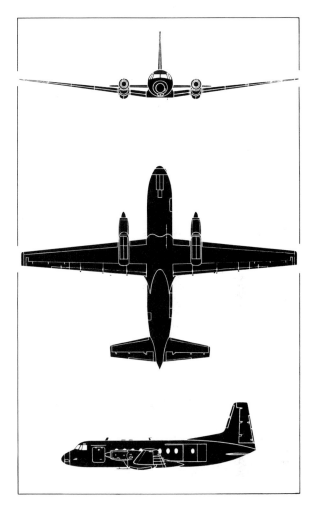

(Top) An example of the British Aerospace HS.748 transport used by the RAE; (immediately above) an HAL-assembled HS.748 in Indian Air Force service; (below) an ex-RAF Andover C Mk 1 serving the RNZAF in No 42 Squadron. (Silhouette) British Aerospace HS.748 (Andover C Mk 2).

Country of Origin: United Kingdom.

Type: General purpose transport.

Power Plant: Two (Srs 2A) 2,280 shp Rolls-Royce Dart 532-2L or (Andover C Mk 1) 3,245 ehp Dart 301 turboprops.

Performance: (HS.748 Srs 2A) Cruising speed, 281 mph (452 km/h) at 38,000 lb (17 236 kg) weight; initial rate of climb, 1,420 ft/min (7.2/m/sec); service ceiling, 25,000 ft (7 620 m); range, 1,066 mls (1 714 km) with max payload, 1,624 mls (2 613 km) with max fuel and 9,527 lb (4 321 kg) payload.

Weights: (HS.748 Srs 2A) Basic operating weight, 25,524 lb (11 577 kg); max payload, 12,976 lb (5 886 kg) or 17,476 lb (7 927 kg) at overload t-o weight; max take-off, 46,500 lb (21 092 kg); optional overload weight, 51,000 lb (23 133 kg).

Dimensions: Span, 98 ft 6 in (30,02 m); length (Srs 2A), 67 ft 0 in (20,42 m), (Andover C Mk 1) 78 ft 0 in (23,77 m); height, (Srs 2A) 24 ft 10 in (7,57 m), (Andover C Mk 1), 30 ft 1 in (9,15 m); wing area, 831·4 sq ft (77,2 m²).

Accommodation: Flight crew of two or three and up to 58 equipped troops, 40 paratroops or 24 stretchers plus attendants.

Status: Prototype HS.748s flown 24 June 1960 and 10 April 1961; prototype Andover (modified HS.748) first flown on 21 December 1963. First production Andover C Mk 1 flown on 9 July 1965. Coastguarder prototype flown 18 February 1977. Total HS.748 production (all types), 357 by mid-1982 including 52 military Srs 2A of which 28 have rear freight door and strengthened floor, and 72 (assembled by HAL) for Indian Air Force.

Notes: Military users of the HS.748, which was designed basically as a civil transport, include the Royal Australian Air Force and Navy, and the air forces of Belgium, Brazil, Brunei, Cameroon, Colombia, Ecuador, Nepal, South Korea, Tanzania, Thailand, Upper Volta, Venezuela and Zambia. Most of these aircraft are used as personnel or VIP transports, in some cases with air-openable rear doors for supply dropping; the RAN HS.748s have been converted for ECM duty. The Andover was derived from the HS.748 with the same wings and forward fuselage but a new rear fuselage with loading ramp and a new tail unit. Total of 31 supplied to RAF but retired in 1975, when six became Andover E Mk 3s for radio calibration duties and 10 sold to the RNZAF, which modified two for VIP duty. The Andover name is also used for six HS.748s in RAF service, these being two Andover CC Mk 2s serving with the Queen's Flight and four Andover C Mk 2s on VIP communications duties. The Coastguarder, flown in prototype form in 1977, is an HS.748 variant specially equipped for maritime surveillance duty, with MEL Marec search radar and a ventral radome. ·

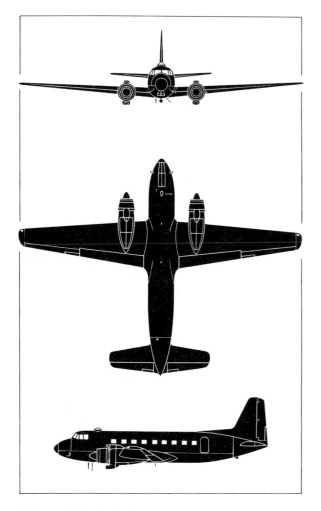

(Above) A line-up of CASA 207 Azor transports in service with Escuadron 351; (immediately below) the Azor T.7-20 serving with Esc. 351 and (bottom) T.7-1, the first production Azor, operated by Esc.405. (Silhouette) CASA 207 Azor.

Country of Origin: Spain.

Type: Short/medium-range general purpose transport.

Power Plant: Two 2,040 hp Bristol Hercules 730 piston-radial engines.

Performance: Max level speed, 261 mph (420 km/h) at 4,920 ft (1 500 m); cruising speed at 64 per cent power, 222 mph (357 km/h) at 10,000 ft (3 050 m); initial rate of climb, 1,080 ft/min (5,5 m/sec); service ceiling, 27,887 ft (8 500 m); range with 6,600 lb (3 000 kg) payload, 1,460 mls (2 350 km).

Weights: (C-207-A) Empty equipped, 23,370 lb (10 600 kg); max payload, 6,806 lb (3 087 kg); max take-off (C-207-A), 35, 275 lb (16 000 kg); (C-207-C), 36,376 lb (16 500 kg).

Dimensions: Span, 91 ft 2½ in (27,80 m); length 68 ft 5 in (20,85 m); height 25 ft 5 in (7,75 m); gross wing area, 923 sq ft (85,8m²).

Accommodation: Flight crew of four and (C-207-A) up to 38 passengers or (C-207-C) up to 7,385 lb (3 350 kg) of freight or 37 troops.

Status: First flown 28 September 1958. Production of 10 C-207-A and 10 C-207-C completed in 1968.

Notes: The largest aircraft of original Spanish design built to date, the Azor was an attempt to produce a 30-38 seat airliner which could be used by the Spanish airlines. However, the type found no commercial customers after prototype testing had been completed and production orders were placed only by the Spanish Ministerio del Aire on behalf of the Air Force. An initial batch of 10 C-207-As was built in personnel transport configuration and a second batch of 10 was then ordered for use as freighters. These were designated C-207-Cs and had re-stressed fuselages with double cargo-loading doors and provision for carrying up to 37 paratroops. The Azors serve with the Spanish Air Force nomenclature T.7A and T.7B, and were originally operated by 351 Escuadron del Mando de Transporte at Getafe, Madrid. The two XT-7 prototypes remained in service for a number of years with the 406 Escuadron de Experimentacion en Vuelo at Torrejon. By 1981, seven Azors remained operational with the Ejercito del Aire, comprising two T-7As and five T-7Bs. These aircraft were all in service with Escuadrón 405, based at Getafe and serving alongside four C-212 Aviocars to provide short-to-medium distance governmental transportation tasks and target-towing for anti-aircraft artillery units. For the latter rôle, the two T-7As have been fitted with Bendix ventral pods to accommodate the drogue targets. The Azors were considered to be near to retirement but no plans for their replacement had been announced.

(Top) A radar-equipped Aviocar of the Uruguayan Air Force; (immediately above) A TE.12B serving as a VIP transport with Escuadron 745; (below) an Aviocar operated by the Royal Jordanian Air Force (Silhouette) CASA Aviocar Series 200.

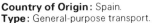

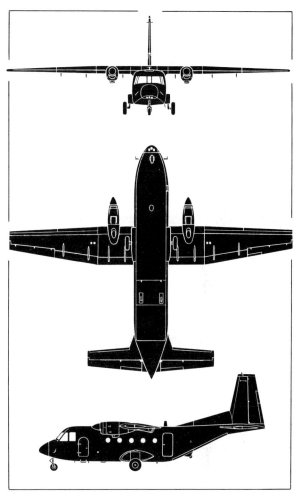

Country of Origin: Spain.

Type: General-purpose transport.

Power Plant: Two 775 ehp Garrett-AiResearch TPE331-5-251C or (Srs 200) 900 shp TPE 331-10-501C turboprops

Performance: (C.212-5) Max speed, 223 mph (359 km/h) at 12,000 ft (3 660 m); economical cruise, 171 mph (275 km/h) at 12,000 ft (3 660 km); initial rate of climb, 1,700 ft/min (8,6 m/sec); service ceiling, 26,700 ft (8 140 m); range with max payload, 300 mls (480 km); range with max fuel, 1,093 mls (1 760 km).

Performance: (Srs 200) Max cruising speed, 227 mph (365 km/h) at 10,000 ft (3 050 m); initial rate of climb, 1,555 ft/min (7,9 m/sec); service ceiling, 28,000 ft (8 535 m); range with max payload, 255 mls (410 km).

Weights: (C.212-5) Empty equipped, 8,610 lb (3 905 kg); max payload, 4,630 lb (2 100 kg); max take-off, 14,330 lb (6 500 kg).

Weights: (Srs 200) Empty equipped, 9 072 lb (4 115 kg); max payload, 4,960 lb (2 250 kg); max take-off, 16,424 lb (7 450 kg).

Dimensions: Span, 62 ft 4 in (19,00 m); length, 49 ft 10½ in (15,20 m); height, 20 ft 8¾ in (6,32 m); wing area, 430·6 sq ft (40,0 m²).

Accommodation: Flight crew of two; provision for 15 troops and a jumpmaster in paratroop versions, or up to 24 troops or 4,960 lb (2 250 kg) of supplies, including light vehicles.

Status: Prototypes first flown on 26 March and 23 October 1971. First pre-production model flown on 17 November 1972. Prototypes of Srs 200 flown on 30 April and 20 June 1978 respectively. Production total, 154 C-212-5 completed 1980; 130 166 200 on order by February 1982 (including 88 for assembly in Indonesia).

Notes: Design of the CASA 212 began in 1965 in response to a Spanish Air Force requirement for a small tactical transport to replace the CASA-built Junkers Ju 52/3m tri-motor transports then still in service. Two prototypes were ordered by the *Ministerio del Aire* in September 1968; these both flew with TPE 331-201 engines rated at 755 ehp, later being re-engined with the more powerful -251Cs selected for production models, subsequently identified as the C.212-5 variant after introduction of Srs 200 with uprated engines and increased weights. Spanish Air Force variants of the Aviocar include the utility transport C.212A (military designation T.12B); VIP transport C.212AV (T.12C); photographic survey C.212B (TR.12A); navigation trainer C.212E (TE.12B) and search and rescue (D.12). Foreign military users include the air forces of Jordan, Portugal, Uruguay and the air force and navy of Indonesia. The Indonesian aircraft are assembled by P T Nurtanio in Bandung.

(Above) One of the US Navy's last remaining VC-131Hs, serving in 1982 with VR-48; (immediately below) an HC-131A used in the search and rescue rôle by the US Coast Guard; (bottom) a CC-109 Cosmopolitan of No 412 Squadron, CAF. (Silhouette) Convair C-131H.

Country of Origin: USA (Canada).

Type: Personnel transport and search and rescue duties.

Power Plant: Two (C-131A) 2,500 hp (with water injection) R-2800-99W piston engines or (C-131H) 3,750 eshp Allison 501D-13 turboprops.

Performance: (C-131A) Max speed, 315 mph (508 km/h) at 15,600 ft (4 755 m); average cruising speed, 209 mph (337 km/h) at 5,000 ft (1 525 m); initial rate of climb, 1,230 ft/min (6,25 m/sec); service ceiling, 22,500 ft (6 860 m); range 1,880 mls (3 030 km) with max payload; ferry range, 2,130 mls (3 427 km).

Performance: (C-131H) Cruising speed, 342 mph (550 km/h) at 20,000 ft (6 100 m); initial rate of climb, 2,050 ft/min (10,4 m/sec); range, 2,270 mls (3 650 km) with 5,000-lb (2 270-kg) payload.

Weights: (C-131A) Empty equipped, 28,538 lb (12 945 kg); normal take-off, 46,955 lb (21 300 kg); max overload, 47,803 lb (21 683 kg).

Weights: (C-131H) Normal take-off, 53,200 lb (24 130 kg); max overload 57,000 lb (25 855 kg).

Dimensions: (C-131A) Span, 91 ft 8½ in (27,95 m); length, 74 ft 8½ in (22,77 m); height, 27 ft 4 in (8,32 m); wing area, 817 sq ft (75,89 m²).

Dimensions: (C-131H) Span, 105 ft 4 in (32,12 m); length, 81 ft

6 in (24,84 m); height, 29 ft 2 in (8,89 m); wing area, 920 sq ft (85,47 m).

Accommodation: Two pilots and (C-131A) up to 29 passengers or 27 stretchers or (C-131H) up to 48 passengers.

Status: Prototype Convair 240 flown 16 March 1947; first C-131A delivered to USAF 1 April 1954; first Convair 340 flown 5 October 1951; first YC-131C (Allison 501D-13 engines) flown 29 June 1954; first Canadair CL-66 (Eland engines) flown 2 February 1959. Production totals: Model 240, 569 (including 176 commercial/airline models); Model 340, 311 (including 212 commercial/airline models); Model 440, 179 (including 153 commercial/airline models); CL-66 (by Canadair), 10.

Notes: By 1981, few examples of the C-131 remained in US military service but one Navy Reserve Squadron, VR-48, was still flying VC-131H transports in the VIP rôle. The US Coast Guard took on strength 20 HC-131As, modified from C-131As (Convair 240) for the search and rescue rôle pending delivery of HU-25A Guardians from 1982 onwards. Seven Canadair-built CL-66s, converted to have Allison 501D-13s, remain in service with the Canadian Armed Forces, operated by No 412 Squadron as VIP and personnel transports with the Canadian designation CC-109 Cosmopolitans.

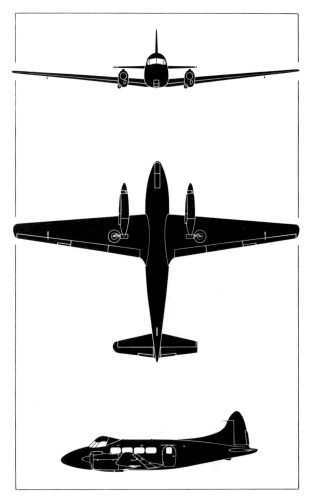

(Top) A pair of Devon C Mk 2s operated by the Air Transport Flight of the RAE, Farnborough; (immediately above and below) two illustrations of Devon C Mk 2s used for communications duties by No 207 Squadron, RAF, based at Northolt. (Silhouette) de Havilland Devon C Mk 2.

Country of Origin: United Kingdom.
Type: Light transport and communications.
Power Plant: Two (C Mk 1) 330 hp de Havilland Gipsy Queen 70-4 or 71 or (C Mk 2) 400 hp Gipsy Queen 175 piston engines.
Performance: Max speed, 210 mph (338 km/h) at 8,000 ft (2 440 m); max cruising speed, 200 mph (322 km/h) at 8,500 ft (2 590 m); economical cruising speed, 179 mph (288 km/h) at 8,000 ft (2 440 m); initial rate of climb, 750 ft/min (3,8 m/sec); service ceiling, 20,000 ft (6 100 m); range, 500 mls (805 km).
Weights: Empty equipped, 5,780 lb (2 621 kg); max take-off, 8,500 lb (3 855 kg).
Dimensions: Span, 57 ft 0 in (17,37 m); length, 39 ft 4 in (11,98 m); height, 13 ft 0 in (3,96 m); wing area, 335 sq ft (31,12 m²).
Accommodation: Two pilots, and seven passenger seats.
Armament: None.
Status: Prototype D.H. 104 Dove first flown on 25 September 1945; total production 544, completed 1967, including more than 200 for military use.
Notes: The Dove was the first post-war product of the de Havilland company—first flown on the 25th anniversary of the foundation of that company—and was also the first new civil

aircraft completed and flown in Britain after the war ended. It was developed primarily as a small airliner, but in 1947 the RAF drew up a specification (C.13/47) for a communications aircraft based on the Dove and ordered into production eventually as the Devon C Mk 1. A total of 44 was built for the RAF, the designation of these aircraft changing to C Mk 2 when Gipsy Queen 175 engines replaced the original Queen 71s or slightly more powerful Queen 70-4s. To meet their specific RAF rôle, the Devons had the forward starboard passenger seat removed to make space for a J-type dinghy, VHF TR 1920 radio installed, a jettisonable cabin door and a two-stage amber canopy to allow for night-flying practice. Later, a number of the Devons were modified to have the enlarged cockpit canopy meanwhile developed for the Heron, and in this form they became Devon C Mk 2/2s. Fourteen Devons remained in service with No 207 Squadron, RAF, in 1981, with no immediate replacement in sight; a few also operated in RAF colours at the RAE, Farnborough. Devons were also acquired by the Indian and New Zealand Air Force, and Doves were purchased in substantial numbers by several other air forces—notably Argentina, with an order for 54. The Royal Navy acquired 13 Doves which served as Sea Devon C Mk 20s until No 781 Squadron stood down in 1981, leaving one or two in Fleet Air Arm service with other units.

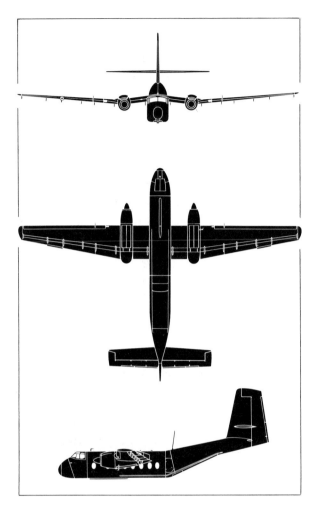

(Above) A DHC-4A Caribou of the Spanish Air Force, which acquired a dozen of these transports under the service designation T.9; (below) a Caribou of the Kenya Air Force. (Silhouette) de Havilland DHC-4A Caribou.

Country of Origin: Canada.

Type: Short range tactical transport.

Power Plant: Two 1,450 hp Pratt & Whitney R-2000-7M2 piston radials.

Performance: Max speed, 216 mph (347 km/h) at 6,500 ft (1 980 m); cruising speed, 182 mph (293 km/h) at 7,500 ft (2 285 m); initial rate of climb, 1,355 ft/min (6,9 m/sec); service ceiling, 24,800 ft (7 560 m); range with max payload, 242 mls (390 km); range with max fuel, 1,307 mls (2 103 km).

Weights: Basic operating, 18,260 lb (8 283 kg); max payload, 8,740 lb (3 965 kg); normal max take-off, 28,500 lb (12 928 kg); max overload, 31,300 lb (14 197 kg).

Dimensions: Span, 95 ft 7½ in (29,15 m); length, 72 ft 7 in (22,13 m); height, 31 ft 9in (9,68 m); wing area, 912 sq ft (84,72 m²).

Accommodation: Crew of two and provision for 32 troops, 26 paratroops, 22 stretchers plus eight seats, two fully loaded jeeps or up to 3 tons of cargo.

Status: Prototype first flown 30 July 1958; first YAC-1 flown March 1953; service deliveries began October 1959. US Type Approval (DHC-4) 23 December 1960, (DHC-4A) 11 July 1961. Production total (including commercial) 307, completed 1973.

Notes: The Caribou was designed primarily to meet a US Army requirement for a tactical transport able to operate from small, unprepared strips close to the front-line, carrying troops and supplies to the front and evacuating casualties on return flights. Following one prototype for company flight testing, de Havilland built five for US Army evaluation with the designation YAC-1 and one for the RCAF as CC-108. The US Army bought 159 AC-1s, later designated CV-2As (gross weight 26,000 lb/11 793 kg) and CV-2Bs (28,500 lb/12 928 kg); when the surviving 134 CV-2s were transferred to the USAF in 1966 these aircraft were redesignated C-7A. The C-7As were widely used by USAF in Vietnam, and some 33 of these were captured by the Vietnamese People's Army Air Force in 1975, and are still in use. By 1981, USAF inventory was down to 35, operated by one AF Reserve Tactical Airlift Wing and one National Guard Tactical Airlift Group. The RCAF (now Canadian Armed Forces) acquired eight more CC-108s (now out of service) and other military users in 1982, with totals acquired, included the Royal Australian Air Force (26), Zambian Air Force (5), Indian Air Force (22), Kenya Air Force (8), Royal Malaysian Air Force (17), Spanish Air Force (12, designated T.9), the United Arab Emirates Air Force (3), Cameroon Air Force (3) and Uganda Police Air Wing (1).

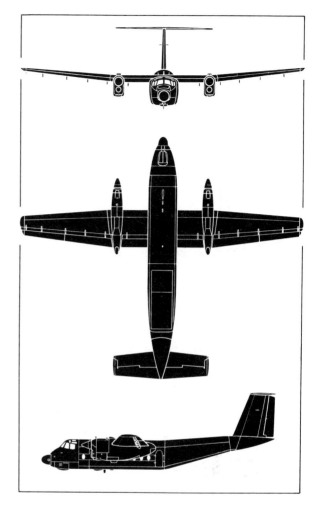

(Top) A de Havilland Canada DHC-5D of the Force Aérienne Zairoise; (immediately above) a Caribou of the United Arab Emirates Air Force in landing configuration; (below) a DHC-5D in Togo insignia. (Silhouette) de Havilland DHC-5 Buffalo.

Country of Origin: Canada.

Type: STOL tactical transport.

Power Plant: Two 2,850 shp General Electric (C-8A) T64-GE-10 turboprops or (CC-115) 3,055 shp CT64-820-1 or (DHC-5D) 3,133 shp CT64-820-4 turboprops.

Performance: (C-8A) Max cruising speed 271 mph (435 km/h) at 10,000 ft (3 050 m); long-range cruise, 208 mph (335 km/h) at 10,000 ft (3 050 m); initial rate of climb, 1,890 ft/min (9,6 m/sec); service ceiling, 30,000 ft (9 150 m); range with max payload, 507 mls (815 km); range with max fuel, 2,170 mls (3 490 km) with 4,000 lb (1 815 kg) payload.

Performance: (DHC-5D) Max cruising speed, 261 mph (420 km/h) at 10,000 ft (3 050 m); initial rate of climb, 380 ft/min (1,93 m/sec); service ceiling, 27,500 ft (8 380 m); range with max payload, 690 mls (1 112 km).

Weights: Operating weight empty, 23,157 lb (10 505 kg); max payload, 13,843 lb (6 279 kg); max fuel load, 13,598 lb (6 168 kg); max take-off, 41,000 lb (18 598 kg).

Weights: (DHC-5D) Empty, 25,160 lb (11 412 kg); max payload, 18,000 lb (8 164 kg); max take-off (STOL from unprepared field), 41,000 lb (18 597 kg); max take-off, 49,200 lb (22 316 kg).

Dimensions: Span 96 ft 0 in (29,26 m); length (C-8A) 77 ft 4 in (23,57 m); length (DHC-5D) 79 ft 0 in (24,08 m); height, 28 ft 8 in (8,73 m); wing area, 945 sq ft (87,8 m²).

Accommodation: Flight crew of three and provision for up to 41 troops, 35 paratroops or 24 stretchers plus six seats.

Status: Prototype first flown 9 April 1964. Deliveries began in April 1965; DHC-5D first flown 1 August 1975. Production totals: DHC-5/CV-7A, 4; DHC-5A, 55, completed 1972; DHC-5D, over 60 up to 1982, including Cameroon, 2; Ecuador, 2; Kenya, 6; Mauritania, 2; Mexico, 2; Oman, 1; Sudan, 4; Tanzania, 4; United Arab Emirates, 4; Zaire, 3; Zambia, 7 and Egypt, 12.

Notes: The first four DHC-5s were delivered for US Army evaluation as CV-7As (original designation YAC-2) but a change of policy led to the Army programme being abandoned and these aircraft were transferred to the USAF as C-8As. The RCAF (now Canadian Armed Forces) purchased 15 improved DHC-5As with the service designation CC-115) and these were delivered in 1967, with uprated engines and radar in the nose. Subsequently, the Brazilian Air Force ordered 24 and the Peruvian Air Force ordered 16. In 1975, de Havilland introduced the DHC-5D, which took advantage of the inherent airframe strength in terms of higher operating weights at reduced g loadings, combined with improved engines.

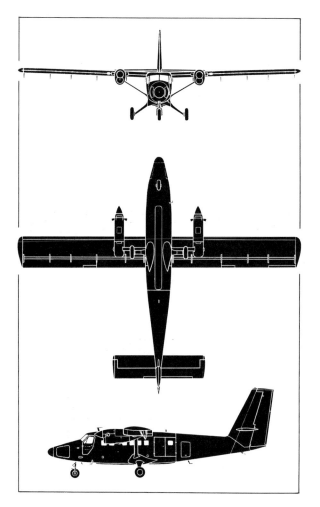

(Above) A DHC-6 Twin Otter with wheel/ski undercarriage operated by the Armada Argentina; (immediately below) a UV-18A Twin Otter of the Alaska National Guard; (bottom) a Twin Otter serving with the Royal Norwegian Air Force. (Silhouette) de Havilland DHC-6 Twin Otter.

Country of Origin: Canada.

Type: Light utility transport.

Power Plant: Two 652 eshp Pratt & Whitney Canada PT6A-27 turboprops.

Performance: Max cruising speed, 210 mph (338 km/h) at 10,000 ft (3 050 m); initial rate of climb, 1,600 ft/min (8,13 m/sec); service ceiling, 26,700 ft (8 140 m); range, 806 mls (1 297 km) with 2,500 lb (1 134 kg) payload and 1,059 mls (1 704 km) with 1,900 lb (862 kg) payload at long-range cruising speed.

Weights: Typical operating weight empty, 7,415 lb (3 363 kg); max payload, 4,280 lb (1 941 kg); max take-off weight, 12,500 lb (5 670 kg).

Dimensions: Span, 65 ft 0 in (19,81 m); length overall (landplane), 51 ft 9 in (15,77 m); length overall (seaplane), 49 ft 6 in (15,09 m); height overall (landplane), 19 ft 6 in (5,94 m); height overall (seaplane), 19 ft 10 in (6,04 m); wing area, 420 sq ft (39,02 m²).

Accommodation: Two pilots side-by-side on flight deck; cabin accommodation for up to 20 passengers, with double freight-loading doors.

Armament: None.

Status: Prototype first flown 20 May 1965. First production delivery, July 1966. Production totals, Series 100, 115; Series 200, 115; Srs 300s, six; Srs 300, more than 500, with production continuing in 1982.

Notes: The Twin Otter originated, as the name suggests, as a twin-engined version of the Otter, utilising many of the same fuselage and wing components. Development was launched by putting down a batch of five, and the first three of these had 579 eshp PT6A-6 engines, the PT6A-20 then being adopted for the inititial production run of Series 100s. The Series 200 differed in having a lengthened nose and internal changes to increase the baggage space. Uprated engines introduced in the Srs 300 allowed higher weights to be utilised. The Twin Otter has been adopted as a utility transport by several air forces, including the Canadian Armed Forces, which acquired nine as CC-138s, the Argentine Air Force (5) and Army (3), the Chilean Air Force (11), Ecuadorean Air Force (3), Jamaica Defence Force (1), the Peruvian Air Force (12, of which 10 are floatplanes), Panamanian Air Force (1), Paraguayan Air Force (1), Royal Norwegian Air Force (5) and Uganda Police Air Wing (1). The US Army bought four Twin Otters for service (optionally on skis) in Alaska, designated UV-18A, and the USAF bought two UV-18Bs in 1977 for operation at the Air Academy, Colorado Springs.

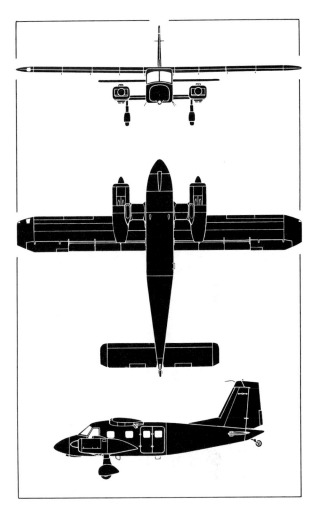

(Top) A Dornier Do 28D serving with the Kenya Air Force; (immediately above) one of the Do 28D-2s supplied to the Luftwaffe; (below) the Dornier 128-2 prototype in maritime reconnaissance configuration. (Silhouette) Dornier Do 28D-2 Skyservant.

Country of Origin: Federal Germany.

Type: Light STOL utility aircraft.

Power Plant: Two (Do 28D and Do 128-2) 380 hp Lycoming IGSO-540-A1E six-cylinder horizontally-opposed engines.

Performance: Cruising speed at 65 per cent power, 169 mph (272 km/h) at 10,000 ft (3 050 m); service ceiling, 25,200 ft (7 680 m); range with max payload, standard fuel, 528 mls (850 km); max range with standard fuel and 1,650 lb (750 kg) payload, 1,243 mls (2 000 km); range with max payload and auxiliary fuel, 700 mls (1 130 km); max range with auxiliary fuel and 1,100 lb (500 kg) payload, 1,925 mls (3 100 km).

Weights: Standard empty weight, 5,128 lb (2 328 kg); operating weight empty (troop transport), 5,755 lb (2 613 kg); max take-off, 8,463 lb (3 842 kg), max take-off with external tanks or stores, 8,844 lb (4 015 kg).

Dimensions: Span, 51 ft 0 in (15,55 m); length, 37 ft 5 in (11,41 m); height, 12 ft 9½ in (3,90 m); wing area, 312·2 sq ft (29,0 m²).

Accommodation: Two seats in cockpit, with full dual controls; up to 10 passengers or 12 troops in cabin, or five stretchers and three seats, or cargo.

Status: Prototype first flown on 23 February 1966, prototype Do 28D-5 (turboprops) flown on 9 April 1978; prototype Do 28D-6 flown 4 March 1980; civil certification (Do 28D) on 24 February 1967 and (Do 28D-1) 6 November 1967. Production total approximately 300 by mid-1982.

Notes: Although resembling the Do 28 in general configuration and size, the Do 28D Skyservant was a completely new design with better performance and payload, as described above. The Skyservant found its largest market among the German armed forces, with orders for 101 Do 28D-2s for the *Luftwaffe* and 20 for the *Marineflieger* in the general utility/communications rôle, and four (Do 28D-1/S) for the *Flugbereitschaftstaffel*, a unit of the *Luftwaffe* providing VIP transport services. In 1980, a programme began to modify these aircraft to Do 28D-2T configuration with TIGO-540 turbosupercharged engines; the first flight was made in March 1980. Other military customers for the Do 28D-2 include the air forces or quasi-military agencies in the Cameroon (2), Ethiopia (2), Israel (15), Kenya (6), Malawi (12), Nigeria (20), Somalia (2), Thailand (3), Turkey (9) and Zambia (10). In 1980 Dornier developed a maritime surveillance version of the Skyservant, with search radar in a 360-deg scan radome under the nose and Morocco was reported to be the first customer for this variant, the current model being designated Do 128.

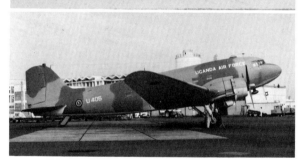

(Above) A Douglas CC-129 in service with the Canadian Armed Forces; (immediately below) an Hellenic Air Force Douglas C-47 at take-off; (bottom) a ground view of a Douglas C-47 in the markings of the Uganda Air Force. (Silhouette) The Douglas C-47 Skytrain and Dakota.

Country of Origin: USA.

Type: General-purpose transport.

Power Plant: Two Pratt & Whitney R-1830-90D or -92 radials of 1,200 hp or (C-117D) Wright R-1820 radials of 1,535 hp.

Performance: (C-47A) Max speed, 229 mph (368,5 km/h) at 7,500 ft (2 286 m); cruising speed, 185 mph (298 km/h) at 7,500 ft (2 286 m); initial rate of climb, 1,500 ft/min (7·5 m/sec); max range 2,125 mls (3 420 km).

Weights: Empty, 16,970 lb (7 700 kg); normal take-off, 26,000 lb (11 793 kg); max overload, 33,000 lb (14 970 kg).

Dimensions: Span, 95 ft 0 in (28,96 m); length, 64 ft 5½ in (19,64 m); height, 16 ft 11 in (5,16 m); wing area, 987 sq ft (91,69 m²).

Accommodation: Flight crew of three, and up to 28 troops.

Status: First flown (as commercial DST) 17 December 1935. First delivery to US Army Air Corps (as C-41) October 1938. First C-47 delivered 1 February 1942. Production totals (built on military contracts): two C-41; 965 C-47; 5,254 C-47A; 3,364 C-47B; 66 R4D-1; 2 R4D-2; 219 C-53; 159 C-53D; 17 C-117A, grand total of 10,048 in USA, plus additional production in Soviet Union (about 2,000 as Li-2) and Japan.

Notes: The C-47 Skytrain, C-53 Skytrooper and Dakota (RAF name for C-47) were all variants of the Douglas DC-3, itself one of the best-known and widely-used of piston-engined civil transports, and became the most widely known and used of any World War II aircraft. The USAF and USN continued to use special-purpose variants until the late 'seventies, new rôles having been found for the C-47 during the Vietnam war, particularly as a heavily-armed gunship (the AC-47D) and for electronic reconnaissance (the EC-47P and EC-47Q). The AC-47 gunship, or weapons platform, which also served with the air forces of South Vietnam, Cambodia, Laos and Thailand, was intended to provide suppressive fire from three 7,62-mm Miniguns fired from side positions. Among the final variants serving with the US Navy were the ski-equipped LC-47H for use in the Antarctic and the C-117D, similar to the commercial Super DC-3 with uprated engines and revised, more angular, wing and tail outlines. Numerous air forces continue to operate C-47 variants in the 'eighties for transport, training and special duties, and although total numbers decline steadily with the introduction of new types, statistics indicate that in 1982, the DC-3 was still being used by more military air arms (at least 60) than any other single type of aircraft. A Soviet licence-built version, the Li-2, remains in service in small numbers with the Soviet Air Force.

DOUGLAS C-54 SKYMASTER

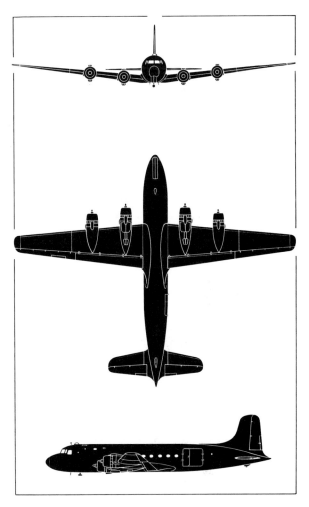

(Top) One of the five DC-4S (ex-South African Airways aircraft) in service with No 44 Squadron, SAAF, in full camouflage finish; (immediately above) a DC-4 of the Ethiopian Air Force and (below) a similar aircraft used by the Mexican Air Force. (Silhouette) Douglas C-54 Skymaster.

Country of Origin: USA.

Type: Medium-range transport.

Power Plant: Four Pratt & Whitney R-2000-7 or -11 radials of 1,350 hp or (C-54G, S and T) R-2000-9 radials of 1,450 hp.

Performance: (C-54D) Max speed, 274 mph (441 km/h) at 14,000 ft (4 267 m); cruising speed, 239 mph (385 km/h) at 15,000 ft (4 572 m); max range, 3,900 mls (6 276 km).

Weights: Empty, 38,200 lb (17 327 kg); normal take-off, 62,000 lb (28 123 kg); max overload, 73,000 lb (33 112 kg).

Dimensions: Span, 117 ft 6 in (35,81 m); length, 93 ft 11 in (28,63 m); height, 27 ft 6¼ in (8,38 m); wing area, 1,463 sq ft (135,91 m²).

Accommodation: Flight crew of five and up to 50 equipped troops or freight load of 32,000 lb (14 515 kg).

Status: First flown 26 March 1942, deliveries to US Army Air Force began December 1942. Production totals: 24 C-54; 207 C-54A; 220 C-54B; 350 C-54D; 75 C-54E; 76 C-54G and 211 R5D variants for US Navy.

Notes: Douglas built a single DC-4E commercial transport prototype, but test flying which began on 21 June 1938 did not lead to large-scale commercial acceptance. Instead, a scaled-down DC-4A was projected, and a production batch of 24 was laid down in 1940 against airline orders. This entire batch was commandeered by the US Army Air Force early in 1942, before the first had flown, and with the designation C-54, these aircraft became the first equipment for Air Transport Command, set up in December 1942 to ferry men and supplies around the world. Subsequent production versions were designated up to C-54G except C-54C, which was a modified C-54A used as a VIP transport by President Roosevelt and known as the "Sacred Cow". Post-war variants and redesignation of US Navy Skymasters led to designations up to C-54M being applied to US service variants of the C-54. A number of examples remain in use with foreign air forces, among the most recent users of the DC-4/C-54 being the air arms of Argentina, Bolivia, the Central African Republic, Chad, Colombia, Ethiopia, France, Honduras, South Korea, Mauritania, Mexico, Paraguay, Peru, Salvador, South Africa, and Zaire. Of these users, the South African Air Force was in 1981 one of those most dependent upon the C-54s, of which five were still serving with No 44 Squadron (in full operational camouflage) alongside DC-3/C-47 Dakotas based at Waterkloof. The ex-civil DC-4s in the inventory of the French *Aéronavale* were equipped for search-and-rescue duty and operated with *Escadrille* 9S from Tontouta in New Caledonia.

(Above and immediately below) Two views of a Douglas C-118B, US Navy version of the commercial DC-6A still serving in 1982; (bottom) a DC-6 operated by the Niger Air Force. (Silhouette) Douglas DC-6A.

Country of Origin: USA.

Type: Medium-long-range transport.

Power Plant: Four 2,500 hp (with water injection) Pratt & Whitney R-2800-52W radial engines.

Performance: (C-118B at max weight) Max speed, 342 mph (550 km/h) at 16,700 ft (5 090 m); average cruising speed, 246 mph (396 km/h) at 10,000 ft (3 050 m); initial rate of climb, 870 ft/min (4,42 m/sec); time to 10,000 ft (3 050 m), 12·9 min; time to 20,000 ft (6 100 m), 40 min; service ceiling, 19,900 ft (6 066 m); range with max payload, 2,300 mls (3 700 km); range with max fuel and 21,000 lb (9 526 kg) payload, 3,820 mls (6 150 km).

Weights: Empty equipped, 56,505 lb (25 630 kg); max payload, 31,610 lb (14 338 kg); max take-off, 112,000 lb (50 803 kg).

Dimensions: Span, 117 ft 6 in (35,81 m); length, 107 ft 0 in (31,61 m); height, 28 ft 8 in (8,74 m); wing area, 1,463 sq ft (135,92 m²).

Accommodation: Flight crew of five (two pilots, flight engineer, navigator, radio operator) and 79 troop seats, or 60 stretchers with six attendants, or up to 76 passengers.

Status: DC-6 prototype (XC-112A) first flown on 15 February 1946; first DC-6 (commercial) flown 29 June 1946; first DC-6A

(commercial) delivered 7 March 1951; first C-118B (R6D-1) flown August 1951 and delivered on 7 September 1951; last military C-118 delivery 23 January 1956; prototype DC-7 flown October 1954. Production totals: XC-112A, 1; VC-118, 1; C-118A, 101; R6D-1/C-118B, 65; commercial DC-6, 174; DC-6A, 74; DC-6B, 288; DC-7, 105; DC-7B, 112; DC-7C, 121, final delivery 10 December 1958.

Notes: The C-118 designation applied originally to USAF versions of the commercial Douglas DC-6, purchased in quantity for service as personnel and logistic transports with MATS. The US Navy purchased similar aircraft as R6D-1s and after transferring 40 of its fleet to the USAF, retained the survivors with the designation C-118B. In 1982, these elderly transports were still serving in four of the nine US Fleet Support Squadrons manned by Naval Reserve personnel, their replacement being dependent upon funding of additional C-9A Skytrain II jet transports as used by four of the other VR squadrons. None of the USAF C-118s remain operational but DC-6, DC-6A and DC-6B variants are still flying with several other air forces (the DC-6 having a shorter fuselage and the DC-6B lacking the freight doors and floor of the DC-6A). The DC-7 was generally similar to, but larger than, the DC-6; few remain in military use.

EMBRAER EMB-110 BANDEIRANTE

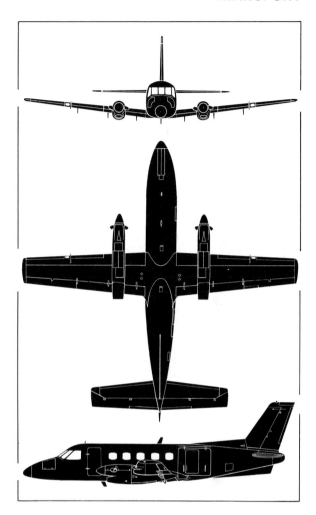

(Top) An EMBRAER EMB-110K1 supplied to the Forces Aeriennes Gabonaises; (immediately above) the EC-95 version of the Bandeirante; (below) a C-95A of the Força Aeréa Brasileira showing the cargo loading door. (Silhouette) EMBRAER EMB-110K1 Bandeirante.

Country of Origin: Brazil.

Type: General purpose light transport.

Power Plant: Two (C-95) 680 shp Pratt & Whitney (Canada) PT6A-27 or (C-95A) 750 shp PT6A-34 turboprops.

Performance: (C-95) Max cruising speed, 260 mph (418 km/h) at 9,840 ft (3 000 m); initial rate of climb, 1,968 ft/min (10 m/sec); service ceiling, 27,950 ft (8 520 m); max range, 1,150 mls (1 850 km) with 30 min reserves.

Weights: (C-95) Empty equipped, 6,437 lb (2 920 kg); max payload, 4,850 lb (2 200 kg); max take-off, 11,243 lb (5 100 kg); max landing, 10,692 lb (4 850 kg).

Dimensions: Span, 50 ft $3\frac{1}{4}$ in (15,30 m); length (C-95), 46 ft $8\frac{1}{4}$ in (14,22 m); length (C-95A), 49 ft $6\frac{1}{2}$ in (15,10 m); height, 16 ft 2 in (4,92 m); wing area 313·2 sq ft (29,1 m²).

Accommodation: Two pilots on flight deck and 6-12 seats in cabin; provision for four stretchers and two seats.

Status: Three EMB-100 (YC-95) prototypes flown on 26 October 1968, 19 October 1969 and 26 June 1970 respectively. First EMB-110 (C-95) production model flown on 9 August 1972. Deliveries began in late 1973. Production and orders: EMB-110 prototypes, 3; C-95, 60; EC-95, 4; RC-95, 6; C-95A, 40; EMB-110(N), 3 (Chile); EMB-110C, 5 (Uruguay); EMB-110K1, 2 (Gabon); EMB-110P1, 1

(Gabon).

Notes: Development of the Bandeirante began under the design leadership of the well-known French designer Max Holste at the PAR-*Departmento de Aeronaves* of the *Centro Tecnico Aeroespacial*, the original designation being IPD/PAR-6504. Following creation of the state-sponsored EMBRAER organisation in August 1969, the Bandeirante became an EMBRAER responsibility and a production contract was placed by the Brazilian Air Force (*Força Aérea Brasileira*) which designates the aircraft C-95 as a transport, able to accommodate up to 12 passengers or four stretchers with two medical attendants. Subsequent development produced several other versions, of which the principal is the EMB-110K1, designated C-95A by the FAB, which has ordered 40. This differs from the original C-95 in having a lengthened fuselage, uprated engines and an enlarged cargo door in the rear fuselage. The FAB also ordered a version of the Bandeirante for radio and navaid calibration, designated EC-95, and another variant with cameras and other special equipment to serve as the RC-95 in the aerial survey rôle. Military versions of the Bandeirante have been exported to Chile (three transports for Naval Aviation); Uruguay (five transports for the air force) and the Gabon (two transports for the air force and one for service with the Presidential Guards).

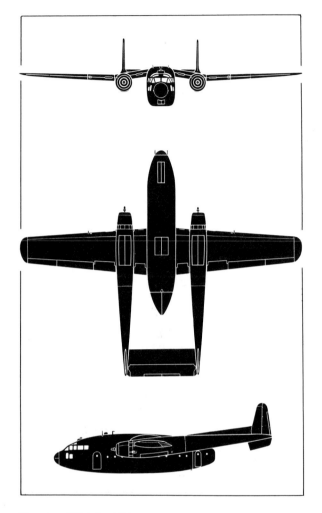

(Above) A Fairchild C-119G of the Chinese Nationalist Air Force; (immediately below) a C-119K, with wing-mounted jet boosters, of the Ethiopian Air Force; (bottom) an Indian Air Force C-119G with dorsal jet-boost engine. (Silhouette) Fairchild C-119G.

Country of Origin: USA.

Type: Medium-range tactical cargo and troop transport.

Power Plant: Two Wright R-3350-85 or 89A radials of 2,500 hp each or (C-119K) R-3350-999-TC18EA2 radials of 3,700 hp each with water injection and (Indian AF C-119 only) one HAL-built 4,700 lb st (2 132 kgp) Orpheus 701 booster turbojet or 3,400 lb st (1 542 kgp) Westinghouse J34 booster turbojet in dorsal pod.

Performance: (C-119K); Max speed, 243 mph (391 km/h) at 10,000 ft (3 050 m); max cruising speed, 187 mph (300 km/h) at 10,000 ft (3 050 m); initial rate of climb (one engine out), 1,050 ft/min (5,3 m/sec); range with max payload 900 mls (1 595 km); ferry range 3,460 mls (5 570 km).

Weights: (C-119K); Empty, 44,747 lb (20 300 kg); max payload, 20,000 lb (9 070 kg); max take-off and landing, 77,000 lb (34 925 kg).

Dimensions: Span, 109 ft 3 in (34,29 m); length, 86 ft 6 in (26,36 m); height, 26 ft 6 in (8,07 m); wing area, 1,447 sq ft (134,43 m²).

Accommodation: Flight crew of four (two pilots, navigator and radio operator) plus loadmaster or jumpmaster and up to 62 fully-equipped troops or assorted items of cargo.

Status: First prototype (C-119A) flown in November 1947. Deliveries began December 1949. Production totalled 1,051, including 88 for Italy, India and Belgium and remainder for USAF/USN.

Notes: The C-119 Flying Boxcar was developed from the C-82 Packet and is sometimes referred to as the Packet also. Production variants were C-119B with R-4360-20 engines, C-119C with -20WA water injection engines, C-119F with -85 engines and 85,000 lb (38 555 kg) overload weight and C-119G, which was similar with Aeroproducts propellers. Later modification programmes produced the AC-119G gunship with four 7,62-mm miniguns in the fuselage, and the C-119K (unarmed) and AC-119K (armed) with underwing pods containing two 2,850 lb st (1 293 kgp) J85-GE-17 turbojets. The C-119 is no longer in service in the USAF or ANG; of the foreign air forces that received C-119s, the Indian Air Force was the principal user in 1982, with some 40 aircraft equipping Nos 12, 19 and 48 Squadrons. About half of these have been modified to have fuselage-top jet pods to boost performance in mountainous regions, the engine being either the Westinghouse J34 or Bristol Siddeley Orpheus. Other C-119s were still serving in small quantities in Ethiopia and Nationalist China.

FAIRCHILD C-123 PROVIDER

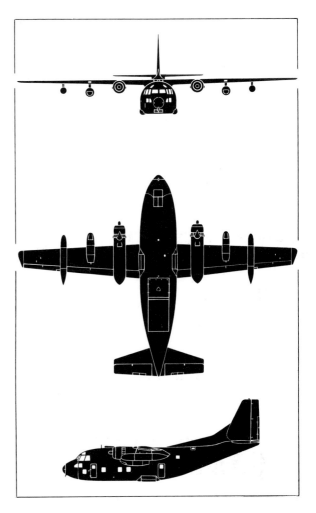

(Top) A fairchild C-123K with underwing jet pods and drop tanks, serving with the US Air Force Reserve; (immediately above) a C-123 of the Royal Thai Air Force; (below) the prototype Mancro C-123T, with Allison T56 turboprops. (Silhouette) Fairchild C-123K Provider.

Country of Origin: USA.

Type: Medium tactical assault transport.

Power Plant: Two 2,500 hp Pratt & Whitney R-2800-99W radials plus (C-123J) two 1,000 lb st (454 kgp) Fairchild J44-R-3 booster turbojets or (C-123K) two 2,850 lb st (1 293 kgp) General Electric J85-GE-17 booster turbojets.

Performance: (C-123K) Max level speed, 228 mph (367 km/h); max cruising speed, 173 mph (278 km/h); initial rate of climb (one engine out) 1,220 ft/min (6,2 m/sec); service ceiling (one engine out) 21,100 ft (6 430 m).

Weights: (C-123K) Empty, 35,366 lb (16 042 kg); basic operating 36,576 lb (16 590 kg); max payload, 15,000 lb (6 800 kg); max take-off and landing, 60,000 lb (27 215 kg).

Dimensions: Span, 110 ft 0 in (33,53 m); length, 76 ft 3 in (23,93 m); height, 34 ft 1 in (10,63 m); wing area, 1,223 sq ft (113,62 m²).

Accommodation: Flight crew of two and up to 60 equipped troops or 50 stretchers plus four seats or miscellaneous cargo loads.

Status: First flown (as XC-123 Avitruc) on 14 October 1949; first Fairchild-built C-123B flown on 1 September 1954; first C-123K flown on 27 May 1966. Production total, five by Chase and 302 by Fairchild.

Notes: The Provider originated in 1949 as an all-metal troop and cargo glider developed by Chase Aircraft and designated XG-20. One of two prototypes was fitted with two R-2800-83 engines in wing nacelles and tested as an assault transport, leading to a USAF production order for 300, placed with the Kaiser-Frazer Corporation, plus five pre-production models to be built by Chase. Fairchild took over the K-F commitment and built 302 C-123Bs between 1954 and 1958. Of this total, 24 were for MAP delivery to Venezuela and Saudi Arabia, and subsequently the USAF transferred some of its C-123s to the air forces of Thailand and Vietnam. Later conversion programmes produced 10 C-123Hs with jet pods at the wing tips, and the C-123K with underwing jet pods (specification above). Between 1966 and September 1968, 183 C-123Bs were converted to C-123Ks, primarily for service in Vietnam. In 1981, the USAF inventory included 52 C-123Ks flown by four AF Reserve squadrons, but this total was to be reduced to 18 by 1982. Two squadrons of the Philippine Air Force operate C-123Ks, some of which were ex-VNAF aircraft; the Chinese Nationalist Air Force has about 10 and the largest user is the Thai Air Force with some 40 in service. A C-123T conversion with Allison T56 turboprops was developed in 1981 by Mancro.

(Above) Fokker F27 Mk 600 in service with the Nigerian Air Force; (immediately below) a radar-equipped F27 Maritime of the Philippine Air Force and (bottom) a ground view of one of the Angolan Air Forces F27 Mk 400 transports. (Silhouette) Fokker F27 Maritime.

Country of Origin: Netherlands.

Type: Tactical transport and maritime surveillance.

Power Plant: (Maritime) Two 2,370 eshp with water methanol injection and 2,020 eshp dry Rolls-Royce Dart RDa7 Mk 536-7R turboprops.

Performance: (Maritime) Max speed 295 mph (474 km/h) at 20,000 ft (6 100 m); cruising speed at 38,000 lb (17 235 kg) weight, 288 mph (463 km/h) at 20,000 ft (6 100 m); typical search speed, 167-201 mph (269-324 km/h) at 2,000 ft (610 m); service ceiling, 25,000 ft (7 620 m); time to climb to 20,000 ft (6 100 m) at normal weight, 27 min; max range, with 30-min loiter and 5 per cent flight fuel reserve, 3,110 mls (5 000 km) at 23,000-25,000 ft (7 010-7 620 m); time on station (high-altitude transit to and from base, loiter at 2,000 ft/610 m at 184 mph/296 km/h), 8 hrs at 230 mls (370 km), 6 hrs at 460 mls (740 km), 4 hrs at 748 mls (1 204 km).

Weights: (Maritime) Manufacturer's weight empty, 27,600 lb (12 519 kg); operational equipped weight 29,352 lb (13 314 kg); normal take-off weight, 45,000 lb (20 412 kg); max overload weight, 47,500 lb (21 546 kg).

Dimensions: Span, 95 ft 2 in (29,00 m); length, 77 ft 3½ in (23,56 m); height, 28 ft 6½ in (8,70 m); wing area, 754 sq ft (70,00 m²).

Accommodation: Flight crew of two with third seat on flight deck for observer or engineer. Typical cabin crew for maritime surveillance comprises two observers, radar operator and tactical commander/navigator. Troopship accommodates up to 46 paratroops, or 24 stretchers with nine attendants.

Status: F27 prototypes flown 24 November 1955 (Dart 507, short fuselage) and 29 January 1957. First production Mk 100 flown on 23 March 1958; first Mk 200 flown 20 September 1959; first Maritime (Mk 100 conversion) flown on 28 February 1976; first production Maritime flown 14 June 1977. Production totals, approximately 526 by Fokker by beginning of 1982 and continuing (plus 206 by Fairchild, complete), including 11 Maritime and approximately 115 transports for military operators.

Notes: Fokker F27 has been one of the most successful post-war commercial transports. Major military version is the Mk 400M, sometimes known as the Troopship, but some air forces also acquired basic civil variants, for VIP use. The Maritime, with search radar and other special features for maritime surveillance, has been ordered by the Peruvian Navy (2); Spanish Air Force (3); Angola (1); Philippine Air Force (3) and the Dutch *Koninklijke Luchtmacht* (2).

(Top and immediately above) Air and ground views of the prototype FMA IA 50 known at first as the Guarani II; (below) a production model IA 50 with tip tanks, serving with the I Brigade Aerea of the FAA. (Silhouette) FMA IA 50.

Country of Origin: Argentina.

Type: General purpose transport.

Power Plant: Two 930 shp Turboméca Bastan VIA turboprops.

Performance: Max speed, 310 mph (500 km/h); high speed cruise 305 mph (491 km/h); long range cruise, 280 mph (450 km/h); initial rate of climb, 2,640 ft/min (13,4 m/sec); service ceiling, 41,000 ft (12 500 m); range with max payload, 1,240 mls (1,995 km); range with max fuel, 1,600 mls (2 575 km).

Weights: Empty equipped, 8,650 lb (3 924 kg); max payload, 3,307 lb (1 500 kg); max take-off, 16,204 lb (7 350 kg); max take-off weight (without tip tanks), 15,873 lb (7 200 kg).

Dimensions: Span 64 ft 3¼ in (19,59 m); length, 50 ft 2½ in (15,30 m); height, 18 ft 5 in (5,61 m); wing area, 450 sq ft (41,81 m²).

Accommodation: Flight crew of two; alternative layouts for 10, 12 or 15 passengers as a transport or six stretchers plus two seats, or six seats as a navigation trainer.

Armament: None.

Status: Prototype first flown on 23 April 1963. Production totals: prototypes, two; pre-production, one; production, 38, completed 1975.

Notes: Originally built as the Guarani II, the IA 50 GII was developed from a single Guarani I prototype, which was in turn a transport derivative of the IA 35 Huanquero. New features of the IA 50 Guarani II were a swept-back single fin and rudder, shorter fuselage and more powerful engines. Two prototypes (with Bastan VIA engines) were built, plus a pre-production model, before the Argentine Air Force placed an initial order for 18, a second batch of 15 being ordered later. Included in the first batch of GIIs were 14 troop transports—one being fitted with skis for operation in the Antarctic—two aerial survey aircraft and one VIP transport for the Argentine Air Force and one staff transport for the Argentine Navy. One GII was also built for the use of the President of Argentina, and four were equipped for aerial survey duties and delivered to the Military Geographic Institute. By 1982, the GII force had been reduced to about 20 aircraft, and these were being operated principally by the I *Esc de Transporte*, as part of the *Fuerza Aérea Argentina's Servicios de Transportes Aéreos Militares*, based at El Palomar. The single example supplied to the *Comando de Aviacion Naval Argentine* operated with the 5 *Escuadra* at the Ezeiza base as part of a mixed transport support force. The GII prototype was flown with wing-tip fuel tanks and this remained an optional installation for production aircraft, although seldom used.

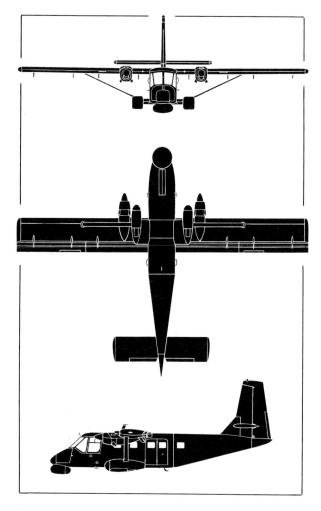

(Above) GAF N22 Missionmaster in service with the Australian Army; (immediately below) an N22 Searchmaster L demonstrator; (bottom) a Missionmaster of the Papua New Guinea Defence Force. (Silhouette) GAF Searchmaster L.

Country of Origin: Australia.

Type: STOL utility transport and maritime surveillance aircraft.

Power Plant: Two 400 ehp Allison 250-B17B turboprops.

Performance: (N22B Missionmaster) Max cruising speed, 193 mph (311 km/h); initial rate of climb, 1,460 ft/min (742 m/sec); service ceiling, 21,000 ft (6 400 m); max range, 668 mls (1 074 km) at sea level, 840 mls (1 352 km) at 10,000 ft (3 050 m).

Weights: Typical operating empty, 4,741 lb (2 150 kg); max payload, 3,110 lb (1 410 kg); max take-off and landing, 8,500 lb (3 855 kg).

Dimensions: Span, 54 ft 1¼ in (16,52 m); length 41 ft 2½ in (12,56 m); height 18 ft 1½ in (5,52 m); wing area, 324 sq ft (30,10 m²).

Accommodation: Flight crew of one or two and up to 12 troops, or miscellaneous freight.

Armament: Missionmaster and Searchmaster have four wing hardpoints to carry up to 500 lb (227 kg) each.

Status: First and second prototypes flown on 23 July and 5 December 1971 respectively. Production total by early 1982, 145 (military and civil) plus next batch of 55 approved for future manufacture. Military sales include: Australian Army, 11 Mission-

master; Indonesian Navy, 16 Searchmaster B and 2 Searchmaster L; Philippine Air Force, 12 Missionmaster; Papua New Guinea Defense Force, 7 Missionmaster; Royal Thai Air Force, 20 Missionmaster.

Notes: Design of the Nomad began in 1965 (as the Project N) to provide the indigenous Australian aircraft industry with a project having export potential in military and civil markets. The prototypes were to basic N22 configuration but most production aircraft since 1974 have been to the N22B standard, with increased gross weight. The GAF also subsequently developed the N24, which has a lengthened fuselage to seat up to 17 passengers and is produced primarily for the commercial market. The military variants are marketed under the variant names Missionmaster and Search-master, the former being a utility transport with wing hardpoints, load-bearing supply-drop doors in the cabin floor, self-sealing fuel cells and military avionics, while the latter is equipped for maritime surveillance and coastal patrol duties. Two standards of equipment are available for the Searchmaster, the 'B' model having Bendix RDR-1400 search radar in a radome in the nose and the Searchmaster 'L' carrying Litton APS-504(V)2 radar with a 360-deg scan aerial in a radome under the nose, together with more sophisticated avionics and navaids.

(Top) A Grumman C-2A Greyhound of fleet tactical transport squadron VR-24 comes aboard the USS "Independence" on a carrier on-board delivery (COD) mission; (immediately above) a C-2A of VRC-50 based in Japan and (below) one of VR-24's Greyhounds in Malta. (Silhouette) Grumman C-2A Greyhound.

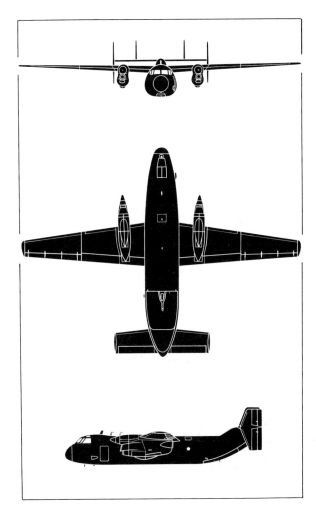

Country of Origin: USA.

Type: Carrier On-board Delivery (COD) transport.

Power Plant: Two Allison T56-A-8A turboprops each rated at 4,050 shp for take-off.

Performance: Maximum speed, 352 mph (567 km/h) at optimum altitude; cruising speed for best range, 297 mph (477 km/h) at 30,000 ft (9 145 m); initial rate of climb, 2,330 ft/min (11,8 m/sec); service ceiling, 28,800 ft; mission range, 1,650 mls (2 658 km) cruising at 297 mph (477 km/h) at 26,200-32,100 ft (7 986-9 784 m) altitude.

Weights: Empty, 31,250 lb (14 175 kg); fuel, 12,400 lb (5 625 kg); normal gross weight, 54,382 lb (24 668 kg).

Dimensions: Span, 80 ft 7 in (24,56 m); span (wings folded), 29 ft 4 in (8,94 m); length, 56 ft 7½ in (17,26 m); height, 15 ft 11 in (4,85 m); wing area, 700 sq ft (65,03 m²).

Accommodation: Flight crew of two with dual controls. Up to 39 passengers or 20 stretchers or up to 10,000 lb (4 540 kg) of cargo.

Armament: None.

Status: First of two YC-2A prototypes (converted E-2As) flown on 18 November 1964. Production deliveries began early 1966 and last of the production batch of 17 delivered in 1968, all for US Navy. Production of 39 more resumed 1982.

Notes: The US Navy has had a requirement for Carrier On-board Delivery (COD) aircraft since World War II, in order to deliver personnel and supplies to its ships at sea. The requirement is met by a mix of helicopters (for VOD, or Vertical On-board Delivery, to ships other than carriers) and fixed-wing transports for the aircraft carriers. With the exception of a single Lockheed US-3A Viking in service in 1981, when two more were under conversion, the COD types used since WWII have been Grumman combat types modified for the role—successively the Avenger, the Tracker and the Hawkeye. The C-2A Greyhound was derived from the Hawkeye by combining a new fuselage with the existing wings, power plant and tail unit (the tailplane, however, having no dihedral). Operated by US Navy squadrons VRC-50 (based at Cubi Point in the Philippines) and VR-24 (based at Sigonella, Sicily), the 12 surviving C-2As of 19 built (including two EC-2A conversions) are undergoing a Service Life Programme (SLEP) at the rate of two a year since 1978, and in-flight refuelling capability was being added from 1980 onwards. The US Navy had an outstanding requirement for more COD aircraft in the 'eighties, and production of the Greyhound was resumed in 1982 to deliver 39 more C-2As between 1985 and 1989.

(Above) An Arava 201 for service with the Salvadorean Air Force; (immediately below) one of the 10 Arava 201s supplied to the Mexican Air Force; (bottom) an Arava 201 used by the Heyl Ha'Avir as an ambulance. (Silhouette) IAI Arava 201.

Country of Origin: Israel.

Type: General purpose STOL transport and gunship.

Power Plant: Two 750 shp Pratt & Whitney PT6A-34 turboprops.

Performance: Max speed, 203 mph (326 km/h) at 10,000 ft (3 050 m); high-speed cruise, 198 mph (319 km/h); long-range cruise, 193 mph (311 km/h); initial rate of climb, 1,290 ft/min (393 m/sec); service ceiling, 25,000 ft (7 620 m); range with max payload, 174 mls (280 km); max range, 808 mls (1 300 km).

Weights: Empty equipped (paratrooper), 8,816 lb (3 999 kg); max payload, 5,184 lb (2 351 kg); max take-off and landing, 15,000 lb (6 803 kg).

Dimensions: Span, 68 ft 9 in (20,96 m); length, 42 ft 9 in (13,03 m); height, 17 ft 1 in (5,21 m); wing area, 470·2 sq ft (43,68 m²).

Accommodation: Flight crew of one or two plus 24 fully-equipped troops or 17 paratroops and one jumpmaster, or eight stretchers plus three seats.

Armament: One 0·5-in (12·7-mm) machine gun can be mounted on each side of fuselage with 250 rpg and provision for single aft-firing 0·5-in (12·7-mm) gun in flexible mount in the rear fuselage. Two hard-points on fuselage with 600-lb (272-kg) capacity each.

Status: Prototype IAI-101s first flown on 27 November 1970

and 8 May 1971; prototype IAI-201 military variant flown 7 March 1972. Production/sales total, over 80 by 1982 including Israeli Air Force, 14; Bolivian Air Force, 6; Colombian Air Force, 3; Ecuadorean Army, 6; Ecuadorean Navy, 3; Guatemalan Air Force, 10; Honduran Air Force, 3; Mexican Air Force, 10; Nicaraguan Air Force, 2; Salvadorean Air Force, 5; Venezuelan National Guard, 4; Swaziland Defence Force, 2, and civil 101B and 102.

Notes: Development of the Arava began in 1966 as the first wholly indigenous product of Israel Aircraft Industries, and in the IAI-101 version was intended primarily as a civil light transport with STOL and rough field capability. Work on the civil variant was suspended on 1972 after prototypes had been tested, to allow IAI to concentrate on development and production of the IAI-201 for the Israeli Air Force and foreign military users. One of the initial Arava prototypes was completed to IAI-201 standard as described above and 15 were on order by October 1973, when the Israeli Air Force operated three during the Yom Kippur war. The Arava versions for civil use are the IAI-101B and IAI-102 and the military model is the IAI-201. A prototype IAI-202 has also been flown, with a lengthened fuselage, a fully "wet" wing and endplate winglets. The IAI-202 has PT6A-36 engines, as also has the IAI-101B, known in the USA as the Cargo Commuterliner.

ILYUSHIN IL-76 (CANDID)

(Top) An Il-76M with, despite Aeroflot insignia, standard tail gun position, (immediately above) an Il-76 with faired tail position and (below) an Il-76T which operates at higher weights. (Silhouette) The standard production Il-76 Candid for the Soviet Air Force.

Country of Origin: Soviet Union.

Type: Heavy duty medium- to long-range freighter and troop transport.

Power Plant: Four 26,455 lb st (12 000 kgp) Soloviev D-30KP turbofans.

Performance: Max speed, 528 mph (850 km/h) at 32,810 ft (10 000 m); max cruise, 497 mph (800 km/h) at 29,500–42,650 ft (9 000–13 000 m); range cruise, 466 mph (750 km/h); range (max payload, 88,185 lb/40 000 kg), 3,290 mls (5 300 km), (max fuel and reserves), 4,163 mls (6 700 km).

Weights: Max take-off, 374,790 lb (170 000 kg).

Dimensions: Span, 165 ft 8⅓ in (50,50 m); length, 152 ft 10¼ in (46,59 m); height, 48 ft 5½ in (14,76 m); wing area, 3,229·2 sq ft (300,00 m²).

Accommodation: Normal flight crew of four with navigator below flight deck in glazed nose. Pressurised hold for container-ised freight, wheeled or tracked vehicles, self-propelled anti-aircraft guns (e.g., one radar-controlled ZSU-57-2 twin-gun with seven-man crew, or two ZSU-23-4 quad-guns with four-man crews), or mobile surface-to-air missile systems (e.g., SA-8 Gecko- or SA-9 Gaskin-equipped vehicles). Troop capacity: 140.

Armament: Twin 23-mm cannon in tail barbette.

Status: First of four prototypes flown on 25 March 1971, with production deliveries to Soviet Air Force commencing in 1974. The air transport component of the Soviet Air Force had received 130–140 Il-76s by the beginning of 1982, when production was running at 30–35 aircraft annually. Small numbers have been supplied to Iraq, Libya and Syria for dual military/civil tasks, and during the course of 1981, the Il-76 was selected by the Indian Air Force as a replacement for the An-12. Deliveries to the Czecho-slovak and Polish air forces were anticipated in 1982.

Notes: The Il-76 is being manufactured in both military and commercial versions, the current military variant being equivalent to the Il-76T which introduced increased fuel capacity and higher take-off weights than the initial production model. A flight-refuelling tanker version of the Il-76 is expected to attain operational capability with the Soviet Air Force in the mid 'eighties, together with an AWACS (airborne warning and control system) version which will markedly extend overwater and overland detection and inteceptor control capability. The AWACS version reportedly features a lengthened forward fuselage and a 'saucer'-type rotating radar antenna. US intelligence sources anticipate that some 50 AWACS Il-76s will have achieved operational status in the mid 'eighties.

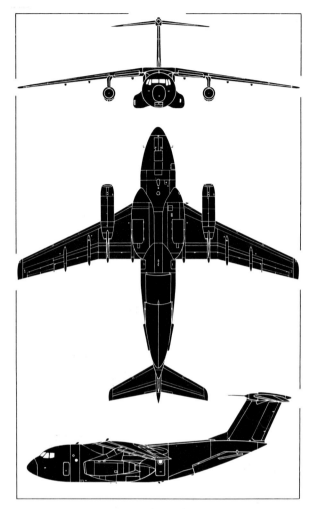

(Above) The second prototype C-1A displaying the air-openable rear door for paradropping; (immediately below and bottom) two views of C-1As in the three-colour camouflage adopted by the JASDF in 1979. (Silhouette) Kawasaki C-1A.

Country of Origin: Japan.

Type: Medium-range transport.

Power Plant: Two 14,500 lb st (6 575 kg) Pratt & Whitney JT8D-M-9 turbofans.

Performance: Max level speed, 500 mph (806 km/h) at 25,000 (7 620 m); long-range cruise, 408 mph (657 km/h); initial rate of climb, 3,500 ft/min (17,8 m/sec); service ceiling, 38,000 ft (11 580 m); range with 17,416-lb (7 900-kg) payload, 807 mls (1 300 km); range with max fuel, 2,050 mls (3 300 km) with payload of 4,850-lb (2 200 kg).

Weights: Empty equipped, 53,572 lb (24 300 kg); max payload, 26,235 lb (11 900 kg); normal take-off, 85,320 lb (38 700 kg); max take-off, 99,210 lb (45 000 kg).

Dimensions: Span, 100 ft 4¾ in (30,60 m); length, 95 ft 1¾ in (29,00 m); height, 32 ft 9¼ in (9,99 m); wing area, 1,297 sq ft (120,5 m²).

Accommodation: Flight crew of four (two pilots, navigator and flight engineer) and loadmaster. Up to 60 equipped troops, 45 paratroops or 36 stretchers plus attendants, or miscellaneous freight on three pallets or loaded individually.

Status: First and second prototypes flown, respectively, on 12 November 1970 and 16 January 1971 and delivered February/ March 1971. Two pre-production C-1As ordered, with first flown 19 September 1973 and both delivered for operational evaluation by February 1974. Total of 27 production C-1As ordered by JASDF, with deliveries starting in December 1974 and completed in October 1981.

Notes: The C-1A was developed to provide the JASDF with a replacement for its aged Curtiss C-46s, which still provided the bulk of Japan's airlift capability in the early 'seventies. Initial design work on the new transport, which was Japan's first large jet-powered design, began in 1966 and was handled by NAMC, an industry consortium that had been responsible for designing and producing the YS-11. NAMC completed a mock-up but the two prototypes, under the designation XC-1A, were assembled by Kawasaki, which later assumed overall responsibility for the design. The last five of the 27 production-model C-1As have additional tankage in the wing centre section for increased range. One of the C-1As was to be used, starting in 1982, as a test-bed for the XF-3 turbofan, and in 1983, the National Aerospace Laboratory is expected to start flight-testing its QSTOL (Quiet-STOL) research aircraft which utilises a C-1 airframe modified to have four FJR-710-600 turbofans and an upper-surface blowing (USB) high lift system.

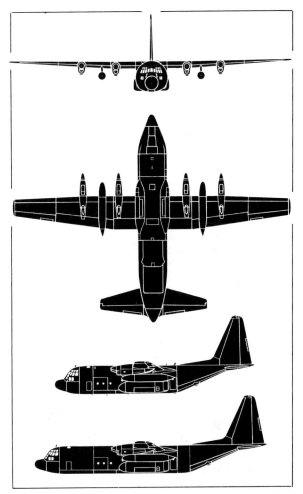

(Top) Lockheed C-130H maritime patrol Hercules of the Malaysian Air Force; (immediately above) an Air National Guard C-130 with combination wheel/ski undercarriage for Arctic operations; (below) Hercules C Mk 3. (Silhouette) C-130H three-view with side view of L-100-30.

Country of Origin: USA.

Type: Medium/long-range military transport.

Power Plant: Four (C-130A, D) 3,750 eshp Allison T56-A-9 or (C-130B, E) 4,050 eshp T56-A-7 or (C-130H, K, P) 4,508 eshp flat-rated T56-A-15 or (C-130F, R) T56-A-16 turboprops.

Performance: (C-130H) Max cruising speed, 386 mph (621 km/h); economical cruise, 345 mph (556 km/h); initial rate of climb, 1,900 ft/min (9,65 m/sec); service ceiling, 33,000 ft (10 060 m); range with max payload, internal fuel only, 2,487 mls (4 002 km); range with external tanks and 20,000-lb (9 070-kg) payload, 4,600 mls (7 410 km).

Weights: (C-130H) Operating weight empty, 75,832 lb (34 397 kg); max payload, 43,310 lb (19 645 kg); normal take-off, 155,000 lb (70 310 kg); max overload, 175,000 kg (79 380 kg).

Dimensions: Span, 132 ft 7 in (40,41 m); length (C-130E, H) 97 ft 9 in (29,79 m), (HC-130H, recovery booms extended), 108 ft 1½ in (32,95 m), (Hercules C Mk 3/C-130H-30), 112 ft 9 in (34,37 m); height, 38 ft 3 in (11,66 m); wing area, 1,745 sq ft (162,12 m²).

Accommodation: Flight crew of four (two pilots, navigator and systems manager) and provision for loadmaster; maximum provision for 92 equipped troops, 64 paratroops or 74 stretchers.

Status: First of two YC-130 prototypes flown 23 August 1954; first production C-130A flown 7 April 1975, first delivery to USAF 9 December 1956; first ski-equipped C-130 (prototype C-130D) flown 29 January 1957; first C-130B flown 10 December 1958, deliveries began 12 June 1959; NC-130B/BLC flown 8 February 1960; first C-130E flown 25 August 1961, deliveries began 6 April 1962; first HC-130H flown 8 December 1964, deliveries began July 1965; first C-130K (C Mk 1) flown 19 October 1966, deliveries began 16 December 1966; Hercules W Mk 2 flown 21 March 1973; first Hercules C Mk 3 conversion (in USA) flown 3 December 1979. Production totals include YC-130, 2; C-130A, 204; RC-130A, 15; C-130B, 132; C-130E, 389; C-130H, over 150, all for USAF and C-130F, 7 for US Navy, plus special-purpose variants (separately described) and exported transports and other variants. Total sales by end-1981, over 1,650 for 51 nations inclusive of 80 commercial Hercules models.

Notes: Lockheed C-130 Hercules is most widely-used tactical transport produced since World War II, serving many air arms in a variety of roles. Majority of transports are C-130E or C-130H, latter with more powerful engines; USAF C-130Ds are ski-equipped versions, for Arctic service, of original C-130A with lower operating weights. Of 66 Hercules C Mk 1 acquired by RAF, 30 are undergoing a 15-ft (4,6-m) stretch to become C Mk 3s.

(Above) Lockheed VC-140B JetStar and (immediately below) a C-140B converted to VC-140B standard, both operated in Europe by the 58th Military Airlift Squadron; (bottom) a JetStar serving with the Saudi Arabian Air Force VIP Flight. (Silhouette) Lockheed C-140 JetStar.

Country of Origin: USA.

Type: VIP transport, and airways inspection.

Powered by: Four 3,000 lb st (1 360 kgp) Pratt & Whitney J60-P-5 turbojets.

Performance: Max speed, 573 mph (922 km/h) at 22,500 ft (6 858 m); cruising speeds, 498 mph (802 km/h) at 33,700 ft (10 270 m); 526 mph (847 km/h) at 41,500 ft (12 650 m); initial rate of climb, 4,750 ft/min (24,1 m/sec); time to 20,000 ft (6 100 m), 6·2 min; time to 30,000 ft (9 150 m), 12·5 min; service ceiling, 36,000 ft (10 973 m); range 1,930 mls (3 100 km) at 498 mph (802 km/h) at 33,700 ft (10 270 m).

Weights: Empty equipped, 22,500 lb (10 206 kg); max take-off, 40,470 lb (18 360 kg).

Dimensions: Span, 53 ft 8½ in (16,37 m); length, 60 ft 6 in (18,44 m); height, 20 ft 6 in (6,25 m); wing area, 542·5 sq ft (50,4 m²).

Accommodation: Normal crew (C-140A) of two pilots, flight inspector, flight traffic specialist and flight mechanic or (VC-140B) two pilots and 8–13 passengers.

Status: First of two prototypes (with two 4,850 lb st/2 200 kgp Bristol Siddeley Orpheus turbojets) flown 4 September 1957. Production total, JetStar I, 162, including five C-140A and 11 C-140B/VC-140B for USAF; JetStar II, 40, completed 1979.

Notes: The JetStar was developed by the California Division of Lockheed aircraft during 1956 in response to the USAF's UCX outline specification for a utility transport that could be purchased 'off-the-shelf' following company-funded design and prototype testing. The two prototypes were each powered by a pair of Orpheus turbojets but the smaller Pratt & Whitney JT12 was selected to power the production aircraft, four of these engines being needed to provide the necessary thrust. The JetStar was put into production primarily for commercial sale, as one of the first specially-designed jet aircraft offered in the business/executive market. USAF orders, in the event, were for five C-140As to be used worldwide to check military navigation aids, six VC-140B eight-seat VIP transports and five C-140B personnel transports; the latter were subsequently converted to VC-140B standard. In 1982, four C-140As remained in service with the 1866th Facility Checking Squadron, six VC-140Bs were attached to the 89th Military Airlift Group, Special Mission, in Washington and five were in service with the 58th Military Airlift Squadron at Ramstein AFB, Germany. JetStars had also been acquired for military or governmental use in Libya, Saudi Arabia, Mexico and Indonesia.

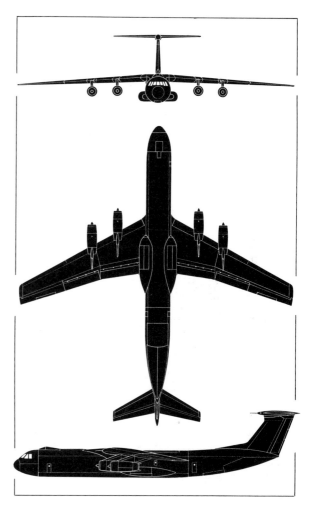

(Top) A stretched-fuselage C-141B StarLifter refuels from a KC-135; (immediately above) an unmodified C-141A about to touchdown; (below) a C-141B of the 63rd MAW. (Silhouette) Lockheed C-141B StarLifter.

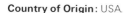

Country of Origin: USA.

Type: Long-range strategic transport.

Power Plant: Four 21,000 lb (9 525 kgp) Pratt & Whitney TF33-P-7 turbojets.

Performance: (C-141B) Max cruising speed, 566 mph (910 km/h); long-range cruise, 495 mph (797 km/h); initial rate of climb, 2,920 ft/min (14,8 m/sec); service ceiling, 41,600 ft (12 680 m); range with max payload, 2,935 mls (4 725 km); range with max fuel, 6,390 mls (10 280 km).

Weights: (C-141A) Empty equipped 133,773 lb (60 678 kg); max payload, 70 847 lb (32 136 kg); max take-off, 316,600 lb (143 600 kg); max landing, 257,500 lb (116 800 kg).

Weights: (C-141B) Empty equipped, 148,120 lb (67 186 kg); max payload, 70,605 lb (32 025 kg) for 2·5 *g* operations, 90,880 lb (41 222 kg) for 2·25 *g*; max take-off, 323,100 lb (146,555 kg) for 2·5 *g* operations, 343,000 lb (155 580 kg) for 2·25 *g*.

Dimensions: Span, 159 ft 11 in (48,74 m); length (C-141A), 145 ft 0 in (44,20 m); length (C-141B), 168 ft 3½ in (51,29 m); height, 39 ft 3 in (11,96 m); wing area, 3,228 sq ft (299,9 m²).

Accommodation: Flight crew of four and 154 equipped troops or 123 paratroops or 80 stretchers plus 16 seats, or miscellaneous freight loaded on 10 pallets or stowed individually.

Status: No prototype. First C-141A flown on 17 December 1963. Entered service October 1964. Production total 285, completed in 1968. First YC-141B ('A' conversion) flown 24 March 1977; first C-141B production conversion delivered 4 December 1979, with 271st completed May 1982.

Notes: Designed to meet a Specific Operational Requirement issued in May 1960, the C-141A StarLifter was the first jet-powered strategic freighter for the USAF, and became the mainstay of Military Airlift Command in place of interim C-135 jet transports and piston-powered C-97s and C-124s. The fuselage, including a rear-loading ramp and clam shell doors, was configured to allow the StarLifter to carry 90 per cent of all the items of air portable equipment in use with the US Army or Air Force. Dimensionally, the C-141A was able to acommodate a complete Minuteman ICBM, in container, but the 86,207 lb (39 103 kg) weight of this item was above the normal payload and a few C-141As were therefore specially modified, with beefed-up structure. The StarLifter remains the principal heavy transport of the USAF's Military Airlift Command, currently equipping a total of 14 squadrons, providing global-range airlift capability. All 271 StarLifters in the inventory have been converted to C-141Bs, featuring fuselage stretch and in-flight refuelling.

(Above) A C-5A Galaxy refuels from a KC-10A; (immediately below) a C-5A displays its multi-wheel undercarriage at take-off; (bottom) a C-5A of the 436th MAW. (Silhouette) Lockheed C-5A Galaxy.

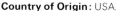

Country of Origin: USA.

Type: Long-range strategic freighter.

Power Plant: Four 41,000 lb st (18 600 kgp) General Electric TF39-GE-1 turbojets.

Performance: Max speed, 571 mph (919 km/h) at 25,000 ft (7 620 m); high speed cruise, 541 mph (871 km/h) at 30,000 ft (9 150 m).; average cruising speed, 518 mph (834 km/h); initial rate of climb, 1,800 ft/min (9,15 m/sec); service ceiling, 34,000 ft (10 360 m); range with max payload, 3,750 mls (6 032 km); range with 112,600-lb (51 074-kg) payload, 6 530 mls (10 505 km); ferry range, 7,990 mls (12 860 km).

Weights: Basic operating weight, empty, 372,500 lb (168 966 kg); design max payload, 220,967 lb (100 228 kg); max take-off weight, 769,000 lb (348 810 kg) for 2·25 g operations.

Dimensions: Span, 222 ft 8½ in (67,88 m); length, 247 ft 10 in (75,54 m); height, 65 ft 1½ in (19,85 m); wing area, 6,200 sq ft (576 m²).

Accommodation: Flight crew of four (two pilots, navigator and system engineer) plus one loadmaster; 15 seats for relief crew, etc, and provision for up to 345 troops, of which total 75 are on upper-deck and 270 on lower deck normally used to carry freight on 36 pallets or loaded individually. Typical loads include two M-

60 tanks, an M-60 tank and two Iroquois helicopters, five M-113 personnel carriers, a 2·5-ton M-59 truck and a 0·5-ton M-151 truck, or 10 Pershing missiles with tow and launch vehicles.

Status: First of eight flight test and evaluation aircraft flown on 30 June 1968. Deliveries began 17 December 1969. Production of 81 completed May 1973. Production reinstated 1982 with order for 50 of enhanced C-5B with deliveries to be completed by 1989.

Notes: Project definition of a very large strategic freighter to serve alongside the C-141 StarLifter began in 1963 and Lockheed was selected in October 1965 to build an aircraft in this category. The requirement was for a freighter that could carry 125,000 lb (56 700 kg) for 8,000 mls (12 875 km), or a maximum of twice that load for a shorter distance. It had to be able to take-off from an 8,000 ft (2 440 m) runway when fully loaded and to land on a 4,000 ft (1 220 m) semi-prepared runway. Because of cost escalation, USAF plans to buy enough C-5As to equip six squadrons were modified to provide a four-squadron force in MAC, each squadron possessing 16 aircraft. The C-5As now operate in the 436th and 60th Military Airlift Wings. On 14 August 1980 Lockheed first flew a C-5A with a modified wing structure to extend service life to 30,000 hrs, and all 77 C-5As still in service are to be so modified by 1987.

(Top) McDonnell Douglas C-9B Skytrain II of US Navy Fleet Tactical Support Squadron VR-1; (immediately above) a C-9A Nightingale operated in Europe on aeromedical airlift duties; (below) a DC-9 Sr 30 used by the Italian Air Force. (Silhouette) McDonnell Douglas C-9A Nightingale.

Country of Origin: USA.

Type: Personnel and supply transport, and aeromedical aircraft.

Power Plant: Two 14,500 lb st (6 577 kgp) Pratt & Whitney JT8D-9 turbofans.

Performance: (C-9A) 581 mph (935 km/h) at 23,100 ft (7 040 m) at mission weight; average cruising speed, 503 mph (809 km/h) at 35,000 ft (10,670 m); initial rate of climb, 2,900 ft/min (14,73 m/sec); time to 35,000 ft (10 670 m), 25 mins; service ceiling, 35,820 ft (10 918 m); range with max payload, 1,050 mls (1 690 km); ferry range, 2,920 mls (4 700 km).

Weights: Basic equipped weight, 62,247 lb (28 235 kg); max payload, 24,750 lb (11 227 kg); max take-off, 108,000 lb (48 990 kg).

Dimensions: Span 93 ft 5 in (28,47 m); overall length, 119 ft 3½ in (36,37 m); height, 27 ft 6 in (8,38 m); wing area, 1,000·7 sq ft (92,97 m²).

Accommodation: (C-9A) Active crew of eight comprising captain, first officer, flight observer, senior flight nurse, nurse, senior medical technician and two medical technicians; up to 40 ambulatory patients or 30 stretchers or combinations.

Status: First DC-9 (Srs 10) flown 25 February 1965; first Srs 30 flown 1 August 1966; first C-9A flown May 1968 and delivered August 1968; first C-9B delivered 8 May 1973. Production total: over 1,050 by early 1982 (mostly commercial); C-9A, 21; C-9B, 15; VC-9C, 3; Kuwait Air Force C-9B, 2.

Notes: The USAF selected a version of the commercial DC-9 in August 1967 to fulfil a requirement for an aeromedical airlift transport, subsequently adopting the appropriate name Nightingale. Basically a DC-9 Srs 30 (specifically, Model 32), the C-9A incorporates the side-loading cargo door of the DC-9F to facilitate loading of stretchers and large items of medical equipment. Special features include provision for a therapeutic oxygen supply and an isolated special care section. The C-9As are used by the 375th Aeromedical Airlift Wing in the USA, the 55th AA Squadron in Germany and the 20th AA Squadron in the Philippines, The USAF also has three VC-9Cs, which are commercial DC-9s with VIP interiors, used by the 89th Military Airlift Group at Andrews AFB, Washington. The US Navy selected the DC-9 in 1972 as a fleet logistics support transport under the designation C-9B, for which the name Skytrain II was adopted. Like the C-9A, the Skytrain II has freight doors but it lacks the special aeromedical facilities; it is operated by four USNR squadrons. The Kuwait Air Force purchased two DC-9s, basically equivalent to the C-9B; the Italian Air Force operates two commercial Srs 30s.

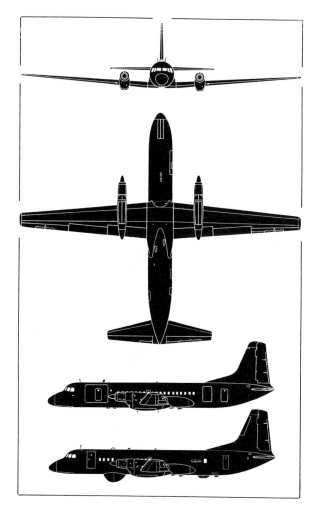

(Above) A YS-11A specially equipped for operation by the Japanese Maritime Safety Board (equivalent to the US Coast Guard); (immediately below) a YS-11A cargo transport and (bottom) radar-equipped YS-11A radar trainer of the JMSDF. (Silhouette) NAMC YS-11A, and extra side-view of radar training version.

Country of Origin: Japan.

Type: Personnel and cargo transport and special purpose trainer.

Power Plant: Two 3,060 eshp with water-methanol injection Rolls-Royce Dart 542-10K turboprops.

Performance: (Srs 200 and 400) Max cruising speed, 291 mph (469 km/h); economical cruise, 281 mph (452 km/h); initial rate of climb, 1,220 ft/min (6,2 m/sec); service ceiling, 22,900 ft (6 980 m); range with max payload, 680 mls (1 090 km); range with max standard fuel, 1,310 mls (2 110 km); range with auxiliary fuel, 2,000 mls (3 215 km).

Weights: Operating weight empty (Srs 200), 33,993 lb (15 419 kg), (Srs 400), 32,639 lb (14 805 kg); max payload (Srs 200), 14,508 lb (6 581 kg), (Srs 400), 15,862 lb (7 195 kg); max take-off, 54,010 lb (24 500 kg).

Dimensions: Span, 104 ft 11¾ in (32,00 m); length, 86 ft 3½ in (26,30 m); height, 29 ft 5½ in (2,88 m); wing area, 1,020·4 sq ft (94,8 m²).

Accommodation: Two pilots and seats for up to 60 passengers in Srs 200 or 42 folding troop seats in Srs 400.

Armament: None.

Status: Two YS-11 prototypes first flown on 30 August and 28 December 1962 respectively. First production YS-11 flown 23 October 1964; first Srs 200 flown 27 November 1967; first Srs 400 flown 17 September 1969. Production totals: prototypes, 2; Srs 100, 47; Srs 200, 95; Srs 300, 16; Srs 400, 9; Srs 500, 4; Srs 600, 9; total 182 completed February 1974; totals include 13 for JASDF and 10 for JMSDF.

Notes: Design of the YS-11 began in 1957 and its development and production became a joint industry undertaking under the direction of a specially-formed management organisation, NAMC (Nihon Aeroplane Manufacturing Co Ltd). The two principal production batches were Srs 100 and Srs 200, the latter having higher operating weights. Similar to the Srs 200 were the mixed traffic Srs 300 and the all-cargo Srs 400; the final 13 aircraft had an increased gross weight to permit higher payloads. The JASDF received four Srs 100s, one Srs 200, one Srs 300 and seven Srs 400, all for use as VIP, personnel or cargo transports. The JMSDF also obtained a few YS-11s as transports but also procured four Srs 200s to be used to train anti-submarine operators, for which purpose they were specially equipped. Apart from these deliveries to the JASDF and JMSDF, all YS-11s were built in the first place for the commercial market, but five Srs 200 were obtained by the Hellenic Air Force in 1980 after lengthy service with Olympic Airways.

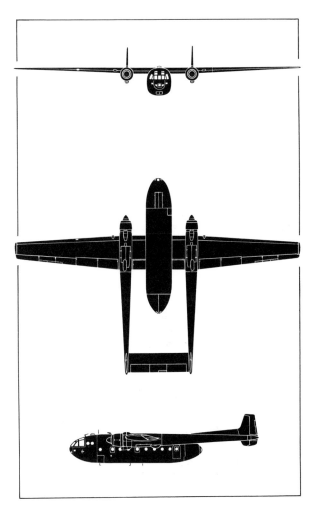

(Top) A Nord 2501 Noratlas troop transport of the Armée de l'Air; (immediately above) a Nord 2501 used for radar calibration by EC 57 Commercy; (below) a Noratlas serving with the Niger Air Force. (Silhouette) Nord 2501 Noratlas.

Country of Origin: France.

Type: Medium-range tactical transport.

Power Plant: Two 2,090 hp SNECMA-Bristol Hercules 738 or 758 piston radials plus (N.2502 and N.2504 only) two 882 lb st (400 kgp) Turboméca Marborè II turbojets.

Performance: Max speed, 251 mph (404 km/h) at 10,000 ft (3 050 m); long-range cruise, 200 mph (322 km/h) at 10,000 ft (3 050 m); initial rate of climb, 1,180 ft/min (5,9 m/sec); service ceiling 23,300 ft (7 100 m); range, 1,710 mls (2 750 km) with payload of 14,994 lb (6 800 kg).

Weights: Empty, 29,327 lb (13 300 kg); payload, 13 227 lb (6 000 kg); max take-off, 48,500 lb (22 000 kg).

Dimensions: Span, 106 ft 7½ in (32,48 m); length, 72 ft 0½ in (21,95 m); height, 19 ft 8¼ in (6,0 m); wing area, 1,089 sq ft (101,0 m²).

Accommodation: Flight crew of four or five and 45 equipped troops, 36 paratroops or 18 stretchers plus medical attendants.

Status: Prototype N.2500 first flown on 10 September 1949; N.2501 prototype first flown on 30 November 1950; N.2502 flown on 1 June 1955; N.2504 flown on 17 November 1958; N.2508 flown on 29 May 1957. Production deliveries began 1951; quantities comprised N.2500, one; N.2501, 267 in France and 161

in Germany; N.2502, 21; N.2503, one; N.2504, five; N.2506, one; N.2508, two.

Notes: The Noratlas was evolved in the period immediately following World War II to provide the *Armée de l'Air* with a troop and paratroop transport and as such it entered service in 1951, continuing as front-line equipment until the advent of the Transall C.160 some 16 years later. The *Armée de l'Air* acquired 200 N.2501s, and the French *Aéronavale* used five N.2504s to train anti-submarine radar operators; the N.2501 was also exported to Israel (30), Portugal (12) and Germany (25), with another 161 built for the *Luftwaffe* in Germany. Surplus Noratlas transports from Germany have entered service with the air forces of Niger and Nigeria, and *Armée de l'Air* Noratlas transports have been supplied to various former French territories, including Djibouti (Afars and Issas) and the Chad Republic, and a few of these are still operating, but the principal operators in 1982 were the *Armée de l'Air*, with about 50 still serving in tactical transport squadrons until delivery of the second batch of Transalls, and the Hellenic Air Force, using 20 ex-*Luftwaffe* aircraft (including one used for radio/calibration). Two former Portuguese aircraft remain in service with the Air Force of the Mozambique Republic. A handful in service in Germany perform special duties for the *Luftwaffe*.

(Above, immediately below and bottom) Air, landing and ground views of Percival Pembrokes in service in the communications rôle with No 60 Squadron in RAF Germany in 1982. (Silhouette) Percival Pembroke C Mk 1.

Country of Origin: United Kingdom.

Type: Light transport and communications.

Power Plant: Two 540 hp Alvis Leonides 127 piston radials.

Performance: Max speed, 224 mph (360 km/h) at 2,000 ft (610 m); max cruising speed, 209 mph (337 km/h) at 5,000 ft (1 525 m) and 199 mph (320 km/h) at 10,000 ft (3 050 m); economical cruising speed, 155 mph (250 km/h) at 8,000 ft (2 440 m); initial rate of climb, 1,070 ft/min (5,4 m/sec); service ceiling, 22,000 ft (6 070 m); range 1,150 mls (1 850 km).

Weights: Empty equipped, 9,178 lb (4 160 kg); eight-passenger payload, 1,732 lb (786 kg); max take-off, 13,500 lb (6 125 kg).

Dimensions: Span, 64 ft 6 in (19,60 m); length, 46 ft 0 in (14,00 m); height, 16 ft 1 in (4,90 m); wing area, 400 sq ft (37,2 m²).

Accommodation: Two pilots and up to 10 rearwards-facing seats in main cabin, or six stretchers with one attendant.

Armament: None.

Status: P.54 Prince prototype first flown 13 May 1948; Sea Prince C Mk 1 first flown 24 March 1950; Sea Prince T Mk 1 first flown 28 June 1951; Pembroke first flown 20 November 1952. Production (excluding commercial Princes): Sea Prince, 15; Pembroke C Mk 1, 46; Pembroke C(PR) Mk 1, 6; Pembroke 51 (Belgium), 12; Pembroke 52 (Sweden, Tp 81), 16; Pembroke 52/2 (Denmark), 6; Pembroke 53 (Finland), 2; Pembroke 54 (Germany), 33; Pembroke 55 (Sudan), 2.

Notes: The Percival (later Hunting) Prince was an early post-war light transport based on the smaller Merganser prototype that was the company's first post-war transport. The Royal Navy acquired Princes for the communication and training rôles, the latter surviving until 1979 when replaced by Jetstream T Mk 2s. The Pembroke was ordered by the Royal Air Force in 1951 as a variant of the Prince with increased wing span and higher operating weights, becoming the principal communications and light utility transport in service throughout the 'sixties. In 1969, a spar modification programme was initiated to prolong the service life of part of the fleet of Pembrokes. Plans were made late in the 'seventies to replace the last remaining dozen or so Pembrokes with the Beech Super King Air 200 or British Aerospace Jetstream 31 (a re-launched and updated version of the original Handley Page aircraft already serving in the RAF & RN as a trainer). However, budgetary restraints prevented orders being placed for either of these types, and at the end of 1982, the RAF still had eight Pembrokes in service with No 60 Squadron, based in Germany for communications duty.

PIAGGIO P.166 (ALBATROSS)

(Top) Air and (immediately above) ground views of the Piaggio P.166 operated by the Italian Air Force for communications duty; (below) a P.166S Albatross operated by No. 27 Squadron of the SAAF. (Silhouette) Piaggio P.166M.

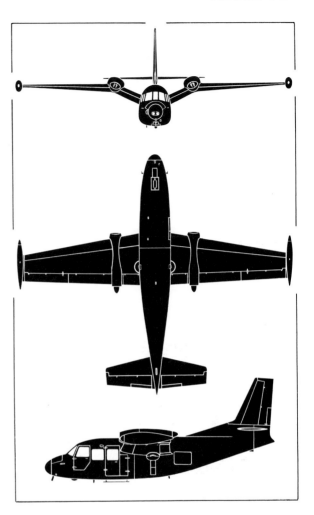

Country of Origin: Italy.

Type: General purpose transport and coastal surveillance aircraft.

Power Plant: Two 340 hp Lycoming GSO-480-B1C6 six-cylinder horizontally-opposed engines or (-DL3) 587 shp Avco Lycoming LTP 101-600 turboprops.

Performance: (P.166M) Max speed, 222 mph (357 km/h) at 9,500 ft (2 900 m); high speed cruise, 207 mph (333 km/h); long range cruise, 174 mph (280 km/h); initial rate of climb, 1,240 ft/min (6,3 m/sec); service ceiling, 25,500 ft (7 770 m); max range, 1,200 mls (1 930 m).

Weights: (P.166M) Empty, 5,180 lb (2,350 kg); max take-off, 8,115 lb (3 680 kg).

Dimensions: Span, (P.166M, over tip tanks), 46 ft 9 in (14,25 m); span, (-DL3, over tip tanks), 48 ft 2½ in (14,69 m); length, 30 ft 3 in (11,90 m); height, 16 ft 5 in (5,0 m); wing area, 286 sq ft (26,56 m²).

Armament: None.

Accommodation: Flight crew of two pilots and accommodation for 6–8 passengers.

Status: Prototype (P.166) first flown on 26 November 1957; certification and deliveries in 1958. First P.166S flown October 1968; certification in 1969. First P.166-DL3 flown 3 July 1976.

Production: P.166M, 51; P.166S, 20; commercial P.166 variants, 43; P.166-DL3, 22 (in production 1982).

Notes: The P.166 evolved from the amphibious P.136, being of similar configuration with two engines on a high wing, but somewhat larger and designed only for land operations. Of more than 100 P.166s built, about half have been for military use, including 51 P.166Ms for the Italian Air Force, which operates the type for communications and light transport duties. The South African Air Force acquired 20 of the P.166S variant, which is specially equipped for search and surveillance duties, with nose radar, individual pilots' doors, cargo door and emergency escape hatch in the cabin roof. The fuel capacity is increased and extensive nav/com equipment is fitted. With the name Albatross, the P.166s serves with No 27 Squadron, SAAF, at Ysterplaat, Cape Town, on short-range patrol and fishery surveillance duties. Several military variants of the basic design were proposed in 1973, but these proposals were superseded by the P.166-DL3 variant which introduced turboprop engines and was available in the same rôles. Production began in 1979 for both civil and military customers, the first announced military user being the Somalian Aeronautical Corps, which acquired two of the four pre-production examples in 1981.

(Above) Rockwell Sabreliner 40A serving the Swedish Air Force as Tp 86; (immediately below) a US Navy T-39D modified to test the nose radar of the F-18 Hornet; (bottom) a T-39A used as a staff transport by the USAF. (Silhouette) Rockwell CRT-39G

Country of Origin: USA.

Type: Communications, light transport and crew training.

Power Plant: Two (T-39A,B,D,F) 3,000 lb st (1 360 kgp) Pratt & Whitney J60-P-3 or -3A or (CT-39E,G) 3,300 lb st (1 497 kgp) Pratt & Whitney JT12A-8 turbojets.

Performance: (T-39A) Max speed, 539 mph (867 km/h) at 21,100 ft (6 431 m); average cruising speed, 502 mph (808 km/h) at 40,000 ft (12 200 m); initial rate of climb, 3,306 ft/min (16,8 m/sec); time to 30,000 ft (9 150 m), 16,9 min; service ceiling, 39,000 ft (11 887 m); range, 2,500 mls (4 020 km) with 30-min loiter and reserves.

Weights: Empty (T-39A), 9,753 lb (4 424 kg), (T-39D), 10,250 lb (4 650 kg); max take-off (T-39A), 18,650 lb (8 460 kg), (T-39D), 17,760 lb (8 056 kg).

Dimensions: Span 44 ft 5 in (13,53 m); length (T-39), 43 ft 9 in (13,33 m), (CT-39G) 46 ft 11 in (14,31 m); height, 16 ft 0 in (4,88 m); wing area, 342·6 sq ft (31,83 m²).

Accommodation: Two pilots; provision for up to seven or (CT-39G) eight passengers, or (T-39D) two students and instructor in cabin.

Status: Prototype NA-246 first flown 16 September 1958; first production T-39A flown 30 June 1960; first deliveries of T-39A, 4 June 1961 and completed autumn 1963; first T-39B flown November 1960, first delivery January 1961; first T-39D flown November 1962, deliveries August 1963–November 1964. Production totals (military only): T-39A, 143; T-39B, 6; T-39D, 42; CT-39E, 7; CT-39G, 12; deliveries complete.

Notes: North American built the NA-246 as a private venture to meet the requirements of the USAF's UTX (utility and 'combat readiness' trainer) specification. The original production version was the T-39A staff transport, communications aircraft and combat readiness trainer. USAF also procured six T-39Bs with radar and Doppler equipment to train F-105 crews and three T-39s were later converted to T-39Fs to train electronic warfare officers for the special 'Wild Weasel' F-105Gs. To train F-8 and F-4 crews in the use of intercept radar, the US Navy bought 42 aircraft similar to the T-39B; originally T3J-1s, they are now T-39Ds. The USN also bought for 'rapid response airlift' examples of the commercial Sabreliner 40 with uprated engines, designated CT-39E, and of the Sabre 60s with lengthened fuselage, which carry the designation CT-39G. Military users of the commercial models include the Argentine Air Force, one Model 75; the Bolivian Air Force, one Model 60 and the Swedish Air Force, one Model 40A with the designation Tp 86.

SHORTS SC-7 SKYVAN

TRANSPORT

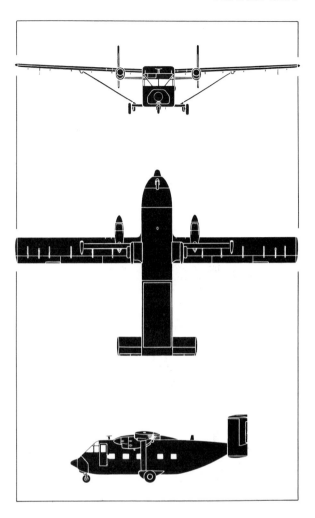

(Top) The pair of Skyvans serving with the Austrian Air Force; (immediately above) a Skyvan operated by the Air Force of the Sultan of Oman; (below) a Skyvan ready for delivery to the Royal Thai Police. (Silhouette) Shorts Skyvan 3M

Country of Origin: United Kingdom.
Type: Utility transport.
Power Plant: Two 715 shp Garrett TPE331-201 turboprops.
Performance: Max cruising speed, 203 mph (327 km/h) at 10,000 ft (3 030 m); economical cruising speed, 173 mph (278 km/h) at 10,000 ft (3 050 m); initial rate of climb, 1,530 ft/min (7,8 m/sec); service ceiling, 22,000 ft (6 705 m); max range, 670 mls (1 075 km) at 173 mph (278 km/h); range with 5,000-lb (2 268-kg) payload, 240 mls (386 km).
Weight: Typical operating weight empty, 7,620 lb (3 456 kg) as a freighter, 8,330 lb (3 778 kg) in troop-carrying configuration; max payload, 5,200 lb (2 358 kg) or 6,000 lb (2 721 kg) at overload take-off weight; normal take-off weight, 13,700 lb (6 214 kg); max overload take-off weight, 14,500 lb (6 577 kg).
Dimensions: Span, 64 ft 11 in (19,79 m); length (including nose radome), 41 ft 4 in (12,60 m); height, 15 ft 1 in (4,60 m); wing area, 373 sq ft (34,65 m²).
Accommodation: Normal flight crew, pilot only, with provision for second pilot. Cabin provides accommodation for maximum of 22 equipped troops, or 16 paratroops with a despatcher or 12 stretchers with two attendants, or cargo loads.
Armament: None.

Status: SC-7 prototype (with Continental engines) first flown 17 January 1963 (with Astazou II engines) on 2 October 1963; first development Srs 2 airframe flown 29 October 1965; first Srs 3 flown 15 December 1967 and second Srs 3 on 20 January 1968; first Srs 3M flown early 1970. Production/sales total 138 by mid-1982 including 54 Srs 3M for military or quasi-military users.
Notes: The Skyvan was developed during 1959 with the object of producing a small utility transport that could efficiently carry bulky and ungainly loads—hence its box-like fuselage and rear loading ramp. The Srs 3M, for military use, operates at higher weights than the commercial version, and has a slightly lower performance consequently. The rear door/loading ramp can be opened in flight to allow supplies or troops to be dropped by parachute. Sales of the Srs 3M include 16 to the Sultan of Oman's Air Force—which is the largest user of the type—six each to the air forces of Ghana and Singapore, five to the Argentinian Naval Prefectura, three each to the Royal Thai Police and the Indonesian Air Force, two each to the Austrian Air Force, Botswana Defence Force, Lesotho Police, Mauritanian Air Force, Royal Nepalese Army and Yeman Arab Republic Air Force and single examples to the Ecuador Army Air Force, Malawi Police and Panama National Guard.

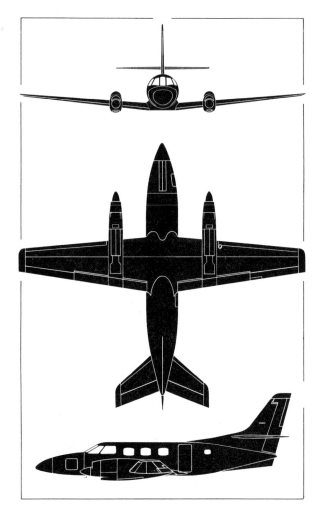

(Above) One of the Swearingen Merlin IIIs supplied to the Force Aérienne Belge; (immediately below) a Merlin IVA used by No 21 Squadron, SAAF; (bottom) the Merlin IV equipped for maritime surveillance. (Silhouette) Swearingen Merlin III.

Country of Origin: USA.

Type: Light personnel and VIP transport and air ambulance.

Power Plant: Two (III) 840 shp Garrett TPE331-3U-303G or (IV) 940 shp with water injection TPE331-3UW-304G turboprops.

Performance: (Merlin III) Max cruising speed, 325 mph (523 km/h) at 16,000 ft (4 875 m); economical cruising speed, 288 mph (463 km/h) at 28,000 ft (8 535 m); initial rate of climb, 2,530 ft/min (12,8 m/sec); service ceiling, 28,900 ft (8 810 m); range with max fuel, 1,968–2,860 mls (3 167–4 602 km) according to speed.

Performance: (Merlin IV) Max cruising speed, 310 mph (499 km/h) at 16,000 ft (4 875 m); economical cruising speed, 276 mph (444 km/h) at 28,000 ft (8 535 m); initial rate of climb, 2,530 ft/min (12,8 m/sec); service ceiling, 28,900 ft (8 810 m); range with max fuel, 1,575–2,095 mls (2 534–3 371 km) according to speed.

Weights: Empty equipped (Merlin III), 7,400 lb (3 356 kg); empty equipped (Merlin IV), 8,200 lb (3 719 kg); max take-off weight, 12,500 lb (5 670 kg).

Dimensions: Span, 46 ft 3 in (14,10 m); length (Merlin III), 42 ft 1¾ in (12,85 m); length (Merlin IV), 59 ft 4¾ in (18,10 m); height, 16 ft 9½ in (5,12 m); wing area, 277·50 sq ft (25,78 m²).

Accommodation: Two pilots side-by-side on flight deck and a maximum of (Merlin III) nine or (Merlin IV) 20 passengers.

Status: Merlin III first flown on 27 July 1970; Merlin IV/Metro first flown on 26 August 1969. Production totals include 92 Merlin III and IIIA, more than 60 Merlin IV and IVA and about 200 Metro II and IIA by 1981 with production continuing.

Notes: The Merlin III was introduced as a further step in the Swearingen company's progressive development of a family of business twins, which started with the Merlin II using the basic wing structure of the Beech Queen Air. The fuselage was a completely new, pressurised component. Most production of the Merlin III has been for the commercial business market, but the Belgian Air Force acquired six Merlin IIIs in 1976 as communication aircraft, and four are in service with the Argentine Army. The Merlin IV was a further development with a much lengthened fuselage and the same wing and power plant, offered for business use or (with the name Metro) as a commuter airliner. Seven Merlin IVs were acquired by the South African Air Force, one of which was equipped as an air ambulance, and these are in service with No 21 Squadron. Other air forces that have acquired this type include the Argentine Air Force with two air ambulance versions, and the Royal Thai Air Force with four.

TRANSALL C-160 TRANSPORT

(Top) A Luftwaffe C.160 of Ltg 63; (immediately above) one of the Transall C.160s of the new production batch, showing the flight refuelling probe; (below) a C.160 serving with the Türk Hava Kuvvetleri, transferred from the Luftwaffe. (Silhouette) Transall C.160, new production batch.

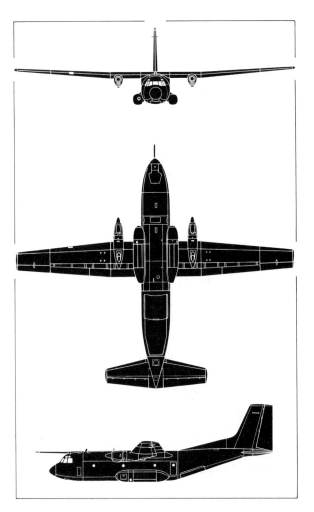

Country of Origin: France and Federal Germany.
Type: Medium-range tactical transport.
Power Plant: Two 6,100 ehp Rolls-Royce Tyne RTy 20 Mk 22 turboprops.
Performance: Max speed, 319 mph (513 km/h) at 16,000 ft (4 875 m); initial rate of climb, 1,360 ft/min (6,9 m/sec); max operating altitude, 30,000 ft (9 145 m); range with max payload, 1,150 mls (1 850 km); range with 17,637-lb (8 000-kg) payload, 3,166 mls (5 095 km); ferry range, 5,500 mls (8 858 km).
Weights: Typical operating weight empty, 63,920 lb (29 000 kg); max payload, 35,270 lb (16 000 kg); normal take-off, 97,450 lb (44 200 kg); max take-off, 112,435 lb (51 000 kg).
Dimensions: Span, 131 ft 3 in (40,0 m); length, 106 ft 3½ in (32,40 m); height, 38 ft 5 in (11,65 m); wing area, 1,723 sq ft (160,1 m²).
Accommodation: Flight crew of four (two pilots, navigator and flight engineer); up to 93 troops, 81 paratroops or 62 stretchers.
Status: First of three prototypes flown in France on 25 February 1963; second and third prototypes flown in Germany 25 May 1963 and 19 February 1964; first of six C-160A pre-production aircraft flown on 21 May 1965; first production C-160D flown in Germany on 2 November 1967 and delivered in April 1968; first C-

160F flown on 13 April 1967 and delivered in October 1967; first C-160Z flown on 28 February 1969 and delivered in July 1969. Production comprised 110 C-160D for Germany, 50 C-160F for France and nine C-160Z for South Africa, completed October 1972. First new-batch C-160 flown in France 9 April 1981; production of 25 for *Armée de l'Air* with deliveries starting late-1981, plus three for Indonesia.
Notes: The Transall project began in 1959 as a joint Franco-German programme to produce a tactical transport to replace the Nord Noratlas. The Transall is operated by two *Luftwaffe* transport groups, three *Armée de l'Air* squadrons and No 28 Squadron of the SAAF at Waterkloof. During 1971, Germany transferred to the Turkish Air Force 20 Transalls and these are now known as C-160Ts. One of the prototypes was later sold to Gabon, and in 1973 four Transalls were modified by SOGERMA under the designation C-160P for the French Postal Service. To meet an *Armée de l'Air* requirement for additional Transalls to replace its remaining Noratlas transports, production was relaunched in 1976, using the same sub-contractors but only one final assembly line. The new-batch aircraft have additional centre-section fuel tanks and provision for in-flight refuelling and (10 aircraft only) a hose drum unit in the port u/c fairing to serve as FR tankers.

147

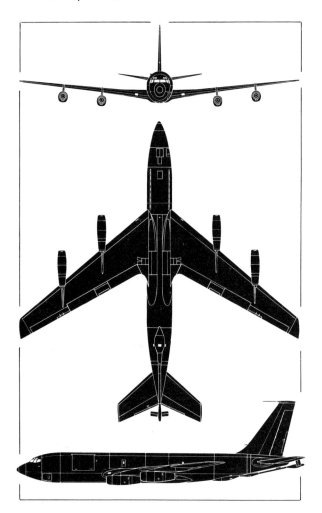

(Above) A Boeing 707 tanker used by the Canadian Armed Forces as a CC-137; (immediately below) the VC-137C US Presidential transport; (bottom) a KC-135A tanker in service with the Ohio Air National Guard. (Silhouette) Boeing KC-135A Stratotanker.

Country of Origin: USA.

Type: In-flight refuelling tanker and transport.

Power Plant: Four (KC-135A, C-135A) 13,750 lb st (6 237 kgp) (with water injection) Pratt & Whitney J57-P-59W turbojets or (C-135B) 18,000 lb st (8 165 kgp) TF33-P-5 turbofans.

Performance: (KC-135A) Typical cruising speed, max load refuelling mission, 532 mph (856 km/h) at 35,000 ft (10 688 m); initial rate of climb, 1,290 ft/min (6,65 m/sec); time to 34,500 ft (9 300 m), 27 min; mission radius, 3,450 mls (5 552 km) to off-load 24,000 lb (10 886 kg) fuel, 1,150 mls (1 850 km) to offload 120,000 lb (54 432 kg) fuel.

Weights: (KC-135A) Operating weight empty, 106,306 lb (48 220 kg); normal take-off weight, 301,600 lb (136 806 kg); max overload weight, 316,000 lb (143 338 kg).

Dimensions: Span, 130 ft 10 in (39,88 m); length overall, 134 ft 6 in (40,99 m); height overall, 41 ft 8 in (12,69 m); wing area, 2,433 sq ft (226,03 m²).

Accommodation: Flight crew of four, comprising two pilots, radio-navigator and boom operator; optional provision for up to 160 troops or 83,000 lb (37 648 kg) of cargo.

Status: First KC-135A flown 31 August 1956; first interim C-135A flown 19 May 1961; first C-135B flown 15 February 1962.

KC-135A entered service 18 June 1957. Production of 732 KC-135A completed in January 1965, plus 15 C-135A, 30 C-135B and 12 C-135F (for France). Fifty-six KC-135Qs by conversion from KC-135As; four KC-135Ds by conversion from RC-135A.

Notes: The basic KC-135A variant remains in service as the principal SAC tanker in 1982, in addition to 11 (of 12 delivered) similar C-135Fs (with probe-and-drogue refuelling) in service in France. KC-135As were operational with some 28 SAC wings or groups in 1982, as well as three AFR and 13 ANG units. A prototype conversion to have CFM-56 turbofans was to fly October 1982, and *Armée de l'Air* C-135Fs are also to be so modified. The C-135A and C-135B (TF33 engines) were built as troop and cargo transports for MAC, having no refuelling boom, and some later became VC-135B government VIP transports and WC-135Bs for weather reconnaissance. Versions of the larger commercial Boeing 707 bought for military service include three VC-137As (later VC-137Bs when fitted with turbofan engines), and two VC-137C Presidential ('Air Force One') transports for the USAF, two as personnel transports for *Luftwaffe*, and two for the RAAF; presidential transports in the Argentine and Egypt; five tanker/transports in the Canadian Armed Forces; 14 supplied to Iran and six for Saudi Arabia for delivery in 1985.

BRITISH AEROSPACE VC10

(Top and immediately above) Two views of VC 10 C Mk 1s serving with No 10 Squadron, RAF; (below) an artist's impression of the VC 10 K Mk 3 tanker conversion of the Super VC 10, with Tornado F Mk 2s. (Silhouette) BAe VC 10 C Mk 1.

Country of Origin: United Kingdom.
Type: Long-range strategic transport and (K Mk 2, K Mk 3) in-flight refuelling tanker.
Power Plant: Four 21,800 lb st (9 888 kgp) Rolls-Royce Conway 301 (R.Co.43D/Mk 550D) turbofans.
Performance: (C Mk 1) Max cruising speed, 568 mph (914 km/h); long-range cruising speed, 425 mph (684 km/h) at 30,000 ft (9 150 m); initial rate of climb, 3,050 ft/min (15,5 m/sec); range with max payload, 3,900 mls (6 275 km).
Weights: (C Mk 1) Max payload, 57,400 lb (26 030 kg); max takeoff weight, 323,000 lb (146 510 kg); max landing weight, 235,000 lb (106 600 kg).
Dimensions: (C Mk 1) Span, 146 ft 2 in (44,55 m); length, 158 ft 8 in (48,36 m); height, 39 ft 6 in (12,04 m); gross wing area, 2,932 sq ft (272,4 m²).
Accommodation: Flight crew of four (two pilots, navigator, engineer). Standard seating (in C Mk 1) for 150 passengers in rearwards-facing six-abreast seats; passenger compartment for 18 (K Mk 2) or 17 (K Mk 3) in rearwards-facing seats.
Status: Prototype VC10 flown 29 June 1962; first production VC10 flown 8 November 1962; first production Super VC10 flown 7 May 1964; first C Mk 1 flown 26 November 1965 and first

delivery 7 July 1966. Production of C Mk 1 completed 1968 and of all VC10 types 1970. Production totals: Prototype, 1, Standard VC10 (commercial), 17; Super VC10 (commercial), 22; C Mk 1 (RAF), 14.
Notes: The VC10 was developed in the late 'fifties to provide BOAC with a long-range jet transport but few sales were achieved other than to BOAC/British Airways. The RAF placed an initial order for five VC10s in September 1961 and eventually acquired 14 in the C Mk 1 configuration, which has the dimensions of the Standard VC10 with the uprated engines and fin fuel tanks of the Super VC10, a large side-loading freight door in the forward fuselage, and a military interior. All but one of these remain in service with No 10 Squadron, RAF. During 1958, the RAF initiated a programme to convert commercial VC10s as three-point tankers to supplement Victor K Mk 2s and British Aerospace received a contract to convert five Standard VC10s to K Mk 2s and four Super VC10s (with longer fuselage) to K Mk 3s. Flight development of these new variants was starting in April 1982. During 1981 the RAF also acquired the last 14 Super VC10s retired by British Airways; three of these airframes were assigned for use as spares and the others are available for future conversion to tankers or transports as may be required.

(Above) A Victor K Mk 2 with all three drogues trailed, (immediately below) a Tornado prototype refuels from a Victor K Mk 2 from No 232 OCU; (bottom) a Victor K Mk 2 on the ground. (Silhouette) Handley Page Victor K Mk 2.

Country of Origin: United Kingdom.

Type: Flight refuelling tanker.

Power Plant: Four 20,600 lb st (9 345 kg) Rolls-Royce Conway 201 (R Co 17) turbojets.

Performance: Max speed over 600 mph (966 km/h) at 40,000 ft (12 192 m); service ceiling, over 50,000 ft (15 250 m); unrefuelled range, 4,600 mls (7 400 km).

Weights: Typical empty weight, 110,000 lb (33 550 kg); max take-off weight, 223,000 lb (101 150 kg).

Dimensions: 117 ft 0 in (35,69 m); length, 114 ft 11 in (35,02 m); height, 30 ft 1½ in (9,18 m); wing area, 2,200 sq ft (204, 38 m²).

Accommodation: Flight crew of five comprising two pilots, navigator-plotter, navigator-radar, airborne electronics officer.

Status: Prototype Victor bomber first flown 24 December 1952; first production B Mk 1 flown on 1 February 1956; first B Mk 2 flown on 20 February 1959; first B(K) Mk 1A tanker conversion flown on 28 April 1965; first K Mk 2 tanker conversion flown on 1 March 1972; first delivery 8 May 1974. Production totals, 50 B Mk 1, 30 B Mk 2, completed in 1962. Total of 24 K Mk 2 conversions, delivered by mid-1977.

Notes: In its original guise as a strategic bomber, the Victor was part of Britain's V-Force which provided the nation's main

deterrent in the 'fifties and 'sixties. Variants were the initial production B Mk1 with 11,050 lb st (5 012 kgp) Armstrong Siddeley Sapphire 202/207 turbojets; B Mk 1A conversions with tail warning radar and other modifications; the K Mk 1 and K Mk 1A refuelling tanker conversions; the B Mk 2 with extra wing span, Conway 103 (RCo 11) engines and increased weights; the B Mk 2R conversions with uprated Conway 201s; the SR Mk 2 conversions for photographic reconnaissance and the K Mk 2 tankers. All conversion programmes but that of the K Mk 2 were handled by Handley Page before its failure in 1970; the K Mk 2 programme, covering 24 aircraft, was taken over by Hawker Siddeley at Woodford, and these aircraft were delivered to the RAF by 1977, forming, in Nos 55 and 57 Squadrons, the sole tanker force until the introduction of VC10 tankers. Pods under each wing contain retractable hose and drogue equipment, allowing two fighter aircraft to refuel simultaneously when required; a similar hose drum unit in the fuselage is normally used to refuel larger aircraft one at a time. As well as having the HDUs installed, the Victor K Mk 2s were modified to have a reduction of 1 ft 6 in (46 cm) at each wing tip to reduce the bending moments resulting from the addition of the wing pods, and thus enhance the fatigue life.

LOCKHEED KC-130 HERCULES

(Top) A Lockheed KC-130F tanker refuelling A-4 Skyhawks; (immediately above) one of the USAF's HC-130P tankers for helicopter refuelling; (below) an HC-130N serving with an MAC Rescue squadron. (Silhouette) Lockheed HC-130P Hercules.

Country of Origin: USA.

Type: Aerial refuelling tanker and transport.

Power Plant: Four (KC-130F) 4,050 eshp Allison T56-A-7 or (KC-130R) 4,508 eshp flat-rated T56-A-16 or (HC-130H, N, P) 4,508 eshp flat-rated T56-A-15 turboprops.

Performance: (KC-130R), 373 mph (600 km/h) at 21,500 ft (6 553 m); average cruise, 331 mph (533 km/h) at 23,000–31,700 ft (7 010–9 662 m); initial rate of climb, 2,990 ft/min (15,2 m/sec); service ceiling, 25,000 ft (7 620 m); refuelling mission radius, 1,150 mls (1 850 km) with one hour loiter; combat range, 2,950 mls (4 747 km) with max payload and 4,300 mls (6 920 km) with max fuel and 12 000-lb (5 443-kg) payload.

Weights: (KC-130R) Empty, 75,368 lb (34 187 kg); max payload, 26,913 lb (12 207 kg) at normal take-off weight and 47,720 lb (21 646 kg) at overload weight; normal take-off, 155,000 lb (70 310 kg); max overload weight, 175,00 lb (79 380 kg).

Dimensions: Span, 132 ft 7 in (40,41 m); length, 99 ft 5½ in (30,32 m); height, 38 ft 3 in (11,66 m); wing area, 1,745 sq ft (162,12 m²).

Accommodation: Flight crew of five (two pilots, flight engineer, navigator and radio operator/loadmaster). Provision for up to 92 combat troops or 64 paratroops with equipment.

Status: YC-130 Hercules prototype first flown 23 August 1954. KC-130F flown 22 January 1960 and delivered 21 March 1960; first KC-130R flown September 1975 and delivered October 1975; first HC-130H flown 8 December 1964; first HC-130N flown January 1970; first HC-130P flown June 1966.

Notes: The first Hercules tankers were ordered by US Marine Corps (with GV-1 designation) in August 1958 after trials with two converted C-130As and 46 were built, with underwing hose drum units for probe-and-drogue refuelling; 15 KC-130Rs were similar but based on improved C-130E airframe. The USAF also acquired HC-130P and HC-130N tankers specially equipped to refuel Air Rescue Helicopter Service helicopters in Vietnam, and foreign users of tanker (KC-130H) Hercules include the Spanish, Argentine, Brazilian, Israeli and Royal Saudi Air Forces. Many special-duty versions have been developed, including, for the USAF, the HC-130H for aerial search, rescue and recovery; AC-130A, E and H gunships, RC-130A, B and S for photo-survey and WC-130B, E and H weather reconnaissance and research, DC-130A, E and H drone launchers, JC-130B and JHC-130H for satellite recovery, EC-130E for electronic surveillance and MC-130E for covert electronic sensing. US Navy uses EC-130G and Q for communications and Coast Guard uses HC-130Bs.

(Above) Two KC-10A Extenders in an aerial refuelling test mission; (immediately above and below) two aspects of the first KC-10A Extender air refuelling tanker/transport for the USAF. (Silhouette) McDonnell Douglas KC-10A Extender.

Country of Origin: USA.

Type: Flight refuelling tanker and cargo aircraft.

Power Plant: Three 52,500 lb st (23 814 kgp) General Electric F103-GE-100 turbofans.

Performance: (Estimated) Max speed, 620 mph (988 km/h) at 33,000 ft (10 060 m); max cruise, 595 mph (957 km/h) at 31,000 ft (9 450 m); long-range cruise, 540 mph (870 km/h) at 31,000 ft (9 450 m); typical refuelling mission, 2,200 mls (3 540 km) from base with 200,000 lb (90 720 kg) of fuel and return; max range (with 170,000 lb/77 112 kg cargo), 4,370 mls (7 033 km).

Weights: Operational empty (tanker), 240,245 lb (108 973 kg); operational empty (cargo configuration), 244,471 lb (110 890 kg); max cargo payload, 169,529 lb (76 897 kg); max take-off, 590,000 lb (267 624 kg).

Dimensions: Span, 165 ft 4 in (50,42 m); length, 181 ft 7 in (55,35 m); height, 58 ft 1 in (17,70 m); wing area, 3,647 sq ft (338,8 m²).

Accommodation: Flight crew of five plus provision for six seats for additional crew and four bunks for crew rest. Fourteen additional seats for support personnel may be provided in the forward cabin. Alternatively, a larger area can be provided for 55 more support personnel, with necessary facilities.

Status: DC-10 prototype flown 29 August 1970; first DC-10 Srs 30 flown 21 June 1972; first DC-10 Srs 30CF flown 28 February 1973; first KC-10A flown 12 July 1980. Total USAF requirement, 60, of which 16 on firm order by mid-1982.

Notes: The Extender is a military tanker/cargo derivative of the commercial DC-10 Series 30CF convertible freighter with refuelling boom, boom operator's station, hose and drogue, military avionics and body fuel cells in the lower cargo compartments. The largest aircraft yet adopted for the in-flight refuelling tanker role, the KC-10A can carry sufficient fuel to replenish a formation of fighter aircraft and at the same time carry in its cabin the fighters' support equipment and support personnel that are needed to accompany operational squadrons on overseas deployment. The Extender, which incorporates a refuelling receptacle so that it can itself receive fuel from another tanker, can refuel all types of military aircraft in USAF, USN, USMC and NATO service, since it carries a hose and drogue unit as well as the 'flying boom' that is standard for USAF aircraft refuelling. The KC-10A Extenders are being operated, from 1982, by one of the tanker squadrons of SAC based at Barksdale AFB, where the first two KC-10As were delivered in March and July 1981.

ANTONOV AN-2 (COLT)

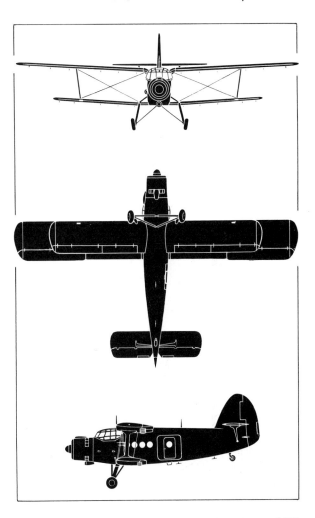

(Top) An An-2 light utility transport in DDR service for parachutist training, and (immediately above and below) An-2s serving with the Polish Air Force. Production of the An-2 continues in Poland and China. (Silhouette) The An-2 Colt.

Country of Origin: Soviet Union (Poland and China)
Type: General-purpose light utility transport.
Power Plant: One 1,000 hp Shvetsov ASh-62M nine-cylinder radial air-cooled engine.
Performance: (An-2T at 11,574 lb/5 250 kg) Max speed, 160 mph (258 km/h) at 5,740 ft (1 750 m); econ cruise, 115 mph (185 km/h); initial climb, 689 ft/min (3,50 m/sec); time to 14,425 ft (4 400 m), 30 min; range (with 1,102-lb/500 kg payload), 560 mls (900 km) at 3,280 ft (1 000 m).
Weights: Empty, 7,605 lb (3 450 kg); max take-off, 12,125 lb (5 500 kg).
Dimensions: Span, 59 ft 8½ in (18,18 m); length, 41 ft 9½ in (12,74 m); height, 13 ft 1½ in (4,00 m); wing area, 765·3 sq ft (71,10 m²).
Accommodation: Crew of two and up to 12 fully-equipped troops or six paratroops, or 3,306 lb (1 500 kg) of freight.
Status: Flown as a prototype on 31 August 1947, the An-2 claims the distinction of having been built in larger numbers than any post-WWII aircraft other than certain US light planes. More than 5,000 An-2s were built in the Soviet Union before, in 1960, all production was transferred to the WSK-Mielec in Poland where manufacture was continuing at the beginning of 1982, more than

9,000 having been built at the Polish facility of which some 8,000 have been exported (including about 7,500 to the Soviet Union). Production of the An-2 is also continuing in China as the C-5, the first Chinese-built example having flown in December 1957 and very large numbers having since been manufactured for the Chinese armed forces, paramilitary organisations, for civil use and for export.
Notes: The An-2 currently serves in the light utility transport role with all the WarPac air forces and with a considerable number of the world's smaller armed forces. The North Korean Army alone possesses some 225 An-2s with which it can lift some 2,000 commandos, this low- and slow-flying aircraft having the ability to evade radar detection. Numerous variants of the An-2 have been manufactured, military tasks including paratroop training, aeromedical, communications and liaison duties. Prior to the termination of production in the Soviet Union, a small series designated An-2M was built, this featuring a redesigned, enlarged and more angular vertical tail, a revised engine mounting and other modifications, metal bonding being introduced into the airframe construction. It is uncertain if any of the An-2M version were delivered to the Soviet armed forces. A turboprop-powered derivative is designated An-3.

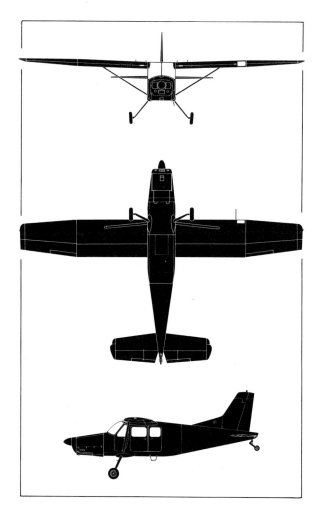

(Above and immediately below) Two views of Atlas C-4M Kudu light transports as used by Nos 41 and 42 Squadrons of the South African Air Force; (bottom) an Aermacchi AL 60 Trojan of the Zimbabwe Air Force. (Silhouette) Atlas C-4M Kudu.

Country of Origin: South Africa (and Italy).

Type: Utility transport.

Power Plant: (Kudu) One 340 hp Piaggio-built Lycoming GSO-480-B1B3 or (AL.60) 400 hp Lycoming IO-720-A1A piston engine.

Performance: (Kudu) Max speed, 161 mph (259 km/h) at 8,000 ft (2 440 m); economical cruising speed, 124 mph (200 km/h); initial rate of climb, 800 ft/min (4,1 m/sec); service ceiling, 14,000 ft (4 270 m); range with 881-lb (400-kg) payload, 460 mls (740 km); max range, 806 mls (1 297 km).

Performance: (AL.60) Max speed, 156 mph (251 km/h) at sea level; economical cruise, 108 mph (174 km/h) at 5,000 ft (1 525 m); initial rate of climb, 1,080 ft/min (5,5 m/sec); service ceiling, 13,600 ft (4 150 m); max range, 645 mls (1 037 km).

Weights: (Kudu) Empty, 2,711 lb (1 230 kg); max payload, 1,235 lb (560 kg); max take-off, 4,497 lb (2 040 kg).

Weights: (AL.60) Empty, 2,395 lb (1 086 kg); max cargo payload, 1,440 lb (653 kg); max take-off, 4,500 lb (2 041 kg).

Dimensions: (Kudu) Span, 42 ft 10¾ in (13,08 m); length, 30 ft 6½ in (9,31 m); height, 12 ft 0 in (3,66 m); wing area, 225·7 sq ft (20,97 m²).

Dimensions: (AL.60) Span, 39 ft 4 in (11,99 m); length, 28 ft 10½ in (8,80 m); height, 10 ft 10 in (3,30 m); wing area, 210·4 sq ft (19,55 m²).

Accommodation: Two pilots and up to six passengers.

Status: Prototype Lockheed L 60 first flown 15 September 1959; first Aermacchi-built AL.60 flown 19 April 1961. Prototype C4M Kudu flown 16 February 1974; first military model Kudu flown 18 June 1975. Production totals, 32 LASA 60 built in Mexico; more than 100 AL 60 built by Aermacchi in Italy; over 40 C4M Kudu built by Atlas in South Africa.

Notes: The AL.60 has its origin in a design by the Lockheed-California company. A batch of these aircraft was built by Lockheed-Azcarate in Mexico as LASA-60s, and in Italy, Aermacchi put the type into production as the AL.60 and several variants were developed; sales included a batch for Rhodesia, where the type remains in service with the Zimbabwe Air Force as the Trojan. A design team from Atlas Aircraft Corp then worked with Aermacchi to develop the AL-60C-4M in which the engine and wing of the AM-3C Bosbok (separately described) were combined with the AL-60C fuselage, adapted to have a single sliding door for paratroop dropping and a hatch in the floor for supply drops. As the Atlas C-4M Kudu, this type then entered production for service with the South African Air Force and is operated by Nos 41 and 42 Squadrons.

BEECHCRAFT U-8 AND QUEEN AIR

(Top) An elderly Beechcraft-Twin Bonanza serving with the Swiss Air Force; (immediately above) a Beechcraft Queen Air operated by the JGSDF and (below) a later Queen Air B80 of the Heyl Ha'Avir. (Silhouette) Beechcraft Queen Air B80.

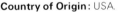

Country of Origin: USA.

Type: Communications and light cargo transport.

Power Plant: Two (U-8F) 340 hp Lycoming IGSO-480-A1A6 or (Queen Air B80) 380 hp IGSO-540-A1D piston engines.

Performance: (U-8F): Max permissible speed, 269 mph (433 km/h); max speed, 239 mph (385 km/h) at critical altitude; cruising speed, 200 mph (322 km/h) at 65 per cent power at 10,000 ft (3 050 m); initial rate of climb, 1,300 ft/min (6,6 m/sec); service ceiling, 27,000 ft (8 230 m); cruising range, 1,370 mls (2 204 km) at 200 mph (322 km/h) at 10,000 ft (3 050 m); max endurance (no reserves), 6·95 hrs.

Performance: (Queen Air B80) Max speed, 248 mph (400 km/h) at 11,500 ft (3 500 m); cruising speed, 225 mph (362 km/h) at 15,000 ft (4 570 m); economical cruise, 183 mph (294 km/h) at 15,000 ft (4 570 m); initial rate of climb, 1,275 ft/min (6.5 m/sec); service ceiling, 26,800 ft (8 168 m); range, 1,517 mls (2440 km) at 183 mph (295 km/h).

Weights: (U-8D) Empty, 4,974 lb (2 256 kg) (U-8F) 4,996 lb (2 266 kg); max take-off (U-8D) 7,000 lb (3 175 kg), (U-8F), 7,700 lb (3 493 kg), (B80) 8,800 lb (3992 kg).

Dimensions: Span (U-8F), 45 ft 10½ in (13,99 m), (B80) 50 ft 3 in (15,32 m); length (U-8F), 33 ft 4 in (10,16 m), (B80) 35 ft 6 in

(10,82 m); height (U-8F), 14 ft 2 in (4,32 m), (B80) 14ft 2½ in (4,33 m); wing area (U-8F), 277 sq ft (25,73 m²) (B80) 294 sq ft (27,3 m²).

Accommodation: One or two pilots and (U-8F) up to four (or (B80) nine passengers.

Status: Prototype Beech Model 50 first flown 15 November 1949; first YL-23 delivered to US Army 30 January 1952; first L-23D flown October 1955; first L-23F flown January 1959. Production: 974 of all models, including YL-23, 4; L-23A, 55; L-23B, 40; XL-23C, 1; L-23D, 85; RL-23D, 20; L-23E, 6; L-23F, 79.

Notes: The US Army adopted the Beech Twin Bonanza as its standard communications, transport and liaison aircraft after buying four examples off-the-shelf for evaluation in 1952. A total of 290 was procured as listed above, including the single XL-23C for USAF evaluation. The RL-23Ds carried side-looking radar in a long ventral fairing, but are no longer in service. All models were redesignated in the U-8 series in 1962, and in 1981 about 50 U-8s remained in service with active Army units, the Army Reserve and the National Guard. A few examples of the commercial Twin Bonanza have entered military service, in Switzerland, Pakistan and Chile. Several air forces also acquired examples of the commercial Queen Air.

(Above) Beech U-21A Ute transport in US Army service; (immediately below) the US Navy's T-44 trainer based, like the U-21, on the commercial King Air; (bottom) a Beechcraft King Air C90 serving with the Spanish Escuela Nacional de Aeronautica (Escuadron 744) with the local designation E.22. (Silhouette) Beechcraft U-21 Ute.

Country of Origin: USA.

Type: (U-21) Utility transport and special reconnaissance and (T-44) training aircraft.

Power Plant: Two (U-21A,D,E and G) 550 shp Pratt & Whitney Canada T74-CP-700 or (U-21F) 680 shp PT6A-28 or (RU-21B and C) 750 shp T74-CP-702 or (UC-6B) 550 shp PT6A-21 or (T-44A) 750 shp PT6A-34B turboprops.

Performance: (U-21A and U-21G) Max speed, 249 mph (401 km/h) at 11,000 ft (3 350 m); max cruising speed, 245 mph (395 km/h) at 10,000 ft (3 050 m); economical cruising speed, 205 mph (328 km/h) at 10,000 ft (3 050 m); initial rate of climb, 2,000 ft/min (10,1 m/sec); service ceiling, 25,500 ft (7 775 m); range with max fuel, 1,676 mls (2 697 km); range with max payload; 1,167 mls (1 878 km).

Weights: Empty equipped (U-21A and U-21G), 5,464 lb (2 478 kg); (U-21F), 6,728 lb (3 051 kg); max payload (U-21A and U-21G), 4,186 lb (1 898 kg); max take-off weight (U-21A, D,E,G), 9,650 lb (4 377 kg); (RU-21B and C), 10,900 lb (4 944 kg) (U-21F), 11,500 lb (5 216 kg).

Dimensions: Span (U-21), 45 ft 10½ in (13,98 m); span (VC-6, T-44), 50 ft 3 in (15,32 m); length (except U-21F), 35 ft 6 in (10,82 m); length (U-21F), 39 ft 11¼ in (12,17 m); height, (except U-21F), 14 ft 2½ in (4,33 m); height (U-21F), 15 ft 4¼ in (4,68 m); wing area (U-21), 279.7 sq ft (25,98 m²), wing area (VC-6, T-44), 293,94 sq ft (27,31 m²).

Accommodation: (U-21) Crew of two with dual control; up to ten combat-equipped troops, or three stretchers plus three seated; or six passengers, or cargo, or special equipment operators.

Status: Prototype (NU-8F) first flown in May 1963. First production U-21A flown in March 1967. Deliveries to US Army began on 16 May 1967. Production totals, U-21A, 124; U-21B, 3; RU-21C, 2; RU-21E, 16; U-21F, 5; U-21G, 17; VC-6B, 1; T-44A, 61.

Notes: The U-21 was derived from the commercial Queen Air (used by the US Army as the U-8) through installation of turboprop engines, producing the NU-8F prototype in 1963. The Army procured 124 U-21As and 17 similar U-21Gs (with updated equipment) for staff and utility transport duties, plus a series of special electronic reconnaissance versions, designated RU-21A (4 U-21As converted), RU-21B, RU-21C, RU-21D (18 U-21As converted) and RU-21H (12 RU-21Es converted) according to equipment and power plant. The five U-21Fs are commercial model King Air A100s acquired by the Army 1971, and a single VC-6A is a C90 acquired by the USAF as a VIP transport. The US Navy T-44As (King Air G90) are multi-engine pilot trainers.

CANADAIR CL-215

(Top) A Canadair CL-215 used in the search and rescue rôle by Esc 404 of the Spanish Air Force; (immediately above) one of the CL-215s of the Royal Thai Navy; (below) first of four CL-215s supplied to Yugoslavia for fire-fighting duty. (Silhouette) Canadair CL-215.

Country of Origin: Canada.

Type: Water-bomber and utility amphibian.

Power Plant: Two 2,100 hp Pratt & Whitney R-2800-83AM-21H or 12AD/CA3 piston radial engines.

Performance: Max cruising speed, 181 mph (291 km/h) at 10,000 ft (3 048 m); initial rate of climb, 1,000 ft/min (5,08 m/sec), range with 6,750 lb (3 060 kg) payload, 610 mls (982 km); range with 4,500 lb (2 040 kg) payload, 1,117 mls (1 797 km).

Weights: Basic operating (tanker), 27,740 lb (12,585 kg), (utility); 27,540 lb (12 490 kg); max payload (tanker), 12,000 lb (5,442 kg), (utility), 6,800 lb (3,085 kg); max take-off (tanker), 43,500 lb (19 728 kg), (utility), 37,700 lb (17 100 kg).

Dimensions: Span, 93 ft 10 in (28,60 m); length 65 ft 0¼ in (19,82 m); height, 29 ft 5½ in (8,92 m); wing area, 1,080 sq ft (100 m²).

Accommodation: Flight crew of two and folding seats for eight passengers; utility version can carry up to 29 passengers or 12 stretchers in rescue rôle or 6,800 lb (3 085 kg) of cargo.

Status: Prototype first flown on 23 October 1967. First deliveries (to French *Protection Civile*) in June 1969. A total of 80 CL-215s had been approved for production by mid-1981 in four batches, with work then in hand on the final 15. Orders by military or government agencies included Spanish Air Force, 17; Hellenic Air Force, 11; Royal Thai Navy, 2; Yugoslav government, 4.

Notes: The CL-215 was developed to meet the need for a specialised aerial tanker for fire-fighting duties in Canada and other heavily-forested areas. Its entire load of 1,200 Imp gal (5 455 l) of water or fire retardent can be dropped in one second and its tanks can be refilled in 12 seconds as the aircraft taxies across a lake. An initial production batch of 30 CL-215s was built in 1968–71, of which 15 went to the Quebec government, 12 to France, two to Spain and one to Greece. Production was resumed in 1973, the CL-215s, for delivery from April 1974 onwards having several new features, including the R-2800-83AM-12AD/CA3 engines, provision for AVQ-21 radar or a camera and infra-red sensor pod in the nose, an extra 312 Imp gal (1 500 l) of fuel and an optional loud hailer in the port nacelle, to allow the crew to pass messages to fire-fighters on the ground. The CL-215s operated by the Spanish Air Force, under the local designation of UD-13, are used for search and rescue duties by *Escuadron* 404, although they are also available for fire-fighting. The Greek CL-215s are used as personnel and supply transports when not required as water bombers, and the Royal Thai Navy flies two on coastal patrol duties.

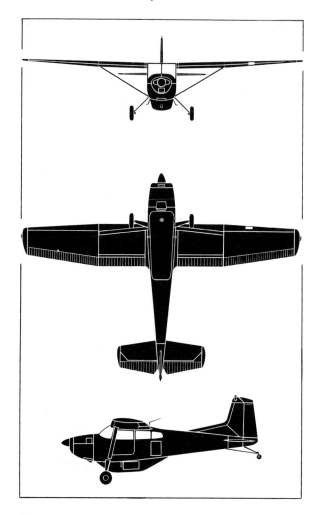

(Top) A Cessna U-17A, the version of the Skywagon widely distributed through US government military aid programmes; (immediately below) a Cessna U-17C variant; (bottom) Cessna 207 Skywagon used by the French Gendarmerie. (Silhouette) Cessna U-17 with cargo pod.

Country of Origin: USA.

Type: General utility monoplane.

Power Plant: One 300 hp Continental IO-520-D six-cylinder horizontally-opposed engine.

Performance: Max speed, 178 mph (286 km/h) at sea level; max cruise, 169 mph (272 km/h) at 7,500 ft (2 285 m); economical cruise, 129 mph (208 km/h) at 10,000 ft (3 050 m); initial rate of climb, 1,010 ft/min (5,1 m/sec); service ceiling, 17,150 ft (5 230 m); range, 660 mls (1 062 km) at max cruise (75 per cent power), range with long-range tanks, 1,075 mls (1 730 km) at economical cruise.

Weights: Empty equipped, 1,585 lb (719 km); max take-off 3,350 lb (1 519 kg).

Dimensions: Span, 35 ft 10 in (10,92 m); length, 25 ft 9 in (7,85 m); height, 7 ft 9 in (2,36 m); wing area, 174 sq ft (16,16 m²).

Accommodation: Pilot and optional arrangements for up to five passengers or cargo in lieu of seats.

Armament: None.

Status: Prototype (Model 185) flown in July 1960. Production totals; U-17A, 262; U-17B, 205; U-17C,7; plus commercial Model 180s and 185s.

Notes: The Cessna Model 185 Skywagon is one of a family of single-engined high-wing Cessna utility aircraft which serve in both military and civil guise. Essentially a multi-purpose derivative of the earlier Model 180 with a strengthened structure, the U-17/Skywagon 185 has removable passenger seats to allow the whole cabin to be used for cargo-carrying. In 1963, the USAF selected the Model 185 for supply to foreign nations receiving US aid through MAP, and the designation U-17 was allocated, although no examples were acquired for use by the USAF itself. The U-17A was equivalent to the Cessna 185C while the U-17B had different equipment. The U-17C was basically the 180H, with O-470-R engine. Nations supplied with U-17s included Bolivia, Costa Rica, Laos, Nicaragua, Turkey and South Vietnam. The South African Air Force acquired 24 similar Cessna 185As in mid-1962 followed by twelve 185Ds and nine 185Es by 1968, all on direct contract; they remained in service in 1981 with No 11 Squadron at Potchefstroom. Numerous other air arms operate Cessna 185s or 180s in small numbers. Some examples operate on skis, floats or as amphibians, and a glass fibre cargo-pak can be carried under the Fuselage. Also operated as a light utility transport are examples of the Cessna U206 Skywagon, T207 Turbo Stationair and the Model 210 Centurion, the last-mentioned featuring a retractable undercarriage.

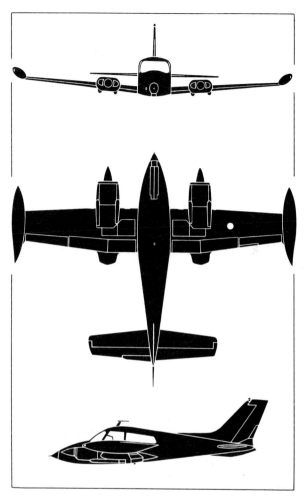

(Top) A Cessna U-3A, originally delivered to the USAF and transferred to the Navy for use at China Lake; (immediately above and below) two views of Cessna 310Ks in service with the Armée de l'Air for communications duty. (Silhouette) Cessna 310R.

Country of Origin: USA.
Type: Communications.
Power Plant: Two (U-3) 240 hp Continental O-470-M or (310K) 260 hp Continental IO-470-V piston engines.
Performance: (U-3A) Max speed, 238 mph (383 km/h) at sea level; typical cruising speed, 181 mph (291 km/h) at 10,000 ft (3 050 m); initial rate of climb, 1,800 ft/min (9,1 m/sec); time to 10,000 ft (3 050 m), 8·6 min; time to 19,800 ft (6 035 m), 34 min; service ceiling, 19,800 ft (6 035 m); range, 1,005 mls (1 617 km) at 181 mph (291 km/h) at 10,000 ft (3 050 m); ferry range, 1,066 mls (1 715 km); max endurance, 6·1 hrs.
Performance: (310K) Max speed, 237 mph (381 km/h) at sea level; max cruising speed, 222 mph (357 km/h) at 75 per cent power at 6,500 ft (1 980 m); economical cruising speed, 179 mph (288 km/h); initial rate of climb, 1,540 ft/min (7,8 m/sec); service ceiling, 19,900 ft (6 065 m); range, 800 mls (1 285 km) at 222 mph (357 km/h) at 6,500 ft (1 980 m).
Weights: (U-3A) Empty equipped, 3,166 lb (1 436 kg); max take-off 4,830 lb (2 190 kg).
Weights: (310K) Empty equipped, 3,110 lb (1 411 kg); max take-off, 5,200 lb (2 360 kg).
Dimensions: Span (U-3A), 35 ft 8½ in (10,88 m); span (310K),

36 ft 11 in (11,25 m); length (U-3A), 27 ft 0 in (8,23 m); length (310K), 29 ft 6 in (8,99 m); height (U-3A), 10 ft 6 in (3,20 m); height (310K), 9 ft 11 in (3,02 m); wing area (U-3A), 175 sq ft (16,26 m²); wing area (310K), 179 sq ft (16,63 m²).
Accommodation: Two pilots and three passengers.
Status: Prototype Cessna 310 first flown on 3 January 1953; first U-3A flown May 1957. Production totals, 5,447 Model 310s, completed 1981, including U-3A, 160 and U-3B, 36.
Notes: The commercial Model 310 was the first of the Cessna twin-engined business transports introduced after World War II, and it remained in production from 1954 until 1981, having undergone progressive development in that time. The USAF contracted on 15 February 1957 for 80 Model 310s to be purchased "off-the-shelf" as communications aircraft, this quantity later being doubled. At first designated L-27As, they were redesignated U-3As and were often known as "Blue Canoes" in the USAF from their blue-and-white finish. Also purchased were 36 U-3Bs, featuring the swept-back fin of later Model 310s, IO-470-D engines and 4,990 lb (2 263 kg) gross weight. Principal U-3A user in 1982 was the US Army National Guard and Army Reserve units with about 40 in service. The French *Armée de l'Air* acquired 12 Model 310Ks for the communications rôle.

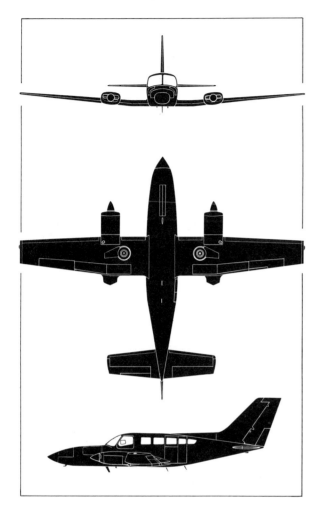

(Above) A Cessna 402 of the Malaysian Air Force; (immediately below) a Cessna 411 used by the Armée de l'Air's VIP transportation unit; (bottom) Cessna 421 operated by No 42 Squadron, RNZAF. (Silhouette) Cessna 402B.

Country of Origin: USA.

Type: Light transport and communications.

Power Plant: Two (402) 300 hp Continental TSIO-520-E or (411) 340 hp Continental GTSIO-520-C piston engines.

Performance: (402) Max speed, 228 mph (367 km/h) at sea level and 261 mph (420 km/h) at 16,000 ft (4 875 m); economical cruise, 215 mph (346 km/h) at 25,000 ft (7 620 m); initial rate of climb, 1,610 ft/min (8,2 m/sec); service ceiling, 26,180 ft (7 980 m); range with standard fuel, 694–808 mls (1 117–1 300 km); range with auxiliary fuel, 972–1,131 mls (1 564–1 820 km).

Performance: (411) Max speed, 232 mph (373 km/h) at sea level and 268 mph (431 km/h) at 16,000 ft (4 875 m); economical cruise, 216 mph (348 km/h) at 25,000 ft (7 620 m); initial rate of climb, 1,900 ft/min (9,7 m/sec); service ceiling, 26,000 ft (7 925 m); max range with standard fuel (no reserves), 1,300 mls (2 090 km).

Weights: (402) Empty equipped, 3,638 lb (1 650 kg); max take-off, 6,300 lb (2 858 kg).

Weights: (411) Empty equipped, 3,865 lb (1 753 kg); max take-off, 6,500 lb (2 948 kg).

Dimensions: (402,411) Span, 39 ft 10¼ in (12,15 m) over tip tanks; length, 33 ft 9 in (10,29 m); height, 11 ft 8 in (3,56 m); wing area (402) 195·7 sq ft (18,18 m²), (411) 200 sq ft (18,58 m²).

Accommodation: Two pilots and up to (411) six or (402) nine passengers in cabin.

Status: Prototype 411 first flown 18 July 1962; prototype 401/402 flown on 26 August 1965; prototype 421 flown 14 October 1965.

Notes: These models in the "400" series are among the largest piston-engined types in the Cessna range of business twins, the Model 411 being the first to appear. Progressive development led to the introduction of the Model 401 as a lower-priced alternative with substantially the same airframe; and the 402 with a reinforced cabin floor and an optional cargo-loading door. The Malaysian Air Force purchased 12 Model 402s, and the French *Armée de l'Air* acquired 12 Model 411s. The Malaysian aircraft, delivered in 1975, are used primarily as crew trainers, with two specially equipped for photographic and liaison duties, and the French 411s are used for communications duty. The Cessna 421 is a little larger and more powerful than the 411 and has a pressurised cabin. Among the users of this variant is the Royal New Zealand Air Force, which acquired three to replace its elderly DH Devons in the communications rôle.

DE HAVILLAND CANADA DHC-2 BEAVER

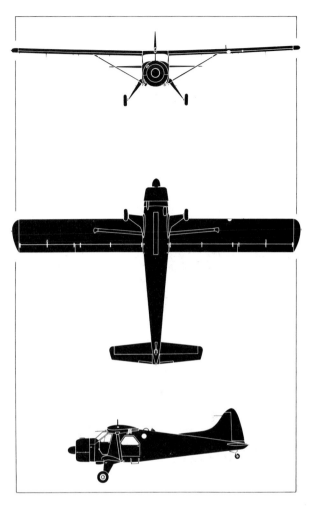

(Top) One of the last few Beaver AL Mk 1s remaining in British Army service in 1982; (immediately above) a Beaver of the Kenya Air Force; (below) a Beaver used by the Indonesian Army (Anghatan Darat). (Silhouette) De Havilland Canada DHC-2 Beaver.

Country of Origin: Canada.
Type: Light utility transport.
Power Plant: One 450 hp Pratt & Whitney R-985-AN Wasp Junior radial.
Performance: Max speed, 140 mph (225 km/h); max cruising speed, 135 mph (217 km/h) at sea level; economical cruising speed, 125 mph (210 km/h); initial rate of climb, 1,020 ft/min (5,2 m/sec); service ceiling, 18,000 ft (5 490 m); range with max payload, 483 mls (777 km); max range, 778 mls (1 252 km).
Weights: Basic operating, 3,000 lb (1 361 kg); max take-off 5,100 lb (2 313 kg).
Dimensions: Span, 48 ft 0 in (14,64 m); length, 30 ft 4 in (9,24 m); height, 9 ft 0 in (2,75 m); wing area, 250 sq ft (23·2 m²).
Accommodation: Pilot and up to seven passengers (provision for dual control if second pilot carried). Floor stressed for freight with lightweight collapsible bush seats interchangeable with cargo attachments.
Status: Prototype first flown August 1947. Certification (civil version) on 12 March 1948. Production deliveries began 1954; total production over 1,657 including 968 for US Army as U-6A (originally L-20A) and six L-20B/U-6B; single Mk II (Leonides engine) first flown in 1953, DHC-2 Mk III Turbo-Beaver first flown

on 30 December, 1963; Volpar/DHC Model 4000 first flown April 1972.
Notes: The Beaver was the second design of the Canadian de Havilland company, and the first of the company's series of "bush" aircraft. It was produced in both civil and military guise, the largest single user being the US Army, which selected the Beaver in 1951. Initially with the designation L-20A, later changed to U-6A, 974 Beavers were supplied to the US services, about one fifth of these going to the USAF, three to the USN, and the remainder to the Army. A few were still in service in 1981. The Beaver was selected for service with the British Army in 1960, 46 being acquired as Beaver AL Mk 1s; 10 of these were still operational in 1981, serving in Northern Ireland. One experimental Beaver II had a Leonides engine; the Beaver III, of which about 60 examples were produced, had a 579 ehp Pratt & Whitney PT6A-6 turboprop, and in 1972 Volpar produced an alternative turboprop conversion scheme using the 715 ehp Garrett AiResearch TPE-331 engine. Beavers entered service in about 70 countries around the world and many air forces acquired examples for use on general transport, communications and liaison duties. Among the more recent operators of the type were Argentina, Colombia, Dominica, Haiti, Indonesia, South Korea, Turkey and Zambia.

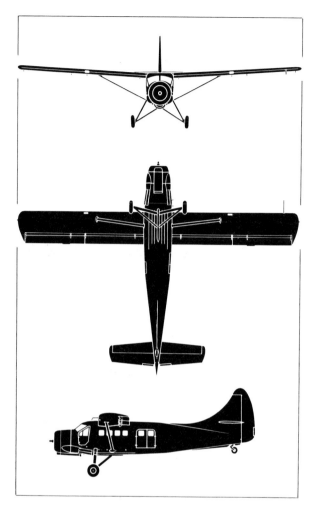

(Above) A de Havilland Otter supplied to the Indian Air Force; (immediately below and bottom) land and water-based examples of the Otter used by the Canadian Air Reserve units as the CSR-123. (Silhouette) De Havilland Canada DHC-3 Otter.

Country of Origin: Canada

Type: Light utility transport.

Power Plant: One 600 hp Pratt & Whitney R-1340-S1H1-G or S3H1-G piston radial engine.

Performance: Max cruising speed, 132 mph (212 km/h) at sea level; best economy cruise, 121 mph (195 km/h) at sea level, initial rate of climb, 850 ft/min (4,3 m/sec); service ceiling (S1H1-G), 18,800 ft (5 730 m), (S3H1-G), 17,400 ft (5,300 m); range with max payload, 875 mls (1 410 km); range with max fuel, 945 mls (1 520 km).

Weights: Basic operating (landplane), 4,431 lb (2 010 kg), (seaplane), 4,892 lb (2 219 kg), (skiplane), 4,652 lb (2 147 kg), (amphibian), 5,412 lb (2 455 kg); max payload 2,100 lb (953 kg); max take-off (landplane, skiplane, amphibian), 8,000 lb (3 629 kg), (seaplane), 7,967 lb (3 614 kg).

Dimensions: Span, 58 ft 0 in (17,69 m); length, 41 ft 10 in, (12,80 m); height, (landplane) 12 ft 7 in (3,83 m), (seaplane), 15 ft 0 in (4,57 m); wing area, 375 sq ft (34,84 m²).

Accommodation: Pilot and co-pilot or passenger side-by-side and nine passengers in main cabin with optional seat for tenth passenger; optional layouts for carriage of six stretchers or assorted freight loads.

Status: Prototype first flown on 12 December 1951. Type certification as landplane and seaplane in November 1952. Production total 460 including 190 for US Army, 16 for the US Navy and 69 for RCAF. Production completed in 1966.

Notes: The Otter evolved from de Havilland experience with the Beaver, having the same primary rôle as a general utility passenger and freight transport to operate in "bush" conditions. From the outset, provision was made for operation of the Otter as a floatplane (in which case a small ventral fin is fitted) and it was the first single-engined aircraft certificated in accordance with the ICAO category D airworthiness requirements. Otters often operate as skiplanes, particularly in Canada, Alaska and Scandinavia, and a later development was an amphibious version, using specially modified Edo floats accommodating retractable main and nose wheels. Major military users of the Otter were the US Army (as the U-1A), the US Navy (as the UC-1, later U-1B) operating in the Antarctic, and the RCAF (later Canadian Armed Forces), which designated the Otter CSR-123. US Army and Navy use has now ended but about 20 CSR-123s were still operational in 1982, some of these with the Canadian Air Reserve, when Otters were also being used in small numbers by a few other air forces in South America and Asia.

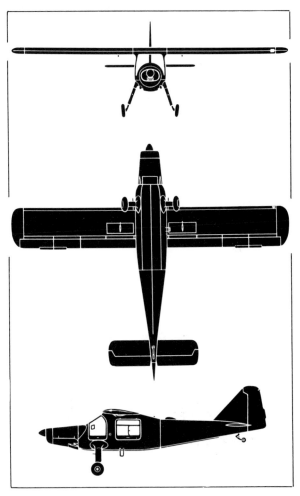

(Top) A Dornier Do 27 (built in Spain by CASA) operated as the L.9 by the Spanish Air Force; (immediately above) Dornier Do 27A serving with the Nigerian Air Force; (below) one of the Do 27As of Israel's Heyl Ha' Avir. (Silhouette) Dornier Do 27.

Country of Origin: Federal Germany.

Type: General utility aircraft and AOP.

Power Plant: (A-4) One 270 hp Lycoming GO-480-B1A6 or (H-2) 340 hp Lycoming GSO-480-B1B6 six-cylinder horizontally-opposed engine.

Performance: (A-4) Max speed, 141 mph (227 km/h) at 3,280 ft (1 000 m); cruising speed (75 per cent power), 130 mph (210 km/h); cruising speed (65 per cent power), 109 mph (175 km/h); initial rate of climb, 650 ft/min (3,3 m/sec); service ceiling, 10,825 ft (3 300 m); range with max fuel (60 per cent power), at 3,280 ft (1 000 m), 685 mls (1 100 km).

Performance: (H-2) Max speed, 152 mph (245 km/h) at 3,280 ft (1 000 m); cruising speed (75 per cent power), 132 mph (212 km/h); cruising speed (65 per cent power), 112 mph (180 km/h); initial rate of climb, 965 ft/min (4,9 m/sec); service ceiling, 22,000 ft (6,700 m); range with max fuel, 845 mls (1 360 km).

Weights: Empty equipped, 2,365 lb (1 072 kg); max take-off, 4,070 lb (1 850 kg).

Dimensions: Span, 39 ft 4½ in (12,0 m); length, 31 ft 6 in (9,6 m); height, 9 ft 2 in (2,8 m); wing area, 208·8 sq ft (19,4 m²).

Accommodation: Two seats side-by-side in cockpit and provi-sion for four to six seats in cabin aft.

Status: First of three prototypes flown on 27 June 1955. First production Do 27A flown on 17 October 1956. Production totals: Do 27A-1, 195; Do 27A-3, 75; Do 17A-4, 52; Do 27B-1, 88; Do 27B-3, 18; Do 27H-1, 1; Do 27H-2, 12; Do 27Q-3, 1; Do 27Q-4, 34; Do 27Q-5, 1; total 571, completed in 1966. In addition, 50 C-127 built by CASA, first example flown on 3 December 1959.

Notes: First post-war design by Professor Claude Dornier was the Do 25, designed and built in Spain to meet a Spanish Air Force requirement for a general purpose light aircraft. Two prototypes were built, the first flight being on 25 June 1954, with a 150 hp ENMA Tigre G-IVB engine, and CASA subsequently built 50 of the production Do 27A version as C-127s for the Spanish Air Force. Examples remaining in service with the *Ejercito del Aire* in 1981 were designated U.9. Principal German production, following three Do 27 prototypes, was for the *Luftwaffe*, which received all the A versions listed above (with only detail differences) and the B version, which had dual control—a total of 428, of which fewer than 50 remained in service in 1981. A few Do 27s were also acquired by other air forces, including those of Burundi, Israel, Malawi, Nigeria, Togo and Turkey, as well as the Swedish Army Aviation Department.

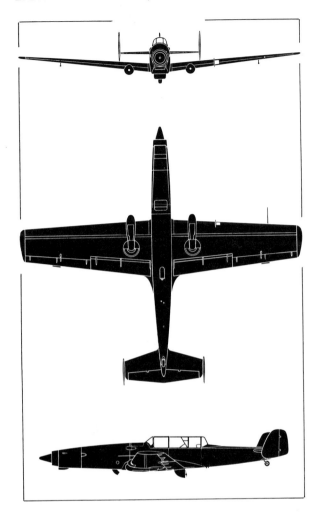

(Above) The prototype EKW C.3605 conversion with turboprop engine; (immediately below and bottom) two of the production-conversion C.3605s in Swiss Flugwaffe service as target tugs. (Silhouette) EKW C.3605.

Country of Origin: Switzerland.

Type: Target towing aircraft.

Power Plant: One 1,150 ehp Avco-Lycoming T5307A (LTC-1) turboprop.

Performance: Max speed, 268 mph (432 km/h) at 10,000 ft (3 050 m); max cruise, 261 mph (420 km/h) at 10,000 ft (3 050 m); economical cruise, 217 mph (350 km/h) at 20,000 ft (6 100 m); initial rate of climb, 2,470 ft/min (12,54 m/sec); service ceiling 32,810 ft (10 000 m); range (internal fuel only) 609 mls (980 km).

Weights: Empty equipped, 5,806 lb (2 634 kg); normal take-off 7,275 lb (3 300 kg); max overload, 8,192 lb (3 716 kg).

Dimensions: Span, 45 ft 1 in (13,74 m); length 39 ft 5¾ in (12,03 m); height, 13 ft 3½ in (4,05 m); wing area, 308·9 sq ft (28·7 m²).

Accommodation: Pilot and observer/winch operator seated in tandem beneath long "glasshouse" canopy.

Status: Prototype (C-3603) first flown on 23 November 1941. Total of 150 delivered to Swiss Air Force by 1948. Prototype conversion to C-3605 flown on 19 August 1968. Conversion of 23 C-3605s completed by end-1972.

Notes: In service with the Swiss Air Force since 1971 as target tugs, the C-3605s are converted from C-3603 reconnaissance bombers, following successful testing of a prototype conversion in 1968/69. The modification, primarily, concerns installation of a Lycoming turboprop in place of the original Hispano-Suiza piston engine, and fitting a winch and target stowage in the fuselage beneath the rear seat. A third, central fin was added after initial testing of the C-3605 prototype with the standard twin fins and rudders of the original design. The C-3605 is not a re-manufactured aircraft, the aim having been to change the engine with minimum alteration to existing structure, an additional section being introduced ahead of the forward fuselage mainframe in order to maintain the existing CG position after installation of the lower-weight turboprop. Both the C-3603 and C-3605 derive from the C-3601 and C-3602 prototypes which were ordered from the EKW concern at Emmen in 1936 and first flew in 1939. A production order was placed in 1940, leading to the appearance of the first C-3603 in November 1941. In addition to 144 C-3603s, the EKW built 10 C-3604s, with more powerful engine and other improvements. Six more C-3603s were assembled from spares in 1947/48 but none now remain in service in the original role. The C-3605s were converted from the 35 C-3603s that had already been converted to serve as target-tugs.

GRUMMAN HU-16 ALBATROSS

(Top) One of the US Coast Guard's HU-16Es, scheduled for retirement from 1982 onwards; (immediately above) an HU-16B serving with the Indonesian Navy; (below) one of the Hellenic Air Force's ASW-equipped HU-16s. (Silhouette) Grumman HU-16E Albatross.

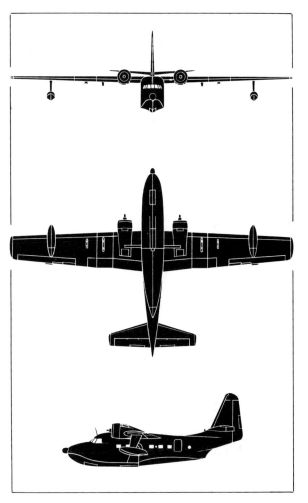

Country of Origin: USA.

Type: Air-sea rescue and reconnaissance amphibian.

Power Plant: Two 1,425 hp Wright R-1820-76A or 76B or (CSR-110) 1,525 hp R-1820-82 radial engines.

Performance: (HU-16B) Max speed, 236 mph (379 km/h); max cruising speed, 224 mph (362 km/h); long range cruise, 124 mph (200 km/h); initial rate of climb, 1,450 ft/min (7,3 m/sec); service ceiling, 21,500 ft (6,550 m); range with max fuel 2,850 mls (4 587 km) with 30 min plus 5 per cent reserve; max endurance (with external tanks) 22·9 hrs.

Weights: (HU-16B) Empty equipped, 22,883 lb (10 380 kg); normal take-off, 30,353 lb (13 768 kg); max overload, 37,500 lb (17 010 kg).

Dimensions: Span (HU-16A), 80 ft 0 in (24,38 m), (HU-16B), 96 ft 8 in (29,46 m); length (HU-16A), 60 ft 8 in (18,49 m), (HU-16B), 62 ft 10 in (19,18 m); height (HU-16A), 24 ft 10 in (7,57 m), (HU-16B), 25 ft 10 in (7,87 m); wing area (HU-16A), 833 sq ft (77,39 m²), (HU-16B), 1,035 sq ft (96,2 m²).

Accommodation: Crew of five or six and up to 12 stretchers (for rescue duty) or up to 22 seats (for transport rôle). Crew of four in ASW rôle.

Armament: (ASW versions only) Four Mk 43 torpedoes or two

Mk 43 torpedoes and two Mk 54-2 or Mk 101 depth charges.

Status: Prototype (XJR2F-1) first flown 24 October 1947; first SA-16B conversion flown 16 January 1956. Production quantities: XJR2F-1, 2; UF-1, 1G, 1L, 111; UF-2, 17; SA-16A, 170; SA-16B, 118, completed 1961.

Notes: Origin of the Albatross was a US Navy requirement for a general-purpose utility amphibian. Production models for the US Navy were UF-1, UF-1L (for Antarctic operation) and UF-1T (trainers), later being redesignated HU-16C, LU-16C and TU-16C. The USAF bought SA-16s (later HU-16As) for air-sea rescue duties, some being completed or later converted to SA-16B (later HU-16B) with bigger wing span and taller tail. Navy aircraft similarly modified became UF-2 (later HU-16D) and the US Coast Guard acquired 34 UF-1G (UF-2G when modified, then redesignated HU-16E). Through MAP and other programmes, the Albatross was supplied to some 12 other nations, and a special ASW version with nose-mounted search radar was supplied to Norway and Spain. The 16 Norwegian aircraft were later passed on to Greece and Spain, and eight continued in service with the Hellenic Air Force in 1981. Other late users of the amphibian included Argentina, Brazil, Chile, Nationalist China, Indonesia, Mexico, Pakistan, the Philippines, Thailand and Venezuela.

(Above) One of the Luftwaffe's VIP transport Hansas, eight of which were acquired; (immediately below and bottom) air and ground views of the Hansajet as equipped for ECM training in Luftwaffe service. (Silhouette) MBB (HFB) 320 Hansa.

Country of Origin: Federal Germany.

Type: VIP transport, radio and radar calibration and ECM missions.

Power Plant: Two 2,850 lb st (1 293 kgp) General Electric CJ610-1 or 2,950 lb st (1 340 kgp) CJ610-5 or 3,100 lb st (1 406 kgp) CJ610-9 turbojets.

Performance: (with CJ610-9 engines); Max cruising speed, 513 mph (825 km/h) at 25,000 ft (7 620 m); best economy cruise, 420 mph (675 km/h) at 35,000 ft (10 670 m); initial rate of climb, 4,250 ft/min (21,6 m/sec); operational ceiling, 40,000 ft (12 200 m); range with max fuel, 1,472 mls (2,370 km).

Weights: Basic operating (passenger); 11,960 lb (5 425 kg), (cargo), 11,874 lb (5,386 kg); max payload (passenger), 3,913 lb (1 775 kg), (cargo) 4,000 lb (1 814 kg); max take-off, 20,280 lb (9 200 kg).

Dimensions: Span, 47 ft 6 in (14,49 m); length 54 ft 6 in (16,61 m); height, 16 ft 2 in (4,94 m); wing area, 324·4 sq ft (30,14m²).

Accommodation: Flight crew of two and typical arrangements for up to seven passengers in executive version and up to 12 passengers and a stewardess in commuter airline versions.

Armament: None.

Status: Two prototypes, first flown on 21 April and 19 October 1964 respectively. First production model flown on 2 February 1966. Production total 47, including 16 for *Luftwaffe*.

Notes: A product of the Hamburger Flugzeugbau before its merger into MBB, the Hansa was notable for its configuration, with the wing swept forward. Intended primarily for the business/executive market, the Hansa sold only in limited numbers. The first 15 Hansas had the CJ610-1 engine, followed by 20 with the -5; the -9 engine was introduced with the 31st aircraft. Optional modifications on the final production batch permitted an increased gross weight of 21,160 lb (9 600 kg) accompanied by an increase of 880 lb (400 kg) in the maximum payload that could be carried. Eight Hansas were originally acquired by the *Luftwaffe*, two going to *Erprobungsstelle* 61 (EST 61) for experimental and communications flying and the other six going to the *Flugbereitschaftstaffel* (FBS) at Köln-Bonn as part of the fleet available for VIP transportation duties. The *Luftwaffe* subsequently acquired eight more Hansas when commercial sales declined, the last of these being delivered in 1980. These later aircraft were modified by MBB with nose radomes and other special equipment to serve in the ECM training rôle, being operated by FVST 61 at Neubiberg, this unit also being responsible for airways calibration flying with the Hansas.

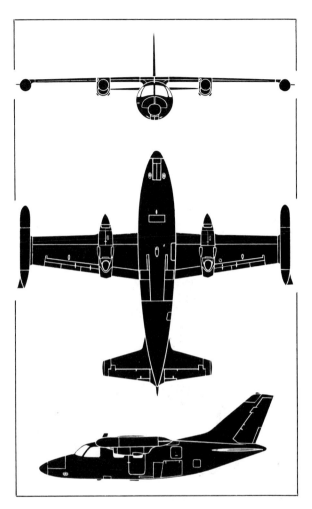

(Top and immediately above) Air and ground views of the Mitsubishi MU-2S as operated by the JASDF for search and rescue missions; (below) the MU-2C used by the JGSDF for liaison and reconnaissance duties. (Silhouette) Mitsubishi MU-2F.

Country of Origin: Japan.

Type: Light transport, liaison and search and rescue aircraft.

Power Plant: Two (MU-2C, MU-2E) 605 ehp Garrett AiResearch TPE 331-25A or (MU-2K) 724 ehp TPE 331-6-251M turboprops.

Performance: Max cruising speed, 310 mph (500 km/h) at 10,000 ft (3 050 m); economical cruising speed, 280 mph (450 km/h) at 20,000 ft (6 100 m); initial rate of climb, 2,220 ft/min (11,3 m/sec); service ceiling, 26,000 ft (7 900 m); max range, 1,300 mls (2 100 km).

Weights: Empty equipped, 5,650 lb (2 560 kg); max take-off (MU-2C) 9,350 lb (4 240 kg), (MU-2E) 10,053 lb (4 560 kg).

Dimensions: Span, over tip tanks, 39 ft 2 in (11,95 m); length, 33 ft 3 in (10,13 m); height, 12 ft 11 in (3,94 m); wing area, 178 sq ft (16,54 m²).

Accommodation: Two pilots side-by-side on flight deck and up to nine passengers in cabin.

Status: Prototype MU-2A first flown on 14 September 1963; first MU-2C (LR-1) flown 11 May 1967; first MU-2E (MU-2S) flown 15 August 1967. First delivery, MU-2C on 30 June 1967. Production total, over 700 by early 1982, including eight MU-2C/LR-1 for JGSDF, 16 MU-2E/MU-2S and seven MU-2K/MU-2A for JASDF.

Notes: The MU-2 was designed primarily to serve as a light business transport and the great majority of those produced have been sold in this role. The original MU-2A prototypes had Turboméca Astazou IIK engines but the Garrett TPE331, in its different versions, has powered all the successive production models, from the MU-2B to the MU-2L, some of which have longer fuselages. The Japanese armed forces were early customers for MU-2s, the Ground Self-Defence Force ordering four MU-2Cs for use in the liaison and communications rôle in 1966. Designated LR-1 in military guise, the MU-2C is unpressurized (unlike its commercial counterpart) and optional equipment includes one vertical and one flexibly-mounted oblique camera for the secondary reconnaissance rôle, or two 13-mm nose-mounted machine guns, bombs and rockets. Four more LR-1s acquired later were similar to the commercial MU-2K, with uprated engines. The Air Self Defence Force has purchased 23 MU-2s to serve in the search and rescue rôle, these featuring Doppler radar for navigation (in a nose radome), bulged observation windows and an air-openable door to permit lifeboats to be dropped. The first 16 of these SAR aircraft were designated MU-2E by Mitsubishi but MU-2S by the JASDF; the final seven, however, were based on the commercial MU-2K and had the official designation MU-2A.

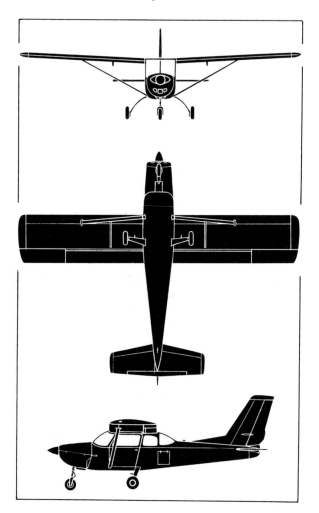

(Above and immediately below) Two views of a Neiva Regente operated as the L-42 for liaison duties with the Fôrça Aérea Brasileira; (bottom) the C-42 version of the Regente, which serves in the communications rôle. (Silhouette) Neiva Regente.

Country of Origin: Brazil.

Type: Air observation post and liaison aircraft.

Power Plant: One (C-42) 180 hp Lycoming O-360-A1D four-cylinder or (L-42) 210 hp Continental IO-360-D six-cylinder horizontally-opposed engine.

Performance: (C-42) Max speed, 137 mph (220 km/h) at sea level; cruising speed, 132 mph (212 km/h) at 5,100 ft (1 550 m); initial rate of climb, 690 ft/min (3,5 m/sec); service ceiling, 11,800 ft (3 600 m); range with max payload, 651 mls (904 km); range with max fuel, 576 mls (928 km).

Performance: (L-42) Max speed, 153 mph (246 km/h) at sea level; max cruising speed, 142 mph (229 km/h) at sea level; cruising speed (75 per cent power), 134 mph (216 km/h) at 5,000 ft (1 525 m); initial rate of climb, 918 ft/min (4,7 m/sec); service ceiling, 15,810 ft (4 820 m); range with max payload, 547 mls (925 km); range with max fuel, 590 mls (950 km).

Weights: (C-42) Empty equipped, 1,410 lb (640 kg); max take-off, 2,293 lb (1 040 kg).

Weights: (L-42) Empty equipped, 1,622 lb (736 kg); max take-off, 2,293 lb (1 040 kg).

Dimensions: Span, 29 ft 11½ in (9,13 m); length, 23 ft 7¾ in (7,21 m); height, 9 ft 7¼ in (2,93 m); wing area, 144·8 sq ft (13,45 m²).

Accommodation: (L-42) Two seats side-by-side for pilot and co-pilot or observer and third seat in rear of cabin for navigator or observer.

Armament: None.

Status: Prototype (Model 360C) first flown on 7 September 1961; first production C-42 flown in February 1965 and production of 80 completed in 1968. Prototype YL-42 flown in October 1967; first production L-42 flown in June 1969 and production of 40 completed in March 1971.

Notes: Brazil's Neiva company (taken over during 1980 by the State-owned EMBRAER) produced a series of light aircraft of conventional high-wing design, the first with an all-metal airframe being the Model 360C Regente in 1961. This type was ordered into production for the Brazilian Air Force, which assigned it the designation U-42 (later changed to C-42) as a light utility aircraft. Eighty were built, these aircraft being four-seaters. A second variant, the Regente 420L, was evolved more specifically for AOP duties, having a cut-down rear fuselage and "all-round" cabin transparencies and was designated L-42 in service. In 1981, the Fôrça Aérea Brasileira had about 50 C-42 Regentes still in service in addition to the L-42s.

PIAGGIO PD-808

(Top) Piaggio PD-808 in service with the Italian Air Force's Reparto Sperimentale di Volo at Pratica di Mare for communications duties; (immediately above and below) the PD-808 light-transport. (Silhouette) Piaggio PD-808.

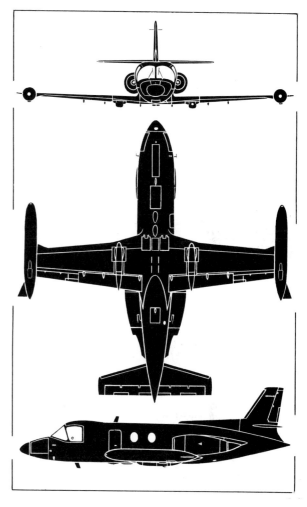

Country of Origin: Italy.

Type: Staff and personnel transport and trainer.

Power Plant: Two 3,360 lb st (1 524 kgp) Rolls-Royce (Piaggio) Viper 526 turbojets.

Performance: Max level speed, 529 mph (852 km/h) at 19,500 ft (5 945 km); high speed cruise, 497 mph (800 km/h) at 36,000 ft (11 000 m); long-range cruise, 449 mph (722 km/h) at 41,000 ft (12 500 m); initial rate of climb, 5,400 ft/min (27,5 m/sec); service ceiling, 45,000 ft (13 715 m); range with max fuel, 1,322 mls (2 128 km) with payload of 840 lb (381 kg).

Weights: Empty equipped, 10,650 lb (4 830 kg); max payload, 1,600 lb (726 kg); max take-off, 18,000 lb (8 165 kg); max landing 16,000 lb (7 257 kg).

Dimensions: Span, 43 ft 3½ in (13,20 m); length, 42 ft 2 in 12,80 m); height, 15 ft 9 in (4,80 m); wing area, 225 sq ft (20,9 m²).

Accommodation: Flight crew of two; six (VIP) or nine (communications) passenger seats in cabin.

Armament: None.

Status: First and second prototypes flown on 29 August 1964 and 14 June 1966 respectively; civil certification on 29 November 1966. Production of 22 completed in 1973.

Notes: Originally known as the Vespa-Jet, the PD-808 was designed basically by the Douglas Aircraft Company's El Segundo Division, with detail design and manufacture undertaken by Piaggio. Intended for the civil market, the PD-808 was in the end ordered only by the Italian Air Force, which in 1965 ordered a batch of 25 (later reduced to 22). Included in the production batch delivered to the Air Force were aircraft in four different configurations, examples of which continued in service in 1982. They included four with VIP interiors, six for electronic counter-measures with special equipment and five-man crew, eight nine-seat communications aircraft, and four for checking Italy's airways and navigational systems. The nine-seat version may also be employed in the navigational training rôle, with one student station at the co-pilot's seat and either two or three more students' stations in the main cabin. The ECM version took the designation PD-808RM and these aircraft are used by the 8° *Gruppe* of the 14° *Stormo Reparto Radiomisure* at Pratica di Mare, this unit also being responsible for operation of the airways checking and calibration aircraft. The PD-808TA transports and the VIP-furnished aircraft are operated principally by the 306° *Gruppo Reparto Volo Stato Maggiore* (Air Staff Flying Unit) based at Rome Ciampino. A projected version of the PD-808 with Garrett TFE 731-1 turbofans was not built.

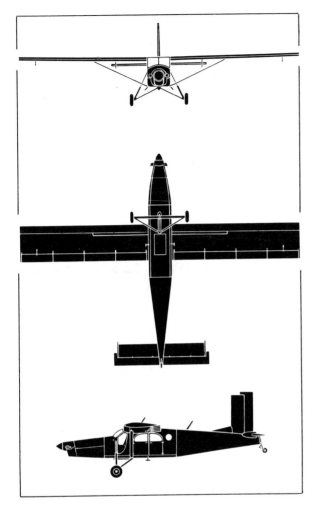

(Above) One of two Turbo Porters operated in Berlin by the US Army as the UV-20 Chiricahua; (immediately below) a Turbo Porter serving with Switzerland's Flugwaffe and (bottom) a similar aircraft operated by the Australian Army. (Silhouette) Pilatus PC-6B Turbo Porter.

Country of Origin: Switzerland/USA.

Type: Light utility and armed observation aircraft.

Power Plant: One (PC-6/A) 523 shp Turboméca Astazou IIG; (PC-6/A1) 573 shp Astazou XII; (PC-6/A2) 573 shp Astazou XIVE; (PC-6/B) 550 shp Pratt & Whitney PT6A-6A; (PC-6/B1) 550 shp PT6A-20; (PC-6/B2) 550 shp PT6A-27; (PC-6/C) 575 shp Garrett TPE 331-25D or (PC-6/C1 and AU-23A) 576 shp TPE 331-1-100 turboprop engine.

Performance: (PC-6/C1 and AU-23A) Max cruising speed, 164 mph (264 km/h) at 10,000 ft (3 050 m); economical cruising speed, 144 mph (231 km/h) at 10,000 ft (3 050 m); initial rate of climb, 1,607 ft/min (8,2 m/sec); service ceiling, 27,875 ft (8 500 m); range with max internal fuel, 683 mls (1 100 km); range with two external fuel tanks, 1,044 mls (1 680 km).

Weights: Empty equipped, 2,612 lb (1 185 kg); max take-off and landing, 4,850 lb (2 200 kg).

Dimensions: Span, 49 ft 8 in (15,13 m); length (Astazou engine), 36 ft 4½ in (11,08 m); length (PT6A engine), 36 ft 1 in (11,00 m); length (TPE 331 engine), 35 ft 9 in (10,90 m); height, 10 ft 6 in (3,20 m); wing area, 310 sq ft (28,80 m²).

Accommodation: Pilot and up to nine other occupants.

Armament: (AU-23A only) One hardpoint under fuselage with capacity of 590 lb (268 kg); four underwing strong points, with capacity of 510 lb (231 kg) inner and 350 lb (159 kg) outer; max external load 2,000 lb (906 kg). Provision in cabin for two 7·62-mm miniguns or one 20-mm cannon.

Status: Prototype PC-6 flown 4 May 1959; first turboprop version (PC-6/A) flown 2 May 1961; first PC-6/B flown 1 May 1964; first PC-6/C (by Fairchild) flown October 1965, (by Pilatus) flown 4 March 1966. Production total, all varients, over 420 by 1982.

Notes: The Turbo-Porter was evolved from the piston-engined Porter (a few examples of which are also in military service). The Australian Army bought a total of 14 PC-6/B-1s, and other customers have included air arms in Argentine, Austria, Bolivia, Burma, Chad, Columbia, Nepal, Peru, Sudan and Switzerland. In 1966, Fairchild in the USA began production of Turbo 100 Porters, and in 1970, an armed version was developed with the characteristics indicated above. The USAF bought 15 of this AU-23A armed variant for evaluation, supplying 13 of these to the Royal Thai Air Force, which subsequently acquired 20 more; the Thai Police bought five. In 1979, the US Army bought two Turbo-Porters for service in Berlin, these aircraft being designated UV-20A and named Chiricahua.

PILATUS BRITTEN-NORMAN DEFENDER AND ISLANDER   LIGHT TRANSPORT/UTILITY

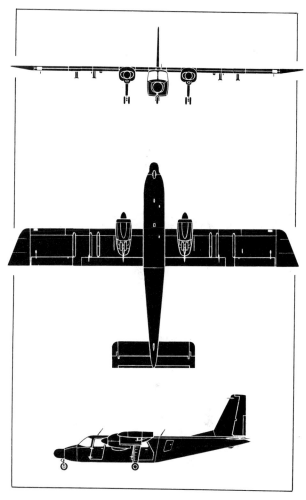

(Top) A Britten-Norman Islander serving with the Hong Kong Auxiliary Air Force; (below) a Mauritanian Air Force Defender with underwing rockets. (Silhouette) Pilatus Britten-Norman Defender with nose radome.

Country of Origin: United Kingdom.

Type: Multi-rôle light utility aircraft.

Power Plant: Two 300 hp Avco Lycoming IO-540-K1B5 piston engines.

Performance: (Clean) Max speed, 174 mph (280 km/h); cruising speeds, 159 mph (255 km/h) at 10,000 ft (3 050 m) at 67 per cent power and 141 mph (227 km/h) at 2,000 ft (610 m) at 59 per cent power; initial rate of climb, 1,300 ft/min (6,6 m/sec); service ceiling, 17,000 ft (5 180 m); range with max payload, 418 mls (672 km); range with standard fuel, 1,260 mls (2 027 km).

Performance: (With stores on wing pylons) Max speed, 166 mph (266 km/h); cruising speeds, 150 mph (242 km/h) at 10,000 ft (3 050 m) at 67 per cent power and 133 mph (215 km/h) at 2,000 ft (610 m) at 59 per cent power; initial rate of climb, 1,170 ft/min (5,9 m/sec); service ceiling, 17,000 ft (5 180 m); range with max payload, 375 mls (603 km).

Weights: Empty equipped, 4,020 lb (1 824 kg); max take-off, 6,600 lb (2 993 kg).

Dimensions: Span, 49 ft 0 in (14,94 m); span with extended tips, 53 ft 0 in (16,15 m); length, without radome; 35 ft 7¾ in (10,86 m); length with nose radome, 36 ft 3¾ in (11,07 m); height, 13 ft 8¾ in (4,18 m); wing area, 325.0 sq ft (30,19 m²).

Accommodation: Pilot and up to nine passengers, or three stretchers with two attendants.

Armament: Four wing strong points with a capacity of 700 lb (317,5 kg) each inboard and 450 lb (204 kg) outboard.

Status: First BN-2 Islander flown 13 June 1965, second prototype flown 20 August 1966; first production BN-2 flown 24 April 1967; first Defender flown 20 May 1971. Production total, over 1,000 including civil BN-2 Islanders by early 1982.

Notes: The Islander was conceived in 1963 as a light transport in the category of a D.H.89A Dragon Rapide replacement, at first powered by 210 hp engines but produced for civil use with 260 hp or 300 hp engines. The original Britten Norman company was later acquired by Fairey and is now part of the Swiss Oerlikon-Buhle group associated with Pilatus. Some Islanders were purchased as light transports for military use, for example by the Abu Dhabi Defence Force, Ghana Air Force and Jamaica Defence Force. More specifically equipped for military duties, the Defender has been acquired in some numbers by the Sultan of Oman's Air Force, Malagasy Air Force, Belgian Army, Indian Navy, Mauritanian Islamic Air Force, Guyana Defence Force, Botswana Defence Force and Philippine Navy, and by several other air arms. Most Defenders have nose-mounted radar and wing pylons.

(Above) One of the Piper U-11A Aztecs originally delivered to the US Navy and operated later by the US Marine Corps; (immediately below) an EMBRAER-built Piper Seneca II used in Brazil as the U-7; (bottom) U-7s of the Fôrça Aérea Brasileira. (Silhouette) Piper U-11 Aztec.

Country of Origin: USA.

Type: Light twin-engined transport and general utility aircraft.

Power Plant: Two (U-11A) 250 hp Lycoming O-540-A1D5 or (U-7) 200 hp Continental TSIO-360-E engines.

Performance: (U-11A) Max speed, 208 mph (335,km/h) at sea level; average cruise, 135 mph (217 km/h) at 31 per cent power at 7,000 ft (2 134 m); initial rate of climb, 1,620 ft/min (8,2 m/sec); time to 20,000 ft (6 100 m); service ceiling, 20,900 ft (6370 m); range, 1,160 mls (1 869 km).

Performance: (U-7) Max speed, 225 mph (361 km/h) at 12,000 ft (3 660 m); cruising speed, 177 mph (285 km/h) at 55 per cent power at 10,000 ft (3 050 m); initial rate of climb, 1,340 ft/min (6,8 m/sec); operational ceiling, 25,000 ft (7 620 m); range, 714 mls (1 148 km).

Weights: (U-11A) Empty, 3,020 lb (1 370 kg); max take-off, 4,800 lb (2 177 kg).

Weights: (U-7) Empty 2,841 lbs (1 289 kg); max take-off, 4,570 lb (2 073 kg).

Dimensions: (U-11A) Span, 37 ft 1¾ in (11,31 m); length, 27 ft 7¾ in (8,43 m); height, 10 ft 3½ in (3,13 m); wing area, 207 sq ft (19,23 m²).

Dimensions: (U-7) Span, 38 ft 10¾ in (11,85 m); length, 28 ft 7½ in (8,72 m); height, 9 ft 10¾ in (3,02 m); wing area, 208·7 sq ft (19,39 m²).

Accommodation: Pilot plus (U-11A) three or (U-7) five passengers.

Status: U-11A Aztec first flown 16 October 1958, first delivered 19 August 1961. PA-34-200T first delivered 1972.

Notes: The U-11A designation applies to the survivors of a batch of 20 Piper PA-23 Aztecs purchased off-the-shelf by the US Navy in 1958 under the designation UO-1. Several other air arms have acquired later variants of the Aztec family, including the Spanish Air Force, which has six Turbo Aztec Es in service as E.19s; these are powered by the 250 hp TIO-540-C1A engines and are used by *Escuadrón* 423 to give refresher training to general duty officers. Among other users of Aztecs are the *Armée de l'Air* in France and the air forces of Malagasy, Nigeria, Senegal and Uganda and the Peruvian Navy. The slightly larger Piper PA-34-200T Seneca serves as a communications aircraft in the Brazilian Air Force with the local desigation U-7, a total of 32 having been acquired since 1976 from the EMBRAER licence-production line. Among the smaller Piper twins in military use are a pair of Twin Comanches serving with Spain's *Arma Aerea de la Armada* (Naval Air Arm) with the designation E.31.

PIPER PA-31 NAVAJO CHIEFTAIN (AND CHEYENNE)   LIGHT TRANSPORT/UTILITY

*(Top) Piper PA-31 used by French Aéronavale for communications flying;
(immediately above) PA-31T Navajo used for instrument training as E.18 by
the Spanish Air Force; (below) PA-31P of the Kenya Air Force. (Silhouette)
Piper PA-31 Navajo.*

Country of Origin: USA.

Type: Light transport, training, survey and maritime patrol.

Power Plant: Two (Chieftain) 350 hp Avco Lycoming TIO-540-J2BD piston engines or (Cheyenne) 620 ehp Pratt & Whitney Canada PT6A-28 turboprops.

Performance: (Chieftain) Max speed, 266 mph (428 km/h); cruising speed, 254 mph (409 km/h) at 75 per cent power at 20,000 ft (6 100 m) and 199 mph (320 km/h) at 55 per cent power at 12,000 ft (3 660 m); initial rate of climb, 1,120 ft/min (5,7 m/sec); service ceiling, 27,200 ft (8 290 m); range, approximately 1,000 mls (1 610 km).

Performance: (Cheyenne) Cruising speed, 325 mph (524 km/h) at 11,000 ft (3 350 m) and 287 mph (463 km/h) at 29,000 ft (8 840 m); initial rate of climb, 660 ft/min (3,35 m/sec); service ceiling, 31,600 ft (9 630 m); max range, 1,740 mls (2 800 km).

Weights: (Chieftain) Empty, 4,221 lb (1 915 kg); max take-off, 7,000 lb (3 175 kg).

Weights: (Cheyenne) Empty, 4,980 lb (2 259 kg); max take-off, 9,000 lb (4 082 kg).

Dimensions: (Chieftain) Span, 40 ft 8 in (12,40 m); length, 34 ft 7½ in (10,55 m); height, 13 ft 0 in (3,96 m); wing area, 229 sq ft (21,3 m²).

Dimensions: (Cheyenne) Span, 42 ft 8¼ in (13,01 m); length, 34 ft 8 in (10,57 m); height, 12 ft 9 in (3,98 m); wing area, 229 sq ft (21,3 m²).

Accommodation: Two pilots side-by-side and up to (Chieftain) eight or (Cheyenne) six passengers in cabin.

Status: PA-31 Navajo prototype first flown on 30 September 1964; Navajo Chieftain introduced 1972; PA-31T Cheyenne prototype first flown 20 August 1969.

Notes: The Navajo, in its original six-eight seat business transport form, was introduced by Piper in 1965 as the largest aircraft in its range. The most important of several subsequent variants was the PA-31-350 Navajo Chieftain, featuring a lengthened fuselage and a reinforced cabin floor for concentrated cargo loads. The Chieftain has found some military applications, as have the earlier versions, the largest single user being the French *Aéronavale* with 12 for communications and instrument training duties. Other users include the Argentine Navy, Chilean Army, and Spanish, Nigerian, Syrian and Kenya air forces. The PA-31T Cheyenne is essentially the Navajo airframe with turboprop engines and wing-tip tanks; a maritime surveillance variant has pod-mounted radar under the port wing and other special equipment and two of these surveillance Cheyennes were supplied in 1981 to Mauritania.

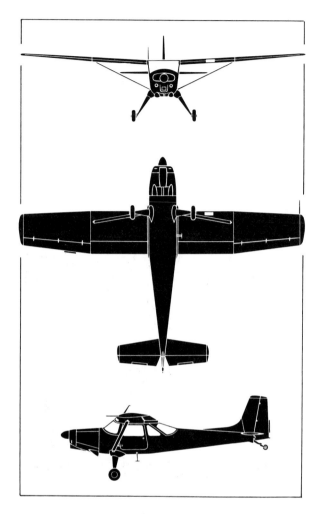

(Above and immediately below) Two views of the UTVA-60 civil prototype, from which the military UTVA-66 was derived for the Yugoslav Air Force; (bottom) an UTVA-66 in military service. (Silhouette) UTVA-66.

Country of Origin: Yugoslavia.

Type: Light utility and observation aircraft.

Power Plant: One (UTVA-60) 270 hp Lycoming GO-480-B1A6, (UTVA-60H) 296 hp Lycoming GO-480-G1H6 or (UTVA-66) 250 hp Lycoming GSO-480-B1J6 six cylinder horizontally-opposed engine.

Performance: (UTVA-60-AT1) Max speed, 157 mph (252 km/h); max cruise, 143 mph (230 km/h); economical cruise, 114 mph (184 km/h); initial rate of climb, 1,260 ft/min (6,4 m/sec); service ceiling, 17,060 ft (5 200 m); range 485 mls (780 km).

Performance: (UTVA-66) Max speed, 155 mph (250 km/h); max cruise, 143 mph (230 km/h); initial rate of climb, 885 ft/min (4,5 m/sec); service ceiling, 22,000 ft (6 700 m); range 466 mls (750 km).

Weights; (UTVA-60-AT1); Empty equipped, 2,100 lb (952 kg); normal take-off, 3,192 lb (1 448 kg); max take-off, 3,571 lb (1,620 kg).

Weights: (UTVA-66); Empty equipped, 2,756 lb (1 250 kg); max take-off, 4,000 lb (1 184 kg).

Dimensions: Span, 37 ft 5 in (11,40 m); length (UTVA-60), 26 ft 11½ in (8,22 m); length (UTVA-66), 27 ft 6 in (8,38 m); height (UTVA-60), 8 ft 11 in (2,72 m); height (UTVA-66), 10 ft 6 in (3,20 m); wing area, 195·5 sq ft (18,08 m²).

Armament: (UTVA-66V) Two wing hardpoints for bombs, rockets, rocket pods or Matra AA. 52 7,62-mm gun pods.

Accommodation: Pilot and three passengers or two stretchers.

Status: Prototype (UTVA-56) flown 22 April 1959; prototype UTVA-60H flown 29 October 1961; prototype UTVA-66 flown in 1966; prototype UTVA-66H flown September 1968; prototype UTVA-66V flown 1974.

Notes: The series of UTVA high-wing light aircraft began in 1959 with the UTVA-56. This was "productionised" as the UTVA-60, and put into production for the Yugoslav Air Force. Several versions were designated, including the UTVA-60-AT1 basic four-seater for utility use; the 60-AT2 with dual controls for use as a trainer; the 60-AG equipped for agricultural duties; the 60-AM ambulance version with accommodation for two stretchers and the 60-H float-plane with twin Edo floats. The UTVA-66 introduced fixed slots on the wing leading edge, larger tail unit and strengthened undercarriage. Variants that have entered service with the Yugoslav Air Force include the basic UTVA-66 and the UTVA-66V with underwing armament. The UTVA-66-AM can carry two stretchers plus attendant and pilot, and the UTVA-66H is a floatplane with BIN-1600 floats.

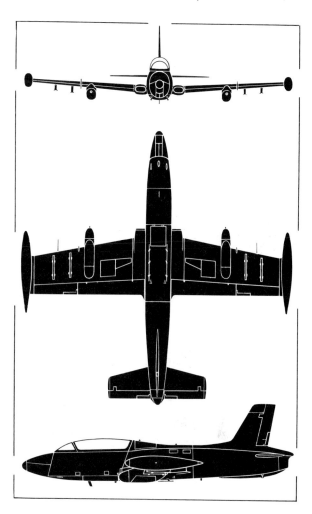

(Top) An Aermacchi MB-326H operating with the Royal Australian Navy; (immediately above) a Brazilian-built MB-326GB (EMBRAER AT-26) Xavante; (below) an MB-326GB of the Argentine Navy. (Silhouette) Aermacchi MB-326GB.

Country of Origin: Italy.

Type: Basic trainer and light strike aircraft.

Power Plant: One 2,500 lb st (1 134 kgp) Rolls-Royce (MB-326B D and H) Viper 11 or (MB 326G, GB, F and M), 3,410 lb st (1 547 kgp) Viper 20 Mk 540 turbojet.

Performance: (MB-326G, clean) Max speed, 539 mph (867 km/h); max cruising speed, 495 mph (797 km/h); initial rate of climb, 6,050 ft/min (31,5 m/sec); service ceiling, 47,000 ft (14 325 m); range, internal and tip tanks, 1,150 mls (1 850 km); range, with underwing tanks, 1,520 mls (2 445 km).

Weights: (MB-326G, unarmed trainer) Basic operating, 6,920 lb (2 685 kg); max take-off (clean), 10,090 lb (4 577 kg); max take-off (armed), 11,500 lb (5 216 kg).

Dimensions: Span (over tip tanks), 35 ft 7 in (10,85 m); length, 35 ft 0¼ in (10,67 m); height, 12 ft 2½ in (3,72 m); wing area, 208·3 sq ft (19,4 m²).

Accommodation: Two in tandem.

Armament: (MB-326F, G) Provision for up to 4,000 lb (1 814 kg) of bombs, gun pods, rockets, etc, on six wing pylons.

Status: Prototype MB-326 (Viper 8) flown on 10 December 1957; first production MB-326 flown on 5 October 1960. First MB-326GB flown in Brazil 3 September 1971. Production totals:

Prototypes, 2; MB-326 (Italian Air Force), 124; MB-326E (Italian Air Force), 6; MB-326B (Tunisia), 8; MB-326D (Alitalia), 4; MB-326F (Ghana), 9; MB-326GB (Zaire), 17, (Argentine Navy), 8, (Zambia), 23; MB-326GB (Brazil), 182 (built by EMBRAER as AT-26 Xavante); MB-326H (Australia), 12 plus 85 built by CAC; MB-326M (South Africa), 151 including 135 produced by Atlas as Impala I, built 1966–1974.

Notes: The Italian Air Force uses the original MB-326, the improved MB-326E which has new equipment and the six wing strong points of the later MB-326G (six conversions and six new-built), and the MB-326M (five conversions) for radio/navaid calibration. Other export models are noted above; in addition, EMBRAER in Brazil sold six Xavante to Togo and nine to Paraguay. Of the 97 supplied to or built in Australia, the RAN uses 10 and RAAF the balance. South Africa imported 16 MB-326Ms for assembly by Atlas in 1966, followed about a year later by the first example of largely local manufacture, the last of 135 being delivered on 29 August 1974. As the Impala I, the MB-326M is used by Nos. 4, 5, 6, 7 and 8 Squadrons, the FTS and No 85 Advanced Flying School. The MB-326L is in effect a two-seat version of the MB-326K (separately described), supplied to Dubai (two) and Tunisia (four).

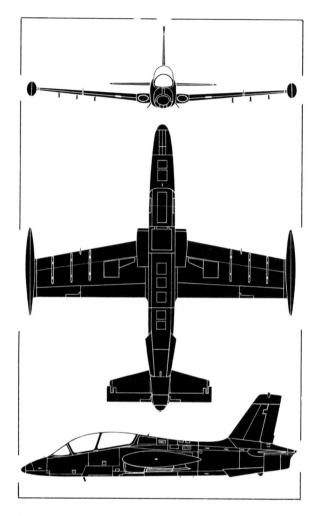

(Above) An Aermacchi MB-339A carrying a variety of weapons while undergoing flight testing; (immediately below) the first production MB-339A and (bottom) an MB-339A in service with the calibration squadron of the AMI at Pratica di Mare. (Silhouette) Aermacchi MB-339A.

Country of Origin: Italy.
Type: Two-seat basic and advanced trainer.
Power Plant: One 4,000 lb (1 814 kg) Fiat-built Rolls Royce Viper 632-43 turbojet.
Performance: Max speed (clean configuration), 558 mph (898 km/h) at sea level, 508 mph (817 km/h) at 30,000 ft (9 145 m) or Mach 0·77; initial climb, 6,600 ft/min (33,5 m/sec); service ceiling, 47,500 ft (14 630 m); max range (clean configuration), 1,094 mls (1 760 km), (ferry configuration with two 143-Imp gal/650-l pylon tanks), 1,310 mls (2 110 km).
Weights: Empty equipped, 6,883 lb (3 125 kg); normal take-off weight (clean), 9,700 lb (4 400 kg); max take-off, 13,000 lb (5 897 kg).
Dimensions: Span, 35 ft 7 in (10,86 m); length, 36 ft 0 in (10,97 m); height, 13 ft 1 in (3,99 m); wing area, 207·74 sq ft (19,30 m²).
Accommodation: Two in tandem.
Armament: A maximum of 4,000 lb (1 815 kg) distributed between six underwing stations.
Status: Two prototypes (MB-339X) flown on 12 August 1976 and 20 May 1977, respectively, and first of six pre-series (MB-339A) aicraft flown on 20 July 1978, with first two examples

accepted by Italian Air Force on 9 August 1979. Sales/orders: Italian Air Force, 100; Argentine Navy (10, first delivery November 1980); Peruvian Air Force (16, first delivery late 1981).
Notes: Based on the airframe of the earlier MB-326 and incorporating the strengthened structure of the MB-326K, the MB-339 incorporates an entirely redesigned forward fuselage providing vertically staggered seats for pupil and instructor. It also has provision to carry an extensive variety of external stores on the six wing hard points, up to a combined total of 4,000 lb (1 815 kg), including AAMs such as the Sidewinder and Matra 550 Magic on the two outer stations, and bombs, rockets or gun pods on all stations. Aermacchi also has developed, in collaboration with Electronica SpA of Rome, an airborne ECM pod for carriage by the MB-339. In addition to its use as a trainer at the *Scuola di Volo Basico-Iniziale Aviogetti*, the MB-339A serves with the AMI's 8° *Gruppo* of the 14° *Stormo Reparto Radiomisure* (Radio Aids Survey and Electronic Warfare Wing). A single-seat version of the MB-339A has also been developed, following the precedent of the MB-326K variant of the MB-326 (separately described); this version is named the MB-339K Veltro 2 (Greyhound), perpetuating the name of the Macchi MC 205 fighter of World War II.

AERO L 39 ALBATROS

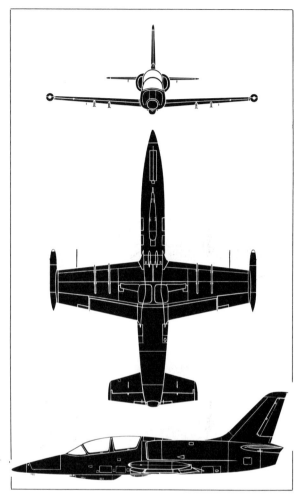

(Top) An Aero L 39 in manufacturer's demonstration finish; (immediately above) an L 39Z of the Czech Air Force with gun pod and underwing AAMs; (below) an L 39 exported to Libya for use at the Air Academy. (Silhouette) Aero L 39Z.

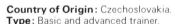

Country of Origin: Czechoslovakia.
Type: Basic and advanced trainer.
Power Plant: One 3,307 lb st (1 500 kgp) Walter Titan (Ivchenko Ai-25 TL) turbofan.
Performance: Max speed, clean, 435 mph (700 km/h) at sea level and 466 mph (750 km/h) at 16,400 ft (5 000 m); initial rate of climb, 4,035 ft/min (20,5 m/sec); service ceiling, 36,100 ft (11 000 m); range on internal fuel only, 680 mls (1 100 km) with 5 per cent reserves; radius of action, single-seat strike with gun and bombs, LO-LO-LO, 330 mls (530 km).
Weights: Empty, 7,859 lb (3 565 kg); max external stores, 2,425 lb (1 100 kg); normal take-off, training mission, 10,028 lb (4 549 kg); max take-off, strike mission, 12,450 lb (5 650 kg).
Dimensions: Span, 31 ft 0½ in (9,46 m); length, 39 ft 9½ in (12,13 m); height, 15 ft 7¾ in (4,77 m); wing area, 202·4 sq ft (18,8 m²).
Accommodation: Two in tandem, full dual control.
Armament: (L 39ZO) Four wing hard points with capacity for 1,100 lb (500 kg) each inboard and 550 lb (250 kg) each outboard; plus (L 39Z) fuselage centre-line mounting for 23-mm gun pod.
Status: First of five prototypes flown on 4 November 1968; first

of pre-production batch of 10 completed in 1971; production deliveries began in 1973. Production of more than 1,000 completed by 1981 (and continuing) for air forces of the Warsaw Pact countries and for export to Iraq, Libya and Afghanistan.
Notes: Development of the L 39 was initiated at the Vodochody works to provide a successor for the L 29 Delfin. A protracted flight test programme was undertaken, using at least five flying prototypes (in addition to two built for static testing) and modifications were made to the intakes before the L 39 entered production. One prototype was tested in the weapon training rôle with underwing stores, and in 1973 a light strike version of the L 39 was also developed with the designation L 39Z, having four wing hard points to carry bombs or rocket pods, and a pod on the fuselage centre-line mounting a 23-mm GSh-23 two-barrel cannon. An alternative weapons training version, without the gun pod, is designated L 39ZO, and the unarmed flying training version is designated L 39C. The total requirement for L 39Cs is thought to be about 3,500 to meet the needs of the air forces of the Warpac countries, in which the Albatros is the standard advanced/weapons trainer, these nations including the Soviet Union, Czechoslovakia, Bulgaria, Hungary and East Germany. Exports have been made to other countries as noted above.

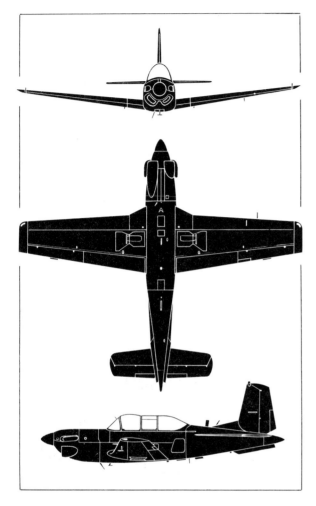

(Above) A Beechcraft T-34C serving with the US Navy; (immediately below) a T-34C-1 Turbine Mentor exported to the Ecuadorian Air Force; (bottom) the armed Turbine Mentor 34C with long-range tanks. (Silhouette) Beechcraft T-34C.

Country of Origin: USA.

Type: Basic trainer and light strike.

Power Plant: One 715 shp (derated to 400 shp) Pratt & Whitney (Canada) PT6A-25 turboprop.

Performance: Max cruise, 246 mph (396 km/h) at 17,500 ft (5 335 m); initial rate of climb, 1,350 ft/min (6,85 m/sec); service ceiling, over 30,000 ft (9 145 m); range, training configuration, 680 mls (1 094 km); range, strike mission with four stores, 345 mls (555 km); range, FAC mission, 115 mls (185 km) with 2·6 hr loiter.

Weights: Empty equipped 3,150 lb (1 423 kg); take-off, trainer, 4,300 lb (1 950 kg); max take-off, strike configuration, 5,500 lb (2 494 kg).

Dimensions: Span 33 ft 5¾ in (10,16 m); length, 28 ft 8½ in (8,75 m); height 9 ft 10⅞ in (3,02 m); wing area, 179·56 sq ft (16,68 m²).

Accommodation: Two in tandem, dual controls.

Armament: (T-34C-1 only) Four wing hardpoints, with capacity of 600 lb (272 kg) each inboard and 300 lb (136 kg) each outboard; maximum combined load, 1,200 lb (544 kg). Possible weapons include Mk 81 bombs, rockets, rocket pods, gun pods and wire-guided anti-tank missiles.

Status: First of two YT-34Cs flown 21 September 1973, and

deliveries to US Navy Air Training Command at Whiting Field began November 1977. UC Navy contracts totalled 196 by 1982; export contracts for T-34C-1 comprise Morocco, 12; Argentina (Navy) 15; Ecuador, 20; Ecuador Navy 3; Gabon Presidential Guard, 4; Indonesia, 16; Peru (Navy), 6 and Uruguay (Navy), 3; Algeria acquired six unarmed Turbine Mentor 34Cs for its National Pilot Training School.

Notes: Beech first developed a jet powered derivative of the Model 45 Mentor (separately described in Trainers section) as the Model 73, first flown on 18 December 1955, and powered by a Continental J69-T-9. After losing the USAF competititon to the Cessna T-37, Beech embarked on a wholly new study for the US Navy in 1972 leading to evolution of the Turbine Mentor. As a trainer, the T-34C is fitted with a torque-limited PT6A-25 turboprop affording 400 shp but the T-34C-1 may be fitted with a version of the PT6A-25 derated to 550 shp, wing racks for external ordnance and an armament control system to permit operation as an armament trainer or light-counter insurgency aircraft. In this configuration, a higher gross weight is applicable, as indicated in the data above. Additional quantities of T-34Cs were to be acquired by the US Navy from 1982 onwards to supplement those already in service.

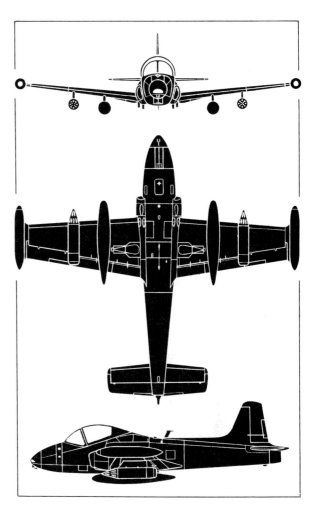

(Top) A pair of Hunting Jet Provost T Mk 5s serving at the RAF College, Cranwell; (immediately above) a Strikemaster Mk 88 of the Royal New Zealand Air Force; (below) Strikemaster Mk 82, Sultan of Oman's Air Force. (Silhouette) British Aerospace Strikemaster.

Country of Origin: United Kingdom.

Type: Basic trainer and light strike aircraft.

Power Plant: One 1,759 lb st (794 kgp) Rolls-Royce Viper (Jet Provost 3 and 51) Mk 102 or (Jet Provost 4,5,52 and 55) 2,500 lb st (1 134 kgp) Viper 202 or (Strikemaster) 3,410 lb st (1,547 kgp) Viper 535.

Performance: (Jet Provost 5) Max speed, 440 mph (708 km/h) at a weight of 6,400 lb (2 900 kg) at 25,000 ft (7 620 m); initial rate of climb, 3,550 ft/min (18 m/sec); service ceiling, 34,500 ft (10 500 m); max range with tip tanks, 900 mls (1 450 km) at 35,000 ft (10 670 m).

Performance: (Strikemaster) Max speed (clean), 472 mph (760 km/h) at 20,000 ft (6 100 m); initial rate of climb, 5,300 ft/min (26 m/sec); radius of action (max armament), 250 mls (400 km); radius of action (max fuel), 735 mls (1 200 km); ferry range, 1,675 mls (2 700 km).

Weights: (Jet Provost) Normal take-off (internal fuel only), 7,629 lb (3 460 kg); max take-off (Mk 55, with tip tanks), 8,524 lb (3,866 kg); max overload 9,200 lb (4 173 kg).

Weights: (Strikemaster) Empty equipped, 6,270 lb (2 844 kg); normal take-off (trainer), 9,200 lb (4 170 kg); normal take-off (strike), 11,500 lb (5 215 kg).

Dimensions: Span, 35 ft 4 in (10,77 m); span (over tip tanks), 36 ft 11 in (11,25 m); length, 33 ft 8½ in (10,27 m); height, 10 ft 2 in (3,10 m); wing area, 213·7 sq ft (19,80 m²).

Armament: Provision for two 7.62-mm machine guns in fuselage. Four (Jet Provost 55) or eight (Strikemaster) wing strong points, for maximum ordnance load of 3,000 lb (1 360 kg).

Status: Prototype Jet Provost first flown 26 June 1954; first JP3 flown on 22 June 1958; first JP5 flown on 28 February 1967; first Strikemaster flown on 26 October 1967. Production totals: Jet Provost 1, 10; JP2, 2; JP3, 201; JP4, 198; JP5, 110; JP51, 22; JP52, 43; JP55, 5; Strikemaster, 141 up to 1982, as listed below.

Notes: Jet Provost was RAF's first jet trainer, Mks 3, 4 and 5 being for RAF service and Mks 51, 52 and 55 for export. RAF still uses in 1982 the T Mk 3A and (with pressurised cockpit) T Mk 5A, following refit programmes in mid 'seventies. Strikemaster (like Jet Provost 5) has pressurised cockpit and users comprise Saudi Arabia, 25 (Mk 80) and 22 (Mk 80A); Oman, 12 (Mk 82) and 12 (Mk 82A); Kuwait, 12 (Mk 83); Singapore, 4 (Mk 81, from South Arabia) and 16 (Mk 84); Kenya, 6 Mk (87); New Zealand, 16 (Mk 88) and Ecuador, 16 (Mk 89). A final batch of 10 Strikemasters was assembled at Hurn in 1980/81 after production at Warton ended, for expected future orders.

(Above) A British Aerospace Hawk T Mk 1 of the RAF Tactical Weapons Unit with Sidewinder AAMs for self defence; (immediately below) the BAe Hawk demonstrator in US Navy colours; (bottom) Hawk Mk 53 of the Indonesian Air Force. (Silhouette) British Aerospace Hawk T Mk 1.

Country of Origin: United Kingdom.

Type: Basic/advanced jet trainer and light strike aircraft.

Power Plant: One 5,200 lb st (2 360 kg) Rolls-Royce Turboméca RT 172-06-11 Adour 151 or (export) 851 turbofan.

Performance: Max speed, 645 mph (1 038 km/h) or Mach 0·88; initial rate of climb, 9,300 ft/min (47,2 m/sec); time to 30,000 ft (9 145 m), 6 mins 6 secs; service ceiling, 50,000 ft (15 240 m); combat radius (weapons training missions, 3,000 lb/1 360 kg external load), 645 mls (1 038 km); combat radius (strike mission, max external load), 345 mls (556 km); ferry range, clean, 1 510 mls (2 433 km); ferry range, two drop tanks, 1,922 mls (3 093 km).

Weights: Empty, 8,040 lb (3 647 kg); normal take-off, trainer, clean, 11,100 lb (5 035 kg); normal take-off, weapons trainer, 12,284 lb (5 572 kg); max take-off weight, 17,085 lb (7 750 kg).

Dimensions: Span, 30 ft 9¾ in (9,39 m); length, 38 ft 10¾ in (11,85 m) including nose probe; height, 13 ft 1 in (3,99 m); wing area, 179,6 sq ft (16,69 m²).

Accommodation: Two in tandem, dual controls.

Armament: Basic aircraft has provision (RAF weapons trainer) to carry external centreline gun pack with 30-mm Aden gun and two inboard wing pylons with a capacity of 1,120 lb (508 kg) each; fuselage centreline position has same capacity for alterna-

tive stores and export Hawk has provision for two outboard wing pylons; max underwing load, 6,500 lb (2 950 kg).

Status: Pre-production Hawk T Mk 1 flown 21 August 1974; first production T Mk 1 flown 19 May 1975. Deliveries (to RAF) began 4 November 1976. Production/sales: T Mk 1 (RAF), 176 (plus follow on order for 18 approved in principle April 1980); Mk 50 (company demonstrator), 1; Mk 51 (Finland), 50 (including 46 assembled by Valmet OY); Mk 52 (Kenya), 12; Mk 53 (Indonesia), 12 (plus four on option); Zimbabwe, 8; United Arab Emirates, 18 (under negotiation, 1982).

Notes: THe RAF adopted the Hawker Sideley P. 1182 project to meet an Air Staff Requirement drawn for an advanced trainer to replace the Gnat and Hunter. In the RAF, the Hawk is used at No. 4 FTS for the advanced stages of flying training (without armament), at Nos 1 and 2 Tactical Weapons Units for weapons training and by the Red Arrows aerobatic team. Total of 72 Hawks at the TWUs are being adapted to carry Sidewinder AAMs on inboard wing pylons for a secondary air defence rôle. RAF aircraft do not make use of outboard wing pylons, available on export aircraft; the Kenyan aircraft also have, as a special option, a braking parachute installation. The Hawk was selected late in 1981 to meet the US Navy's VTX-TS requirements.

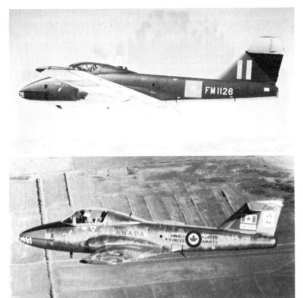

(Top) A Canadair CL-41G light strike aircraft of the Malaysian Air Force; (immediately above) a CL-41 serving the Canadian Armed Forces as the CT-114; (below) a CT-114 of the Snowbirds aerobatics team. (Silhouette) Canadair CL-41

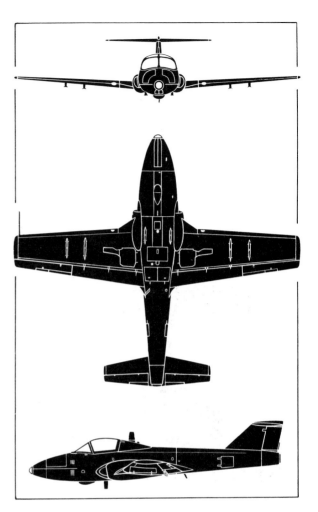

Country of Origin: Canada.
Type: Basic trainer and light attack aircraft.
Power Plant: One (CL-41G) 2,950 lb st (1 340 kgp) General Electric J85-J4 or (CL-41A) 2,633 lb st (1 195 kgp) Oreuda-built J85-CAN-40 turbojet.
Performance: (CL-41A) Max speed 498 mph (801 km/h) at 28,500 ft (8 700 m); initial rate of climb, 4,220 ft/min (21,4 m/sec); service ceiling, 43,000 ft (13 100 m); range 944 mls (1 519 km).
Performance: (CL-41G) Max speed, 480 mph (774 km/h) at 28,500 ft (8 700 m); service ceiling, 42,200 ft (12 800 m); range (with six external tanks) 1,340 mls (2 157 km).
Weights: (CL-41A) Empty 4,895 lb (2 220 kg); max take-off 7,397 lb (3 355 kg).
Weights: (CL-41G) Empty, 5,296 lb (2 400 kg); max take-off 11,288 lb (5 131 kg).
Dimensions: Span 36 ft 6 in (11,13 m); length 32 ft 0 in (9,75 m); height, 9 ft 3¾ in (2,84 m); wing area, 220 sq ft (20,44 m²).
Accommodation: Two side-by-side, with dual controls.
Armament: (CL-41G) Six wing hardpoints for up to 3,500 lb (1 590 kg) of bombs, rockets, mini-gun pods, etc.
Status: Prototype first flown on 13 January 1960; first production CL-41A flown in October 1963, CL-41R flown on 13 July 1962.

First CL-41G flown in June 1964. Production totals: two prototypes, 190 CL-41A and 20 CL-41G, completed in 1968.
Notes: Canadair built a prototype of its CL-41A basic jet trainer as a private venture, powered by a 2,400 lb st (1 088 kgp) Pratt & Whitney JT12A-5 turbojet. After evaluation, this design was selected by the RCAF as its new basic trainer and 190 were built. These aircraft carry the Canadian Armed Forces Designation CT-114 Tutor. The 15th production CL-41A was modified to prototype CL-41G light strike and weapon trainer configuration, with four underwing strong points. The production CL-41G has, in addition, two strong points under the centre section. Twenty delivered to the Royal Malaysian Air Force in 1967–68 have the local name of Tebuan (Wasp) and are used at Kuantan by No 9 Jebat (Civet) Squadron for training and No 6 Naga (Dragon) Sqdn for light strike duties. The CT-114 remains the standard basic trainer of the Canadian Armed Forces serving in 1982 at No 2 FTS, Moose Jaw, and also equipping the CAF's national aerobatic team, the 'Snowbirds'. Of about 140 remaining in the CAF inventory, some 40 are in storage, but have undergone avionics/equipment updating by Northwest Industries. The single CL-41R was an experimental systems trainer with NASARR radar in a lengthened nose.

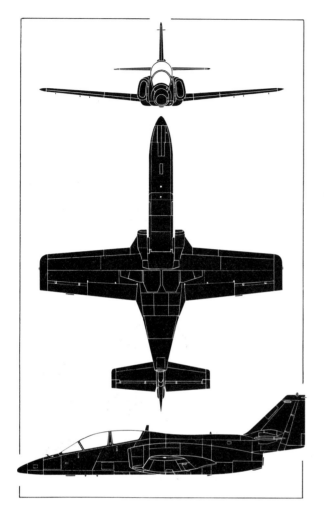

(Above) An air view of the CASA 101 Aviojet, serving with Escuadron 733 of the Spanish Air Force; (immediately below and bottom) landing and ground views of the CASA 101, for which the Spanish Air Force designation is E.25. (Silhouette) CASA 101 Aviojet.

Country of Origin: Spain.

Type: Basic and advanced trainer.

Power Plant: One 3,500 lb st (1 588 kgp) Garrett AiResearch TFE 731-2-2J turbofan.

Performance: (At 10,362 lb/4 700 kg) Max speed 479 mph (770 km/h) or Mach 0·7 at 28,000 ft (8 535 m), 404 mph (650 km/h) or Mach 0·53 at sea level; initial rate of climb 3,350 ft/min (17 m/sec); time to 25,000 ft (7 620 m), 12 min; service ceiling, 41,000 ft (12,495 m); range (internal fuel at 11,540 lb/5 235 kg), 2,485 mls (4 000 km).

Weights: Basic operational empty, 6,790 lb (3,080 kg), loaded (pilot training mission with outer wing tanks empty), 10,362 lb (4 700 kg), (with max internal fuel), 11,540 lb (5 235 kg); max take-off, 12,346 lb (5 600 kg).

Dimensions: Span, 34 ft $9\frac{3}{4}$ in (10,60 m); length, 40 ft $2\frac{1}{4}$ in (12,25 m); height, 13 ft 11 in (4,25 m); wing area 215·3 sq ft (20,00 m²).

Accommodation: Two in tandem, dual controls.

Armament: (C101ET) Seven external stores stations (six wing and one fuselage) for maximum of 3,707 lb (1 500 kg) of ordnance. Provision is made for a semi-recessed pod beneath the aft cockpit for a 30-mm cannon or two 7.62-mm Miniguns. Warload options

include four Mk 83 or six Mk 82 bombs, or four AGM-65 Maverick missiles.

Status: Four C-101 prototypes first flown, respectively, on 27 June 1977, 30 September 1977, 26 January 1978 and 17 April 1978. Sixty ordered by Spanish Air Force in March 1978, of which the first flew on 8 November 1979; first four accepted by the Air Academy on 17 March 1980, and follow-on batch of additional 28 aircraft ordered subsequently. Eight (plus eight on option) ordered by Chilean Air Force, designated C-101BB.

Notes: The standard C-101EB basic trainer has replaced the Ha-200 Saeta, the T-6 Texan and the T-33A in the Spanish Air Force trainer inventory, service entry having been made in March 1980 in *Escuadron* 793 at the *Academia General del Aire* (Air Academy). In Spanish service, the Aviojet is designated E.25, as a basic/advanced trainer, this being the C-101EB, ordered in sufficient quantity to replace T-33As and T-6D/Gs in the refresher training rôle in 41 and 42 *Grupo*, as well as the HA-200s in the *Academia*. CASA also has projected an armed version, the C-101ET, which could succeed the HA-220 in the weapons training and light strike rôle, but orders had not been placed up to the beginning of 1982. The C-101BB is an export model, for the Chilean Air Force, with a 3,700 lb, st (1 678 kgp) TFE 731-3-1J turbofan.

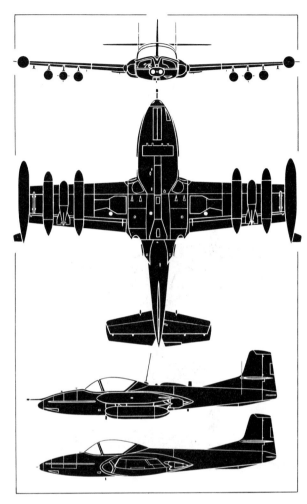

(Top) Cessna T-37B, the "Tweety Bird" basic trainer of the USAF; (immediately above) a T-37B serving in the Hellenic Air Force; (below) an A-37B armed variant of the Cessna trainer, as used by Air National Guard units. (Silhouette) Cessna A-37B with extra side view of the T-37B.

Country of Origin: USA.

Type: Basic trainer, weapons trainer, (A-37) light attack and (OA-37) forward air control.

Power Plant: Two (T-37B, C) 4,025 lb st (465 kgp) Continental T69-T-25 or (A-37A) 2,400 lb st (1 090 kgp) General Electric J85-GE-5 or (A-37B) 2,850 lb st (1 293 kgp) J85-GE-17A turbojets.

Performance: (T-37B) Max speed, 405 mph (652 km/h) at 10,000 ft (3 050 m); average cruising speed, 318 mph (512 km/h) at 25,000 ft (7 620 m); initial rate of climb, 3,040 ft/min (15,4 m/sec); service ceiling, 35,000 ft (10 670 m); range, 527 mls (848 km); training mission endurance, 1, 4 hrs.

Performance: (A-37B) Max speed, 479 mph (771 km/h) at 15,500 ft (4 724 m); average cruising speed, 298 mph (480 km/h) at 25,000 ft (7 620 m); initial rate of climb, 4,420 ft/min (22,5 m/sec); service ceiling, 25,000 ft (7 620 m); combat radius with 1,858 lb (843 kg) bomb load, 236 mls (380 km); combat radius with max armament, 146 mls (234 km); ferry range, 930 mls (1 497 km).

Weights: Empty (T-37B), 4,067 lb (1 845 kg), (A-37B), 6,008 lb (2 725 kg); max take-off (T-37B), 6,800 lb (3 084 kg), (A-37B), 14,000 lb (6 350 kg).

Dimensions: Span, 33 ft 9¼ in (10,30 m); span over tip tanks (A-37B), 38 ft 5 in (11,70 m); length, 29 ft 3½ in (8,93 m); length over refuelling boom (A-37B), 31 ft 10 in (9,69 m); height, 9 ft 2 in (2,8 m); wing area, 183,9 sq ft (17,09 m²).

Accommodation: Two, side-by-side with dual controls.

Armament: (T-37A, B) unarmed; (T-37C) has two wing pylons, capacity 250 lb (113,5 kg) each; (A-37A, B) one 7,62-mm GAU-2B/A gun in front fuselage; four wing pylons with total capacity of 5,680 lb (2 576 kg) for bombs, rockets, stores dispensers, etc.

Status: Prototype XT-37 first flown 12 October 1954; first production T-37A flown 27 September 1955; first of two YAT-37D flown 22 October 1963. Production totals: XT-37, 3; T-37A, 444; T-37B, 552; T-37C, 198; A-37B, 577, completed 1975.

Notes: T-37B is standard USAF basic trainer, also used by *Luftwaffe* for its US-based pilot training programme and by several air forces supplied through MAP or by sale of surplus USAF aircraft. Armed T-37C was built for MAP supply to Brazil, Chile, Columbia, Greece, Pakistan, Peru, Portugal, South Korea and Turkey. All T-37As, with T69-T-9 engines, were converted to T-37B, or A-37A (39 aircraft) pending production of definitive A-37B. Several South American air forces now fly A-37Bs, as well as one US Air Force Reserve unit, and three ANG units fly OA-37Bs in forward air control rôle.

(Above) A production model Dassault-Breguet/Dornier Alpha Jet of the Groupement Ecole 314 of Armée de l'Air; (immediately below) a Dornier-built Alpha Jet serving with the Luftwaffe's Jabo G 49; (bottom) a Nigerian Air Force Alpha Jet. (Silhouette) Dassault-Breguet/Dornier Alpha Jet E.

Country of Origin: France/Federal Germany.

Type: Basic/advanced trainer and light strike aircraft.

Power Plant: Two 2,975 lb st (1 350 kgp) SNECMA/Turboméca Larzac O4-C5 turbofans.

Performance: Max speed, 622 mph (1 000 km/h) at sea level, or Mach 0·826, and 567 mph (912 km/h) at 32,810 ft (10,000 m), or Mach 0·84; initial rate of climb, 11,220 ft/mins (57 m/sec); service ceiling, 48,000 ft (14 630 m); tactical radius (training mission, LO-LO-LO), 267 mls (430 km); tactical radius (strike mission, with gun pack, external stores and tanks), 351 mls (565 km) LO-LO-LO and 639 mls (1 028 km) HI-LO-HI; ferry range, 1,785 mls (2 872 km).

Weights: Empty equipped, trainer, 7,374 lb (3 345 kg), close support, 7,749 lb (3 515 kg); normal take-off, trainer, clean, 11,023 lb (5 000 kg); max take-off weight with external stores, 16,535 lb (7 500 kg).

Dimensions: Span, 29 ft 11 ins (9,11 m); length (trainer), 40 ft 3¼ in (12,29 m); length (close support), 43 ft 5 in (13,23 m); height, 13 ft 9 in (14,19 m); wing area, 188·4 sq ft (17,50 m²).

Accommodation: Two in tandem, dual controls, or (close support version) pilot only.

Armament: (Weapon trainer and close support option) External centreline gun pod with (Alpha Jet E) 30-mm DEFA 533 or (A) 27-mm Mauser cannon. Four wing hardpoints for maximum extenal load of 5,510 lb (2 500 kg).

Status: Basic prototype flown on 26 October 1973 (in France) and 9 January 1974 (Germany) followed by representative prototypes of Alpha Jet A on 6 May 1974 (France) and Alpha Jet E on 11 October 1974. Pre-production E flown 4 November 1977 and first fully definitive production E on 19 May 1978; first production A flown 12 April 1978 and first 1B (Belgium) on 20 June 1978. Production/sales: Prototypes, 4; Alpha Jet E (France), 175; Alpha Jet A (Germany), 175; Alpha Jet 1B (Belgium), 33; Ivory Coast, 6; Morocco, 24, Nigeria, 15; Qatar, 6, Togo, 5, Egypt, 30 and Cameroon, 6; total 479 by end-1981 of which some 390 delivered.

Notes: Alpha Jet is subject of joint development programme launched by France and Germany in July 1969, with Dassault Breguet and Dornier as the principal design/production companies, each responsible for a final assembly line. French Alpha Jet E is used by *Armée de l'Air* as basic/advanced trainer, entering service in summer 1978. The *Luftwaffe* Alpha Jet A is a dedicated close air support aircraft flown as a single-seater (with full canopy retained), and entered service in March 1980. Alpha Jet 1Bs for the Belgian Air Force were assembled by SABCA.

EMBRAER EMB-312 (T-27) TUCANO   TRAINER/LIGHT STRIKE

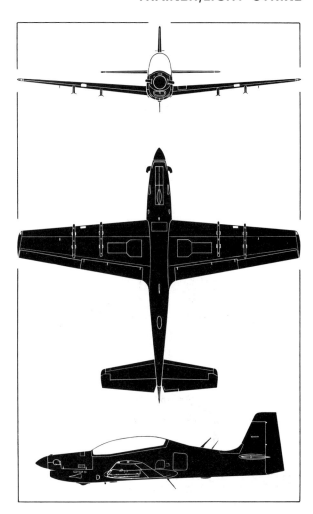

(Top and immediately above) Two photographs of the first prototype of the EMBRAER T-27 trainer on an early test flight. (Below) The second prototype of the T-27, which has been named Tucano by the Força Aérea Brasileira. (Silhouette) EMBRAER T-27 Tucano.

Country of Origin: Brazil
Type: Basic trainer and light strike aircraft.
Power Plant: One 750 shp Pratt & Whitney (Canada) PT6A-25C turboprop.
Performance: Max speed (at 3,307 lb/1 500 kg), 302 mph (486 km/h) at 10,000 ft (3 050 m), (at 5,181 lb/2 350 kg) 296 mph (476 km/h) at 8,000 ft (2 440 m); max continuous cruise, 272 mph (438 km/h), initial rate of climb (at 5,070 lb/2 300 kg), 2,126 ft/min (10,80 m/sec); max range (30-min reserves), 1,312 mls (2 112 km); tactical radius HI-LO-HI (with four 250 lb/113 kg Mk 81 bombs), 161 mls (260 km), (with two Mk 81 bombs), 602 (970 km).
Weights: Basic empty weight, 3,487 lb (1 582 kg); max take-off 5,180 lb (2 350 kg).
Dimensions: Span, 36 ft 6½ in (11,14 m); length 32ft 4¼ in (9,86 m); height, 11 ft 1⅞ in (3,40 m); wing area, 204·52 sq ft (19,00 m²).
Accommodation: Two in tandem with full dual controls.
Armament: Four wing hard points, each with a capacity of 300 lb (150 kg); max combined load, 1,234 lb (560 kg). Typical ordnance loads include two 0·5-in (12,7-mm) machine gun pods with 350 rpg, four pods each with seven 37-mm or 70-mm rockets or

four 250 lb (113 kg) Mk 81 bombs.
Status: First of two prototypes flown on 16 August 1980, with deliveries against order for 168 for the Brazilian Air Force scheduled to commence beginning of 1983 at a rate of five monthly.
Notes: The EMB-312 has been developed initially to meet local Brazilian requirements for a basic trainer to replace the Cessna T-37 serving at the *Academia de Força Aérea* (Air Academy) at Pirassununga. Use of a turboprop type to replace a turbojet trainer is in line with current efforts to achieve fuel economies, and is result of a lengthy period of design evolution in Brazil, starting with studies for a turboprop derivative of the Neiva T-25 Universal. This project received no official backing, but EMBRAER considered the possibility of developing the piston-engined Universal II (as the EMB-301) and the turboprop version (as the EMB-311) before embarking on design of the almost wholly new EMB-312. This design, which is unusual among aircraft in its class for having ejection seats, received formal approval of the Brazilian Ministry of Aeronautics on 6 December 1978, when four prototypes were ordered, including one each for fatigue and static testing. Production plans were confirmed in 1981, in which year the name Tucano was adopted for the T-27.

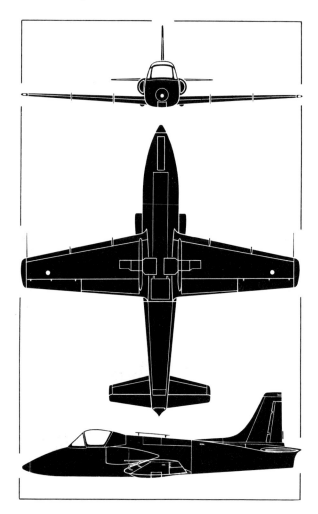

(Above) An HAL Kiran Mk IA serving with the Indian Air Force; (immediately below) a ground view of the Kiran I; (bottom) the Kiran IA showing underwing rocket pods. (Silhouette) HAL Kiran I.

Country of Origin: India.

Type: Basic trainer.

Power Plant: One 2,500 lb st (1 135 kg) Rolls-Royce Bristol Viper 11 turbojet.

Performance: Max speed, 432 mph (695 km/h) at sea level and 427 mph (688 km/h) at 30,000 ft (9 150 m); max cruising speed, 201 mph (324 km/h); initial rate of climb, 4,774 ft/min; (24.1 m/sec); time to reach 30,000 ft (9 144 m), 20 min; service ceiling 30,000 ft (9 150 m); range 465 mls (748 km) at 265 mph (426 km/h) at 30,000 ft (9 144 m); endurance, 1 hr 45 min at 30,000 ft (9 150 m) at 265 mph (426 km/h) on full internal fuel capacity.

Weights: Empty, 5,644 lb (2 560 kg); normal take-off, 7,936 lb (3 600 kg); max overload, 9,039 lb (4 100 kg) with two 50-Imp gal (227-l) drop tanks.

Dimensions: Span, 35 ft 1¼ in (10,70 m); length, 34 ft 9 in (10,60 m); height, 11 ft 11 in (3,64 m); wing area, 204·5 sq ft (19,00 m²).

Accommodation: Two side-by-side, with full dual control.

Armament: (Mk IA) Two wing hardpoints for up to 500 lb (227 kg) each. (Mk II) Two 7,62 mm machine guns in nose; four wing hardpoints for up to 500 lb (227 kg) bombs or rocket pods each, or four drop tanks.

Status: Prototype first flown 4 September 1964; second prototype flown August 1965; pre-production deliveries began March 1968; Mk II prototype flown 30 July 1976; second Mk II prototype flown in February 1979. Production totals: Prototypes 2; pre-production, 24; Mk I, 94; Mk IA, 67; Mk II, 20 ordered 1981 for delivery 1983. Production of Mk 1A completed November 1981.

Notes: Design of the Kiran (Ray of Light) began at the HAL plant in Bangalore in 1961m by a team led by Dr V M Chatage, with the object of developing a basic jet trainer to replace the licence-built HAL/DH Vampire, 281 examples of which had been built in India in several versions. A pre-production batch of 24 Kirans was built the first six of these being handed over to the Indian Air Force in March 1968. During the course of 1973, the Kiran entered service with the Indian Air Force Academy at Dundigal where it was standard equipment in 1981 in its unarmed Mk I and weapons-training Mk IA versions, the latter differing only in having two wing hardpoints. A few Mk Is serve with the Indian Navy in INAS 550 and INAS 551. The more fully-armed Mk II, capable of light strike duties, entered production in 1981 for service introduction in 1983. This is powered by a derated version of the Orpheus 701 turbojet affording 3,400 lb st (1 542 kgp).

LOCKHEED T-33A SHOOTING STAR

(Top) A Canadair-built T-33A-N Silver Star in CAF service as CT-133; (immediately above) a Lockheed T-33A in Spanish service as an E.15; (below) a T-33A of the Royal Saudi Air Force. (Silhouette) Lockheed T-33A.

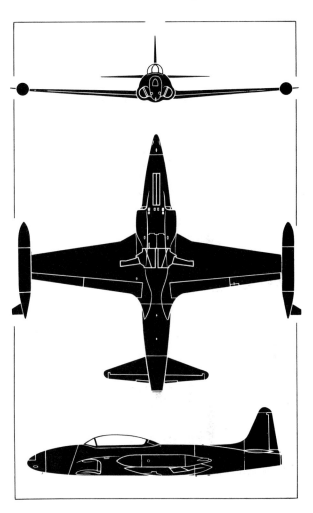

Country of Origin: USA.

Type: Advanced trainer and light strike aircraft.

Power Plant: One 5,200 lb st (2 360 kgp) Allison J33-A-35 turbojet or (T-33A-N) 5,100 lb st (2 313 kgp) Rolls-Royce Nene 10 turbojet.

Performance: (T-33A) Max speed, 600 mph (960 km/h) at sea level and 524 mph (843 km/h) at 10,000 ft (3 050 m); average cruising speed 433 mph (697 km/h) at 40,000 ft (12 200 m); initial rate of climb, 3,220 ft/min (16,14 m/sec); service ceiling, 40,500 ft (1 235 m); mission radius, 435 mls (700 km); ferry range, 1,195 mls (1 923 km); max endurance, 2.8 hrs.

Weights: (T-33A) Empty, 8,365 lb (3 794 kg); max take-off, 15,100 lb (6 850 kg).

Dimensions: Span, 38 ft 10½ in (11,85 m); length 37 ft 9 in (11,48 m); height, 11 ft 8½ in (3,57 m); wing area, 235 sq ft (21,81 m²).

Armament: Two 0·50-in (12,7-mm) M.3 machine guns. Provision on wing strongpoints for up to 2,000 lb (908 kg) of bombs or 10 air-to-ground rockets.

Accommodation: Two in tandem, full dual controls.

Status: Prototype (TF-80C) first flown on 22 March 1948. Production of 5,771 by Lockheed completed between 1948 and

1959. Under license, Kawasaki built 210 in Japan and Canadair built 656 (CL-30) in Canada.

Notes: This two-seat training version of the F-80 Shooting Star (the USAF's first operational jet fighter) was evolved in 1947 to meet Air Force requirements for an advanced jet trainer. Initial production aircraft were designated TF-80C by the USAF and TV-2 for the US Navy. Of the production total, the Navy received 649, and 1,058 were procured by USAF for supply to foreign nations through MAP, some of these being armed for close support and interdiction with guns, rockets or bombs and designated AT-33A. Also included in the MAP-supplied batches were 85 RT-33As with lengthened, camera-carrying nose and special equipment replacing the rear seat. For service with the RCAF, Canadair built 656 Silver Star Mk 3s (CL-30), after a trial installation of the Nene powerplant in a Lockheed airframe as the Silver Star Mk 2. Twenty standard T-33As served with the RCAF as Silver Star Mk 1s. T-33A 'T-Birds' remain in service in 1982 with many air forces, including those of Brazil, Canada, Chile, Colombia, Ethiopia, Greece, Italy, Japan, Mexico (AT-33A), Pakistan, Portugal, Spain and most of the Central American nations. Several of these countries also continue to operate the RT-33A in the tactical reconnaissance rôle.

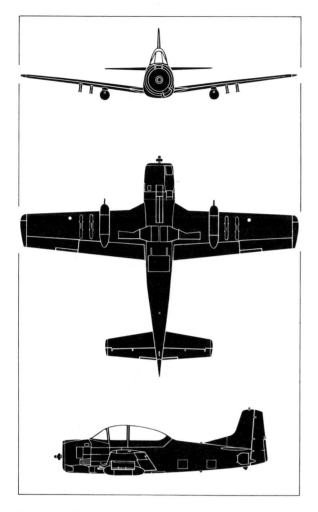

(Above) North American T-28B Trojan basic trainer of the US Navy at Pensacola; (immediately below) an armed T-28D in service with the Royal Thai Air Force; (bottom) one of the T-28As of the Mexican Air Force. (Silhouette) North American T-28D.

Country of Origin: USA.

Type: Basic trainer and light attack aircraft.

Power Plant: One (T-28A) 800 hp Wright R-1300-1 or (T-28B and C) 1,425 hp Wright R-1820-86 or (T-28D) 1,300 hp R-1820-56S engine.

Performance: (T-28B) Max speed 346 mph (557 km/h) at 18,000 ft (5,486 m); normal cruising speed, 219 mph (352 km/h); initial rate of climb, 3,830 ft/min (1,9 m/sec); service ceiling 37,000 ft (11 278 m); max range, 907 mls (1 460 km).

Performance: (T-28D) Max speed 352 mph (566 km/h) at 18,000 ft (1 167 m); max range, 1,184 mls (1 820 km) cruising at 203 mph (327 km/h).

Weights: (T-28D) Empty, 6,512 lb (2 953 kg); loaded, 8,118 lb (3 682 kg).

Dimensions: Span, 40 ft 7½ in (12,37 m); length, 32 ft 10 in (10,00 m); height, 12 ft 8 in (3,86 m); wing area, 272·1 sq ft (25,3 m²).

Accommodation: Two in tandem.

Armament: (T-28D only) Six underwing strong points carry two 0·50-in (12,7-mm) gun pods and assorted bombs, rockets, etc, to a total weight of 4,000 lb (1 815 kg).

Status: First of two prototypes (XT-28) flown on 26 September

1949; first T-28B flown in 1954; first T-28C flown on 19 September 1955; first T-28D flown in 1961; first T-28D-5 flown in 1965; first of three YAT-28Es flown 15 February 1963. Production totals, XT-28, 2; T-28A, 1,194; T-28B, 489; T-28C, 299. (Other variants were conversions). Production completed in 1957.

Notes: The NA.159 design was an attempt to produce a post-war successor to the NA.16/T-6 family of trainers. The T-28A was built for the USAF and the T-28B and T-28C were for the US Navy, the latter having an arrester hook for dummy deck-landing approaches. Through MAP and other programmes T-28As were supplied to several overseas air forces, particularly in South America and South East Asia, and the T-28D conversion was evolved with a heavy underwing armament, several hundred surplus T-28As being converted by North American and Fairchild, with the final batches by the latter company being designated AT-28Ds. A similar conversion scheme was undertaken by the Sud Aviation in France, which delivered 245 modified T-28As to the Armée de l'Air as Fennecs for service in North Africa. In 1982, T-28s were still serving as basic trainers with a few air forces, but larger numbers were in use in the light strike rôle, particularly in the Philippines and Thailand. The YAT-28E variant developed by North America featured a turboprop engine.

PILATUS PC-7 TURBO TRAINER

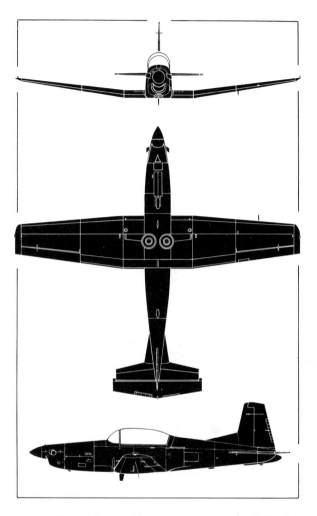

(Above) One of the two PC-7s evaluated by the Swiss Flugwaffe prior to confirmation of a production order; (below) two examples of the Turbo Trainer in Swiss markings keep company with an example destined for Burma. (Silhouette) Pilatus PC-7 Turbo Trainer.

Country of Origin: Switzerland.

Type: Basic/advanced trainer.

Power Plant: One 550 shp (flat rated from 650 shp) Pratt & Whitney Canada PT6A-25A turboprop.

Performance: (At 4,189 lb/1 900 kg) Max speed 239 mph (385 km/h) at sea level, 264 mph (425 km/h) at 16,405 ft (5 000 m); cruising speed, 186 mph (300 km/h) at sea level, 205 mph (330 km/h) at 16,405 ft (5 000 m); initial rate of climb, 2,000 ft/min (10,2 m/sec); time to 16,400 ft (5 000 m), 10 min; service ceiling, 32,000 ft (9 755 m); max range (at 40% power with 5% plus 20 min reserve), 777 mls (1 250 km); endurance, 3·38 hrs.

Weights: Empty, 2,866 lb (1 300 kg); max take-off (clean), 4,189 lb (1 900 kg), (external stores), 5,952 lb (2 700 kg).

Dimensions: Span, 34 ft 1½ in (10,40 m); length, 31 ft 11⅞ in (9,75 m); height, 10 ft 6½ in (3,21 m); wing area 178·68 sq ft (16,60 m²).

Accommodation: Two in tandem with full dual controls.

Armament: Six wing hardpoints permit external loads up to 500 lb (250 kg) on inner pylons, 353 lb (160 kg) on centre pylons and 242·5 lb (110 kg) on outer pylons. Max external load, 2,293 lb (1 040 kg).

Status: First of the two PC-7 prototypes flown (as P-3B with PT6A-20 engine) on 12 April 1966; first production PC-7 flown 12 August 1978. Initial production batch launched in 1977. Production orders in excess of 290 by the beginning of 1982, including Bolivia, 36; Burma, 17; Chilean Navy, 10; Guatemala, 12; Iraq, 52; Mexico, 55; Swiss *Flugwaffe*, 40, United Arab Emirates, 14 and Royal Malaysian Air Force, 44. Other reported customers include Argentine Navy and Philippine Air Force.

Notes: Derived from the piston engined P-3 basic trainer (the two prototypes being conversions of the original P-3 prototype and a series-production P3-05), the PC-7 has undergone extensive structural redesign in its production form. This redesign, which included a completely new electrically-activated undercarriage and a low-fatigue one-piece wing, was undertaken in conjunction with Dornier, which is responsible for marketing the Turbo Trainer in Germany. The Swiss *Flugwaffe* placed an order for 40 PC-7s during 1981, after operating two early production examples for an extended evaluation. By then, the trainer had already been ordered by some 10 foreign air arms, the major user being the Mexican Air Force which had ordered a small initial batch as trainers and then a larger batch for use in the light strike role, replacing aged North American T-28Ds.

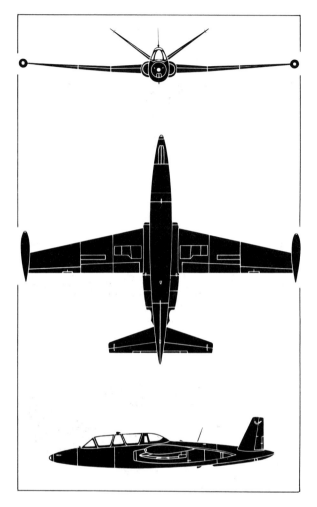

(Above) A formation of three Potez CM-170 Magisters of the Irish Army Air Corps; (immediately below) a CM-170 of Israel's Heyl Ha'Avir; (bottom) one of the French Navy's CM-175 Zephyr trainers. (Silhouette) Potez CM-170 Magister.

Country of Origin: France.

Type: Basic trainer.

Power Plant: Two (CM 170-1 and CM 175) 880 lb st (400 kgp) Turboméca Marborè IIA or (CM 170-2 Super Magister) 1,058 lb st (480 kgp) Marborè VIC turbojets.

Performance: (CM 170-2) Max speed, 435 mph (700 km/h) at sea level and 463 mph (745 km/h) at 29,520 ft (9 000 m); initial rate of climb, 3,540 ft/min (18 m/sec); service ceiling 44,300 ft (13 500 m); range, 775 mls (1 250 km); endurance 2 hr 50 min.

Weights: Empty equipped (CM 170-1), 4,740 lb (2 150 kg), (CM 170-2), 5,093 lb (2 310 kg); normal take-off, 6,835 lb (3 100 kg); max take-off, 7,055 lb (3 200 kg).

Dimensions: Span, 37 ft 5 in (11,40 m); span over tip tanks, 39 ft 10 in (12,15 m); length, 33 ft 0 in (10,06 m); height, 9 ft 2 in (2,80 m); wing area, 186·1 sq ft (17,30 m²).

Accommodation: Two in tandem, full dual controls.

Armament: Two 7,5-mm or 7,62-mm fixed machine guns in nose, underwing strong points for bombs, rockets or missiles.

Status: First of three protoypes flown on 27 June 1951; first pre-production on 7 July 1954; first production on 29 February 1956; first CM 175 Zephyr flown 30 May 1959. Production total 916 comprising: prototypes, 3; pre-production, 10; *Armée de l'Air*, 387;

CEV, 5; *Aéronavale*, 32; Brazil, 7; Germany, 250; Israel 52; Austria, 18; Finland, 82; Belgium, 48; Cambodia, 4; Congo (Leopoldville) 6; Lebanon, 4. Production was also undertaken in Finland (62 by Valmet OY), Israel (36 by IAI) and Germany (188 by Flugzeug Union Sud).

Notes: The CM 170 was originally designed to a French Air Force specification and entered service as the standard basic trainer at French flying schools. Of the 400 delivered to the French Air Force, 130 were to CM 170–2 Super Magister standard, as were seven supplied to Brazil. The *Aéronavale* CM 175 Zephyr had an arrester hook. Several of the former French territories in Africa received Magisters from *Armée de l'Air* stocks, including Algeria, Cameroon, Morocco, Rwanda and Senegal; others were supplied to Bangladesh, Guatemala and Salvador, and in 1975 the Irish Air Corps acquired six CM170-2s that were ex-Austrian and ex-Belgian Congo, and were completely refurbished by Aérospatiale before delivery. With a dual training light strike role, the Irish CM 170-2s remain operational in 1982; the *Armée de l'Air* remains the major Magister user, with some 300 expected to stay in service until 1990. The type is also the principal basic trainer for the *Heyl Ha'Avir* in Israel and IAI Bedek division is refurbishing these during 1982 to a new standard named the Amit.

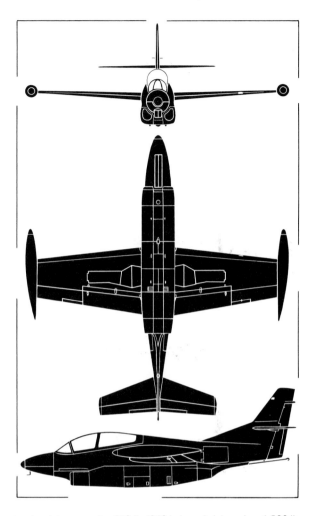

(Top) A Rockwell T-2B Buckeye of US Navy Training Squadron VT-4; (immediately above) a T-2E of the Hellenic Air Force; (below) one of the T-2Ds supplied to the Venezuelan Air Force. (Silhouette) Rockwell T-2C Buckeye.

Country of Origin: USA.

Type: Basic trainer and light attack aircraft.

Power Plant: Two (T-2B) 3,000 lb st (1 360 kgp) Pratt & Whitney J60-P-6 or (T-2C and T-2D) two 2,950 lb st (1,339 kgp) General Electric J85-GE-4 turbojets.

Performance: (T-2B) Max speed, 543 mph (874 km/h) at sea level; average cruising speed, 414 mph (667 km/h) at 44,000 ft (13 411 m); initial rate of climb, 6,100 ft/min (30,99m/sec); service ceiling, 42, 600 ft (12 984 m); range, training mission with tip tanks, 1,112 mls (1 790 km).

Performance: (T-2C) Max speed, 522 mph (840 km/h) at 25,000 ft (7 620 m); initial rate of climb, 6,200 ft/min (31.5 m/sec); service ceiling, 40,414 ft (12 320 m); max range, 1,047 mls (1 685 km).

Weights: Empty, 8,115 lb (3 680 kg); normal take-off (T-2C) 13,179 lb (5,977 kg); max take-off (T-2D, E), 16,500 lb (7 484 kg).

Dimensions: Span (over tip tanks), 38 ft 1½ in (11,62 m); length, 38 ft 3½ in (11,67 m); height, 14 ft 9½ in (4,51 m); wing area, 255 sq ft (23,69 m²).

Accommodation: Two in tandem, full dual controls.

Armament: (T-2B, C, optional) one store station beneath each wing with capacity of 320 lb (145 kg) each; (T-2D, E), six wing hard-points, capacity 750 lb (340 kg) each inboard and 500 lb (227 kg) each intermediate and outboard.

Status: First production model T2J-1 (no prototypes built) first flown on 31 January 1958; first T2J-2 (T-2B) conversion flown on 30 August 1962; first production T-2B flown on 21 May 1965; first T-2C prototype flown on 17 April 1968; first production T-2C flown on 10 December 1968. Production quantities, T-2A, 217; T-2B, 97; T-2C 231; T-2D, 24; T-2E, 40; production complete.

Notes: The North American NA-241 design met a US Navy requirement for a basic jet trainer, and was powered by a single 3,400 lb st (1 540 kgp) Westinghouse J34-WE-36 or -48 engine. It was in service as the T2J-1 by mid-1959, finally retiring from USN service early in 1973, by which time the designation had changed to T-2A. The T-2B differed from the T-2A primarily in having two J60 engines, and the T-2C followed, with another change of power plant; some 200 T-2Cs remained in the US Navy inventory in 1982, as basic pilot trainers. The first export order came from Venezuela in 1972, for 12 T-2Ds for the Air Force Academy; a second batch of 12 incorporated the full six-pylon armament option first offered by Rockwell in 1973, and the 40 T-2Es supplied to Greece in 1976 have a similar capability for use in the light strike role.

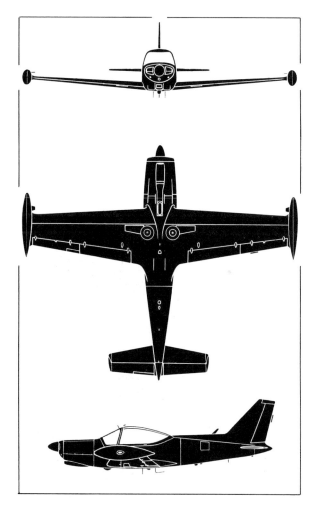

(Above) A pair of Siai Marchetti SF 260s of the Zambian Air Force; (immediately below) an SF 260 serving in the Belgian Air Force as a primary/basic trainer; (bottom) the prototype SF.260W Warrior light armed aircraft. (Silhouette) Siai Marchetti SF 260.

Country of Origin: Italy

Type: Primary trainer and light attack aircraft.

Power Plant: One 160 hp Avco Lycoming O-540-E4A5 six-cylinder horizontally-opposed engine.

Performance: (SF.260M) Max speed, 211 mph (340 km/h) at sea level; max cruising speed, 200 mph (322 km/h) at 75 per cent power at 4,925 ft (1 500 m); initial rate of climb, 1,558 ft/min (7,9 m/sec); service ceiling, 15,300 ft (4 665 m); range with max fuel, 1,025 mls (1 650 km); radius of action (SF.260W) strike mission with max ordnance, 345 mls (556 km).

Weights: Empty equipped (M), 1,761 lb (799 kg), (W), 1,794 lb (814 kg); max take-off (M), 2,645 lb (1 200 kg), (W) 2,886 lb (1 300 kg).

Dimensions: Span, 26 ft 11¾ in (8,25 m); span over tip-tanks, 27 ft 4¾ in (8,35 m); length, 23 ft 3½ in (7,10 m); height, 7 ft 11 in (2,41 m); wing area, 108·7 sq ft (10,10 m²).

Accommodation: Two seats side-by-side with full dual controls and third seat behind.

Armament: (SF 260W only) Two or four wing strongpoints with max capacity of 660 lb (300 kg); typical loads can include two SIAI or Matra gun pods each containing two 7,62-mm guns; rocket pods or 110-lb (50-kg) or 264·5-lb (120-kg) bombs.

Status: Prototype (as Frati F.250) flown on 15 July 1964. First SF.260MX flown 10 October 1970. First SF 260W Warrior flown in May 1972. Production quantities include: Belgium, 36 SF.260M; Bolivia, 6 SF.260M; Burma, 10 SF.260MB and 9 W; Dubai, one SF.260WD; Ecuador, 12 SF.260ME; Eire, 10 SF.260WE; Italy, 25 SF.260AMI; Libya, 230 SF.260ML; Morocco, two SF.260MM; Philippines, 32 SF.260MP and 16 SF.260WP; Singapore, 22 SF.260MS; Somalia, 6 SF.260WS; Thailand, 12 SF.260MT; Tunisia, 6 SF.260M and 12 SF.260WT; Zaire, 23 SF.260MC; Zambia, 8 SF.260MZ; Zimbabwe, 22 SF.260WC.

Notes: The SF.260MX is the generic designation for the export military version of the SF.260 three-seat high performance lightplane. The SF.260W Warrior differs from the SF.260M primarily in having a strengthened wing with two pylons for the carriage of assorted weapon loads, as indicated above, and entered production in 1973. Siai Marchetti also developed a variant of the SF.260W for maritime surveillance, search and rescue and supply missions, as the Sea Warrior, with enlarged tip tanks, one containing RDR-1400 lightweight radar and the other a photographic reconnaissance system. Warriors acquired by the Rhodesian Air Force (now the Zimbabwe Air Force) by way of the Comores Islands and Belgium, have the local name Genet.

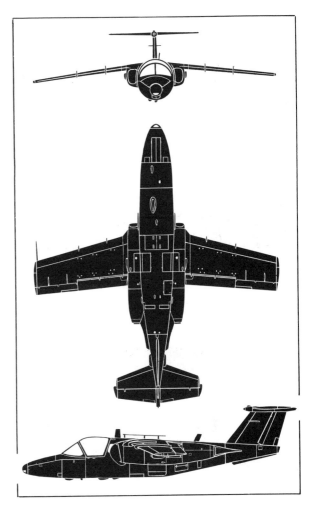

(Top) A Saab 105OE of the Austrian Air Force; (immediately above) one of the SK 60C reconnaissance versions of the Saab 105 serving the Swedish Air Force; (below) an SK 60C with wing armament. (Silhouette) Saab 105.

Country of Origin: Sweden.

Type: Basic trainer and light attack aircraft.

Power Plant: Two (SK 60) 1,640 lb st (743 kg) Turboméca Aubisque turbofans or (Saab-105XT, 105XH and 105G) 2,850 lb st (1 293 kgp) General Electric J85-GE-17B turbojets.

Performance: (SK 60 at gross weight of 8,820 lb/4 000 kg): Max speed 475 mph (765 km/h) at 20,000 ft (6 000 m); cruising speed 475 mph (765 km/h) at 20,000 ft (6 000 m); cruising speed 435 mph (700 km/h) at 20,000 ft (6 000 m) and 426 mph (685 km/h) at 30,000 ft (9 000 m); initial rate of climb, 3,440 ft/min (17,5 m/sec); service ceiling, 39,400 ft (12 000 m); range, 1,106 mls (1 780 km).

Performance: (105XT at max weight) Max speed, 603 mph (970 km/h) at sea level and 544 mph (875 km/h) at 33,000 ft (10 000 m); time to 33,000 ft (10 000 m) 4–5 mins; range at 43,000 ft (13 100 m) at 435 mph (700 km/h) with 20-min reserve, 1,423 mls (2 290 km).

Weights; (SK 60) Empty, 5,534 lb (2 510 kg); max take-off according to rôle—aerobatic, 8, 380 lb (3 800 kg), utility, 8,930 lb (4 050 kg) and ground attack, 9,920 lb (4 500 kg).

Weights: (105XT) Empty, 6,173 lb (2 800 kg); normal take-off (trainer), 10,174 lb (4 615 kg); max take-off (armed), 14,330 lb

(6 500 kg).

Dimensions: Span, 31 ft 2 in (9,50 m); length (SK, 60), 34 ft 5 in (10,50 m); length (105XT), 35 ft 5¼ in (10,80 m); height 8 ft 10 in (2,70 m); wing area, 175 sq ft (16,3 m²).

Accommodation: Two side-by-side dual controls. Optional provision for two additional seats if ejection seats not fitted.

Armament: Wing stressed for six strong points to carry (SK 60B) up to 1,543 lb (700 kg) or (105XT) up to 4,410 lb (2 000 kg) total stores.

Status: Two prototypes first flown on 29 June 1963 and 17 June 1964 respectively. First production SK 60A flown on 27 August 1965; prototype SK 60C flown on 18 January 1967; 105XT flown on 29 April 1967; 105Ö flown 17 February 1970; 105G flown on 26 May 1972. Production of 150 for Swedish Air Force, 40 for Austrian Air Force completed.

Notes: The multi-purpose Saab 105 was adopted by the Royal Swedish Air Force as its standard trainer (SK 60A), for weapons training and light strike duties (SK 60B) and for reconnaissance (SK 60C). The SK 60B/Cs are used by one squadron of the F 21 wing at Lulea, but in time of war, the SK 60A trainers would be used to equip four more operational units for light strike duties. Austrian Saab 105Ös serve as basic and weapons trainers.

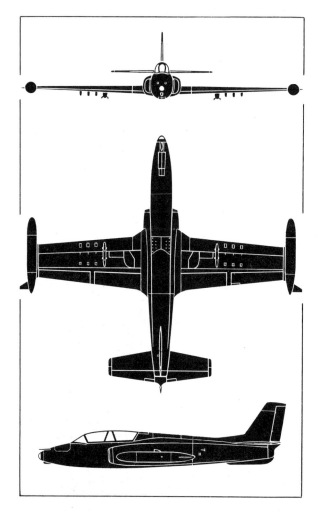

(Above) One of the prototypes of the Soko Galeb; (immediately below) a Galeb of the Yugoslav Air Force about to touch down and (bottom) a ground view of a production model of the Galeb, Yugoslavia's standard basic trainer. (Silhouette) Soko Galeb.

Country of Origin: Yugoslavia.

Type: Basic jet trainer.

Power Plant: One 2,500 lb st (1 134 kgp) Rolls-Royce Viper II Mk 22–6 turbojet.

Performance: Max speed, 470 mph (756 km/h) at sea level and 505 mph (812 km/h) at 20,350 ft (6 200 m); max cruising speed 453 mph (730 km/h) at 19,680 ft (6 000 m); initial rate of climb, 4,500 ft/min (22,8 m/sec); time to climb to 19,680 ft (6 000 m), 5.5 min and to 29,520 ft (9 000 m), 10.2 min; service ceiling, 39,370 ft (12 000 m); max range, 770 mls (1 240 km) at 29,520 ft (9 000 m) with full tip tanks; max endurance at 23,000 ft (7 000 m), 2 hr 30 min.

Weights: Empty equipped, 5,775 lb (2 620 kg); max take-off weights according to mission: aerobatic (clean), 7,438 lb (3 374 kg); basic trainer (clean), 7,690 lb (3 488 kg); navigation trainer (with tip-tanks), 8,439 lb (3 828 kg); weapons trainer, 8,792 lb (3 988 kg); strike 9,480 lb (4 300 kg).

Dimensions: Span, 34 ft 4½ in (10,47 m); span over tip-tanks, 38 ft 1½ in (11,62 m); length, 33 ft 11 in (10,34 m); height, 10 ft 9 in (3,28 m); wing area, 209.14 sq ft (19,43 m²).

Accommodation: Two in tandem, with full dual control.

Armament: Two 0·50-in (12,7-mm) machine guns in nose and underwing pylons for two 100-lb (50-kg) or 220-lb (100-kg) bombs, plus four 57-mm or two 127-mm rockets.

Status: First of two prototypes flown in May 1961; first pre-production example flew in February 1963 and deliveries to Yugoslav AF began in 1965.

Notes: Design of the Galeb (Seagull) began in 1957 and after prototypes had been evaluated the type became the first jet-powered aircraft of Yugoslavian design to enter production. In addition to the Yugoslav Air Force, which has adopted the type as its standard trainer, the Galeb G2-A is used by the Zambian Air Force, which received two in 1970, together with four single-seat Jastreb strike aircraft. A version powered by the 3,395 lb st (1 540 kgp) Viper 532 was designated Galeb-3 and made its first flight on 19 August 1970, but did not enter production. Closely related to the Galeb, and the production equivalent of the Galeb-3, however, is the two-seat weapons training version of the Jastreb, which in its basic single-seat form was itself developed from the Galeb and is in service in some numbers with the Yugoslav Air Force. Production of both the Galeb and the Jastreb for indigenous use ended by the late 'seventies, but delivery of 50 improved Galeb G2-AEs to the Libyan Arab Republic Air Force was not completed until 1980.

AERO L 29 DELFIN

TRAINER

Country of Origin: Czechoslovakia
Type: Basic Trainer.
Power Plant: One 1,960 lb st (890 kgp) M-701 VC-150 or S-50 turbojet.
Performance: Max speed, 382 mph (615 km/h) at sea level and 407 mph (655 km/h) at 16,400 ft (5 000 m); normal cruising speed, 340 mph (547 km/h) at 16,400 ft (5 000 m); initial rate of climb, 2,755 ft/min (14 m/sec); service ceiling, 36,100 ft (11 000 m); max range with internal fuel, 397 mls (640 km); range with drop tanks, 555 mls (894 km).
Weights: Empty, 5,027 lb (2 280 kg); normal take-off, 7,231 lb (3 280 kg); max overload, 7,804 lb (3 540 kg).
Dimensions: Span, 33 ft 9 in (10,29 m); length, 35 ft 5½ in (10,81 m); height, 10 ft 3 in (3,13 m); wing area, 213·1 sq ft (19,80 m²).
Accommodation: Two in tandem, full dual control.
Armament: Wing strong points can carry (in place of drop tanks) two bombs of up to 220 lb (100 kg) weight, two 7,62-mm gun pods or eight air-to-ground rockets.
Status: First Prototype (XL 29) flown on 5 April 1959 and second in July 1960. First production model flown in April 1963. Production ended in 1974, by which time more than 3,500 had been built.
Notes: The L 29 was one of three designs built as prototypes to meet a requirement for a basic jet trainer for use in the Soviet Bloc nations. After competitive evaluation it was adopted for use by all the Warsaw Pact air forces except that of Poland, which chose to proceed with the indigenous TS-11. The Delphin also has been supplied to Syria, Indonesia and Egypt, and small numbers were supplied to Uganda and Nigeria, some being used in an attack rôle during the war against Biafra.

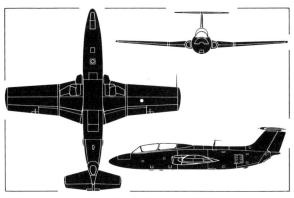

(Silhouette) Aero L 29 Delfin. (Below) An L 29 Delfin serving with the Hungarian Air Force.

AEROSPACE CT/4 AIRTRAINER

TRAINER

Country of Origin: New Zealand.
Type: Basic trainer.
Power Plant: One 210 hp Continental IO-360-D six-cylinder horizontally-opposed engine.
Performance: Max speed 178 mph (286 km/h) at sea level and 163 mph (262 km/h) at 10,000 ft (3 050 m); cruising speed at 75 per cent power, 144 mph (232 km/h) at 10,000 ft (3 050 m); cruising speed at 65 per cent power, 145 mph (233 km/h) at sea level and 139 mph (224 km/h) at 5,000 ft (1 524 m); initial rate of climb, 1,345 ft/min (6,8 m/sec); service ceiling 17,900 ft (5 455 m); range with 10 per cent reserve, 790 mls (1 271 km) at 5,000 ft (1 525 m).
Weights: Empty equipped, 1,490 lb (675 kg); max take-off, 2,400 lb (1 088 kg).
Dimensions: Span, 26 ft 0 in (7,92 m); length, 23 ft 2 in (7,06 m); height, 8 ft 6 in (2,59 m); wing area, 129 sq ft (12,00 m²).
Accommodation: Two seats side-by-side with full dual control.
Status: Prototype first flown on 23 February 1972. First delivery to R Thai AF on 23 October 1973. Production totals, 51 for RAAF, 24 for Royal Thai AF, 19 (CT-4B) for RNZAF, completed 1977.
Notes: The origins of the Airtrainer can be traced back to 1953 when a two-seat light aircraft by Henry Millicer (then chief aerodynamicist of the Australian Government Aircraft Factories) won a competition organised by the British Royal Aero Club. This design eventually was put into production and became the basis for a four-seat development, the Victa Aircruiser. Using the same revised structure as the Aircruiser restressed for g limits of +6 to −3, the Airtrainer is dimensionally similar to the Airtourer but has a number of modifications to suit it to the military training rôle, including provision for the carriage of 13-Imp gal (59-l) wing-tip fuel tanks.

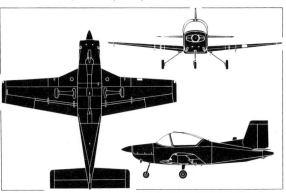

(Above) An Aerospace CT-4 serving at the RAAF Central Flying School. (Silhouette) Aerospace CT-4 Airtrainer.

TRAINER

AÉROSPATIALE TB 30 EPSILON

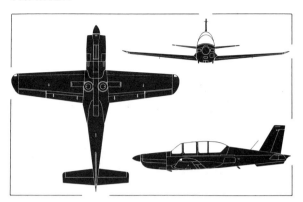

Country of Origin: France.
Type: Primary-basic trainer
Power Plant: One 300 hp Avco Lycoming IO-540-L1B5-D piston engine.
Performance: Max speed, 230 mph (370 km/h) at sea level; initial rate of climb, 1,700 ft/min (8,6 m/sec); service ceiling 20,000 ft (6 100 m); endurance, 3 hr 45 min.
Weights: Empty equipped, 1,935 lb (878 kg); max take-off, 2,650 lb (1 200 kg).
Dimensions: Span 25 ft 11½ in (7,92 m); length 24 ft 10½ in (7,59 m); height 8 ft 9 in (2,66 m); wing area 103·5 sq ft (9,60m²).
Accommodation: Two in tandem with full dual controls.
Status: First prototype flown 22 December 1979, second prototype flown 12 July 1980. Both prototypes subsequently modified and flight testing resumed with first of these on 31 October 1980. Production order for 30 Epsilons for *Armée de l'Air* confirmed 5 March 1982, with deliveries to begin September-1983; eventual requirement, 50 aircraft.
Notes: The Epsilon programme was launched by the *Armée de l'Air* in 1977, with initial studies directed towards a pure-jet type. Interest then shifted to a side-by-side piston trainer based on the SOCATA TB 10, but when the *Armée d l'Air* opted for tandem seating in 1978, virtually all commonality was lost. The TB 30B proposal provided the basis for prototype development, contracted in June 1979, but unacceptable pitch/yaw coupling charactersitics demonstrated by the prototype resulted, during 1980, in the application of extended, rounded and upswept wingtips, redesign of the rear fuselage and vertical tail surfaces, the lowering of the tailplane and the addition of a ventral fin. The Epsilon is to be employed by the *Armée de l'Air* for the first 80–100 hours of flying training.

(Silhouette) Aérospatiale TB.30 Epsilon. (Below) The second prototype Epsilon after modification.

TRAINER

AEROTEC T-23 UIRAPURU AND T-17 TANGARA

(Above) The prototype YT-17 Tangará, an updated version of the T-23 Uirapuru.-(Silhouette) Aerotec T-23 Uirapuru.

Country of Origin: Brazil.
Type: Primary trainer.
Power Plant: One 160 hp Lycoming O-320-B2B four-cylinder horizontally-opposed piston engine.
Performance: Max speed, 140 mph (225 km/h); max cruising speed, 115 mph (185 km/h) at 5,000 ft (1 525 m); initial rate of climb, 787 ft/min (4 m/sec); service ceiling, 14,760 ft (4 500 m); max range, 495 mls (800 km); endurance 4 hrs.
Weights: Empty, 1,190 lb (540 kg); max take-off, 1,825 lb (840 kg).
Dimensions: Span 27 ft 10¾ in (8,50 m); length, 21 ft 8 in (6,60 m); height, 8 ft 10 in (2,70 m); wing area, 145·3 sq ft (13,50 m²).
Accommodation: Two seats side by side with full dual control.
Status: Prototype first flown on 2 June 1965; first pre-production T-23 flown on 23 January 1968. Prototype A-132 Uirapuru II/T-17 Tangará flown 26 February 1981. Production totals, 100 for Brazilian Air Force, 18 for Bolivia, 8 for Paraguay.
Notes: The original A-122 Uirapuru was a private venture prototype designed by two Brazilian engineers and flown in 1965 with a 108 hp Lycoming O-235-C1 engine. Early in 1968 the Brazilian Air Force adopted the Uirapuru as a replacement for its locally-built Fokker S.11 and S.12 Instructor primary trainers, and placed an order for 30, with the Brazilian Air Force designation T-23. Further orders were placed in 1969 to bring the total Brazilian Air Force purchase of T-23s to 100. The Paraguayan Air Force purchased eight and the Bolivian Air Force, 18. An improved version, at first known as the A-132 Uirapuru II, features an improved cockpit canopy and increased span of 29 ft 6 in (9,00 m). As the T-17 Tangará, this variant may replace the T-23 in the Brazilian Air Force.

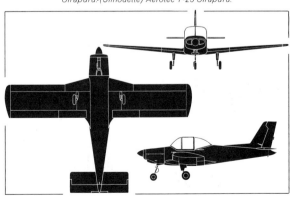

196

AIDC T-CH-I

Country of Origin: Taiwan.
Type: Primary/basic trainer.
Power Plant: One 1,450 eshp Avco Lycoming (Taiwan licence built) T53-L-701 turboprop.
Performance: Max speed, 368 mph (592 km/h) at 15,000 ft (4 570 m); max cruising speed, 253 mph (407 km/h) at 15,000 ft (4 570 m); economical cruise, 196 mph (315 km/h) at 15,000 ft (4 570 m); initial rate of climb, 3,400 ft/m (17,3 m/sec); service ceiling, 32,000 ft (9 755 m); range, 1,250 mls (2 010km).
Weights: Empty, 5,750 lb (2 608 kg); normal take-off (clean), 7,500 lb (3 402 kg); max take-off, 11,150 lb (5 057 kg).
Dimensions: Span, 40 ft 0 in (12,19 m); length 33 ft 8 in (10,26 m); height, 12 ft 0 in (3,66 m); wing area, 271·0 sq ft, (25,18 m²).
Accommodation: Two in tandem, dual controls.
Armament: Provision for wing pylons.
Status: First prototype flown 23 November 1973; second (armed) prototype flown 27 November 1974. Production batch of 50 launched 1976.
Notes: Aircraft design and manufacture in Taiwan is the responsibility of the Aero Industry Development Centre of the Chinese Air Force (AIDC/CAF) at Taichung. The first AIDC product of local development is the T-CH-I basic trainer which closely resembles the North American T-28 in most respects apart from the engine. The two prototypes were designated XT-CH-IA and XT-CH-IB respectively, the latter being an armed version for weapons training or light strike duty. Although design provision has thus been made for wing hardpoints, the production batch of 50 T-CH-Is built between 1976 and 1981 are unarmed and have entered service with the Chinese Air Force as basic trainers onto which pupils progress after an ab initio phase on the PL-IB.

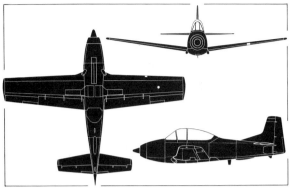

(Silhouette) AIDC T-CH-1. (Below) A production model T-CH-1 trainer in service in Taiwan.

BEECH 45 (T-34) MENTOR

Country of Origin: USA.
Type: Primary trainer.
Power Plant: One 225 hp Continental O-470-13A six-cylinder horizontally-opposed engine.
Performance: Max speed, 189 mph (304 km/h) at sea level; economical cruise, 170 mph (274 km/h) at 7,500 ft (2 286 m); initial rate of climb, 1,100 ft/min (5,6 m/sec); service ceiling, 17,300 ft (5 273 m); range, 737 mls (1 186 km).
Weights: (T-34A) Empty, 2,156 lb (978 kg); max take-off, 2,950 lb (1 338 kg).
Dimensions: Span, 32 ft 10 in (10 m); length, 25 ft 11 in (7·9 m); height, 10 ft 0¼ in (3·04 m); wing area, 177·6 sq ft (16·49 m²).
Accommodation: Two in tandem, dual controls.
Status: Prototype (Model 45) first flown 2 December 1948. First pre-production YT-34 flown in May 1950; production deliveries of T-34A began in 1954. First T-34B flown October 1954, deliveries began May 1955. Production totals: 350 T-34A and 423 T-34B and 170 export Model B45s by Beech, 100 T-34A and 25 Model 45A by Canadian Car and Foundry, 176 Model 45 by Fuji and 75 in Argentina, final deliveries 1962.
Notes: Mentor prototype was a derivative of the civil Bonanza. Design was adopted by USAF on 4 March 1953 and by US Navy on 17 June 1954, designation being T-34A and T-34B respectively, the latter with O-470-4 engine. US government supplied T-34s through MAP to Spain (as E.17) and Saudi Arabia. Beech exported similar Model B45s to Argentina (15), Chile (66), Colombia (41), Mexico (4), El Salvador (3) and Venezuela (41). In Japan, Fuji built 140 Model B45s for the JASDF and 36 for the Philippine Air Force, and another 75 B45s were assembled at Cordoba for the Argentina Air Force. CCF-built T-34s used by RCAF later transferred to Turkey and Greece.

(Above) A Beechcraft T-34 Mentor serving in the Spanish Air Force as an E.17. (Silhouette) Beechcraft T-34 Mentor.

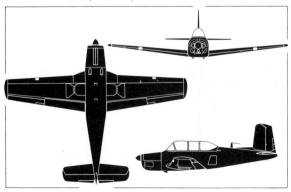

TRAINER

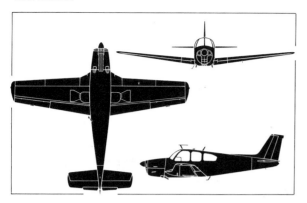

(Silhouette) Beechcraft F33 Bonanza. (Below) F33C Bonanzas in Spanish Air Force service as E.24s.

BEECHCRAFT MODEL 33 BONANZA

Country of Origin: USA.
Type: Primary trainer.
Power Plant: One 285 hp Continental IO-520-BB piston engine.
Performance: Max speed, 209 mph (338 km/h) at sea level; cruising speed, 198 mph (319 km/h) at 75 per cent power at 6,000 ft (1 830 m) and 157 mph (253 km/h) at 45 per cent power at 8,000 ft (2 440 m); initial rate of climb, 1,167 ft/min (5,9 m/sec); service ceiling, 17,860 ft (5 445 m); range 824 mls (1 326 km) at 75 per cent power, 1,023 mls (1 648 km) at 8,000 ft (2 440 m).
Weights: Empty equipped, 2,132 lb (967 kg); max take-off and landing 3,400 lb (1 542 kg).
Dimensions: Span, 33 ft 6 in (10,21 m); length, 26 ft 8 in (8,13 m); height, 8 ft 3 in (2,51 m); wing area, 181 sq ft (16,80 m²).
Armament: None.
Accommodation: Two pilots, side-by-side; two additional passenger seats in rear of cabin.
Status: Prototype Bonanza (Model 35) first flown 22 December 1945; first Model 33 flown 14 September 1959. Production total approximately 2,400 (Model 33s only) including, for military or quasi-military use, 18 F 33A and 27 F 33C to Imperial Iranian Air Force, five F 33C to Mexican Navy, 20 F 33C to the Mexican Air Force, 16 F 33C to Netherlands Government Flying School and 12 F 33A and 29 F 33C to the Spanish Air Force (plus 12 F 33A to Spanish Government for civil flying school).
Notes: The original Bonanza was distinguished by its 'butterfly' tail; the F 33 variant (described above) was introduced as the Debonair with conventional tail unit and is also now known as the Bonanza. In Spanish Air Force service, the type is known as the E.24A (F 33A) and E.24B (F 33C), operating alongside T-34As in *Escuadrone* 791 at the *Academia General del Aire* (Air Academy) at San Javier.

TRAINER

(Above) A Beechcraft CT-134 Musketeer in service with the Canadian Armed Forces. (Silhouette) Beechcraft Musketeer Sport.

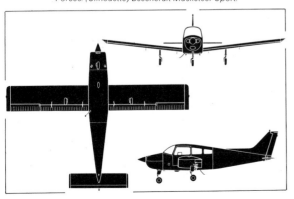

BEECHCRAFT MUSKETEER AND SUNDOWNER

Country of Origin: USA.
Type: Primary trainer.
Power Plant: One (Musketeer) 150 hp Lycoming O-320-E2C or (Sundowner) 180 hp Avro Lycoming O-360-A4K piston engine.
Performance: (Musketeer) Max speed, 140 mph (225 km/h) at sea level; max cruise, 131 mph (211 km/h) at 75 per cent power at 7,000 ft (2 135 m); initial rate of climb, 740 ft/min (3,6 m/sec); service ceiling, 11,900 ft (3 630 m); range, 883 mls (1 420 km) at 55 per cent power.
Performance: (CT-134A) Max speed, 141 mph (228 km/h) at sea level; cruising speed, 113 mph (182 km/h) at 59 per cent power; initial rate of climb, 792 ft/min (4,0 m/sec); service ceiling 12,600 ft (3 840 m); range, 687 mls (1 106 km).
Weights: (CT-134A) Empty equipped, 1,502 lb (681 kg); max take-off (Musketeer), 2,250 lb (1 020 kg); max take-off (CT-134A) 2,450 lb (1 111kg).
Dimensions: Span, 32 ft 9 in (9,98 m); length (Musketeer), 25 ft 0 in (7,62 m); length (CT-134A), 25 ft 9 in (7,85 m); height, 8 ft 3 in (2,51 m); wing area, 146 sq ft (13,57 m²).
Accommodation: Two pilots side-by-side; optional provision for two passengers in rear of cabin.
Status: Musketeer prototype first flown on 23 October 1961; name Musketeer dropped in 1974 when three current models became the Sundowner 180, Sierra 200 and Sport 150. Over 5,000 aircraft built since 1962; military sales include 20 for Mexico and 25 Musketeer and 21 Sundowner 180 for Canada.
Notes: In service with the Canadian Armed Forces as a primary trainer, the Musketeer was designated CT-134; the 25 Sundowners acquired in 1981 to supplement them are CT-134As, renamed Musketeer IIs in Canada only. The Mexican Air Force uses Musketeers as Instrument trainers.

BEECHCRAFT T-42 COCHISE (AND BARON)   TRAINER

Country of Origin: USA.
Type: Instrument flying trainer.
Power Plant: Two 260 hp Continental IO-470-L piston engines.
Performance: Max speed 236 mph (380 km/h) at sea level; cruising speed, 195 mph (314 km/h) at 50 per cent power at 10,000 ft (3 050 m); initial rate of climb, 1,670 ft/min (8,5 m/sec); service ceiling, 19,300 ft (5 880 m); range, 1,225 mls (1 971 km) at 45 per cent power at 10,000 ft (3 050 m).
Weights: Empty equipped, 3,233 lb (1 466 kg); max take-off 5,100 lb (2 313 kg).
Dimensions: Span, 35 ft 10 in (11,53 m); length, 28 ft 0 in (8,53 m); height, 9 ft 7 in (3,93 m); wing area, 199·2 sq ft (18,5 m²).
Armament: None.
Accommodation: Two pilots (pupil and instructor); two passenger seats in rear.
Status: Prototype Model 95-55 flown 29 February 1960; Model 99-B55 certificated September 1963; T-42A (Model 95-B55B) ordered 1965. Production/sales total over 2,400 including T-42A (US Army), 65; T-42A (Turkey), 5; Model 95-B55 (Spain), 19.
Notes: The Baron is one of the range of Beech twin-engined business transports, in production since 1961 in a number of versions; production quantities quoted above refer only to the original Model 55. The US Army made an off-the-shelf purchase of 65 Barons in 1965/66 to be used as instrument flying trainers and these were still in service in 1982, having been passed on to units of the Army Reserve and National Guard. In 1971, the Army procured five more T-42As, which were supplied to the Turkish Army through MAP. Spain acquired a total of 19 Barons which serve (as E.20s) in *Escuadrone* 423 at Getafe to give refresher training to HQ staff and other officers not permanently attached to flying units.

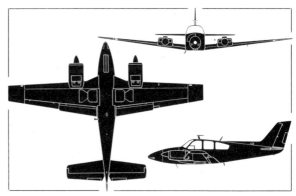

(Silhouette) Beech T-42A Cochise. (Below) A Beechcraft B55 Baron used by the Spanish Air Force as E.20.

BRITISH AEROSPACE (SAL) BULLDOG   TRAINER

Country of Origin: United Kingdom.
Type: Primary trainer.
Power Plant: One 200 hp Avco-Lycoming IO-360-A1B6 piston engine.
Performance: Max speed, 150 mph (241 km/h) at sea level; economical cruising speed, 121 mph (194 km/h) at 55 per cent power at 4,000 ft (1 220 m); initial rate of climb 1,034 ft/min (5,25 m/sec); service ceiling 16,000 ft (4 880 m); range with max fuel, no reserves, 621 mls (1 000 km).
Weights: Empty equipped, 1,430 lb (649 kg); max take-off (non-aerobatic), 2,350 lb (1 066 kg); max take-off (aerobatic, Srs 120) 2,238 lb (1 015 kg).
Dimensions: Span, 33 ft 0 in (10,06 m); length, 23 ft 3 in (7,08 m); height, 7 ft 5¾ in (2,28 m); wing area, 129·4 sq ft (12,02 m²).
Accommodation: Two side-by-side, full dual control.
Armament (optional): Four hardpoints in wings.
Status: Prototype (by Beagle) first flown on 19 May 1969; second prototype (by Scottish Aviation) flown on 14 February 1971. First production Srs 100 flown on 22 July 1971; first Model 102 flown on 25 November 1971; first Model 103 flown on 25 April 1972; first Srs 120 flown on 30 January 1973. Production/sales totals; Sweden (Model 101/Sk 61), 78; Malaysia (Model 102), 15; Kenya (Model 103), 5; RAF (Model 121), 130; Ghana (Model 122/122A), 13; Nigeria (Model 123), 36; Jordan (Model 125), 23; Lebanon (Model 126), 6; Kenya (Model 127), 9; Hong Kong (Model 128), 2; Botswana, 6.
Notes: The Bulldog originated as a military derivative of the Beagle Pup. After Srs 100s had been built for Sweden, Malaysia and Kenya, the Srs 120 was re-stressed to permit semi-aerobatic manoeuvres at the full gross weight.

(Above) Scottish Aviation Bulldog for service with the Malaysian Air Force. (Silhouette) British Aerospace Bulldog T Mk 1.

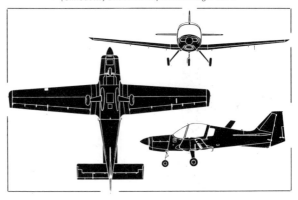

TRAINER

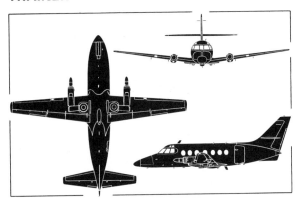

(Silhouette) British Aerospace Jetstream. (Below) A Scottish Aviation-built Jetstream T Mk 2 in Royal Navy service.

BRITISH AEROSPACE (SAL) JETSTREAM

Country of Origin: United Kingdom.
Type: Crew trainer.
Power Plant: Two 996 eshp Turboméca Astazou 16D turboprops.
Performance: Max speed, 282 mph (454 km/h) at 10,000 ft (3 050 m); cruising speed 269 mph (433km/h) at 15,000 ft (4 575 m); initial rate of climb, 2,500 ft/min (12·7 m/sec); service ceiling, 25,000 ft (7 620 m); max range 1,380 mls (2 224 km).
Weights: Typical empty equipped weight, 8,741 lb (3 973 kg); max take-off weight, 12,500 lb (5 670 kg).
Dimensions: Span 52 ft 0 in (15,58 m); length, 47 ft 1½ in (14,37 m); height, 17 ft 5½ in (5,32 m); wing area, 270 sq ft (25,0m²).
Accommodation: (T Mk 1) Two pilots (pupil and instructor) plus four seats in cabin. (T Mk 2) Two pilots, two trainee observers and navigating instructor in cabin.
Status: Prototype (HP Jetstream 1) first flown on 18 August 1967; first Jetstream T Mk 1 (assembled/converted by Scottish Aviation) flown on 13 April 1973; last of 26 T Mk 1s flown 2 December 1976. First T Mk 2 (aerodynamic test) flown 7 April 1977. First T Mk 2 delivered 21 October 1978.
Notes: The RAF ordered 26 Jetstream T Mk 1s from Scottish Aviation to fill a requirement for a multi-engined pilot trainer. Included in this batch were seven HP-built airframes, 14 assembled from HP components and five new-build. The Jetstream T Mk 1s entered service with 5 FTS early in 1974 but were withdrawn December 1974 when RAF multi-engine training was cut back. Fourteen were then converted to T Mk 2s, with nose radome for weather/search radar and equipped for naval observer training duties with No 780 squadron. Remaining T Mk 1s re-entered RAF service at 6 FTS on 25 November 1976.

TRAINER

(Above) One of the surviving CASA 1.131L trainers still used by the Spanish Air Force. as E.3Bs. (Silhouette) CASA (Bücker) Jungmann.

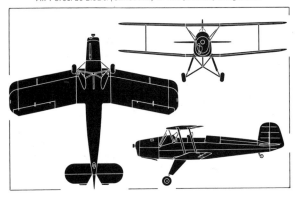

CASA (BUCKER) BU 131 JUNGMANN

Country of Origin: Spain (Germany).
Type: Primary trainer.
Power Plant: One 125 hp ENMA Tigre G-IV piston engine.
Performance: Max speed 124 mph (200 km/h); cruising speed, 95 mph (153 km/h); initial rate of climb, 1,202 ft/min (5,2 m/sec); service ceiling, 17,710 ft (5 398 m); range, 310 mls (500 km).
Weights: Empty, 992 lb (450 kg); max take-off, 1,587 lb (720 kg).
Dimensions: Span, 24 ft 3 in (7,39 m); length, 22 ft 1 in (6,73 m); height, 7 ft 5 in (2,26 m); wing area, 145 sq ft (13,47 m²).
Accommodation: Two in tandem in individual open cockpits.
Status: Prototype Bü 131 first flown (in Germany) 27 April 1934. Production by CASA in Spain began 1939, completed 1963; total of 550 CASA 1.131Es built.
Notes: First flown in Germany in 1934, the Bü 131 Jungmann can claim to be the oldest design still in active military service in 1981, although a handful of Stearman PT-13 Kaydets used as primary trainers by the Mexican Air Force are probably the most elderly airframes, having been built in the early years of World War II. The PT-13 originated in the USA a year or two after the Bücker Jungmann, but production of the latter continued much longer, and ended only in 1963. CASA in Spain had acquired a licence to build the Bü 131 as early as 1939, this being one of several German designs adopted for production at that time by Spanish companies following the successful support extended to General Franco by Germany during the Spanish Civil War. The Bü 131 was developed in Spain as the CASA 1.131E, with the indigenous Tigre G-IV engine, and became the standard primary trainer in the *Ejercito del Aire*. With the local designation of E-3B, about 40 Jungmanns were still serving in this rôle in 1982 for grading and initial flying training at the *Academia General del Aire* at San Javier, with *Escuadrone* 781.

CESSNA T-41 MESCALERO

Country of Origin: USA.
Type: Primary trainer.
Power Plant: One (T-41A) 150 hp Lycoming O-320-E2D four-cylinder or (T-41B/C/D) 210 hp Continental IO-360-D six-cylinder horizontally-opposed engine.
Performance: (T-41B) Max speed, 153 mph (246 km/h); max cruising speed, 105 mph (169 km/h) at 10,000 ft (3 050 m); initial rate of climb, 880 ft/min (4,5 m/sec); service ceiling, 17,000 ft (5 180 m); range, 1,010 mls (1 625 km).
Weights: Empty equipped, 1,405 lb (637 kg); max take-off and landing, 2,550 lb (1 156 kg).
Dimensions: Span, 35 ft 10 in (10,92 m); length, 26 ft 11 in (8,20 m); height, 8 ft 9½ in (2,68 m); wing area, 174 sq ft (16,16 m²).
Accommodation: Two crew side-by-side with dual control and two passenger seats.
Status: Commercial Model 172 introduced in November 1955. First USAF order for T-41A announced July 1964 with delivery of the first batch between September 1964 and July 1965. Production totals, T-41A, 259; T-41B, 255; T-41C, 52; T-41D, 226.
Notes: The USAF selected the commercial Cessna Model 172 in July 1964 when it was decided to abandon the "all-through" jet training programme and to provide 30 hrs on a piston-engined primary trainer for all *ab initio* students. For use at the USAF Academy in Colorado, the USAF purchased a version of the commercial R172E with more powerful engine, as the T-41C. The US Army had previously ordered a similar model as the T-41B, for use on training and site support duties. The T-41D differed only in slight details and was built for foreign nations supplied through MAP. Several air forces have also acquired Cessna 172s or Rheims-built FR 172s, similar to T-41s, in off-the-shelf purchases.

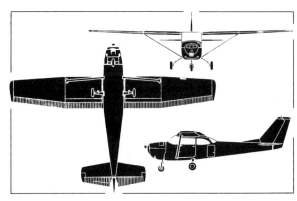

(Silhouette) Cessna T-41 Mescalero. (Below) A Cessna T-41D primary trainer of the Philippine Air Force.

DASSAULT-BREGUET MYSTERE 10 MER

Country of Origin: France.
Type: Multi-purpose trainer.
Power Plant: Two 3,230 lb st (465 kgp) Garrett TFE 731-2 turbofans.
Performance: Max cruising speed, 566 mph (912 km/h) at 25,000 ft (7 620 m); maximum range, 2,209 mls (3 555 km) cruising at 495 mph (796 km/h) at 41,000 ft (12 500 m); range with max payload, 1,400 mls (2 253 km) at 566 mph (912 km/h) at 31,000 ft (9 450 m).
Weights: Empty equipped, 10,760 lb (4 880 kg); max payload, 2,337 lb (1 060 kg); max take-off weight, 18,740 lb (8 500 kg).
Dimensions: Span, 41 ft 11 in (13,08 m); length, 40 ft 11 in (12,47 m); height, 15 ft 1½ in (4,61 m); wing area, 259 sq ft (24,1 m²).
Accommodation: Two pilots and up to four passengers in the cabin.
Status: Mystère 10 prototype first flown (with CJ610 engines) 1 December 1970; second prototype (with TFE 731-2 engines) flown 15 October 1971 and third prototype flown on 14 October 1972. First production Mystère 10 flown 30 April 1973 and deliveries began 1 November 1973. Production/sales total (principaly for commercial use) over 200 by 1982.
Notes: The Mystère/Falcon 10 is the second member in the Dassault-Breguet family of biz-jets. One or two examples have been purchased for quasi-military use as VIP transports but the principal military variant is the Mystère 10 MER, four examples of which have been acquired by *Aéronavale* for multi-rôle use. The major mission of the 10 MERs is to serve as intruder targets for the intercept training of Super Etendard pilots. They are also equipped for operation as conventional instrument and night flying pilot trainers.

(Above) One of the Dassault-Breguet Mystère 10 MER trainers of the Aéronavale. (Silhouette) Dassault-Breguet Mystère 10.

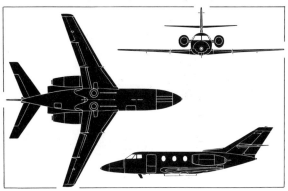

TRAINER

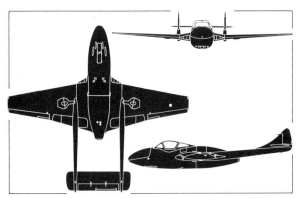

(Silhouette) De Havilland Vampire T Mk 11. (Below) A single-seat Vampire FB Mk 6 weapons trainer in Switzerland.

DE HAVILLAND D.H.115 VAMPIRE

Country of Origin: United Kingdom.
Type: Advanced trainer.
Power Plant: One 3,500 lb st (1 588 kgp) de Havilland Goblin 35 turbojet.
Performance: (T Mk 11, clean): Max speed, 538 mph (866 km/h) at sea level, 549 mph (885 km/h) at 20,000 ft (6 100 m); normal cruising speed, 403 mph (649 km/h) at 40,000 ft (12 200 m); initial rate of climb, 4,500 ft/min (22,8 m/sec); time to climb to 40,000 ft (12 200 m), 16·3 min; still air range, 853 mls (1 370 km).
Weights: Empty, 7,380 lb (3 347 kg); loaded (clean), 11,150 lb (5 060 kg); loaded (two 100 Imp gal/455 1 drop tanks), 12,920 lb (5 860 kg).
Dimensions: Span, 38 ft 0 in (11,59 m); length, 34 ft 6½ in (10,51 m); height, 6 ft 2 in (1,88 m); wing area, 261 sq ft (24,25 m²).
Accommodation: (T Mk 11,55) Two side-by-side, full dual controls; (FB Mk 6) Pilot only.
Armament: (T Mk 11) two or (T Mk 55) four 20 mm Hispano 404 cannon and provision for eight 25 lb (11·3 kg) or 60 lb (27·2 kg) rockets and two 500 lb (227 kg) bombs.
Status: Prototype D.H.100 Vampire single-seat fighter first flown on 20 September 1943; first D.H.115 Vampire Trainer flown on 15 November 1950; first production T Mk 11 flown on 1 December 1951. Production totals, 731 T Mk 11 and T Mk 55; 73 T Mk 22; 36 T Mk 33; 5 T Mk 34; 68 T Mk 35.
Notes: A two-seat training version of the Vampire fighter was designated Vampire T Mk 11 and the T Mk 55 was for export; examples remain in service in 1981 in Dominica, Switzerland and Zimbabwe. Some single-seat Vampires are also in use as advanced trainers, Switzerland being the largest single user. Many of the Swiss Vampire FB Mk 6s have UHF radio fitted in modified nose.

TRAINER

(Above) A Chipmunk T Mk 10 attached to the Army Air Corps. (Silhouette) De Havilland Canada Chipmunk T Mk 10.

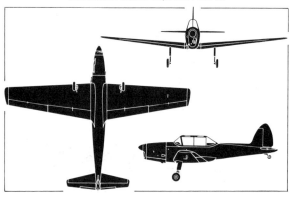

DE HAVILLAND DHC-1 CHIPMUNK

Country of Origin: Canada.
Type: Primary trainer.
Power Plant: One 145 hp de Havilland Gypsy Major 8 (military) or Gipsy Major 10 Mk 2 (civil) four-cylinder inverted in-line engine.
Performance: Max speed, 138 mph (222 km/h) at sea level, cruising speed, 119 mph (191 km/h) at sea level; initial rate of climb, 840 ft/min (4·27 m/sec); service ceiling, 15,800 ft (4 820 m); range, 280 mls (445 km) at 116 mph (187 km/h) at 5,000 ft (1 525 m).
Weights: Empty, 1,425 lb (647 kg); normal loaded, 2,014 lb (914 kg); max take-off, 2,100 lb (953 kg).
Dimensions: Span, 34 ft 4 in (10,46 m); length, 25 ft 5 in (7,75 m); height, 7 ft 0 in (2,13 m); wing area, 172 sq ft (15,98 m²).
Accommodation: Two in tandem, full dual controls.
Status: Prototype first flown 22 May 1946; production deliveries began 1947. First British production aircraft completed September 1949. Production totals: DHC-1B-1, 157; DHC-1B-2, 60; T 10, 740; T Mk 20, 231; Mk 21, 29; by OFEMA in Portugal, 60.
Notes: The Chipmunk was the first original design by the Canadian associate of the de Havilland company. Initial sales were of the DHC-1B-1 version, and the RCAF then bought 60 of the DHC-1B-2 version with a one-piece blown canopy over the cockpits, which was designated Chipmunk T Mk 30. In 1948 the Chipmunk was adopted for service with the RAF and a production line was established at the Chester factory of the parent company, where 889 were completed, plus another 111 at the Hatfield works. The majority of these were Chipmunk T Mk 10s for the RAF, but examples were exported for military use to at least a dozen other nations and a few of these remain in service in 1981. In the UK, the RAF retains the Chipmunk in Air Experience Flights.

EMBRAER EMB-121 XINGU

Country of Origin: Brazil.
Type: Light transport and multi-engined trainer.
Power Plant: Two 680 shp Pratt & Whitney Canada PT6A-28 turboprops.
Performance: Max cruise, 280 mph (450 km/h) at 11,000 ft (3 353 m); initial rate of climb, 1,400 ft/min (7,11 m/sec); service ceiling, 26,000 ft (7 925 m); range (with 1,985-lb/900-kg payload), 1,036 mls (1 668 km) at 20,000 ft (6 100 m); max range (with 1,344-lb/610-kg payload), 1,462 mls (2 353 km).
Weights: Empty equipped, 7,716 lb (3 500 kg); max take-off 12,500 lb (5 670 kg).
Dimensions: Span, 47 ft 5 in (14,45 m); length, 40 ft 2¼ in (12,25 m); height, 15 ft 6½ in (4,74 m); wing area, 296 sq ft (27,50 m²).
Armament: None.
Accommodation: Two seats side-by-side on flight deck and individual seats for five-six passengers in main cabin.
Status: Prototype flown 10 October 1976; first production aircraft flown on 20 May 1977. Deliveries began 1978; over 50 delivered by 1981, including six for Brazilian Air Force. Between March 1982 and December 1983, France to receive 41 Xingu ordered January 1981 for *Armée de l'Air* (25) and *Aéronavale* (16) for liaison and training duties.
Notes: The Xingu was derived from the EMB-110 Bandeirante using the same basic wing with a smaller fuselage. Six of the first EMB-121s off the line were delivered to the Brazilian Air Force, for use (designated VU-9) by the 6° *Esquadrao de Transporte Aereo* based at Brasilia. The *Armée de l'Air* adopted the Xingu to replace its ancient Flamants and the *Aéronavale* chose the Brazilian aircraft to replace its DC-3s used as navigation trainers. The Xingu II has uprated PT6A-135 engines.

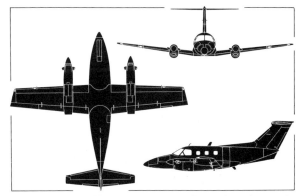

(Silhouette) EMBRAER EMB-121 Xingu I. (Below) One of the early-production Xingu Is used by Brazilian Air Force as VU-9s.

FFA AS 202 BRAVO

Country of Origin: Switzerland.
Type: Primary trainer.
Power Plant: One (AS 202/15) 150 hp Avco Lycoming O-320-E2A or (AS 202/18A) 180 hp AEIO-360-B1F piston engine.
Performance: (AS 202/18A) Max speed, 150 mph (241 km/h) at sea level; max cruising speed, 141 mph (226 km/h) at 8,000 ft (2 440 m); economical cruise, 126 mph (203 km/h) at 55 per cent power at 10,000 ft (3 050 m); initial rate of climb, 905 ft/min (4,6 m/sec); service ceiling, 18,000 ft (5 490 m); range, 600 mls (965 km); max endurance, 5½ hrs.
Weights: (AS 202/18A) Empty equipped, 1,543 lb (700 kg); max take-off, 2,315 lb (1 050 kg).
Dimensions: Span, 31 ft 11¾ in (9,75 m); length, 24 ft 7¼ in (7,50 m); height, 9 ft 2¾ in (2,81 m); wing area, 149·2 sq ft (13,86 m²).
Accommodation: Two seats side-by-side with dual controls; provision for third occupant in rear when non-aerobatic.
Status: Prototypes flown on 7 March 1969 (in Switzerland), 7 May 1969 (in Italy) and 16 June 1969 (in Switzerland). First production AS 202 flown 22 December 1971. Production/sales totals by end-1982, more than 150 including Iraqi Air Force, 48 AS 202/18A-1; Indonesian Air Force, 20; Moroccan Air Force, 14 and Uganda Army Air Force, 6.
Notes: The AS 202 Bravo was the product of an agreement concluded between Siai Marchetti in Italy and Flug-und Fahrzeugwerke AG in Switzerland providing for joint development of a trainer and light sporting aircraft. All production has been handled by FFA and embraces the two differently-powered variants noted above. During 1978 a prototype was flown of the AS 202/26A with a 260 hp Avco Lycoming engine, but this variant had not been ordered up to the end of 1981.

(Above) An FFA AS-202/18 Bravo in service for primary training with the Indonesian Air Force. (Silhouette) FFA AS-202.

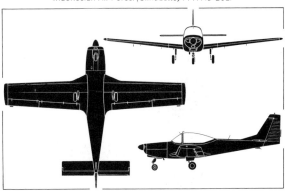

FUJI T1

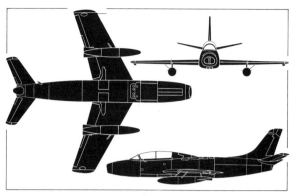

(Silhouette) Fuji T.1B. (Below) A Fuji T.1B, the second production version of the JASDF basic/intermediate trainer.

Country of Origin: Japan.
Type: Basic trainer.
Power Plant: One (T1A) 3,990 lb st (1 810 kgp) Rolls-Royce Bristol Orpheus 805, or (T1B) 2,645 lb st (1 200 kgp) Ishikawajima-Harima J3-IHI-3 or (T1C) 3,085 lb st (1 400 kgp) J3-IHI-7 turbojet.
Performance: (T1A): Max speed (clean) 575 mph (925 km/h) at 20,000 ft (6 100 m); max speed with external tanks, 510 mph (825 km/h) at 25,000 ft (7 600 m); cruising speed, 357 mph (575 km/h) at 10,000 ft (3 050 m) and 385 mph (620 km/h) at 30,000 ft (9 150 m); initial rate of climb, 6,500 ft/min (33 m/sec); service ceiling, 47,244 ft (14 400 m); max range (clean), 805 mls (1 300 km); max range (external fuel) 1,210 mls (1 950 km).
Performance: (T1B): Max speed, 518 mph (834 km/h) at 19,685 ft (6 000 m); cruising speed, 357 mph (575 km/h); initial rate of climb, 4,724 ft/min (24,0 m/sec), service ceiling 39,370 ft (12 000 m).
Weights (T1A): Empty, 6,078 lb (2 755 kg); normal take-off, 9,502 lb (4 310 kg); max overload, 11,005 lb (5 000 kg).
Dimensions: Span, 34 ft 5 in (10,5 m); length, 39 ft 9 in (12,1 m); height, 13 ft 4½ in (4,1 m); wing area, 239·2 sq ft (22,22 in²).
Accommodation: Two in tandem, dual controls.
Status: First of two prototypes flown on 8 January 1958; first T1B flown on 17 May 1960; first T1C flown in April 1965. Production totals: two prototypes, four pre-production, 40 T1A and 20 T1B, all for JASDF; production ended 1963.
Notes: The T1F2 with imported Orpheus engines, and entered service with the designation T1A; the T1F1 with indigenous J3 engine was delivered with the JASDF designation T1B. The T1F3 was re-engined with the uprated J3-IHI-7 and retrospectively designated T1C.

FUJI T-3 (AND LM-I, KM-2)

(Above) A Fuji KM-2 primary trainer, derived from the Beechcraft T-34 Mentor. (Silhouette) The Fuji T-3 (KM-2B).

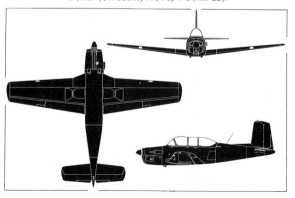

Country of Origin: Japan.
Type: Primary trainer (and light liaison).
Power Plant: One 340 hp Avco Lycoming IGSO-480-A1F6 engine.
Performance: Max speed 234 mph (377 km/h) at 16,000 ft (4 875 m); max cruise, 204 mph (328 km/h) at 8,000 ft (2 440 m); economical cruise, 158 mph (254 km/h) at 8,000 ft (2 440 m); initial rate of climb, 1,520 ft/min (7,7 m/sec); service ceiling, 26,800 ft (8 170 m); range with max fuel, 600 mls (965 km).
Weights; Empty, 2,504 lb (1 136 kg); max take-off, 3,400 lb (1 542 kg).
Dimensions: Span, 32 ft 10 in (10,00 m); length, 26 ft 4¼ in (8,04 m); height, 9 ft 11 in (3,02 m); wing area, 177·6 sq ft (16,50 m²).
Accommodation: Two in tandem, dual controls.
Status: First LM-1 Nikko flown 6 June 1955; prototype KM-2B (T-3) flown 26 September 1974; first production T-3 flown 17 January 1978. Production/sales totals: LM-1, 27 (JGSDF); KM-2, 25 (JMSDF); T-3, 50 (JASDF), completed 1981.
Notes: Fuji evolved the Nikko as a four-seat derivation of the Beech 45 Mentor having a widened centre fuselage but the same wing. The Ground Self-Defence force bought 27 Nikkos for liaison duty under the designation LM-1, some being later converted to LM-2 with uprated engine and an optional fifth seat. Procurement began in 1980 of the TM-1, an improved version of the KM-2 for the GSDF. The KM-2s bought by the Maritime Self-Defence Force were similar to the LM-1 but had 340 hp Lycoming IGSO-480-A1C6 engines and were used as primary trainers. Fuji evolved the KM-2B in 1974, in which the original Beech 45 type cockpit was combined with the improved airframe of the KM-2, and this type was selected by JASDF for production as the T-3.

GOMHOURIA (BÜ 181)

Country of Origin: Egypt (Germany).
Type: Primary trainer.
Power Plant: One (Mks 1, 4 and 5) 105 hp Walter Minor 4-III, or 145 hp Continental (Mks 2 and 3) C-145 or (Mks 6, 7 and 8) O-300 six cylinder horizontally-opposed engine.
Performance: (Mk 6) Max speed, 133 mph (215 km/h) at sea level; normal cruise, 115 mph (185 km/h) at 6,560 ft (2 000 m); initial climb, 785 ft/min (4,0 m/sec); max range, 600 mls (960 km); endurance, 5·5 hrs; service ceiling, 15,740 ft (4 800 m).
Weights: (Mk 6) Empty, 1,146 lb (520 kg); max loaded, 1,840 lb (835 kg).
Dimensions: Span, 34 ft 9 in (10,60 m); length, 25 ft 11 in (7,90 m); height, 6 ft 8½ ins (2,05 m); wing area, 145·3 sq ft (13,50 m²).
Armament: None.
Accommodation: Two side by side with dual controls.
Status: Essentially the Bücker Bü 181 Bestmann of 1939 vintage, the Gomhouria (Republic) entered production during 1950 at Kader, near Cairo, being manufactured in successive versions until 1979, by which time more than 300 had been built in Egypt.
Notes: The Gomhouria remains the standard primary trainer of the Egyptian Air Force, and some 200 Egyptian-built examples of this Bestmann derivative were in service with the EAF and flying clubs mid-1982, when a new blown clear-vision cockpit canopy was being progressively introduced. Most remaining aircraft are powered by the Continental O-300 engine and the final production model was the Mk 8R which featured an improved engine starting system and upgraded communications and navigation equipment. The Gomhouria will be progressively relegated to grading during the mid 'eighties the Egyptian Air Force currently possessing no plans for procurement of a replacement.

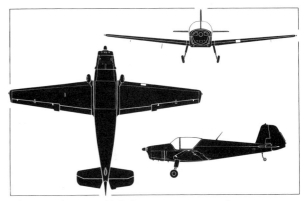

(Silhouette) Gomhouria Mk 8. (Below) A late production Gomhouria with the new canopy and windscreen now being standardised.

GRUMMAN TC-4C ACADEME

Country of Origin: USA.
Type: Bombardier/navigator trainer.
Power Plant: Two 1,910 shp Rolls-Royce Dart 529-8X turboprops.
Performance: Max speed, 359 mph (578 km/h) at 5,000 ft (1 525 m); average cruising speed, 288 mph (463 km/h) at 5,000 ft (1 525 m); initial rate of climb, 1,880 ft/min (9,5 m/sec); time to 25,000 ft (7 620 m), 21·9 min; service ceiling, 30,000 ft (9 150 m); range, 1,146 mls (1 845 km) at 5,000 ft (1 525 m) and 1,836 mls (2 954 km) at 25,000 ft (7 620 m).
Weights: Empty, 24,575 lb (11 147 kg); max take-off, 36,000 lb (16 330 kg).
Dimensions: Span, 78 ft 4 in (23,87 m); length, 67 ft 10¾ in (20,69 m) height, 23 ft 4 in (7,11 m); wing area, 610·3 sq ft (56,69 m²).
Accommodation: Two pilots, five students and two instructors.
Status: Grumman G-159 development aircraft first flown on 14 August 1958, 11 November 1958 and 17 January 1959. First TC-4C flown 14 June 1967. Production total, 200 including one VC-4A and nine TC-4C.
Notes: The US Navy adopted a version of the Grumman Gulfstream I executive aircraft in December 1966 to meet a requirement for training bombardier/navigators in use of the DIANE nav/attack weapon systems of the A-6 Intruder. A simulated A-6 cockpit is located in the rear of the cabin, which also houses four identical radar/navigation training consoles. Eight TC-4Cs operational in 1982 fly with VA-42 and VA-128 (three each) and the USMC VMAT-202; all have been converted to cover the latest TRAM-equipped A-6E. The single VC-4A is an executive transport used by the US Coast Guard. The Greek Air Force also operates a Gulfstream I as a VIP transport.

(Above) One of the US Navy TC-4Cs serving with VA-128 for observer training. (Silhouette) Grumman TC-4C Academe.

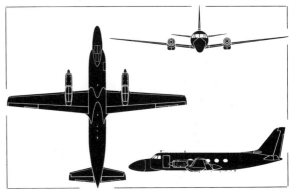

TRAINER

HAL HPT-32

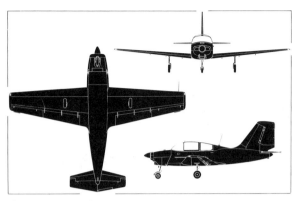

(Silhouette) HAL HPT-32. (Below) One of the prototypes of India's new primary trainer, the HPT-32.

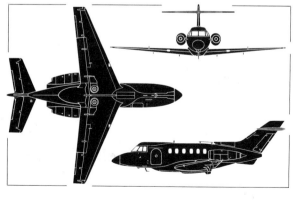

Country of Origin: India.

Type: Primary/basic trainer.

Power Plant: One 260 hp Avco Lycoming AEIO-540-D4B5 engine.

Performance: Max speed 135 mph (217 km/h) at sea level; initial rate of climb, 1,100 ft/min (5,6 m/sec); service ceiling, 15,580 ft (4 750 m); range, 435 mls (700 km) at 5,000 ft (1 525 m) with standard fuel; endurance, 4 hrs.

Weights: Empty, 2,041 lb (926 kg); normal take-off 2,756 lb (1 250 kg); max take-off 3,031 lb (1 375 kg).

Dimensions: Span 31 ft 2 in (9,50 m); length 25 ft 4 in (7,72 m); height, 10 ft 8¾ in (3,27 m); wing area, 161 sq ft (15,00 m²).

Accommodation: Two side-by-side, dual controls.

Armament: None.

Status: Two prototypes flown 6 January 1977 and 12 March 1979 respectively. Third (improved) prototype flown 31 July 1981. Initial Indian Air Force contract for 24 placed 1981, with deliveries to start 1983.

Notes: The HPT-32 was designed as a successor to the HT-2 as a primary-cum-basic trainer in Indian Air Force service, and although the prototypes have fixed undercarriages, the trainer has been designed from the outset for a fully retractable undercarriage (this being fixed on the prototypes by introduction of tie rods and exclusion of power control boosters and hydraulic pumps). Later production aircraft may switch from the Lycoming to a new 260 hp engine of indigenous design. Provision is made for an optional third seat or an auxiliary fuel tank in the cabin. Testing of a prototype in definitive production configuration began in mid-1981, at which time the Kanpur factory of Hindustan Aerospace Ltd was authorised to proceed with an initial production batch of HPT-32s against a prospective total requirement for 100–150.

TRAINER

HAWKER SIDDELEY (BAE) DOMINIE (AND HS.125)

(Above) A Hawker Siddeley Dominie T Mk 1 serving the RAF as a navigation trainer. (Silhouette) HSA Dominie T Mk 1.

Country of Origin: United Kingdom.

Type: Navigation trainer and communications aircraft.

Power Plant: Two (Dominie, HS.125), 3,000 lb st (1 360 kgp) Rolls Royce Viper 301 turbojets or (HS.125 Srs700) 3,700 lb st (1 680 kgp) Garett-AiResearch. TFE 731-3-1H turbofans.

Performance: (Dominie), Max speed, 500 mph (805 km/h) at 30,000 ft (9 145 m); typical operating speed, 368 mph (593 km/h) at 35,000 ft (10 680 m); initial rate of climb, 4,000 ft/min (20,3 m/sec); service ceiling, 40,000 ft (12 200 m).

Weights: Basic weight, 10,100 lb (4 581 kg); radio and navaids, 1,390 lb (631 kg); max take-off, 21,200 lb (9 615 kg); max landing, 19,550 lb (8 865 kg).

Dimensions: Span, 47 ft 0 in (14,33 m); length (Dominie, HS.125 CC Mk 1), 47 ft 5 in (14·45 m); length (HS.125 CC Mk 2, Srs 700) 50 ft 8½ in (15,46 in); height, 16 ft 6 in (5,03 m); wing area, 353 sq ft (32·8 m²).

Accommodation: (Dominie) Two pilots with dual control (provision for single-pilot operation); four seats in cabin.

Status: Prototype D.H.125 first flown on 13 August 1962. First HS.125 Srs 2 Dominie flown on 1 December 1964. Production of 20 Dominies for RAF completed in 1966; more than 520 HS.125s produced for military and civil use, continuing in 1982.

Notes: The Hawker Siddeley (de Havilland) 125 business jet was selected in September 1962 to meet RAF needs for a new navigation trainer, and a batch of 20 was produced. These remain in service with No 6 Flying Training School at Finningley, with the designation Dominie T Mk 1. The RAF uses HS.125s in the communications rôle, having acquired five Srs 400s and two Srs 600s, with the official designation of HS.125 CC Mk 1 and CC Mk 2 respectively. Several other air forces have also bought the HS.125 for various rôles.

HISPANO HA-200 SAETA AND HA-220 SUPER SAETA
TRAINER

Country of Origin: Spain.
Type: Basic trainer and light attack aircraft.
Power Plant: (HA-200A, B & D) Two 880 lb st (400 kgp) Turboméca Marboré II turbojets or (HA-220) two 1,058 lb st (480 kgp) Marboré VI turbojets.
Performance: (HA-220) Max speed, 435 mph (700 km/h) at 23,000 ft (7 000 m); normal cruising speed, 354 mph (570 km/h) at 19,700 ft (6 000 m); initial rate of climb, 3,346 ft/min (17,0 m/sec); service ceiling, 42,650 ft (13 000 m); range with max fuel, 1,055 mls (1 700 km).
Weights: (HA-220) Basic empty, 4,894 lb (2 200 kg); max take-off, 8,157 lb (3 700 kg).
Dimensions: Span, 34 ft 2 in (10,42 m); span over tip tanks, 35 ft 10 in (10,93 m); length, 29 ft 5 in (8,97 m); height 9 ft 4 in (2,85 m); wing area, 187·2 sq ft (17,40 m²).
Accommodation: Two in tandem, full dual controls.
Armament: Two 7,7-mm Breda machine guns in upper front fuselage; two strong points under fuselage with 375-lb (170-kg) capacity each and four underwing strong points.
Status: First prototype flown on 12 August 1955; first HA-200A flown on 11 October 1962; first HA-200B flown on 21 July 1960; first HA-200D flown in April 1965; first HA-220 flown 25 April 1970. Production quantities; two prototypes· HA-200, 10; HA-200A, 30; HA-200D, 55; HA-220, 25; Al Kahira, 63 (in Egypt).
Notes: The HA-200 was adopted by the Spanish Air Force under the designation E.14, together with the similar AE.10As used for weapons training. In the more powerful HA-220 (A.10C), the place of the second seat is taken by an extra fuel tank The E.14 and AE.10A were replaced by the CASA 101 in 1981, but no plans announced for replacement of the A.10Cs and armed AE.10Bs in *Esc* 214. A dozen examples of the Egyptian-built Al Kahira were maintained in airworthy condition early 1982.

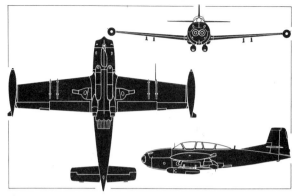

(Silhouette) Hispano HA-220 Saeta. (Below) One of the Hispano HA-220s used by Escuadron 214 of the Spanish Air Force.

McDONNELL DOUGLAS TA-4 SKYHAWK
TRAINER

Country of Origin: USA.
Type: Advanced pilot trainer.
Power Plant: One, 8,500 lb st (3 856 kgp) Pratt & Whitney J52-P-6 turbojet.
Performance: Max speed, 630 mph (1 010 km/h) at sea level, or Mach 0·82; average cruising speed, 470 mph (757 km/h) at 35,000 ft (10 670 m); operational ceiling, over 40,000 ft (12 200 m); typical mission radius, 800 mls (1 290 km) at 470 mph (757 km/h) at high altitudes and 390 mph (630 km/h) at sea level; mission endurance, up to 3·5 hrs with external tanks.
Weight: Operating weight empty, 11,050 lb (5 012 kg); normal take-off weight, clean, 15,500 lb (7 030 kg); max take-off weight, 20,000 lb (9 065 kg).
Dimensions: Span, 27 ft 6 in (8,38 m); length overall (excluding refuelling probe), 42 ft 7¼ in (12,98 m); height overall, 15 ft 3 in (4,66 m); wing area, 260 sq ft (24,16 m²).
Accommodation: Two in tandem, dual controls.
Armament: Two 20-mm MK-12 cannon in wing roots and one fuselage and four wing strongpoints.
Status: Prototype TA-4E two-seat Skyhawk first flown 30 June 1965; first TA-4J flown 21 November 1969. Production totals, TA-4E, 1; TA-4F, 241; TA-4G, 2; TA-4H, 10; TA-4J, 292; TA-4K, 4; TA-4KU, 6.
Notes: As well as serving as an operational conversion trainer, the two-seat variant of the Skyhawk is in service as the standard US Navy advanced/weapons trainer in the pilot training syllabus. The TA-4E prototype and TA-4F production variant had the 9,300 lb st (4 218 kgp) J52-P-8A engine but the TA-4J for the training schools (VT-3, 4, 7, 21, 22, 24, 25 and 86 in 1981) has the lower rated J52-P-6 engine and lacks the in-flight refuelling provision.

(Above) The McDonnell Douglas TA-4J advanced trainer of the US Navy. (Silhouette) McDonnell Douglas TA-4J.

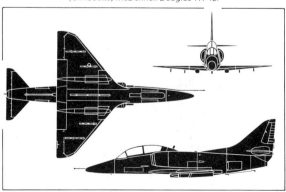

TRAINER

MBB (CASA) 223 FLAMINGO

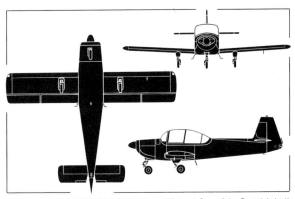

(Silhouette) MBB (CASA) 223 Flamingo. (Below) One of the Spanish-built examples of the MBB 223 Flamingo primary trainer.

Country of Origin: Germany (and Spain).
Type: Primary trainer.
Power Plant: One 200 hp IO- or AIO-360-C1B piston engine.
Performance: (223 K1) Max speed, 155 mph (249 km/h); cruising speed, 138 mph (222 km/h) at 75 per cent power; initial rate of climb, 1,220 ft (6,2 m/sec); service ceiling, 17,390 ft (5 300 m); range, over 310 mls (500 km).
Weight: Empty equipped, 1,510 lb (685 kg); max take-off, (223K1) 1,810 lb (821 kg); (223 A1) 2,160 lb (980 kg).
Dimensions: Span, 27 ft 2 in (8,28 m); length, 24 ft 4½ in (7,43 m); height, 8 ft 10¼ in (2,70 m); wing area, 123·8 sq ft (11,50 m²).
Accommodation: Two in tandem, dual controls.
Status: SIAT 223 prototype first flown 1 March 1967; first Hispano-built CASA 223 flown 14 February 1972; prototype Flamingo trainer flown (in Germany) 25 April 1979. Production/sales: 50 by MBB, 50 by CASA; 16 by Farnerwerke; deliveries include 20 to a Turkish governmental training establishment and 48 to Syrian Air Force.
Notes: The Flamingo, designed in Germany by the SIAT concern before being absorbed into MBB, has the unusual distinction of having been built in three countries in succession using the same jigs. SIAT/MBB built 50, including 15 for Turkish Air Force and then transferred the jigs to Spain, where production was continued by CASA in the former Hispano Aviacion factory that had become part of CASA group. Of 50 built in Spain, 32 were supplied to the Syrian Air Force. Farnerwerke in Switzerland then acquired the jigs, tools and a number of components, which it used to assemble 16 more Flamingos for the Syrian Air Force. The wheel came full circle in 1979 when MBB flew the prototype of an improved Flamingo trainer, the T-1 with changes in construction, equipment and materials.

TRAINER

MIKOYAN-GUREVICH MIG-15UTI (MIDGET)

(Above) The two-seat MiG-15UTI, still in large-scale service. (Silhouette) The MiG-15UTI.

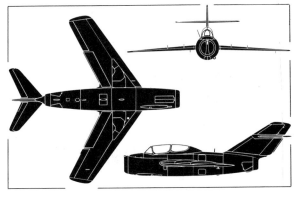

Country of Origin: Soviet Union.
Type: Tandem two-seat advanced trainer.
Power Plant: One 5,952 lb st (2 700kgp) Klimov VK-1 turbojet.
Performance: Max speed (clean), 630 mph (1 015 km/h) or Mach 0·826 at sea level, (with two slipper tanks), 559 mph (900 km/h) or Mach 0·73; initial climb, 10,235 ft/min (52 m/sec); time to 32,810 ft (10 000 m), 6·8 min; service ceiling, 47,980 ft (14 625 m); range (clean), 422 mls (680 km) at 16,405 ft (5 000 m), 590 mls (950 km) at 32,810 ft (10 000 m).
Weights: Empty, 8,818 lb (4 000 kg); loaded (clean), 10,692 lb (4 850 kg); max take-off, 11,905 lb (5 400 kg).
Dimensions: Span, 33 ft 0⅞ in (10,08 m); length, 32 ft 11¼ in (10,04 m); height, 12 ft 1⅝ in (3,70 m); wing area, 221·74 sq ft (20,60 m²).
Armament: Training armament can comprise one 12,7-mm UBK-E machine gun with 150 rounds or one 23-mm NS-23 cannon.
Status: Derived from the MiG-15 (Fagot) single-seat fighter, the MiG-15UTI two-seat trainer appeared as a prototype in 1949, subsequently being built in extremely large numbers. Licence manufacture was undertaken in China (as the FT-2), Czechoslovakia (as the CS 102) and Poland (as the SBLim-1), and the MiG-15UTI remains in widespread service with the Soviet Air Force and the air arms of Afghanistan, Albania, Algeria, Bangladesh, Bulgaria, Cuba, China, Czechoslovakia, Finland, Egypt, East Germany, Iraq, Guinea, Mali, North Korea, Nigeria, Poland, North Yemen and Vietnam. From 1967, all Polish (SBLim-1) trainers were fitted with the power plant, rear fuselage and tail surfaces of the MiG-15bis fighter (becoming SBLim-2 trainers). Because of its limited internal fuel, the MiG-15UTI is normally flown with auxiliary tanks. Small numbers of the Chinese-built version, the FT-2, have been exported (e.g., Pakistan, Albania, etc.).

MITSUBISHI T-2

Country of Origin: Japan.

Type: Advanced trainer.

Power Plant: Two 4,600 lb st (2 086 kgp) dry and 6,950 lb st (3 150 kgp) with reheat Rolls-Royce Turboméca RB.172 Adour 801 turbofans.

Performance: (clean): Max speed, 1,056 mph (1 700 km/h) or Mach 1·6 at 40,000 ft (12 190 m); initial rate of climb, 35,000 ft/min (177,8 m/sec); service ceiling, 50,000 ft (15 250 m); max ferry range, 1,610 mls (2 595 km).

Weights: Operational empty, 13,893 lb (6 302 kg); max take-off 21,161 lb (9 805 kg).

Dimensions: Span, 25 ft 10¼ in (7,88 m); length, 58 ft 6¼ in (17,84 m); height, 14 ft 4¼ in (4,38 m); wing area, 228·0 sq ft (21,2 m²).

Accommodation: Two in tandem, full dual controls.

Armament: Provision for one 20-mm rotary cannon in lower front fuselage; provision for external stores on fuselage centre line and wing pylons and at wing tips.

Status: Two prototypes flown on 20 July 1971 and 2 December 1971. Two pre-production aircraft flown on 28 April and 20 July 1972. Production deliveries began 1975. Production totals, XT-2, 2; pre-production T-2, 2; T-2, 32; T-2A, 44.

Notes: Mitsubishi was selected in September 1967 to proceed with development of an advanced trainer with strike potential. It has been produced in two versions; the T-2 advanced trainer and the T-2A weapons trainer, which carries a 20-mm multi-barrel cannon in the front fuselage. The T-2s serve with the 4th Air Wing of the JASDF, at Matsushima. A single-seat close support fighter variant of the T-2, the Mitsubishi F-1 (FS-T-2Kai), was developed subsequently and has entered production and service (separately described).

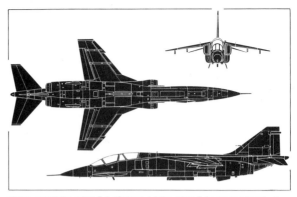

(Silhouette) Mitsubishi T-2. (Below) A Mitsubishi T-2 carrying bombs for a weapons training sortie.

MORANE-SAULNIER MS-760 PARIS

Country of Origin: France.

Type: Basic trainer, photo-survey and liaison aircraft.

Power Plant: Two (MS-760A) 880 lb st (400 kgp) Turboméca Marboré IIC or (MS-760B) 1,058 lb st (480 kgp) Marboré VI turbojets.

Performance: (MS-760B) Max speed, 432 mph (695 km/h) at 25,000 ft (7,600 m); max cruising speed, 393 mph (633 km/h) at 16,400 ft (5 000 m); economical cruising speed, 342 mph (550 km/h); initial rate of climb, 2,460 ft/min (12·5 m/sec); service ceiling 39,370 ft (12 000 m); max range, 1,080 mls (1 740 km).

Weights: Empty, equipped, 4,557 lb (2 067 kg); max take-off, 8,642 lb (3 920 kg).

Dimensions: Span, 33 ft 3 in (10,15 m); length, 33 ft 7 in (10,24 m); height, 8 ft 6 in (2,60 m); wing area, 193·7 sq ft (18 m²).

Accommodation: Side-by-side seats with full dual control.

Armament: Optional provision (for training) for two 7,5-mm machine guns plus four 3·5-in rockets or two bombs.

Status: Prototype (MS-760-01) first flown on 29 July 1954; first production model (MS-760A) flown on 27 February 1958; first MS-760B flown on 12 December 1960. Production totals: one prototype, 150 MS-760A (including 48 assembled in Argentina) and 63 MS-760B (including 48 assembled in Brazil).

Notes: The Paris was built by the original Morane-Saulnier company as a development of the MS-755 Fleuret, one of the first light aircraft to be powered by jet engines. It was adopted by the French *Armée de l'Air* for use in the communications rôle (about 50 still in service in 1982), and a small batch was supplied to the *Aéronavale* which was operating 10 in 1982 for advanced and instrument training. Export orders for the Paris were obtained from the Argentine Air Force (which still had about a dozen in service in 1981) and the Brazilian Air Force (no longer·in service).

(Above) A Morane Saulnier MS-760 Paris serving with the Armée de l'Air. (Silhouette) Morane Saulnier MS-760.

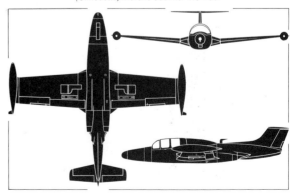

TRAINER   MUDRY CAP 10

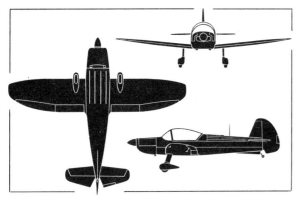

(Silhouette) Mudry CAP 10. (Below) A CAP 10B as used for pilot grading by the Armée de l'Air.

Country of Origin: France.
Type: Primary and aerobatic trainer.
Power Plant: One 180 hp Avco Lycoming IO-360-B2F piston engine.
Performance: Max speed, 168 mph (270 km/h) at sea level; max cruise, 155 mph (250 km/h) at 75 per cent power; initial rate of climb, over 1,180 ft/min (6 m/sec); service ceiling, 16,400 ft (5 000 m); range, 745 mls (1 200 km).
Weights: Empty equipped, 1,190 lb (540 kg); max take-off, aerobatic category, 1,675 lb (760 kg); max take-off, utility category, 1,829 lb (830 kg).
Dimensions: Span, 26 ft 5$\frac{1}{4}$ in (8,06 m); length, 23 ft 6 in (7,16 m); height, 8 ft 4$\frac{1}{2}$ in (2,55 m); wing area, 116·8 sq ft (10,85 m²).
Accommodation: Two side-by-side, dual controls.
Armament: None.
Status: Prototype CAP 10 flown August 1968, certificated 4 September 1970. Production total, about 120, including 50 for *Armée de l'Air* and six for *Aéronavale*.
Notes: The CAP 10 lightplane, built by Avions Mudry et Cie, was derived from the Piel Emeraude, and was developed for the *Armée de l'Air* to serve in the rôle of aerobatic trainer at the *Equipe de Voltige Aérienne* at Salon-de-Provence. It is also used by the *Armée de l'Air* as a grading and *ab initio* trainer for the NCO pilot training syllabus at the basic flying training school at Clermont-Ferrand-Aulnat and has more recently been introduced at the primary training school at Cognac. Six CAP 10s are used by the *Aéronavale* at its pilot selection centre at St Raphael. The *Armée de l'Air* also has acquired six of the single-seat CAP 20s, which are similar to the CAP 10 in general characteristics but are slightly smaller; these are also used by the EVA at Salon-de-Provence for aerobatic indoctrination.

TRAINER   NEIVA T-25 UNIVERSAL

(Above) The Neiva T-25, the Brazilian Air Force's basic flying trainer. (Silhouette) Neiva T-25 Universal.

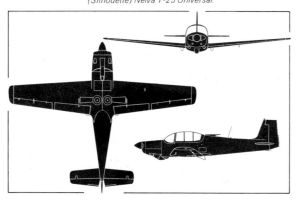

Country of Origin: Brazil.
Type: Basic trainer.
Power Plant: One 300 hp Lycoming IO-540-K1D5 six-cylinder horizontally-opposed engine.
Performance: Max speed, 195 mph (315 km/h) at sea level, cruising speed, 172 mph (278 km/h) at sea level; initial rate of climb, 1,380 ft/min (7,0 m/sec); service ceiling, 19,700 ft (6 000 m); range with max payload, 447 mls (720 km); range with max fuel, 975 mls (1 570 km).
Weights: Empty equipped, 2,425 lb (1 100 kg); max take-off and landing, 3,748 lb (1 700 kg).
Dimensions: Span, 36 ft 1 in (11,0 m); length, 28 ft 2$\frac{1}{2}$ in (8,60 m); height, 9 ft 9$\frac{3}{4}$ in (3·0 m); wing area, 185·14 sq ft (17,20 m²).
Accommodation: Two seats side-by-side, with full dual control, and optional third seat to rear.
Status: Prototype first flown on 29 April 1966; first production model flown on 7 April 1971; prototype YT-25B flown 22 October 1978. Production deliveries began late summer of 1971; total built, 140 for Brazilian Air Force, 10 for Chilean Air Force.
Notes: The Universal was developed by the Neiva company to meet a Brazilian Air Force requirement for a basic trainer which could replace the North American T-6 Texan and the Fokker S-11/S-12 Instructor. Unlike the texan it had to replace, the new trainer was required to provide side-by-side seating, with provision for a third occupant behind the two pilots. After the prototype had been tested in 1966/67, the Brazilian Air Force ordered the Universal into production and assigned it the designation T-25. In 1978, Neiva flew the improved YT-25B Universal II with 400 hp IO-720 engine and increased wing ordnance loads but development was discontinued when EMBRAER acquired Neiva in 1980, and initiated development of the EMB-313 Tucano.

NORTH AMERICAN T-6 TEXAN

TRAINER

Country of Origin: USA.

Type: Basic trainer.

Power Plant: One 550 hp Pratt & Whitney R-1340-AN-1 radial.

Performance: (T-6G) Max speed, 212 mph (341 km/h) at 5,000 ft (1 524 m); max cruising speed, 170 mph (274 km/h); economical cruising speed, 146 mph (235 km/h); initial rate of climb, 1,643 ft/min (8,3 m/sec); service ceiling, 24,750 ft (7 338 m); normal range, 870 mls (1 400 km).

Weights: Empty, 4,271 lb (1 938 kg); max take-off, 6,617 lb (2 546 kg).

Dimensions: Span, 42 ft 0¼ in (12,80 m); length, 29 ft 6 in (8,99 m); height, 11 ft 8½ in (3,56 m); wing area, 253·7 sq ft (23,56 m²).

Accommodation: Two in tandem, dual controls.

Status: Prototype (NA-26) flown in 1937. Production and remanufacture of variants of basic design continued until 1952. Production of all variants (excluding fixed-undercarriage types) totalled nearly 16,000 in the USA plus another 3,920 that were built under licence in Canada and Australia. Production continued in Canada until 1954 as the T-6J for the USAF and Harvard Mk 4 for the RCAF.

Notes: The T-6 Texan or (British name) Harvard is a member of the famous North American family of trainers that began in April 1935 with the NA-16. Initial versions had fixed undercarriage legs but a redesign of the basic airframe in 1937 produced the NA-26 prototype with retractable undercarriage and more powerful engine. Production derivatives of the NA-26 were widely used throughout World War II, and thousands of examples that became surplus at the end of the war were distributed world wide. More than a dozen air forces were continuing to use T-6s for training duties in 1982.

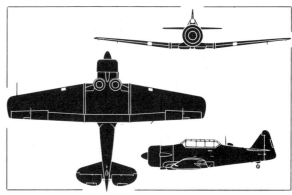

(Silhouette) North American T-6 Texan. (Below) A T-6G of the Spanish Air Force, designated as the E.16.

NORTHROP T-38 TALON

TRAINER

Country of Origin: USA.

Type: Advanced trainer.

Power Plant: Two 2,680 lb st (1 216 kgp) dry and 3,850 lb st (1 748 kgp) with reheat General Electric J85-GE-5 or 5A turbojets.

Performance: Max speed, 804 mph (1 295 km/h) or Mach 1·22 at 36,000 ft (11 000 m) at half fuel weight; cruising speed, 578 mph (930 km/h) at 40,000 ft (12 200 m); initial rate of climb at half fuel weight, 30 000 ft/min (152,4 m/sec); service ceiling at half fuel weight, 45,000 ft (13 716 m); range with max fuel, 20 min reserve, two crew, 973 mls (1 566 km).

Weights: Empty, 7,410 lb (3 361 kg); max take-off and landing, 11,761 lb (5 335 kg).

Dimensions: Span, 25 ft 3 in (7,70 m); length, 46 ft 4½ in (14,13 m); height, 12 ft 10½ in (3,92 m); wing area, 170 sq ft (15,80 m²).

Accommodation: Two in tandem, full dual control.

Status: First YT-38 prototype (YJ85-GE-1 engines) flown on 10 April 1959; first flight with reheat engines, January 1960; first production T-38A flown in May 1960. Production of 1,187 T-38As completed in January 1972.

Notes: The T-38A Talon was an outgrowth of the Northrop programme to develop a lightweight supersonic fighter, the N-156F Freedom Fighter, which eventually went into production as the F-5 (separately described). Design of the similar N-156T trainer proceeded in parallel with that of the N-156F for two years as a private venture, until the USAF drew up a requirement for a supersonic basic/advanced trainer and ordered prototypes of the Northrop design. The production total included 46 T-38As funded by the *Luftwaffe* for its US-based training programmes. From US stocks, T-38As have been supplied to Taiwan (25), Portugal (12) and Turkey (30).

(Above) Northrop T-38A used to train Luftwaffe pilots at Sheppard AFB. (Silhouette) Northrop T-38A Talon.

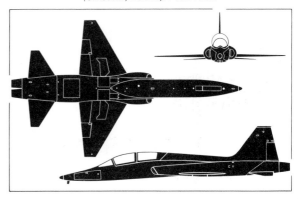

TRAINER

(AIDC) PAZMANY PL-1B CHIENSHOU (AND PL-2)

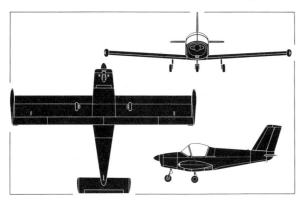

(Silhouette) Pazmany PL-1B. (Below) Pazmany PL-1B trainers built by the Aero Industry Development Centre, Taiwan.

Country of Origin: Taiwan.
Type: Primary trainer.
Power Plant: One 150 hp Lycoming O-320-E2A piston engine.
Performance: Max speed, 150 mph (241 km/h) at sea level; max cruising speed, 130 mph (209km/h); economical cruise, 115 mph (185 km/h) at sea level, initial rate of climb, 1,600 ft/min (8,13 m/sec); range with max fuel, 405 mls (650 km).
Weights: Empty equipped, 950 lb (431 kg); max take-off, 1,440 lb (653 kg).
Dimensions: Span, 28 ft 0 in (8,53 m); length, 19 ft 8¼ in (5,99 m); height, 7 ft 4 in (2,24 m); wing area, 116 sq ft (10,78 m²).
Accommodation: Two side-by-side, dual controls.
Status: Prototype first flown 26 October 1968. Production totals: PL-1A prototypes, 3; PL-1B, 45 for Chinese Nationalist Air Force and 10 for Chinese Nationalist Army. Delivery completed 1974.
Notes: The PL-1B was designed by Ladislao Pazmany, a well-known member of the home-building aircraft movement in the USA. His PL-1 was first flown on 23 March 1962 and was used extensively to prove the soundness of the basic design. In 1968, the Aeronautical Research Laboratory—then a branch of the Bureau of Aircraft Industry in Taiwan and now incorporated into the Aero Industry Development Center (AIDC)—chose the P-1 for production in Taiwan. After construction of three prototypes (known as PL-1As) and extensive testing, the Air Force confirmed its intention of adopting the type as its new primary trainer, and a total of 45 PL-1Bs (as the production version was designated) was built for the air force in addition to 10 for the Army. The Pazmany PL-2 closely resembles the PL-1B, and examples are reported to have been built by air force personnel in Vietnam, Thailand and South Korea.

TRAINER

PIAGGIO P.149D

(Above) Piaggio P 149, as in service for primary training with the Luftwaffe. (Silhouette) Piaggio P 149.

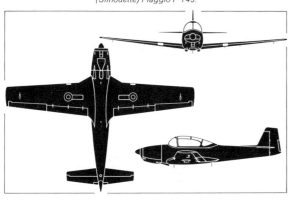

Country of Origin: Italy.
Type: Basic (and grading) trainer.
Power Plant: One 270 hp Lycoming GO-480 B1A6 six-cylinder horizontally-opposed engine.
Performance: Max speeds, 192 mph (304 km/h) at sea level and 177 mph (285 km/h) at 6,560 ft (2 000 m); cruising speed, 165 mph (266 km/h) on 67 per cent power at 7,500 ft (2 300 m) and 145 mph (234 km/h) on 56 per cent power at 10,800 ft (3 300 m); initial rate of climb, 980 ft/min (5 m/sec); service ceiling, 19,800 ft (6 050 m); range with full tanks, 30-min reserve, 680 mls (1 090 km) at 10,800 ft (3 300 m).
Weights: Empty, 2,557 lb (1 160 kg); max take-off weight, 3,704 lb (1 680 kg).
Dimensions: Span, 36 ft 6 in (11,12 m); length, 28 ft 9½ in (8,80 m); height, 9 ft 6 in (2,90 m); wing area, 203 sq ft (18,81 m²).
Accommodation: Two pilots side-by-side with full dual control for training rôle, with seats in rear for two-three passengers.
Status: Prototype first flown on 19 June 1953. First delivery from Italian production line, May 1957; first delivery from German production line, October 1957. Production totals, two prototypes and 72 by Piaggio; 190 by Focke-Wulf, completed 1959.
Notes: Piaggio developed the P.149 as a civil four-seat light aircraft using many structural components of the P.148 including the wing. Major production began after a modified version, with a one-piece rearward sliding hood, had been adopted by the *Luftwaffe.* Piaggio supplied 72 complete aircraft to Germany, and a licence plus 16 sets of assemblies to the Focke-Wulf company. Designated P.149D, the *Luftwaffe* version was adopted for both basic training and liaison tasks, but remained in use in 1982 only as a grading aircraft at WS-50, Fürstenfeldbrück. A few P.149Ds also serve in Uganda Air Force.

PILATUS P.3

Country of Origin: Switzerland.
Type: Basic trainer.
Power Plant: One 260 hp Lycoming GO-435-C2A six-cylinder horizontally-opposed engine.
Performance: Max speed, 193 mph (310 km/h) at 6,560 ft (2 000 m); max cruising speed, 170 mph (275 km/h); economical cruising speed, 157 mph (252 km/h); initial rate of climb, 1,378 ft/min (7,0 m/sec); service ceiling, 18,040 ft (5 500 m); max range, 465 mls (750 km).
Weights: Empty equipped, 2,447 lb (1 110 kg); normal loaded, 3,120 lb (1 415 kg); max take-off, 3,307 lb (1 500 kg).
Dimensions: Span, 34 ft 1 in (10,40 m); length, 28 ft 8 in (8,75 m); height, 10 ft 0 in (3,05 m); wing area, 177 sq ft (16,5 m²).
Accommodation: Two in tandem, full dual control.
Armament: (Optional): Provision for underwing armament comprising one 7·9 mm gun pod with 180 rounds, one carrier for two practice bombs and two rocket launchers, plus a gun camera.
Status: First of two prototypes flown on 3 September 1953. Production batch of 72 supplied to Swiss Air Force and six supplied to Brazil. Production completed.
Notes: Development of the P-3 was initiated in Switzerland in 1951 to provide the *Schweizerische Flugwaffe* (Swiss Air Force) with a replacement for its North American T-6 intermediate trainers. Following successful testing of two prototypes, the type was ordered into production and a batch of 72 was built. They have served since 1955 at Flying Schools to provide basic training, the performance and characteristics of the P.3, despite its low power, being such that pupils could progress straight from this type to Vampire Trainers. Provision is made in the P.3 design for underwing stores, allowing its use as a weapons trainer. The only other customer for the P.3 was the Brazilian Navy.

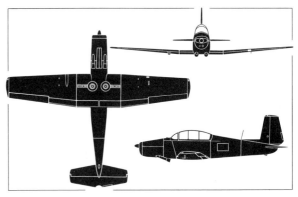

(Silhouette) Pilatus P-3. (Below) Pilatus P-3 serving with Swiss Flugwaffe as a primary trainer.

PIPER PA-28 CHEROKEE (AND CHINCUL) ARROW

Country of Origin: USA.
Type: Primary trainer and light liaison.
Power Plant: One (Arrow II) 200 hp Lycoming IO-360-C1C or (Chincul) 260 hp Lycoming AEIO-540 piston engine.
Performance: (Arrow II) Max speed, 175 mph (282 km/h); max cruise, 165 mph (266 km/h); initial rate of climb, 900 ft/min (4,6 m/sec); service ceiling, 15,000 ft (4 575 m); range, 850 mls (1 368 km) at 55 per cent power.
Performance: (Chincul) Max speed, 195 mph (314 km/h); max cruise, 180 mph (290 km/h); initial rate of climb, 780 ft/min (3,9 m/sec) service ceiling, 13,000 ft (3 962 m); range, 840 mls (1 352 km) at 75 per cent power.
Weight: Empty (Arrow II), 1,531 lb (694 kg), (Chincul) 1,730 lb (785 kg); max take-off, (Arrow II), 2,650 lb (1 202 kg); (Chincul), 2,900 lb (1 315 kg).
Dimensions: Span (Arrow II), 32 ft 2½ in (9,82 m), (Chincul), 35 ft 0 in (10,67 m); length (Arrow), 24 ft 7¼ in (7,50 m), (Chincul) 23 ft 9½ in (7,25 m); height (Arrow), 8 ft 0 in (2,44 m) (Chincul) 7 ft 3½ in (2,23 m); wing area (Arrow and Chincul), 170 sq ft (15,79 m²).
Accommodation: Two-side-by-side with dual controls; provision for two in rear.
Armament: (Chincul) Provision for one 7,62-mm machine gun in lower front fuselage; two wing strongpoints.
Status: PA-28R in production in USA as member of the Warrior/Archer/Arrow family. Chincul first flown 1977.
Notes: Four Arrow IVs purchased by Finnish Air Force in 1980, having longer span wing than Arrow II described above and a retractable undercarriage. Tanzanian Air Force uses Cherokee 140s as trainers and larger Cherokee Six for liaison. Chincul was developed in Argentina as an armed light trainer. The older and slightly larger PA-24 Comanche is used by Spanish Navy as E.30.

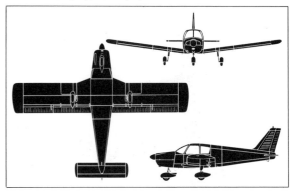

(Above) The Chincul Arrow, developed in Argentina from the Cherokee Arrow. (Silhouette) Piper PA-28 Cherokee 140.

TRAINER

PIPER PA-28R-300XBT PILLAN

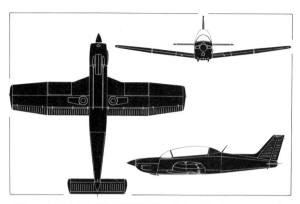

(Silhouette) Piper PA-28R-300XBT Pillan. (Below) The first prototype of the Pillan, built by Piper in the USA.

Country of Origin: USA.

Type: Primary/basic trainer.

Power Plant: One 300 hp Avco Lycoming IO-540 piston engine.

Performance: Max speed, 199 mph (321 km/h); cruising speed, 185 mph (298 km/h) at 75 per cent power at 7,500 ft (2 290 m); cruising speed, 176 mph (284 km/h) at 55 per cent power at 15,000 ft (4 630 m); initial rate of climb, 1,240 ft/min (6,3 m/sec); time to 6,560 ft (2 000 m), 6·5 min; time to 9,840 ft (3 000 m), 11·0 min; service ceiling, 18,400 ft (5 610 m); range, 702 mls (1 130 km) with 45-min reserve.

Weights: Max take-off, 2,900 lb (1 315 kg).

Dimensions: Span, 28 ft 11 in (8,81 m); length, 26 ft 1 in (7,97 m); height, 7 ft 8½ in (2,34 m); wing area, 147 sq ft (13,64 m²).

Armament: None.

Accommodation: Two in tandem, dual controls.

Status: First of four prototypes flown spring of 1981, second prototype flown late 1981.

Notes: The PA-28R-300XBT was developed by Piper at its Lakeland, Florida, facilities, in the first instance to meet the specific needs of the Chilean Air Force for a fully aerobatic primary trainer to replace the Beech 45 Mentor. Two prototypes were built by Piper, with the second being delivered to Chile while the first remained with the manufacturer, and subject to satisfactory complietition of flight testing that was under way in 1982, the Chilean Air Force was expected to acquire about 100. These were to be assembled, using components produced by Piper, at the El Bosque maintenance workshops of the air force, where the Piper PA-28-236 Dakota was already being assembled. The name Pillan, adopted by the Chilean Air Force, means Demon in the dialect of the Araucanos Indians.

TRAINER

SAAB 91 SAFIR

(Above) A Saab Safir primary trainer of the Finnish Air Force. (Silhouette) Saab 92 Safir.

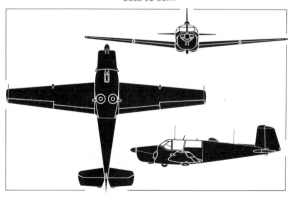

Country of Origin: Sweden.

Type: Basic trainer and communications aircraft.

Power Plant: One (91B and C) 190 hp Lycoming O-435-A six-cylinder horizontally-opposed or (91D) 180 hp Lycoming O-360-AIA four-cylinder horizontally-opposed engine.

Performance: (91D): Max speed, 165 mph (265 km/h) at sea level; max cruising speed, 146 mph (235 km/h); economical cruising speed, 136 mph (220 km/h); initial rate of climb, 800 ft/min (4,1 m/sec); service ceiling, 16,400 ft (5 000 m); max range, 660 mls (1 062 km).

Weights: (91D): Empty equipped, 1,570 lb (710 kg); max take-off, 2,660 lb (1 205 kg); max aerobatic weight, 2,320 lb (1 050 kg).

Dimensions: Span, 34 ft 9 in (10,60 m); length (91B) 26 ft 0 in (7,92 m), (91D) 26 ft 4 in (8,03 m); height, 7 ft 2⅔ in (2,20 m); wing area, 146·3 sq ft (13,60 m²).

Accommodation: Two pilots side-by-side, with full dual control, plus one (91A, B and D) or two (91C) passenger seats in rear.

Status: Prototype first flown on 20 November 1945; first 91B flown on 18 January 1949; first 91C flown in September 1953; first 91D flown in 1957. Total production for military and civil use approximately 320, including 10 91A for Swedish Air Force (Tp 50A), 16 91A to Ethiopian AF, 75 91B to Swedish AF (Sk 50B); 18 91B to Ethiopian AF; 25 91B to R Norwegian AF; 14 91C to Swedish AF (Sk 50C); 14 91C to Ethiopian AF; 24 91D to Austrian AF; 35 91D to Finnish AF and 15 91D to Tunisia.

Notes: Saab completed the prototype Saab 91 Safir in 1945 as a two-three-seat lightplane for the civil market, with a 130 hp DH Gipsy Major 1C engine. A switch to the Lycoming engine was made in the Saab 91B, which was adopted as the standard primary trainer for the Swedish Air Force and built under licence by De Schelde in Holland.

SAAB SAFARI AND SUPPORTER

Country of Origin: Sweden.

Type: Primary trainer and liaison aircraft.

Power Plant: One 200 hp Avco Lycoming IO-360-A1B6 or (TS) 210 hp Continental TSIO-360 turbosupercharged engine.

Performance: (TS) Max speed, 158 mph (254 km/h) at sea level; cruising speed, 138 mph (222 km/h) at sea level and 151 mph (243 km/h) at 12,000 ft (3 660 m); initial rate of climb, 945 ft/min (4,8 m/sec); service ceiling, more than 20,000 ft (6 100 m).

Weights: Empty, equipped, 1,499 lb (680 kg); max take-off 2,645 lb (1 200 kg); max take-off, aerobatic category, 1,984 lb (900 kg).

Dimensions: Span, 29 ft 0½ in (8,85 m); length, 23 ft 3½ in (7,10 m); height, 8 ft 6½ in (2,60 m); wing area 128·1 sq ft (11,90 m²).

Accommodation: Two side-by-side, with dual controls and optional third (rearward facing) seat.

Armament: Optional provision for six wing hardpoints.

Status: Prototype MFI-15 flown 11 July 1969 with 160 hp engine and 26 February 1971 with 200 hp engine. First MFI-17 flown early summer 1972. Production/orders: Royal Danish Air Force and Army, 32; Royal Norwegian Air Force, 16; Zambian National Defence Forces, 20; Pakistan Air Force and Army, 117 (assembled in Pakistan).

Notes: MFI-15 design originated with MFI company as derivative of the Andreasson-designed MFI-9/Bölkow Junior, developed by Saab. Name Safari originally used for civil MFI-15 now applies also to MFI-17 military trainer, which has wing hardpoints and was first known as Supporter. In Pakistan, type is known as Mushak and is being assembled/part manufactured at Risalpur (first 87) and Kamra. A version of the MFI-15 with tailwheel undercarriage is also available.

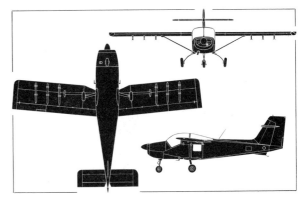

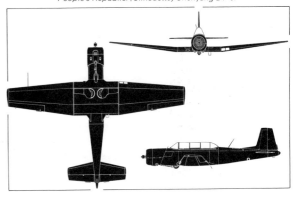

(Silhouette) Saab MFI-17 Supporter. (Below) A Saab Supporter (Mushak) of the Pakistan Air Force.

SHENYANG BT-6

Country of Origin: Chinese Republic.

Type: Primary trainer.

Power Plant: One 285 hp Jia Hou-sai 6 (AI-14R) nine-cylinder radial air-cooled engine.

Performance: Max speed, 178mph (286 km/h); cruising speed, 143 mph (230 km/h); initial rate of climb 1,248 ft/min (6,33 m/sec); service ceiling, 16,680 ft (5 085 m); endurance 3·6 hrs.

Weights: Empty, 2,415 lb (1 095 kg); max take-off, 3,088 lb (1 400 kg).

Dimensions: Span, 35 ft 1¼ in (10,70 m); length 27 ft 10¾ in (8,50 m); height, 10 ft 6 in (3,20 m).

Accommodation: Two in tandem, dual controls.

Status: The BT-6 entered production in 1974–75 in succession to the licence-built Yak-18A (BT-5), some 2,000 examples of which had been built in China, and the BT-6 has since been exported to Bangladesh, North Korea and Zambia.

Notes: The BT-6 (Type 6 Basic Training Aircraft, or Chichao Lienchi Sinshi-liyu), although similar in configuration to the Yak-18A, is, in fact, of original indigenous design and has largely replaced the licence-built Soviet trainer in service with the so-called Air Force of the People's Liberation Army. Development of the BT-6 was undertaken by the State Aircraft Factory at Shenyang, but series production is understood to be undertaken by another factory (either Beijing or Harbin), and the export of this trainer began in 1978, the most recent recipient being the air arm of Bangladesh which procured a number of BT-6s for primary-basic training at the newly-established Jessore flying school early in 1979. In China, the BT-6 appears to be used for all stages of pilot training up to the advanced stage, the next step for pupil pilots being onto the two-seat MiG-15UTI.

(Above) A line-up of Shenyang BT-6 primary trainers serving in the Chinese People's Republic. (Silhouette) Shenyang BT-6.

TRAINER

SHENYANG FT-5

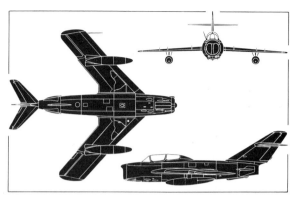

(Silhouette) Shenyang FT-5. (Below) An FT-5 advanced trainer of the PAF Fighter Conversion Unit.

Country of Origin: China.
Type: Tandem two-seat advanced trainer.
Power Plant: One 5,952 lb st (2 700 kgp) Shenyang TJ-5D (Klimov VK-1) turbojet.
Performance: Max speed, 560 mph (902 km/h) at 32,000 ft (9 753 m); service ceiling, 45,000 ft (13 715 m); max endurance (with two 88 Imp gal/400 1 drop tanks), 2·63 hrs; initial climb, 5,315 ft/min (27 m/sec).
Weights: Loaded (clean), 11,700 lb (5 307 kg); max. take-off, 13,400 lb (6 078 kg).
Dimensions: Span, 31 ft 7⅛ in (9,63 m); length, 37 ft 7¼ in (11,46 m); height, 12 ft 5⅝ in (3,80 m); wing area, 243·26 sq ft (22,60 m²).
Status: An exclusively Chinese derivative of the Soviet MiG-17 single-seat fighter (licence-built in China as the F-5), the FT-5 was apparently developed in the late 'sixties, and currently serves in substantial numbers with the Chinese air arm. It has also served with Pakistan since 1975 and Sudan since 1978.
Notes: Purely a Chinese derivative of the MiG-17, no equivalent Soviet version of the fighter having been developed, the FT-5 grafts the forward fuselage and tandem cockpit canopy of the MiG-15UTI, alias FT-2, onto the basic MiG-17 airframe. Unlike the single-seat F-5 version of the MiG-17, however, the FT-5 has a non-afterburning engine and is normally equipped with a single 23-mm NR-23 cannon in the starboard side of the nose for gunnery training in conjunction with a radar-ranging sight for which the antenna is mounted in an extended upper engine air intake lip. Production of the FT-5 followed on that of the single-seat F-5 and is believed to have phased out at Shenyang in the period 1974–75, but large numbers remain in service, with the Chinese air arm, pupils graduating from the FT-5 to the FT-6.

TRAINER

SHENYANG FT-6

(Above) An FT-6 serving with the No 25 Squadron (OCU) of the Pakistan Air Force. (Silhouette) Shenyang FT-6.

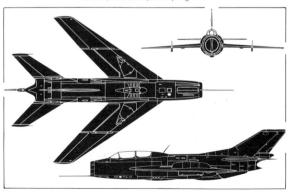

Country of Origin: China.
Type: Tandem two-seat advanced trainer.
Power Plant: Two 5,732 lb st (2 600 kgp) and 7,165 lb st (3 250 kgp) reheat Wopen WP-6 (Tumansky RD-9B-811) turbojets.
Performance: Max speed (clean), 902 mph (1 450 km/h) or Mach 1·35 at 32,800 ft (10 000 m), 832 mph (1 340 km/h) or Mach 1·16 at 1,000 ft (305 m); initial climb, 21,000 ft/min (106,7 m/sec); max range (with drop tanks), 1,240 mls (1 995 km) at 45,920 ft (14 000 m).
Weights: Max take-off (with two 167 Imp gal/760 1 drop tanks), 19,274 lb (8 742 kg).
Dimensions: Span, 29 ft 6⅓ in (9,00 m); length (excluding probe), 44 ft 1 in (13,44 m); height, 12 ft 9½ in (3,90 m); wing area, 269·1 sq ft (25,00 m²).
Armament: One 30-mm NR-30 cannon.
Status: An exclusively Chinese derivative of the Soviet MiG-19 alias F-6 (see page 35) single-seat fighter, the FT-6 was developed in the late 'seventies at Shenyang and remained in production at the beginning of 1982 for the Chinese air arm and for export, recipients including Pakistan and Egypt.
Notes: Although a two-seat trainer derivative of the MiG-19 was developed in the Soviet Union as the MiG-19UTI, its production was not pursued and the FT-6 bears no relationship to this two-seater other than in its precursor. Whereas the MiG-19UTI accommodated the additional cockpit within the overall dimensions of the single-seater from which it was derived, the forward fuselage of the FT-6 has been lengthened and to compensate for the loss of fuel capacity resulting from the second cockpit, extra fuel tanks are inserted in the bays previously occupied by the wing root cannon. Pupil pilots graduate to the FT-6 from the FT-5.

PZL-MIELEC TS-11 ISKRA

Country of Origin: Poland.
Type: Basic trainer.
Power Plant: One 2,205 lb st (1 000 kgp) OKL SO-1 turbojet.
Performance: Max speed, 447 mph (720 km/h) at 16,000 ft (5 000 m); normal cruising speed, 373 mph (600 km/h); initial rate of climb, 3,150 ft/min (16,0 m/sec); service ceiling, 41,000 ft (12 500 m); range with max fuel, 907 mls (1 460 km).
Weights: Empty, 5,423 lb (2 460 kg); normal take-off, 8,068 lb (3 660 kg); max loaded, 8,377 lb (3 800 kg); max landing weight, 7,716 lb (3 500 kg).
Dimensions: Span, 33 ft 0¼ in (10,07 m); length, 36 ft 10¾ in (11,25 m); height, 10 ft 8 in (3,25 m); wing area, 188·37 sq ft (17,5 m²).
Accommodation: Two in tandem, full dual controls.
Armament: (Iskra 100 only): One 23-mm fixed forward-firing cannon in nose, with gun camera, and four wing strong-points each stressed to carry 110 lb (50 kg) load.
Status: Prototype first flown on 5 February 1960. Production deliveries to Polish Air Force began in March 1963; 50 supplied to Indian Air Force, October 1975–March 1976.
Notes: The TS-11 was designed to meet the requirement for a standardised jet basic trainer for use by the Warsaw Pact countries. After an evaluation programme using four prototypes each powered by the 1,700 lb st (771 kgp) HO-10 turbojet, the TS-11 was placed second to the Czech L29 Delfin and the latter type was adapted for service in the Soviet Union and other Warsaw pact nations. Nevertheless, the Polish Air Force decided to adopt the home design for its own use. A variant for weapon training was also produced, with a nose gun, and wing pylons, and designated Iskra 100. The Indian Air Force operates Iskras as advanced trainers at the Fighter Training Wing.

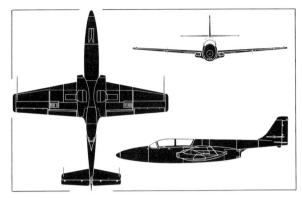

(Silhouette) PZL-Mielec TS-11 Iskra. (Below) A TS-11 Iskra operated at the Indian Air Force's Air Academy.

VALMET L-70 MILTRAINER

Country of Origin: Finland.
Type: Primary trainer.
Type: One 200 hp Avco Lycoming AEIO-360-A1B6 engine.
Performance: Max speed (at 2,204 lb/1 000 kg), 149 mph (240 km/h) at sea level, (at max take-off weight), 143 mph (230 km/h); cruise (75 per cent power), 130 mph (320 km/h) at sea level; initial rate of climb, 1,122 ft/min (5,7 m/sec); service ceiling, 15,090 ft (4 600 m); range (max payload and no reserves), 534 mls (860 km).
Weights: Empty equipped, 1,691 lb (767 kg); max take-off (aerobatic), 2,293 lb (1 040 kg), (normal category), 2,756 lb (1 250 kg).
Dimensions: Span, 32 ft 3¾ in (9,85 m); length, 24 ft 7¼ in (7,50 m); height, 10 ft 0½ in (3,31 m); wing area, 150·69 sq ft (14,00 m²).
Accommodation: Two side-by-side, dual controls.
Armament: Four wing hardpoints with total combined capacity of 660 lb (300 kg) for gun pods, bombs or rockets, for weapons training or light strike rôle.
Status: L-70X prototype first flown 1 July 1975, and first production aircraft flown December 1979; initial delivery against order for 30 for Finnish Air Force on 13 October 1980, with deliveries to be completed during 1982.
Notes: Assigned the name Vinka (Blast) by the Finnish Air Force, the Miltrainer is replacing the Saab Safir as the service's primary-basic trainer. It is followed in the training sequence by the Potez CM 170 Magister, from which Finnish Air Force student pilots then progress to the British Aerospace Hawk 51, which Valmet is assembling in Finland. The L-70 Miltrainer has a roomy cockpit in which it is possible to fit two additional seats if the aircraft is operated in a liaison rôle.

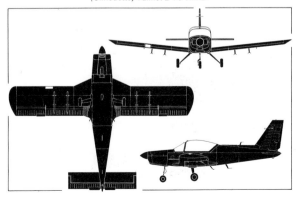

(Above) The first production example of the Vinka for the Finnish Air Force. (Silhouette) Valmet L-70 Vinka.

TRAINER

YAKOVLEV YAK-18A (MAX)

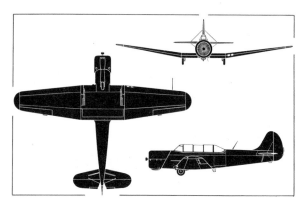

Country of Origin: Soviet Union.
Type: Tandem two-seat primary training monoplane.
Power Plant: One 300 hp Ivchenko AI-14RF nine-cylinder radial air-cooled engine.
Performance: Max speed, 186 mph (300 km/h); cruise, 161 mph (259 km/h); initial climb, 1,575 ft/min (8,0 m/sec); service ceiling, 16,600 ft (5 060 m); range, 435 mls (700 km).
Weights: Empty, 2,259 lb (1 025 kg); max. take-off, 2,910 lb (1 320kg).
Dimensions: Span, 34 ft 9¼ in (10,60 m); length, 27 ft 4¾ in (8,35 m); height, 11 ft 0 in (3,35 m); wing area, 183 sq ft (17,00 m²).
Status: The Yak-18 was flown for the first time in 1946, and was subsequently built in progressively improved versions, more than 8,000 being manufactured and production was continuing at the beginning of 1982 of an extensively revised model, the Yak-18T, suitable for both training and liaison tasks.
Notes: The initial series versions of the Yak-18 were powered by the 160 hp M-11-FR five-cylinder radial, but the Yak-18A, which has been built in larger numbers than all other versions and remains standard Soviet Air Force primary training equipment, was a re-engined and modernised model. Developed in parallel with the Yak-18A was the single-seat Yak-18P, and the Yak-18PM and PS were further single-seat aerobatic models with nosewheel and tailwheel undercarriages respectively. The current production Yak-18T has a four-seat cabin and a 360 hp Vedeneev M-14P nine-cylinder radial engine, and is the standard basic trainer employed by Aeroflot schools. A small number serve with the Soviet Air Force for liaison and communications tasks. Early variants of the Yak-18 are being replaced by the Yak-52 in Soviet military primary flying training schools.

(Silhouette) Yakovlev Yak-18A. (Below) A ski-equipped Yak-18A, of the type still in large-scale Soviet service.

TRAINER

YAKOVLEV YAK-52

(Above) A Yak-52 serving in the Soviet Union, showing the undercarriage retracted. (Silhouette) Yakovlev Yak-52.

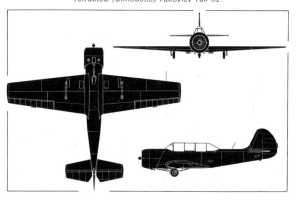

Country of Origin: Soviet Union (Romania).
Type: Tandem two-seat primary trainer.
Power Plant: One 360 hp Vedeneev M-14P nine-cylinder radial air-colled engine.
Performance: Max speed 177 mph (285 km/h); initial climb, 1,970 ft/min (10 m/sec); service ceiling, 19,700 ft (6 000 m); max range, 341 mls (550 km).
Weights: Basic, 2,205 lb (1 000 kg); max take-off, 2,844 lb (1 290 kg).
Dimensions: Span, 31 ft 2 in (9,50 m); length, 25 ft 2¼ in (7,68 m); height, 9 ft 8¼ in (2,95 m); wing area, 161·5 sq ft (15,00 m²).
Status: The prototype Yak-52 was flown in 1976, and all production is being undertaken by the Romanian aircraft industry under the COMECON programme, the first series aircraft having flown early in 1980, and the first deliveries to the Soviet Union having commenced late in that year.
Notes: Intended as a successor to the Yak-18 has the standard primary trainer of the Soviet Air Force and paramilitary flying schools in the Soviet Union, the Yak-52 was developed in parallel with a single-seat version of the same basic design, the Yak-50, which preceded the two-seater into flight test. Apart from tandem seating, the Yak-52 differs from the Yak-50 in undercarriage arrangement, a tricycle undercarriage replacing the tailwheel undercarriage of the single-seat model. Although intended primarily as a primary trainer, the Yak-52 is fully aerobatic and possesses a high power-to-weight ratio in aerobatic configuration. All three wheels remain fully exposed after retraction to offer a greater safety factor. All production of the Yak-52 at the Romanian Bacav factory at the beginning of 1982 was earmarked for the Soviet Union.

ZLIN 526

Country of Origin: Czechoslovakia.
Type: Primary trainer.
Power Plant: One 160 hp Walter Minor 6-III piston engine.
Performance: Max speed, 151 mph (243 km/h) at sea level; cruising speed 129 mph (208 km/h) at 70 per cent power; initial rate of climb, 985 ft/min (5,0 m/sec); service ceiling, 16,350 ft (5 000 m); range 610 mls (980 km) with auxiliary fuel in wing-tip tanks.
Weights: Empty, 1,499 lb (680 kg); normal take-off (aerobatic catagory), 2 072 lb (940 kg); max take-off, 2,150 lb (975 kg).
Dimensions: Span, 34 ft 9 in (10,60 m); length, 25 ft 7 in (7,80 m); height, 6 ft 9 in (2,06 m); wing area 166·3 sq ft (15,45 m²).
Accommodation: Two in tandem, dual controls.
Armament: None.
Status: Prototype Z 26 first flown 1947; Z 126 appeared in 1953; Z 226 appeared in 1955; first Z 326 flown 1957; prototype Z 526 flown 1968; prototype Z 526L flown August 1969; prototype Z 526 AFS flown October 1970; Z 726 appeared in 1973. Production, nearly 2,000, all versions, including civil use; production completed by 1980.
Notes: The Zlin Z 26 family has continued the pre-war Czech reputation for the production of first-rate light aircraft, having been built in larger numbers than most other post-war European lightplanes. Designed originally to an official requirement for a primary/basic trainer for military and State flying club use, it has evolved through many variants, with fixed or retractable under-carriages and including single-seat aerobatic versions. The Z 526 serves in the Czech Air Force as a primary trainer and this or earlier versions are also used in the military training rôle in Cuba, East Germany and Mozambique.

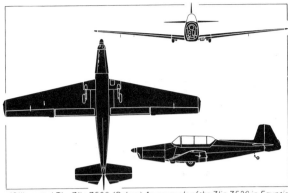

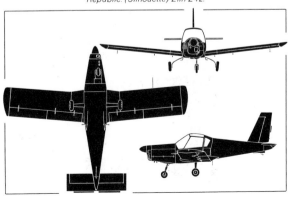

(Silhouette) The Zlin Z526. (Below) An example of the Zlin Z526 in Egyptian Air Force service.

ZLIN 42M and 43

Country of Origin: Czechoslovakia.
Type: Basic trainer and communications.
Power Plant: One (42M) 180 hp Avia M 137 AZ or (43) 210 hp Avia M-337 A piston engine.
Performance: (42M) Max speed, 138 mph (223 km/h) at sea level; cruising speed, 131 mph (211 km/h) at sea level; initial rate of climb, 945 ft/min (4,8 m/sec); service ceiling, 12,470 ft (3 800 m); range, 330 mls (530 km).
Performance: (43) Max speed, 146 mph (235 km/h) at sea level; cruising speed, 130 mph (210 km/h); initial rate of climb, 690 ft/min (3,5 m/sec); service ceiling, 12,470 ft (3 800 m) range, 685 mls (1 100 km).
Weights: (42M) Empty, 1,422 lb (645 kg); max take-off, 2,138 lb (970 kg).
Weights: (43) Empty, 1,477 lb (670 kg); max take-off, 2,976 lb (1 350 kg).
Dimensions: (42M) Span, 29 ft 10¾ in (9,11 m); length, 23 ft 2½ in (7,07 m); height, 8 ft 10 in (2,69 m); wing area, 141·5 sq ft (13,15 m²).
Dimensions: (43) Span, 32 ft 0¼ in (9,76 m); length, 25 ft 5 in (7,75 m); height, 9 ft 7 in (2,91 m); wing area, 156·1 sq ft (14,50 m²).
Accommodation: Two pilots side-by-side and (Zlin 43 only) two passengers in rear cabin.
Status: Prototype Zlin 42 first flown 17 October 1967; first Z42M flown November 1972; Z43 prototype flown 10 December 1968. Production: Zlin 42/42M, over 200, Zlin 43, about 100.
Notes: The Zlin Z42 was adopted as a primary trainer by the air force of the Democratic Republic of Germany. The four-seat Z43, is used in small numbers by the East German and Czechoslovak Air Forces for liaison.

(Above) A Zlin Z43 communications aircraft of the German Democratic Republic. (Silhouette) Zlin Z42.

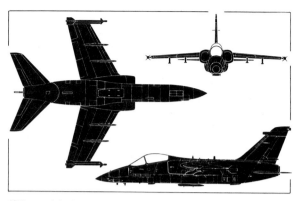

(Silhouette) Aeritalia-Aermacchi-EMBRAER AMX. (below) A model of the AMX in Brazilian Air Force markings.

AERITALIA-AERMACCHI-EMBRAER AMX

Country of Origin: Italy/Brazil
Type: Close air support.
Power Plant: One 11,030 lb st (5 000 kgp) dry Rolls-Royce Spey 807 turbofan.
Performance: (Design requirements) Max speed, 720 mph (1 160 km/h) or Mach 0·95 at 1,000 ft (305 m); average cruise, 590 mph (950 km/h) or Mach 0·77 at 2,000 ft (610 m); combat radius, 207 mls (335 km) LO-LO-LO with 3,000 lb (1 360 kg) ordnance and two drop tanks.
Weights: Normal take-off, 23,150 lb (10 500 kg); max take-off, 26,455 lb (12 000 kg).
Dimensions: Span 29 ft 1½ in (8,88 m); length, 44 ft 6½ in (13,57 m); height, 15 ft 0 in (4,58 m); wing area, 226 sq ft (21,0 m²).
Accommodation: Pilot only.
Armament: One 20-mm M61A-1 multi-barrel cannon in forward fuselage. Fuselage centreline hardpoint and two inner wing hardpoints with 2,000 lb (910 kg) capacity each and two outboard wing hardpoints with 1,000 lb (454 kg) capacity each. Provision for one AIM-9 Sidewinder at each wing tip.
Status: Initial design study for G.91 replacement by Aeritalia 1973/74; design studies for Aermacchi MB 340, 1976/77; Aeritalia-Aermacchi design study mid-1978; Italian/Brazilian agreement for joint development and production of AMX agreed 27 March 1981. Prototype first flight scheduled Autumn 1983; entry into service scheduled late 1986.
Notes: AMX is a proposed lightweight close air support and interdiction aircraft that meets joint Italian and Brazilian requirements and is expected to be assembled in both countries. The AMI requires 187 for eight squadrons; the FAB requires 79, the Brazilian version having a pair of 30-mm DEFA cannon.

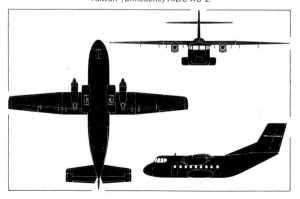

(Above) The prototype XC-2 tactical transport developed by the AIDC in Taiwan. (Silhouette) AIDC XC-2.

AIDC XC-2

Country of Origin: Taiwan.
Type: Light transport and utility aircraft.
Power Plant: Two 1,450 eshp Avco Lycoming (Taiwan licence-built) T53-L-701 turboprops.
Performance: Max speed, 244 mph (392 km/h) at sea level; max cruising speed, 230 mph (370 km/h) at 10,000 ft (3050 m); economical cruising speed, 207 mph (333 km/h); initial rate of climb, 1,500 ft/min, (7,6 m/sec); service ceiling, 26,300 ft (8 015 m); range with max payload, 298 mls (480 km); range with max fuel, 1,032 mls (1 660 km).
Weights: Empty, 15,500 lb (7031 kg), max payload, 8,500 lb (3,855 kg); max take-off 27,500 lb (12 474 kg).
Dimensions: Span, 81 ft 8½ in (24,90 m); length, 65 ft 11½ ins (20,10 m); height, 25 ft 3¾ in (7,72 m); wing area 704 sq ft (65,40 m²).
Accommodation: Crew of three (pilot, co-pilot and flight engineer); provision in cabin for up to 38 passenger seats, with quick-change capability for all-cargo or mixed passenger operations.
Armament: None.
Status: Prototype flown 26 February 1979.
Notes: The XC-2 is the second indigenous design of the Aero Industry Development Centre of the Chinese Air Force (AIDC/CAF) at Taichung, following the successful development and production of the T-CH-1 basic trainer (separately described). Work on the XC-2 began in 1973 with the objective of producing a light transport suitable for military or civil operation. Features of particular use in the military rôle include the two-section loading ramp/rear door in the underside of the rear fuselage, which is also air-openable for dropping of paratroops or supplies. No decision as to possible production had been taken by mid-1982.

ANTONOV AN-72 (COALER)

Country of Origin: Soviet Union.
Type: Short-haul STOL (Short Take-off and Landing) transport.
Power Plant: Two 14,330 lb st (6 500 kgp) Lotarev D-36 turbofans.
Performance: Max cruising speed, 447 mph (720 km/h); range (with max payload, 16,534 lb/7 500 kg, and 30 min reserves), 620 mls (1 000 km), (max fuel), 1,990 mls (3 200 km); normal operating altitude, 26,250-32,800 ft (8 000–10 000 m); max operating altitude, 36,100 ft (11 000 m).
Weights: Loaded (for 3,280-ft/1 000-m runway), 58,420 lb (26 500 kg); max take-off, 67,240 lb (30 500 kg).
Dimensions: Span, 84 ft 9 in (25,83 m); length, 87 ft 2½ in (26,58 m); height, 27 ft 0 in (8,24 m).
Accommodation: Flight crew of two-three and up to 32 troops on fold-down seats along cabin sides, or 24 casualty stretchers and one medical attendant in aeromedical role.
Status: First of two prototypes flown on 22 December 1977, and production status uncertain at beginning of 1982, but manufacture of a pre-series is believed to have been initiated.
Notes: Apparently primarily military in potential (commercial use is likely to restricted by high operating costs to areas inaccessible to more conventional aircraft), the An-72 utilises upper surface blowing to achieve STOL performance, engine exhaust gases flowing over the upper wing surfaces and the inboard double-slotted flaps. Capable of operating from short, semi-prepared strips, the An-72 would seem suitable for use in support of any future generation of V/STOL combat aircraft that may be introduced by the Soviet Union. The high-set engines avoid the problems of foreign object ingestion, and the bogie-type under-carriage, with its low-pressure tyres, will facilitate operations from rough surfaces or snow-covered fields.

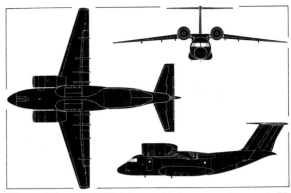

(Silhouette) Antonov An-72. (photograph) A prototype Antonov An-72 displayed at the Paris Air Show.

CAPRONI VIZZOLA C 22J

Country of Origin: Italy.
Type: Primary-basic trainer.
Power Plant: Two 202 lb st (92 kg) Microturbo TRS 18-046 turbojets, or (production option) two 242 lb st (110 kgp) Klockner-Humboldt-Deutz KHD-317 turbojets.
Performance: (Estimated, with KHD-317 engines) Max speed 289 mph (465 km/h) at sea level and 292 mph (470 km/h) at 16,400 ft (5 000 m); econ cruise, 186 mph (300 km/h) at 9,840 ft (3 000 m); initial climb 1,814 ft/min (9,2 m/sec); time to 26,405 ft (5 000 m), 12 min; range (internal fuel with 10 per cent reserves), 660 mls (1,060 km); endurance, 3 hr 20 min.
Weights: Empty, 1,124 lb (510 kg); normal load, 1,984 lb (900 kg); max take-off, 2,425 lb (1 100 kg).
Dimensions: Span, 32 ft 9½ in (10,00 m); length, 20 ft 3¼ in (6,19 m); height, 6 ft 2 in (1,88 m); wing area, 94·2 sq ft (8,75 m²).
Accommodation: Two side-by-side, dual controls.
Armament: The C 22J may be fitted with two or four standard NATO underwing pylons, typical loads including four 97-lb (44-kg) or 440-lb (200-kg) practice bombs, two 7,62-mm gun pods with 500 rounds, or two pods each with eighteen 2-in (5-cm) rockets.
Status: Prototype C 22J flown 21 July 1980.
Notes: The C 22J was one of the first of the new generation of lightweight jet trainers offering low initial procurement and minimum operational costs. The fuselage pod of the C 22J, which utilises a fibreglass shell, is designed to act as a lifting body. During 1981, Siai Marchetti (a member of the Agusta group of companies) reached agreement with Caproni Vizzola in respect of joint development of the C 22J and plans were announced for its further development both as a grading and *ab initio* trainer and for reconnaissance and patrol duties as the C 22 R.

(Above) The prototype C.22J light jet trainer, featuring side-by-side seating. (Silhouette) Caproni C.22J.

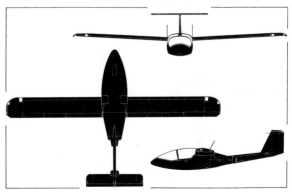

PROTOTYPE/EXPERIMENTAL

DASSAULT-BREGUET SUPER MIRAGE 4000

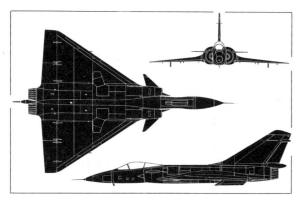

(Silhouette) Dassault-Breguet Mirage 4000. (Below) The prototype Mirage 4000 showing the leading-edge canards.

Country of Origin: France.

Type: Multi-rôle fighter.

Power Plant: Two 12,230 lb st (5 600 kgp) dry and 19,840 lb st (9 000 kgp) with reheat SNECMA M53-5 turbofans.

Performance: (Estimated) Max sustained speed, 1,452 mph (2 336 km/h) or Mach 2·2 above 36,090 ft (11 000 m), 915 mph (1 474 km/h) or Mach 1·2 at sea level; max climb rate, 50,000 ft/min (254 m/sec); operating ceiling, 65,000 ft (19 810 m).

Weights: (Estimated) Loaded (clean), 37,500 lb (17 000 kg); max take-off, 45,000 lb (20 410 kg).

Dimensions: Span, 39 ft 4½ in (12 00 m); length, 61 ft 4¼ in (18 70 m); wing area 786 sq ft (73 00 m²).

Accommodation: Pilot only.

Armament: Two 30-mm DEFA 554 cannon and up to 15,000 lb (6 804 kg) of ordnance on nine external stations (four wing and five fuselage).

Status: Prototype Super Mirage 4000 flown on 9 March 1979.

Notes: Developed as a private venture, the Super Mirage 4000 is optimised for the deep penetration rôle but is also suitable for intercept and air superiority missions, and is most closely comparable with the McDonnell Douglas F-15 Eagle. It closely resembles the Mirage 2000 in aerodynamic, structural and systems layout, sharing with the smaller aircraft such features as fly-by-wire controls, artificial stability, leading-edge flaps and the use of carbon-fibre composites, components using these materials including the fin and rudder, the elevons and the canard surfaces attached to the outer sides of the intake ducts. The prototype was to be equipped with the Thomson-CSF RDM multi-mode radar and other weapon systems equipment from the Mirage 2000 for continued flight development pending possible production orders from overseas customers.

PROTOTYPE/EXPERIMENTAL

FMA IA 63

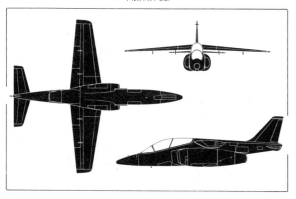

(Above) A full-scale mock-up of the IA-63 displayed during 1981. (Silhouette) FMA IA-63.

Country of Origin: Argentina.

Type: Basic/advanced trainer.

Power Plant: One 3,432 lb st (1 557 kgp) Garrett TFE 731-2-2N turboprop.

Performance: Max speed, 510 mph (821 km/h) or Mach 0·75 at 29,530 ft (9 000 m); limiting Mach number, 0·8; service ceiling (50 per cent fuel), 45,930 ft (14 000 m); ferry range (auxiliary tanks on centreline and two wing points), 1,553 mls (2 500 km).

Weights: Loaded (clean), 7,694 lb (3 490 kg).

Dimensions: Span, 31 ft 9⅓ in (9,69 m); length, 35 ft 10¼ in (10,93 m); height, 14 ft 0½ in (4,28 m); wing area, 168·24 sq ft (15,63 m²).

Armament: Provision for weapons pylons on fuselage centreline and four wing hard-points.

Accommodation: Two in tandem, dual controls.

Status: Design studies initiated April 1979; project definition contract placed with Dornier GmbH 5 May 1980; construction of six prototypes (including static and fatigue test specimens) initiated 1981; first flight scheduled October 1983; entry into service with Argentine Air Force scheduled 1985.

Notes: The IA 63 is being developed in Argentina at the Fabrica Militar de Aviones, Cordoba, in collaboration with Dornier, the latter company having been retained to provide technical design assistance and engineer-training, with the Argentine government wholly responsible for funding. The *Fuerza Aérea Argentina* has a requirement for about 60 to 80 aircraft of IA 63 type for pilot training, but it is expected that the total market may increase to as many as 200 with the inclusion of two-seat and possibly single-seat armed versions for weapons training and the light strike rôle. Final design definition was under way in 1981. The fourth prototype is to be fitted with a JT15D-5 turbofan.

GULFSTREAM AMERICAN PEREGRINE 600

Country of Origin: USA.
Type: Basic trainer.
Power Plant: One 3,000 lb st (1 360 kgp) Pratt & Whitney (Canada) JTD15D-5 turbofan.
Performance: (Production model, estimated); Max speed, 441 mph (710 km/h) at 30,000 ft (9 145 m); average cruise, 425 mph (684 km/h) at 30,000 ft (9 145 m); time to 40,000 ft (12 190 m), 16·5 min; service ceiling, 48,000 ft (14 630 m); range (internal fuel), 1,243 mls (2 000 km).
Weights: Max loaded, 6,200 lb (2 812 kg).
Dimensions: Span, 34 ft 5½ in (10,50 m); length 38 ft 4 in (11,68 m); height, 13 ft 5 in (4,08 m); wing area, 192·76 sq ft (17,90 m²).
Accommodation: Two side-by-side, dual controls.
Status: Prototype first flown 22 May 1981.
Notes: Based on the design of the Hustler 500 business executive transport, production plans for which were discontinued in 1980, the Peregrine 600 prototype was developed by the Gulfstream American company with the objective of meeting the USAF requirement for a Next Generation Trainer (NGT). The prototype was powered by a 2,500 lb st (1 134 kgp) JT15D-4, with which a speed of 393 mph (632 km/h) was achieved at 30,000 ft (9 145 m). Production versions of the Peregrine were expected to be available by 1984 at a fly-away price of about $1·5 million in 1981 values. The company has estimated that on a typical three-hour mission, the Peregrine 600 will have a fuel consumption of about 80 US gal (303 l/h), representing a 30 per cent improvement on contemporary trainers. Proposed variants to meet NGT requirement on offer spring 1982 featured optional power plant comprising paired 1,500 lb st (680 kgp) Williams FJ 44 turbofans fed via individual dorsal intakes.

PROTOTYPE/EXPERIMENTAL

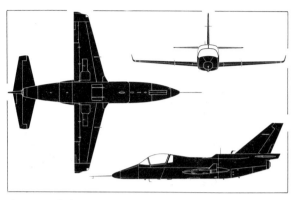

(Silhouette) Gulfstream American Peregrine I. (Below) The prototype Peregrine I military jet trainer.

MICROTURBO MICROJET 200

Country of Origin: France.
Type: Basic trainer.
Power Plant: Two 202 lb st (92 kgp) Microturbo TRS-18-046 turbojets.
Performance: (200B, estimated) Max cruising speed, 288 mph (463 km/h); initial rate of climb, 1,740 ft/min (8,84 m/sec); operating ceiling, 30,000 ft (9 150 m); range, 535 mls (860 km).
Weights: Empty equipped 1,460 lb (663 kg); max take-off 2,535 lb (1 150 kg).
Dimensions: Span, 24 ft 10⅜ in (7,58 m); length, 21 ft 6 in (6,55 m); height, 6 ft 2¾ in (1,90 m); wing area, 65,88 sq ft (6,12 m²).
Accommodation: Two in staggered side-by-side arrangement.
Armament: None.
Status: Prototype Microjet 200 first flown 24 June 1980; construction of three pre-series aircraft proceeding early 1982; production aircraft scheduled for delivery from mid-1983.
Notes: With the Caproni Vizzola C 22J (separately described), the Microjet 200 is one of the first of a new generation of lightweight jet trainers. The prototype is of wooden construction, but the pre-series 200B aircraft have metal fuselages and wings of plastic composite construction. A staggered side-by-side seating arrangement, with the right-hand seat positioned 21·6 in (55 cm) aft of that on the left (which is occupied by the pupil) permits some small reduction in fuselage cross section (by comparison with a conventional side-by-side arrangement) and is claimed to simulate more closely the forward cockpit of a tandem seater to which the pupil will graduate. The Microjet 200 prototype was evaluated by the *Armée de l'Air* and *Aéronavale* at the CEV Istres during 1981 and further evaluation of the pre-production 200B was planned.

PROTOTYPE/EXPERIMENTAL

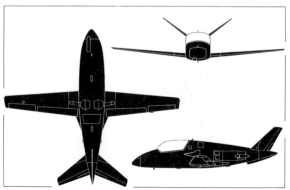

(Above) The prototype Microjet 200 as configured in mid-1981. (Silhouette) Microturbo Microjet 200B (pre-production).

PROTOTYPE/EXPERIMENTAL

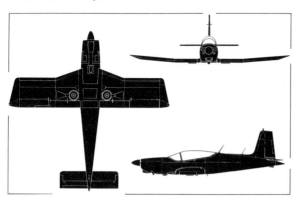

(Silhouette) NDN Aircraft Firecracker. (Below) The NDN-1 Firecracker military trainer, with tandem seating.

NDN AIRCRAFT FIRECRACKER

Country of Origin: United Kingdom.
Type: Basic trainer.
Power Plant: One (NDN-1) 260 hp Lycoming AEIO-540-B4D5 or (NDN-1A) 300 hp Lycoming IO-540 piston engine or (NDN-5) 550 shp Pratt & Whitney Canada PT6A-25A turboprop.
Performance: Max speed at sea level, 203 mph (326 km/h); max cruise (75 per cent power) at 7,000 ft (2 286 m), 192 mph (309 km/h); initial rate of climb, 1,450 ft/min (7,36 m/sec); service ceiling, 18,000 ft (5 485 m); range with max fuel (no reserves), 1,405 mls (2 260 km).
Weights: Empty equipped, 1,930 lb (875 kg); max gross, 2,840 lb (1 288 kg); max landing, 2,700 lb (1 225 kg).
Dimensions: Span, 26 ft 0 in (7,92 m); length, 25 ft 3 in (7,7 m); height, 9 ft 10 in (3,0 m); gross wing area, 126 sq ft (11,71 m²).
Accommodation: Two in tandem, dual controls.
Armament: Provision for four wing hardpoints with total capacity of (NDN-1A) 600 lb (272 kg) or (NDN-5) 1,000 lb (454 kg).
Status: Prototype (NDN-1) first flown 26 May 1977; second prototype (NDN-5) with turboprop to fly 1982.
Notes: The NDN-1 was developed as a private venture, with the objective of producing a relatively light military basic trainer capable of reproducing the handling characteristics of typical swept-wing jet combat aircraft. This is achieved by careful aerodynamic design and the use of a wing of unusually low aspect ratio. A turbosupercharged piston engine is a production option (in the NDN-1A) and a turboprop variant has been designated the NDN-5. The company also proposes to offer the Firecracker as part of a technology transfer package, in which foreign industries would progressively assume responsibility for its licence-production.

PROTOTYPE/EXPERIMENTAL

(Above) First of two prototypes of the Siai Marchetti S.211 jet trainer flying in 1981. (Silhouette) Siai Marchetti S.211.

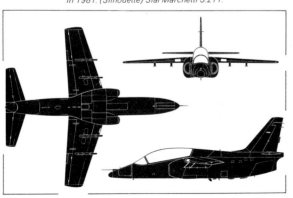

SIAI MARCHETTI S.211

Country of Origin: Italy.
Type: Basic jet trainer and light strike aircraft.
Power Plant: One 2,500 lb st (1 134 kgp) Pratt & Whitney Canada JT15D -4C turbofan.
Performance: Max speed 450 mph (723 km/h) at 25,000 ft (7 620 m); limiting Mach number, 0·8; max cruise, 437 mph (704 km/h) at 25,000 ft (7 620 m); max climb, 4,950 ft/min (25,15 m/sec); service ceiling, 42,000 ft (12 800 m); max range (with 30 min reserve), 1,185 mls (1 910 km) at 30,000 ft (9 145 m), (with two 77 Imp gal/350 l external tanks), 1,672 mls (2 693 km) at 30,000 ft (9 145 m).
Weights: Empty, 3,186 lb (1 445 kg); normal loaded (training mission), 5,070 lb (2 300 kg); max take-off 6,173 lb (2 800 kg).
Dimensions: Span, 26 ft 2½ in (8,00 m); length, 30 ft 5⅓ in (9,28 m); height, 12 ft 2¾ in (3,73 m); wing area 135·63 sq ft (12,60 m²).
Accommodation: Two in tandem, with full dual control.
Armament: No built-in weapons. Provision for four wing strong points with capacity of 660 lb (300 kg) each inboard and 300 lb (150 kg) each outboard for bombs, gun/rocket pods etc.
Status: First of two prototypes flown 10 April 1981.
Notes: The S.211 was launched by Siai Marchetti company (now part of the Agusta group) in 1977 with the objective of producing a basic jet trainer that would have a lower first cost than any competitive type, and would also offer a broad spectrum of performance in the training rôle ranging from *ab initio* into what is usually regarded to be the advanced portion of the flying training syllabus. Up to a dozen air forces were reported in 1982 to be in various stages of discussion or negotiation to obtain production aircraft, the first of which were expected to be ready for delivery late-1982.

AÉROSPATIALE ALOUETTE II

HELICOPTER

Country of Origin: France.
Type: Light utility helicopter.
Power Plant: One (SA 318C) 523 shp Turboméca Astazou IIA or (SA 315B) 870 shp Artouste IIB turboshaft.
Performance: (SA 318C) Max speed, 127 mph (205 km/h) at sea level; max cruise, 112 mph (180 km/h); max inclined climb, 1,396 ft/min (7,1 m/sec); hovering ceiling (IGE), 5,085 ft (1 550 m), (OGE), 2,960 ft (900 m); range with max fuel, 447 mls (720 km); range with max payload 62 mls (100 km).
Weights: (SA 318C) Empty, 1,961 lb (890 kg); max take-off 3,630 lb (1 650 kg).
Dimensions: Rotor diameter, 33 ft 5 in (10,20 m); fuselage length, 31 ft 11¾ in (9,75 m); height, 9 ft (2,75 m).
Status: As the Sud-Est SE 3130, prototype first flown on 12 March 1955; prototype SA 318C Alouette II Astazou first flown on 31 January 1961. Production totals: prototypes, 2; pre-production, 3; SE 313B, 923; SA 318C, 377; grand total, 1,305.
Armament: None.
Accommodation: Pilot and four passengers.
Notes: The Alouette II was first flown on 12 March 1955, powered by a 360 shp Artouste IIC6 turboshaft, as a product of the Sud-Est company, as indicated by its designation SE 3130. Production Alouette IIs by Sud-Est were designated SE 313B after the company had simplified its system of nomenclature. Further development after Sud-Est and Sud-Ouest merged to form Sud-Aviation led to the SA 318C, which differed in having an Astazou IIA turboshaft, as indicated by the above data. The Lama, combining features of the Alouette II and Alouette III, is separately described. A substantial proportion of the total Alouette II production was for military customers and about 20 air arms still had this variant in service in 1982.

Examples of the Aérospatiale Alouette II serving with (above) the Armée de l'Air and (below) Aéronavale.

AÉROSPATIALE ALOUETTE III

HELICOPTER

Country of Origin: France.
Type: Light utility helicopter.
Power Plant: One (SA 316C) 870 shp Turboméca Artouste IIID or (SA 319B) 789 shp Astazou XIV turboshaft.
Performance: (SA 319B) Max speed, 136 mph (220 km/h) at sea level; max cruise, 122 mph (197 km/h); max inclined climb, 853 ft/min (4,32 m/sec); hovering ceiling (IGE), 5,740 ft (1 750 m); range with six passengers, 375 mls (605 km).
Weights: (SA 319B) Empty, 2,403 lb (1 090 kg); max take-off 4,960 lb (2 250 kg).
Dimensions: Rotor diameter, 36 ft 1¾ in (11,02 m); fuselage length; 32 ft 10¾ in (10,03 m), height, 9 ft 10 in (3,0 m).
Armament: Optional provision for one 7,62-mm or one 20-mm gun in or alongside cabin; or four AS.11 or four AS.12 wire-guided missiles; or four 68-mm rocket pods; or (ASM version) two AS.12s or two Mk 44 homing torpedoes.
Accommodation: Pilot and up to six passengers.
Status: Prototype SE 3160 first flown 28 February 1959; SA 316B flown 27 June 1968; first SA 319B flown in 1967. Production/sales total, approximately 1,430 including 250 Chetaks built by HAL in India, 180 by IAR in Romania and 60 by FFA in Switzerland.
Notes: The Alouette III was a development of the Alouette II (separately described) with 870 shp Artouste IIIB turboshaft. Initial production model was SA 316A, followed by SA 316B with higher weights and SA 316C with Artouste IIID engine. The SA 319B (date above) has an Astazou engine and increased range. Among many military users of the Alouette III, which is believed to have been adopted by more air arms than any other single type of helicopter, is the *Aéronavale*, using the ASW Alouette III/ASM. In India, the Alouette III Astazou is built by HAL as the Chetak.

(Above) An Alouette III with torpedoes aboard a frigate of the French Navy and (below) an SA 316B Alouette III of the Libyan Air Force.

HELICOPTER

The HAL Cheetah, a license-built version of the SA 315 Lama built in India, is shown in the photographs above and below.

AÉROSPATIALE SA 315 LAMA

Country of Origin: France.
Type: Light general-purpose helicopter.
Power Plant: One 870 shp Turboméca Artouste IIIB turboshaft.
Performance: Max cruising speed, 75 mph (120 km/h); initial rate of climb, 768 ft/min (3,9 m/sec); service ceiling, 9,840 ft (3 000 m); hovering ceiling, IGE, 9,675 ft (2 950 m); hovering ceiling, OGE, 5,085 ft (1 550 m).
Weights: Empty, 2,251 lb (1 021 kg); normal take-off, 4,300 lb (1 950 kg); max take-off with slung load, 5,070 lb (2 300 kg); max slung load, 2,500 lb (1 135 kg).
Dimensions: Main rotor diameter, 36 ft 1¾ in (11,02 m); overall length, rotor turning, 42 ft 4¾ in (12,92 m); height overall, 10 ft 1¾ in (3,09 m).
Accommodation: Enclosed cabin seats two pilots (or pilot and passenger) plus three passengers.
Armament: None.
Status: Prototype first flown 17 March 1969; first Indian-assembled example flown on 6 October 1972. Production, approximately 360 by mid-1982.
Notes: The Lama was developed during 1968/69 as a variant of the Alouette II/III family of designs specially suited to high-altitude operations, and was intended in particular to meet an Indian Air Force requirement. It combines the basic airframe of the Alouette II with the more powerful dynamic components of the Alouette III, and consequently has a better performance, especially when flying loads out of high altitude airfields. Following acceptance of the Lama for service in the Indian Air Force, in which it is known as the Cheetah, production was initiated by HAL at Bangalore, and about 100 had been delivered by 1981. The Venezuelan Air Force ordered six from the Brazilian assembly line, where the type has the local name of Gaviao.

HELICOPTER

(Above) An SA 321G amphibious helicopter of the Aéronavale and (below) an SA 321GM delivered to Libya.

AÉROSPATIALE SA 321 SUPER FRELON

Country of Origin: France.
Type: Medium transport and multi-purpose helicopter.
Power Plant: Three 1,550 shp Turboméca Turmo IIICB turboshafts.
Performance: Max speed, 171 mph (275 km/h) at sea level; max cruise, 155 mph (250 km/h); max inclined climb, 1,312 ft/min (6,7 m/sec); hovering ceiling (IGE), 7,120 ft (2 170 m); hovering ceiling, (OGE), 1,804 ft (550 m); range, 634 mls (1 020 km).
Weights: Empty, 14,775 lb (6,702 kg); max take-off, 28,660 lb (13 000 kg).
Dimensions: Rotor diameter, 62 ft 0 in (18,90 m); fuselage length, 63 ft 7¾ in (19,40 m); height, 21 ft 10¼ in (6,66 m).
Armament: (SA 321G) Four homing torpedoes or two ASM 39 Exocet anti-shipping missiles can be carried.
Accommodation: Two pilots and (SA 321G) three tactical/sonar operators or (SA 321H) up to 30 troops or 15 stretchers.
Status: SA 3210-01 and -02 prototypes first flown, respectively, on 7 December 1962 and 28 May 1963; SA 321F first flown 7 April 1967; SA 321G flown on 30 November 1965; SA 321Ja flown on 6 July 1967. Production total, 99 including 24 SA 321G for *Aéronavale*, 16 SA 321L for SAAF, 12 SA 321K for Israel Defence Force, 16 SA 321Ja for Chinese People's Republic, 13 SA 321H for Iraq, and nine SA 321GM for Libya.
Notes: Derived from the smaller Frelon prototypes, the Super Frelon entered production as the SA 321G amphibious model for the *Aéronavale* with Sylph radar in outrigger floats and up to four torpedoes and other ASW stores; they are operated by *Flottille* 32F and in 1980/81 were being fitted with ORB 32 Heracles II radar of greatly improved performance. Non-amphibious transport versions were developed as the SA 321F for commercial use and the SA 321H,K and L for specific military customers.

AÉROSPATIALE (WESTLAND) SA 330 PUMA

HELICOPTER

Country of Origin: France.
Type: Multi-rôle medium helicopter.
Power Plant: Two (SA 330B and E) 1,328 shp Turboméca Turmo IIIC4 or (C, F and H) 1,400 shp Turmo IVA or 1,435 hp Turmo IVB or (G, later H, J and L) 1,575 shp Turmo IVC turboshafts.
Performance: (SA 330L) Max permissible speed, 163 mph (263 km/h); normal cruise, 160 mph (258 km/h); initial rate of climb, 1,200 ft/min (6,1 m/sec); service ceiling, 15,750 ft (4 800 m); hovering ceiling, IGE, 7,545 ft (2 300 m); hovering ceiling, OGE, 5,575 ft (1 700 m); max range, no reserves, 341 mls (550 km).
Weights: Empty, 7,970 lb (3 615 kg); max take-off, 16,315 lb (7 400 kg) or 16,535 lb (7 500 kg) with slung load.
Dimensions: Rotor diameter, 49 ft 2½ in (15,00 m); fuselage length, 46 ft 1½ in (14,06 m); height, 16 ft 10½ in (5,14 m).
Armament: Optional provision for 7,62 mm machine gun pods, wire-guided·missiles, rocket pods, etc. on fuselage side.
Accommodation: Two pilots and optional third seat on flight deck; up to 20 troops or six stretchers and six seated patients.
Status: Prototype SA 330 flown on 15 April 1965; first production Puma flown September 1968; first SA 330B flown January 1969; first SA 330E Puma HC Mk 1 flown 25 November 1970 in UK. Production/sales totals, approx 750 by beginning of 1982, including 130 SA 330B for French Army and 48 for RAF.
Notes: The SA 330 became one of three helicopters in Anglo-French co-production agreement in 1967 after it had been selected by the French Army (SA 330B) and RAF (SA 330E). SA 330C and H were military export models, followed by SA 330L in 1976 with composite rotor blades and higher operating weights. Major users include South Africa, Indonesia, Pakistan, Kuwait, Morocco, Spain and United Arab Emirates.

(Above) An SA 330E Puma HC Mk 1 assembled by Westland; (below) an SA 330 VIP transport in the Armée de l'Air.

AÉROSPATIALE SA 341/342 GAZELLE

HELICOPTER

Country of Origin: France.
Type: Light observation and general purpose helicopter.
Power Plant: One (SA 341B) 592 shp Turboméca Astazou IIIN or (SA 341F) Astazou IIIC or (SA 341H) Astazou IIIB or (SA 342K) 870 shp Astazou XIVH or (SA 342M) 859 shp Astazou XIVM turboshaft.
Performance: (SA 342) Max permissible speed, 193 mph (310 km/h) at sea level; max cruise, 164 mph (264 km/h); economical cruise, 148 mph (238 km/h); initial rate of climb, 2,010 ft/min (10,2 m/sec); service ceiling, 14,100 ft (4 300 m); hovering ceiling, IGE, 11,970 ft (3 650 m); hovering ceiling, OGE, 9,430 ft (2 875 m); max range, 469 mls (755 km).
Weights: (SA 342) Empty 2,105 lb (955 kg); max take-off, 4,190 lb (1 900 kg).
Dimensions: Rotor diameter, 34 ft 5½ in (10,50 m); fuselage length, 31 ft 3¼ in (9,53 m); height, 10 ft 2¾ in (3,15 m).
Armament: (SA 342M) Four HOT anti-tank missiles; (SA 342L) provision for two rocket pods, or four or six wire-guided missiles, and two forward-firing 7,62-mm machine guns.
Accommodation: Pilot and co-pilot plus three passsengers.
Status: Prototype SA 340-01 flown on 7 April 1967; second prototype flown on 12 April 1968; first production SA 341 flown 6 August 1971; first SA 341C (Royal Navy) flown 6 July 1972 in UK. Production total, 900 by April 1982, including: prototypes, 2; pre-production, 4; Gazelle AH Mk 1, 184; Gazelle HT Mk 2, 36; Gazelle HT Mk 3, 24; Gazelle HCC Mk 4, 1; SA 341F (French Army), 170; SA 342, (French Army), 120.
Notes: SA 341 was put into production jointly by Aérospatiale and Westland to meet requirements of French Army and British Army, Navy and RAF. SA 341H military export model is assembled by SOKO in Yugoslavia and SA 342K was developed for Kuwait.

(Above) A Westland-built SA 341 Gazelle HT Mk 3 in RAF service; (below) an SA 342 armed with six HOT anti-tank missiles.

227

HELICOPTER

(Above) An Aérospatiale AS 350 used by the French Gendarmerie; (below) a Helibras-assembled Esquilo of the Brazilian Navy.

AÉROSPATIALE AS 350 ECUREUIL

Country of Origin: France.

Type: Light training and general purpose helicopter.

Power Plant: One (AS 350B) 641 shp Turboméce Arriel or (AS 350D) 616shp Avco Lycoming LTS 101-600 A.2 turboshaft.

Performance: (AS 350B) Max permissible speed, 169 mph (272 km/h) below 1,640 ft (500 m); max cruising speed, 144 mph (232 km/h); initial rate of climb 1,615 ft/min (8,2 m/sec); service ceiling, 16,000 ft (4 875 m); hovering ceiling IGE, 9 840 ft (3 000 m); hovering ceiling, OGE, 7,380 ft (2 250 m); range with max fuel (no reserves), 441 mls (710 km).

Weights: Empty (AS 350B), 2,304 lb (1 045 kg), (AS 350D) 2359 lb (1 070 kg); normal take-off, 4,300 lb (1 950 kg); max take-off with slung load, 4,630 lb (2 100 kg).

Dimensions: Rotor diameter, 35 ft 0¾ in (10,69 m); overall length, 42 ft 8 in (13,00 m); height, 10 ft 1¾ in (3,08 m).

Accommodation: Two pilots (or pilot and passenger) plus four passengers.

Status: AS 350 prototype (LTS 101 engine) first flown 27 June 1974; second prototype (Arriel engine) flown 14 February, 1975; production deliveries began April 1978; prototypes of AS 355E Ecureuil 2 first flown 27 September and 14 November 1979; first production AS 355E flown 11 March 1980. Sales (including commercial), about 600 AS 350B/C/D and over 200 AS 350E/F.

Notes: The AS 350 was developed by Aérospatiale as the successor to the highly successful Alouette family. Initial production and sales concentrated on the single-engined Ecureuil (Squirrel), which is marketed in North America as the Astar. To offer better performance and twin-engined safety, the AS 355E and F Ecureuil 2/Twinstar was developed subsequently. The first specifically military purchase was made by the Brazilian Navy, which bought six, assembled in Brazil with the name Esquilo.

HELICOPTER

(Above) An Aérospatiale HH-65A (AS 365G) for the US Coast Guard; (below) the AS 365F with Agrion radar and AS 15 TT missiles.

AÉROSPATIALE AS 365/366 DAUPHIN 2

Country of Origin: France.

Type: Search and rescue, anti-shipping and general purpose medium helicopter.

Power Plant: Two (AS 365) 700 shp Turboméca Arriel 1C or (AS 366) 690 shp Avco Lycoming LTS 101-750 turboshafts.

Performance: (AS 365N) Max permissible speed, 201 mph (324 km/h) at sea level; max cruising speed, 178 mph (287 km/h) at sea level; economical cruise, 149 mph (240 km/h); initial rate of climb, 1,515 ft/min ·(7,7 m/sec); hovering ceiling, IGE, 5,250 ft (1 600 m); hovering ceiling, OGE, 3,115 ft (950 m); max range, no reserves, 571 mls (920 km); search and rescue range (AS 366 N), 191 mls (307 km); max range (AS 366N), 483 mls (778 km); search endurance (AS 365F), 1 hr 40 min at 80 mph (130 km/h) at a distance of 56 mls (90 km) from base.

Weights: Empty (AS 365N), 4,277 lb (1 940 kg), (AS 366N), 5,577 lb (2 530 kg); max take-off, 8,380 lb (3 800 kg).

Dimensions: Rotor diameter, (AS 365N,366G), 38 ft 4 in (11,68 m), (AS 365 F), 39 ft 1½ in (11,93 m); overall length (AS 365N, 366G), 37 ft 4 in (11,38 m), (AS 365F), 39 ft 10½ in (12,15 m); height, 12 ft 6 in (3,81 m).

Armament: (AS 365F) Four Aérospatiale AS 15TT ASMs.

Accommodation: Pilot and (AS 365N) nine passengers or (AS 365F) observer/weapons officer.

Status: Prototype SA 365C first flown 24 January 1975; prototype AS 365N flown on 31 March 1979; first AS 366G/HH-65A flown on 23 July 1980. Production/sales include 20 AS 365F and four AS 365N for Saudi Arabian Navy and 90 HH-65A for US Coast Guard (23 on firm contract to end 1981).

Notes: The SA 365C evolved as a twin-engined derivative of the SA 360 Dauphin and AS 365N is a further improvement with retractable undercarriage.

AGUSTA A 109

Country of Origin: Italy.
Type: General purpose military and naval helicopter.
Power Plant: Two 420 shp Allison 250-C20B turboshafts.
Performance: (At 5,400 lb/2 450 kg gross weight) Max permissible speed, 193 mph (311 km/h); max cruising speed, 165 mph (266 km/h); cruising speed, 143 mph (231 km/h); initial rate of climb, 1,600 ft/min (8,1 m/sec); service ceiling, 16,300 ft (4 968 m); hovering ceiling, IGE, 9,800 ft (2 987 m); hovering ceiling, OGE, 6,800 ft (2 073 m); max range, 382 mls (615 km) at 6,500ft (2 000 m); max endurance, 3 hr 30 min.
Weights: Empty, 3,120 lb (1 415 kg); max take-off, 5,730 lb (2 600 kg).
Dimensions: Main rotor diameter, 36 ft 1 in (11,00 m); fuselage length, 36 ft 5½ in (11,11 m); height, 10 ft 10¾ in (3,32 m).
Armament: For the armed military rôle, two 7.629 mm flexibly-mounted machine guns and up to four stores positions on fuselage-side sponsons. For the anti-submarine, anti-shipping and other naval rôles, two homing torpedoes, or AS-12 or AM-10 wire-guided missiles.
Accommodation: Pilot and up to seven troops or two stretchers and two attendants or (naval rôle) pilot and two or three systems operators.
Status: First (of three) A 109 prototypes flown on 4 August 1971; deliveries of A 109A began early 1976. Production approx 140 by beginning of 1982, including 10 each for Italian Carabinieri and Italian Police, five for Italian Army, nine for the Argentine Army and 12 for the Portuguese Air Force.
Notes: Under development in 1982, the naval version has a number of special features including more comprehensive instruments, extra internal fuel, fixed landing gear, rescue hoist option and provision for search radar.

(Above) The Armed Agusta A 109 in service with the Italian Army; (below) an A 109 used by the Italian Police.

AGUSTA A 129 MANGUSTA

Country of Origin: Italy.
Type: Combat helicopter.
Power Plant: Two 960 shp (1,035 shp 20-sec contingency, one engine out) Rolls-Royce Gem 2–3 turboshafts.
Performance: Max continuous speed, 168 mph (270 km/h) at sea level; cruising speed, 155 mph (250 km/h) at 6,500 ft (2 000 m); initial rate of climb, 1,970 ft/min (10 m/sec); hovering ceiling, IGE, 9,577 ft (2 920 m); hovering ceiling, OGE, 6,560 ft (2 000 m); range, 547 mls (880 km) with two external tanks at 155 mph (250 km/h); endurance, 2 hr 30 min cruising at 6,560 ft (2 000 m).
Weights: Empty, 5 575 lb (2 529 kg); normal take-off, 8 060 lb (3 655 kg).
Dimensions: Main rotor diameter, 46 ft 10 in (11,90 m); fuselage length, 40 ft 3 in (12,275 m); height, 10 ft 11 ½ in (3,35 m).
Armament: Four hardpoints on fuselage side sponsons, with capacity of 440 lb (200 kg) each outboard and 660 lb (300 kg) inboard loads can include eight Hellfire missiles on outboard pylons; or eight TOW missiles outboard plus two seven-tube rocket pods or machine-gun pods.
Accommodation: Pilot and co-pilot/gunner in tandem.
Status: Five prototypes ordered by Italian Army; first flight scheduled for summer 1983, with production deliveries from 1985.
Notes: Agusta has been developing this combat helicopter since the mid-seventies, originally on the basis of the A 109 dynamic components, with a new slender profile fuselage. Agusta first proposed using Avco Lycoming LTS 101-850A-1 turboshafts but in 1981 made a final decision to use the Rolls-Royce Gem. The A 129 Mangusta (Mongoose) is offered with the Martin Marietta mast-mounted sight, for use in conjunction with an integrated helmet and display sight system and night vision aids.

(Above and below) A full-scale mock-up of the Agusta A 129, as under development for the Italian Army.

HELICOPTER

(Above) A Bell 47G in service with the New Zealand Army; (below) a Bell 47 of the Maltese Task Force Helicopter Flight.

Country of Origin: USA.

Type: Light utility and training helicopter.

Power Plant: One (OH-13G & TH-13M) 200 hp Franklin 6V-200-C32 or (OH-13H and UH-13H) 240 hp Lycoming VO-435-A1A, A1B or A1D or (OH-13S and TH-13T) 260 hp Lycoming TVO-435-A1A engine.

Performance: (OH-13S) Max speed, 105 mph (169 km/h) at sea level; max cruise, 86 mph (138 km/h) at 5,000 ft (1 524 m); initial climb, 1,190 ft/min (6,05 m/sec); hovering ceiling, IGE, 18,000 ft (5 486 m); range, 324 mls (521 km).

Weights: Empty, 1,936 lb (877 kg); loaded 1,850 lb (1,293 kg).

Dimensions: Rotor diameter, 37 ft 1½ in (11,31 m); fuselage length, 32 ft 7 in (9,93 m); overall height, 9 ft 3¾ in (2,82 m).

Armament: None.

Accommodation: Pilot and two passengers or (training variants) two pilots side-by-side.

Status: Prototype Model 47 flown on 8 December 1945; first Agusta-built (Model 47G) flown on 22 May 1954. Production of more than 4,000 completed by Bell in 1974 and of more than 1,200 completed by Agusta in 1976; Westland built 216 Sioux AH Mk 1 and 15 HT Mk 2 between 1965 and 1968; in Japan, Kawasaki built 239 Model 47D and 47G.

Notes: The Bell 47 was evolved during 1945 from the company's earlier Model 30, first flown in 1943, and its production run extending over 30 years in four countries exceeded that of any US helicopter prior to Model 206. Large numbers were procured for military use, as well as for a wide variety of civil duties, and although major use by the US Air Force, Navy and Army, the British Army and other large users has now ended, Bell 47s were still serving in 1981 in more than 20 national air arms for helicopter pilot training and general utility duties.

HELICOPTER

(Above) A Bell AH-1G serving in Israel with Heyl Ha'Avir; (below) the US Army AH-1S variant of the Hueycobra.

Country of Origin: USA.

Type: Combat helicopter.

Power Plant: One (AG-1G, 1Q) 1,400 shp Avco Lycoming T53-L-13 or (AH-1R,-1S) 1,800 shp T53-L-703 turboshaft.

Performance: (AH-1S) Max permissible speed, 195 mph (315 km/h); max operating speed, TOW configured, 141 mph (227 km/h); initial rate of climb, 1,620 ft/min (8,23 m/sec); service ceiling, 12,200 ft (3 720 m); hovering ceiling, IGE, 12,200 ft (3 720 m); max range, 315 mls (507 km).

Weights: Operating weight empty (-1G), 6,073 lb (2 754 kg), (-1S), 6,479 lb (2 939 kg); mission weight (-1G), 9,407 lb (4 266 kg), (-1S), 9,875 lb (4 524 kg); max take-off weight, (-1G), 9,500 lb (4 309 kg), (-1S), 10,000 lb (4 535 kg).

Dimensions: Main rotor diameter, 44 ft 0 in (13,41 m); fuselage length, 44 ft 7 in (13,59 m); height, 13 ft 6¼in (4,12 m).

Armament: (All models) M-28 nose turret containing two 7,62-mm Miniguns or two 40-mm M-129 grenade launchers (or one of each) plus fuselage-side sponsons with four hardpoints for (-1G, -1R) rocket pods or gun pods or (-1Q, -1S) eight TOW missiles on two pylons plus gun or rocket pods and ("Up-gun"-1S only) universal nose turret for 20-mm three-barrel Vulcan gun or 30-mm Hughes Chain Gun.

Accommodation: Pilot and co-pilot/gunner in tandem.

Status: Model 209 prototype first flown 7 September 1965. Production/sales exceed 1,800 including 1,078 AH-1G for US Army of which 93 converted to AH-1Q and then to AH-1S, and 197 converted to AH-1S, and 297 AH-1S in three configurations.

Notes: The single-engined HueyCobras are US Army's principal attack helicopters. Overseas deliveries include 12 AH-1Gs to Israel (plus AH-1S on order), five AH-1Gs to Spanish Navy (Z.14), and two AH-1S to Japan (with plans for licence production.)

BELL 209 SEACOBRA

Country of Origin: USA.

Type: Armed tactical helicopter.

Power Plant: One (AH-1J) 1,800 shp (single-engined emergency) Pratt & Whitney (Canada) T400-CP-400 or (AH-1T) 1,970 shp (single-engined emergency) T400-WV-402 twin turboshaft.

Performance: (-1J) Max speed, 161 mph (259 km/h) at 2,000 ft (610 m) and 160 mph (257 km/h) at sea level; average cruising speed, 163 mph (263 km/h); initial rate of climb (clean), 2,230 ft/min (11,3 m/sec); operational ceiling, 10,000 ft (3 050 m); hovering ceiling (with stores), OGE, 4,200 ft (1 280 m); range, 331 mls (533 km) clean, 154 mls (248 km) with stores.

Performance: (-1T) Max speed, 181 mph (291 km/h) at sea level; average cruising speed, 167 mph (269 km/h) at sea level; initial rate of climb (clean), 2,880 ft/min (14,6 m/sec); hovering ceiling OGE (with stores), 5,350 ft (1 631 m); combat radius, attack mission, 130 mls (209 km); max endurance 2·62 hrs.

Weights: Empty (-1J), 6,503 lb (2 950 kg), (-1T), 8,030 lb (3 642 kg); max take-off, (-1J), 10,000 lb (4 540 kg), (-1T), 14,000 lb (6 350 kg).

Dimensions: Main rotor diameter, (-1J), 44 ft 0 in (13,41 m); (-1T), 48 ft 0 in (14,63 m); fuselage length (-1J), 44 ft 7½ in (13,59 m), (-1T), 45 ft 4 in (13,81 m); height (-1J), 13 ft 7½ in (4,15 m), (-1T), 14 ft 4 in (4,36 m).

Armament: One 20-mm triple-barrel cannon in nose turret; fuselage side sponsons with four hardpoints.

Accommodation: Pilot and co-pilot/observer in tandem.

Status: First AH-1J flown November 1969; first AH-1T flown 20 May 1976; first delivery to USMC 15 October 1977. Production: AH-1J, 69; AH-1J/TOW (Iran Army), 202; AH-1T, two prototypes (AH-1J converted) and 57 production.

(Above) A Bell AH-1J Sea Cobra serving with US Marine Squadron HMM-165; (below) the improved AH-1T version of the Sea Cobra.

BELL OH-58 KIOWA AND MODEL 406

Country of Origin: USA.

Type: Observation scout helicopter.

Power Plant: One (OH-58A) 317 shp Allison T63-A-700 or (OH-58C) 420 shp T63-A-720 or (AHIP) 650 shp Allison 250-C30R turboshaft.

Performance: (OH-58A) Max permissible speed, 138 mph (223 km/h); speed for best range, 117 mph (184 km/h); loiter speed for best endurance, 56 mph (90,5 km/h); initial rate of climb, 1,780 ft/min (8,7 m/sec); service ceiling, 18,900 ft (5 760 m); hovering ceiling, IGE, 13,600 ft (4 145 m); hovering ceiling, OGE, 8,800 ft (2 682 m); max range at sea level, 300 mls (481 km).

Weights: Empty equipped (OH-58A), 2,313 lb (1 049 kg), (OH-58C) 2,434 lb (1 104 kg); max take-off (OH-58A), 3,000 lb (1 360 kg), (OH-58C), 3,200 lb (1 451 kg).

Dimensions: Main rotor diameter, 35 ft 4 in (10,77 m); fuselage length, 32 ft 7 in (9,93 m); height, 9 ft 6½ in (2,91 m).

Accommodation: Pilot and co-pilot/observer plus two passengers.

Status: Prototype Bell 206 (Army designation HO-4, then OH-4A) first flown 8 December 1962; first production OH-58A delivered to US Army 23 May 1969. Production totals: OH-4A, five; OH-58A, 2,200; OH-58B (Austria), 12; COH-58A (CAF CH-136), 74; Model 206B-1 Kiowa (Australian Army) 12 plus 40 assembled by Commonwealth Aircraft Corporation.

Notes: Bell Model 206 (OH-4A) was entry in original Army Light Observation Helicopter competititon won by Hughes, with OH-58A selected later. The Canadian Armed Forces CH-136s, Australian Army Kiowas and Austrian Air Force OH-58Bs are all basically similar to the OH-58A. In 1976 Bell converted three A models to OH-58Cs with uprated engines, "Black hole" IR reduction features and improved avionics; Army ordered conversion of 275 more.

(Above) A Bell CH-136 JetRanger used by the CAF; (below) the OH-58C version of the US Army Kiowa.

BELL MODEL 206 JETRANGER

(Above) A Bell 206 JetRanger in service with Heyl Ha'Avir in Israel; (below) the prototype Bell 206L-3 TexasRanger.

Country of Origin: USA (and Italy).
Type: Light utility helicopter.
Power Plant: One (206A) 317 shp Allison 250-C18 or (206B) 400 shp Allison 250-C20A or 420 shp 250-C20B or (Texas Ranger) 650 shp Allison 250-C30P turboshaft.
Performance: (206B) Max permissible speed, 140 mph (225 km/h); max cruising speed, 133 mph (214 km/h) at sea level and 134 mph (216 km/h) at 5,000 ft (1 525 m); initial rate of climb, 1,260 ft/min (6,4 m/sec); service ceiling, 13,500 ft (4 115 m); hovering ceiling, IGE, 12,800 ft (3,900 m); hovering ceiling, OGE, 8,800 ft (2 680 m); range with max fuel and no reserves, 341 mls (549 km) at sea level and 378 mls (608 km) at 5000 ft (1 525 m).
Weights: (206B) Empty, equipped, 1,615 lb (732 kg); max take-off, 3,200 lb (1 451 kg).
Dimensions: Rotor diameter, 33 ft 4 in (10,16 m); fuselage length, 31 ft 2 in (9,50 m); height, 9 ft 6½ in (2,91 m).
Status: Model 206A JetRanger first flown 10 January 1966; commercial deliveries begun early 1967. Production total, more than 7,000 Model 206/OH-58 variants (including production by Agusta in Italy) of which more than 3,400 for military use.
Notes: The Bell 206A was introduced in 1966, using the basic dynamics system developed for the Model 206 submitted in the Army LOH competition (see OH-58A Kiowa, separately described). In 1968, the US Navy selected the Model 206A as its new basic helicopter trainer and purchased a total of 40 as TH-57A Sea Rangers. JetRangers have been sold in about 100 countries, many of them for military use; 14 for the CAF in 1981 are designated CH-139. In 1981 Bell flew a prototype Model 206L Texas Ranger as an armed multi-mission variant of the LongRanger, which is a Model 206 with lengthened fuselage.

BELL MODEL 204 IROQUOIS AND HUEY (AND AB 204AS)

(Above) A Bell TH-1L helicopter trainer used by Navy Helicopter Squadron HT-8; (below) Bell UH-1E in US Marine Corps service.

Country of Origin: USA (and Italy).
Type: General purpose, utility and anti-submarine helicopter.
Power Plant: One (UH-1E) 1,150 shp (five-minute limit Lycoming T53-L-9 or (UH-1F, 204As) 1,325 shp (five-minute limit) General Electric T58-GE-3 turboshaft.
Performance: (UH-1E) Max speed, 138 mph (222 km/h) at sea level; typical cruising speed, 113 mph (182 km/h) at 10,000 ft (3 050 m); initial rate of climb, 1,985 ft/min (10,1 m/sec); service ceiling, 19,700 ft (6 085 m); range, 280 mls (450 km) with two crew, 264 mls (426 km) with five occupants, 246 mls (396 km) with eight occupants; ferry range 631 mls (1 018 km) with external tanks, pilot only.
Weights: Empty (UH-1E), 4,734 lb (2 147 kg); max take-off (UH-1E), 8,500 lb (3 856 kg); (204 AS), 9,500 lb (4 310 kg).
Dimensions: Main rotor diameter (UH-1E), 44 ft 0 in (13,41 in), (204AS), 48 ft 0 in (14,63 m); fuselage length, 41 ft 7 in (12,66 m); height, 14 ft 9 in (4,50 m).
Armament: (204 AS) Fuselage-side strongpoints for two Mk 44 torpedoes.
Accommodation: Pilot and up to seven troops or three stretchers and one attendant.
Status: Bell Model 204 first flown 22 October 1956; first delivery (UH-1A), 30 June 1959.
Notes: First of the famed Huey family (official name Iroquois) was the UH-1A (originally HU-1A) for US Army. UH-1B had a larger cabin and was supplied to numerous air arms in addition to US Army UH-1D had uprated engine, UH-1E, HH-1K, TH-1L and UH-1L were Navy/Marine Corps versions, and UH-1F with engine change was USAF variant. Fuji in Japan and Agusta in Italy built the 204B and Agusta developed the ASW AB 204AS for Italian and Spanish Navy use.

BELL MODEL 205/UH-1 IROQUOIS

Country of Origin: USA.
Type: General purpose, utility and rescue helicopter.
Power Plant: One (UH-ID) 1,100 shp Lycoming T53-L-11 or (UH-1H) 1,400 shp Lycoming T53-L-13B turboshaft.
Performance: (UH-1H) Max permissible speed, 127 mph (204 km/h); max operational speed, 127 mph (204 km/h); initial rate of climb, 1,600 ft/min (8,13 m/sec); service ceiling, 12,600 ft (3,840 m); hovering ceiling, IGE, 13,600 ft (4 145 m); hovering ceiling, OGE, 4,000 ft (1 220 m); range with max fuel, 260 mls (420 km) with typical payload; ferry range, 680 mls (1 095 km).
Weights: Basic operating weight (UH-1H, troop carrier mission), 5,557 lb (2 520 kg); max take-off, 9,500 lb (4 309 kg).
Dimensions: Main rotor diameter, 48 ft 0 in (14,63 m); fuselage length, 41 ft 10¾ in (12,77 m); height, 14 ft 6 in (4,42 m).
Armament: Normally unarmed; provision for pintle-mounted machine gun in cabin, firing through side door.
Accommodation: Pilot and up to 14 troops in cabin, or six stretchers with two attendants.
Status: Bell Model 205 first flown on 16 August, 1961. Production total, more than 7,000 by 1982 (including about 200 by Fuji, 118 by AIDC in Taiwan, 352 by Dornier and others by Agusta.)
Notes: The Bell Model 205 was evolved from the Model 204 (separately described), having an enlarged cabin and larger rotor to increase the payload. As the UH-1D it entered production for the US Army, with deliveries starting in August 1963; Dornier built UH-1Ds for the German Army, Fuji built 90 for the JASDF and Agusta built a similar version for military and civil use in Italy and for export. The UH-1H was similar with an uprated engine and was built for the US Army in large numbers. The Canadian Armed Forces bought similar CUH-1Hs for service as CH-118s and USAF bought the HH-1H for search and rescue.

(Above) A Bell UH-1N transport helicopter in USAF service; (below) the UH-1D operational with the US Army.

BELL MODEL 212, AB 212ASW, 412

Country of Origin: USA (and Italy).
Type: Light transport and general utility helicopter.
Power Plant: One 1,800 shp Pratt & Whitney (Canada) PT6T-3B Turbo Twin Pac coupled turboshaft.
Performance: Max permissible speed, 161 mph (259 km/h) at sea level; max cruising speed, 142 mph (230 km/h) at sea level; max cruising speed (212 ASW, armed), 115 mph (185 km/h); initial rate of climb, 1,320 ft/min (6,7 m/sec); service ceiling, 14,200 ft (4 330 m); hovering ceiling, IGE, 11,000 ft (3 350 m); max range (no reserves), 261 mls (420 km) at sea level; search endurance (212 ASW), 1 hr 36 min at 83 mls (133 km) from base.
Weights: Empty equipped (212), 6,143 lb (2 787 kg), (212 ASW), 7,540 lb (3 420 kg); max take-off (212, 212ASW), 11,200 lb (5 080 kg), (412), 11,600 lb (5 262 kg).
Dimensions: Main rotor diameter (212, 212 ASW), 48 ft 2¼ in (14,69 m), (412), 46 ft 0 in (14,0 m); fuselage length, 42 ft 4¾ in (12,92 m); height, 14 ft 10¼ in (4 53 m).
Armament: (212 ASW) Fuselage side strongpoints to carry two Mk 46 homing torpedoes or depth charges or ASMs.
Accommodation: Pilot and (212,412) up to 14 combat troops or (212 ASW) second pilot and two observers.
Status: Model 212 first flown 1968. Production/sales include 79 UH-1N (USAF), 221 UH-1N/VH-1N for USN and USMC, 50 CUH-1N (CH-135) for Canadian Armed Forces, 25 for Israel, eight for Argentine Air Force, seven for Brunei and six each for Bangladesh and South Korea; Agusta-built AB 212 sales include 24 to Austrian Air Force, 10 to Lebanon and Saudi Arabia and five to Morocco; AB 212ASW sales include 18 to Spanish Navy (as Z.18), eight to Iraqi Air Force and six each to Peruvian and Turkish Navies.
Notes: Bell 412 and AB 412 have a four-bladed main rotor, are otherwise similar to Bell 212 and AB 212.

(Above) A Bell 212 used by the Royal Brunei Defence Force; (below) an Agusta-built AVB 212 ASW of the Peruvian Navy.

(Above and below) Two views of the Model 214A, as developed by Bell for the Iranian Army.

Country of Origin: USA.

Type: Medium lift helicopter.

Power Plant: 2,930 shp Avco Lycoming LTC4B-8D turboshaft.

Performance: Max cruising speed, 161 mph (259km/h) clean, 115 mph (185 km/h) with slung load; service ceiling, 16,400 ft (5000 m) clean and 12,400 ft (3 780 m) with slung load; hovering ceiling, OGE, 12,200 ft (3 719 m) clean and 5,400 ft (1 646 m) with slung load; range with 10 per cent reserve, 294 mls (473 km) clean and 104 mls (167 km) with slung load; endurance, 2·6 hrs.

Weights: Empty 7,588 lb (3 442 kg); normal take-off, 13,800 lb (6 260 kg); max take-off with slung load, 15,000 lb (6 804 kg).

Dimensions: Main rotor diameter, 50 ft 0 in (15,24 m); fuselage length, 48 ft 0¼ in (14,63 m); overall height, 12 ft 10 in (3,90 m).

Accommodation: Two pilots, crew chief and 13 troops.

Armament: None.

Status: Prototype Model 214 Huey Plus first flown in 1970. First production Model 214A flown on 13 March 1974 and first delivery to Iran on 26 April 1975. Production total, 293 Model 214A and 39 Model 214C for Iran.

Notes: The Model 214 Huey Plus was developed as improved version of the UH-1H with a 1,900 shp Lycoming T53-702 turboshaft, enlarged main rotor, strengthened airframe and higher weights. The further improved Model 214A with T55-L-7C engine was demonstrated in Iran leading to a contract for 287 (plus six added later) Model 214A Isfahan helicopters to serve as troop and supply transports, and for 39 similar Model 214Cs for search and rescue duty. Bell put the Model 214B into production for commercial use and developed a larger-capacity helicopter as the 214ST, now entirely a US product following the revolution in Iran and termination of the plans for Model 214 assembly/production in that country.

(Above) CH-113A Voyageur in service with No 424 Squadron, CAF; (below) a KV-107/11 search and rescue helicopter of the JASDF.

Country of Origin: USA (Japan).

Type: Assault, vertical replenishment and transport helicopter.

Power Plant: Two (CH-46D) 1,400shp General Electric T58-GE-10 or (CH-46E) T58-GE-16 or (KV-107/II) 1,250 shp General Electric CT58-110-1 or CT58-IHI-110-1 or (HKP 4C) R-R Gnome H-1200 or (KV-107/IIA) 1,400 shp CT58-140-1 or CT58-IHI-140-1 turboshafts.

Performance: (CH-46D) Max speed, 166 mph (267 km/h) at sea level; typical cruising speed, 163 mph (263 km/h) at sea level and 147 mph (237 km/h) at 10,000 ft (3 050 m); initial rate of climb, 1,900 ft/min (9,7 m/sec); service ceiling, 14,000 ft (4 267 m); hovering ceiling, OGE, 8,370 ft (2 551 m); range, 237 mls (382 km) with 4,000 lb (1815 kg) load; ferry range, 890 mls (1 434 km).

Weights: Empty, 13,134 kg (5 958 kg); max take-off, 23,000 lb (10 433 kg).

Dimensions: Main rotor diameter, 51 ft 0 in (15,55 m); length, blades folded, 45 ft 7½ in (13,91 m); height, 16 ft 11½ in (5,17 m).

Accommodation: Crew of three and 17 equipped troops.

Status: Prototype Vertol 107 first flown 22 April 1958; CH-46A first flown 16 October 1962. Production: CH-46A, 160; CH-46D, 266; CH-46F, 186; UH-46A, 14; UH-46D, 10; CH-113 Labrador (CAF), 6; CH-113A Voyageur (CAF), 12; HKP-4, 13. First Kawasaki-built KV-107/II first flown in May 1962; first KV-107/IIA flown on 3 April 1968. Production totals include two KV-107/II-3 and seven IIA-3 for JMSDF, 42 KV-107/II-4 and 18 IIA-4 for JGSDF, 16 KV-107/II-5 and 16 IIA-5 for JASDF and eight KV-107/II-5 for Swedish Navy (HKP4C).

Notes: Starting 1977, a total of 273 CH-46A/D/Fs are being modified to CH-46Es for US Marine Corps with uprated engines and other improvements. UH-46As and Ds serve with USN. Kawasaki became sole source for the type in 1965.

BOEING VERTOL CH-47 CHINOOK

HELICOPTER

Country of Origin: USA.
Type: Medium lift helicopter.
Power Plant: Two (CH-47A) 2,200 shp Avco Lycoming T55-L-5 or 2,650 shp T55-L-7 or (CH-47B) 2,850 shp T55-L-7C or (CH-47C) 3,750 shp T55-L-11A or (CH-47D) 4,500 shp T55-L-712.
Performance: (CH-47C) Max speed, 146 mph (235 km/h) at sea level; average cruising speed, 131 mph (211 km/h); initial rate of climb, 1,380 ft/min (7,0 m/sec); service ceiling, 8,400 ft (2 560 m); hovering ceiling, OGE, 9,200 ft (2 805 m) at 38,500 lb (17 463 kg); mission radius, 115 mls (185 km) with 11,650 lb (5 284 kg) payload.
Weights: Empty (CH-46C), 21,464 lb (9 736 kg); max take-off (CH-47C), 46,000 lb (20 865 kg); (CH-147), 50,000 lb (22 680 kg); (CH-47D) 53,000 lb (24 267 kg).
Dimensions: Rotor diameter, 60 ft 0 in (18,29 m) each; fuselage length, 51 ft 0 in (15,54 m); height, 18 ft 7¾ in (5,68 m).
Accommodation: Crew of three and 33–44 troops.
Status: First of five prototypes (YHC-1B/YCH-47A) flown 21 September 1961; first production CH-47A delivered 16 August 1962; first CH-47B flown October 1966, delivered 10 May 1967; CH-47C flown on 14 October 1967; first Chinook HC Mk 1 flown 23 March 1980; first YCH-47D flown 11 May 1979. Production totals: YHC-1B, 5; CH-47A, 354; CH-47B, 108; CH-47C, 270, all for US Army. Exports include R Thai AF, four CH-47A; VNAF, 70 (A/B/C from US Army inventory); RAAF, 12 Model 165; Argentine AF, three Model 308; CAF, nine Model 173/CH-147; Spanish AF, 10 Model 176 and three Model 414 (HT.17); RAF, 33 Model 352 Chinook HC Mk 1. Agusta production in Italy includes Italian Army, 26; Iran, 95; Libya, 20; Morocco, six, Tanzania two and Egypt 15.
Notes: US Army Chinook inventory totalled 454 in 1980; 148 CH-47A, 78 CH-47B and 200 CH-47C for conversion to CH-47D.

(Above) A Boeing Vertol Chinook HC Mk 1 of No 18 Squadron, RAF; (below) an Agusta-built CH-47C of the Italian Army.

EH INDUSTRIES EH-101

HELICOPTER

Country of Origin: Italy/United Kingdom.
Type: Anti-submarine and general purpose helicopter.
Power Plant: (Prototypes) Three 1,690 shp General Electric T700-GE-401 turboshafts.
Performance: (ASW, at 28,660 lb/13 000 kg gross weight), Max speed, 189 mph (304 km/h) at sea level; hovering ceiling OGE, 4,800 ft (1 463 m); still air range, no reserves, 1,210 mls (1 945 km); endurance, 7·2 hrs on three engines at sea level and 8·6 hrs on two engines at 3,000 ft (915 m).
Weights: Basic empty, 15,050 lb (6 827 kg); standard gross weight, 28,660 lb (13 000 kg); alternate gross weight, 30,000 lb (13 600 kg).
Dimensions: Main rotor diameter, 60 ft 0 in (18,29 m).
Armament: Fuselage-side strong points for four Mk 46 homing torpedoes or two Aérospatiale AM-39 Exocet air-to-surface-vessel missiles.
Accommodation: Two pilots and additional crew members according to rôle; up to 24 Rangers or 31 troops in cabin.
Status: Joint Anglo-Italian project definition phase launched 12 June 1981. Future programme embraces up to seven prototypes with first flight planned for 1985 and production deliveries starting 1988.
Notes: The EH-101 has its origins in the Westland WG34, a project design conceived to meet Royal Navy requirements for a replacement for the Sea King anti-submarine helicopter in the late 'eighties. Westland and Agusta agreed to collaborate on a single design, leading to the setting up of EH Industries as a jointly-owned company and the placing of a contract for project definition funded by the UK and Italian governments. Production aircraft probably will be powered by the Rolls-Royce Turboméca RTM 321 engine.

Artist's impression of the EH-101 in the markings of (above) the Royal Navy and (below) the Italian Navy.

HELICOPTER

(Above) The US Army's TH-55A Osage training helicopter; (below) a
Hughes 300 in Spanish service.

HUGHES TH-55 OSAGE AND MODEL 300

Country of Origin: USA.
Type: Light training helicopter.
Power Plant: One 180 hp Lycoming HIO-360-B1A piston engine.
Performance: Max permissible speed, 86 mph (138 km/h); max
cruising speed, 75 mph (121 km/h); economical cruising speed,
66 mph (106 km/h); initial rate of climb, 1,140 ft/min (5,8 m/sec);
hovering ceiling, IGE, 5,500 ft (1 675 m); hovering ceiling, OGE,
3,750 ft (1 145 m); range with max fuel, 204 mls (318 km); max
endurance, 2 hr 35 mins.
Weight: Empty, 1,000 lb (457 kg); max take-off, 1,670 lb (757 kg).
Dimensions: Main rotor diameter, 25 ft 3½ in (7,71 m); fuselage
length, 21 ft 11¾ in (2,50 m); height, 8 ft 2¾ in (2,50 m).
Accommodation: Two side-by-side (three in Model 300).
Armament: None.
Status: First Hughes 269 prototype flown in October 1966.
Production total, 792 TH-55A, completed March 1969; plus about
550 commercial and export models of the 300.
Notes: The prototype Hughes 269 was developed as a lightweight two-seat helicopter; the US Army evaluated five pre-
production examples in the observation rôle under the designation
YHO-2HU. It was developed into the Model 269A for commercial
sale, deliveries starting in October 1961. An improved version, the
Model 269B, was marketed as the Hughes 300, between 500 and
600 being built up to 1980. Meanwhile, the US Army decided to
adopt the Model 269A as a primary trainer for helicopter pilots,
and orders for this TH-55A eventually totalled 792. In 1982, the
Army inventory of TH-55As was a little short of 250. Several
foreign nations acquired examples of the Model 269, and a few of
these may remain in use, including Algeria (six), Columbia (six) the
Argentine Air Force, Haiti (two), India (four), Sierra Leone (three)
and Spain (17, with the local Air Force designation HE.20).

HELICOPTER

(Above) A Hughes OH-6A Cayuse of the US Army's Silver Eagles display
team; (below) a Hughes 300 of the Argentine Air Force.

HUGHES OH-6 CAYUSE

Country of Origin: USA.
Type: Light observation helicopters.
Power Plant: One (OH-6A) 317 shp Allison T63-A-5A turboshaft
derated to 252·2 shp for take-off or (OH-6C) 400 shp Allison 250-
C20 turboshaft.
Performance: Max cruising speed, 150 mph (241 km/h) at sea
level; cruising speed for best range, 134 mph (216 km/h); initial
rate of climb, 1,840 ft/min (9,3 m/sec); service ceiling, 15,800 ft
(4 815 m); hovering ceiling, IGE, 11,800 ft (3 595 m); hovering
ceiling, OGE, 7,300 ft (2 225 m); range, 380 mls (611 km); ferry
range 1,560 mls (2 510 km).
Weights: Empty equipped, 1,229 lb (557 kg); normal take-off,
2,400 lb (1 090 kg); max overload, 2,700 lb (1 225 kg).
Dimensions: Main rotor diameter, 26 ft 4 in (8,03 m); fuselage
length, 23 ft 0 in (7,01 m); height, 8 ft 1½ in (2,48 m).
Armament: Provision for armament pack on port side of fuselage,
comprising one 7,62-mm gun or XM-75 grenade launcher.
Accommodation: Two crew (pilot and observer) side-by-side
and provision for up to four fully-equipped troops in cabin.
Status: First of five OH-6A prototypes (originally HO-6) flown 27
February 1963; production total, 1,434 OH-6As for US Army.
Notes: As the Hughes 369, the OH-6A originated as one of the
three helicopters selected for development in 1961 to meet the
US Army Light Observation Helicopter (LOH) requirement, and
was named the winner in May 1965. A single OH-6C was a
converted Cayuse with an uprated Allison turboshaft, five-blade
main rotor, four-blade tail rotor and engine muffling to reduce
external noise levels. The OH-6D was projected to meet the
Army's Advanced Scout Helicopter (ASH) requirement. The basic
Model 369 entered production for the commercial market as the
Hughes 500, (described separately).

HUGHES 500 DEFENDER

Country of Origin: USA.
Type: Light observation, attack and ASW helicopter.
Power Plant: One 420 shp Allison 250-C20B turboshaft derated to 375 shp for take-off.
Performance: (500 M-D) Max speed, 175 mph (282 km/h) at sea level; cruising speed, 160 mph (258 km/h) at sea level; initial rate of climb, 1,920 ft/min (9,75 m/sec); hovering ceiling, IGE, 8,800 ft (2 682 m); max range 290 mls (467 km); endurance, 3 hrs.
Weights: Typical empty, 1,295 lb (588 kg); payload with max fuel, 949 lb (431 kg); max slung load, 2,000 lb (908 kg); normal take-off 3,000 lb (1 360 kg); max take-off, slung load, 3,620 lb (1 642 kg).
Dimensions: Main rotor diameter, 26 ft 5 in (8,05 m); fuselage length, 21 ft 5 in (6,53 m); height, 8 ft 11 in (2,73 m).
Armament: Options include one or two seven-tube 2·75-in (7-cm) rocket launchers, or one rocket launcher with one 7,62-mm minigun, or one Hughes 30-mm Chain Gun, or up to four BGM-71A TOW air-to-surface missiles, or two Stinger air-to-air missiles or two MK 44 or Mk 46 homing torpedoes.
Accommodation: Pilot and gunner/observer; up to six passengers.
Status: Deliveries of Model 500M began April, 1968, first production Model 500D flown 9 October 1975. Production includes licence manufacture or assembly in Italy (Breda Nardi), Argentina (RACA), Japan (Kawasaki) and South Korea.
Notes: Hughes Model 500M is unarmed military observation and training helicopter supplied to air arms in Colombia, Denmark, Mexico, Philippines, Spain, Japan, Argentine and South Korea. Armed 500M-D Defender has been delivered to air arms in Mauritania, Israel, Kenya, Colombia and South Korea, while the Taiwanese Navy has radar- and torpedo-equipped variant.

(Above) A TOW-armed Hughes 500M-D Defender in Israeli service; (below) a 500M-D prototype with mast-mounted weapon sight

HUGHES AH-64 APACHE

Country of Origin: USA.
Type: Attack helicopter.
Power Plant: Two (YAH-64), 1,536 shp General Electric T700-GE-700 or (AH-64A) 1,693 shp T700-GE-701 turboshafts.
Performance: (AH-64 estimated, at primary missions gross weight). Max permissible speed, 235 mph (3 78 km/h) at sea level; max operational speed, 192 mph (309 km/h); max cruising speed, 182 mph (293 km/h); max vertical rate of climb, 2,880 ft/min (14,6 m/sec); service ceiling, 20,500 ft (6 250 m); hovering ceiling, IGE, 15,200 ft (4 633 m); hovering ceiling, OGE, 12,400 ft (3 780 m); max range on internal fuel, 380 mls (611 km); ferry range, 1,120 mls (1 804 km); max endurance on internal fuel, 3 hr 23 min.
Weights: Empty, 10,268 lb (4 657 kg); max take-off, 17,650 lb (8 006 kg).
Dimensions: Main rotor diameter, 48 ft 0 in (14,63 m); fuselage length, 49 ft 5 in (15,06 m); height, 12 ft 7 in (3,83 m).
Armament: One Hughes XM230E1 30-mm Chain gun in under-fuselage turret with 1,200 rounds. Four hardpoints on stub wings can carry up to 16 Rockwell Hellfire anti-tank missiles.
Accommodation: Co-pilot/gunner and pilot in tandem.
Status: Two Hughes Model 77 prototypes ordered by US Army on 22 June 1973, first flown respectively on 30 September and 22 November 1975. Army selection of AH-64 for further development announced November 1976 and prototype modified to pre-production configuration first flown 28 November 1978. First of three additional pre-production YAH-64s (with low mounted tailplane) flown 31 October 1979 and third, with definitive tail rotor and tailplane, first flown 16 March 1980.
Notes: Army testing of the YAH-64 prototype was completed late 1981; US Army plans total procurement of 446 Apaches.

(Above and below) Pre-production models of the AH-64A Apache under development for the US Army.

HELICOPTER

(Above) A Kaman SH-2F Seasprite of Marine Light Helicopter Anti-submarine Squadron HSL-33 and (below) with HSL-31.

KAMAN SH-2 SEASPRITE

Country of Origin: USA.
Type: Light anti-shipping helicopter.
Power Plant: Two 1,350 shp General Electric T58-GE-8F turboshafts.
Performance: Max speed, 165 mph (265 km/h) at sea level; normal cruising speed, 150 mph (241 km/h); initial rate of climb, 2,440 ft/min (12,4 m/sec); service ceiling, 22,500 ft (6 860 m); hovering ceiling, IGE, 18,600 ft (5 670 m); hovering ceiling OGE, 15,400 ft (4 695 m); normal range with max fuel, 422 mls (679 km).
Weights: Empty, 7,040 lb (3 193 kg); normal take-off, 12,800 lb (5 805 kg); overload, 13,300 lb (6 033 kg).
Dimensions: Main rotor diameter, 44 ft 0 in (13,41 m); length (folded), 38 ft 4 in (11,68 m); height, 13 ft 7 in (4,14 m).
Armament: Fuselage-side mounting for one or two torpedoes.
Accommodation: Pilot, co-pilot and sensor operator, plus spare provision for up to four passengers or two stretchers.
Status: First of four prototypes of Kaman Model K-20 (HU2K-1) flown on 2 July 1959; first HU2K-1 production deliveries December 1962; two prototype UH-2Cs first flown 14 March and 20 May 1966; first SH-2D flown 16 March 1971; YSH-2E prototypes flown 7 March and 28 March 1972 respectively; first SH-2F operational deployment, September 1973. Production totals: HU2K-1 prototypes, 4; HU2K-1/UH-2A, 88; HU2K-IU/UH-2B, 102; UH-2C, 40 (A/B conversions); HH-2C, six (A/B conversions); SH-2D, 20 (conversion); SH-2F, 98 (conversion) by 1982; production of 18 SH-2F resumed 1981.
Notes: The original UH-2A and UH-2B were single-engined long-range search and rescue helicopters, from which the UH-2C derived as a conversion programme. SH-2D development, followed by SH-2F, was to meet US Navy Light Airborne Multi-Purpose System (LAMPS) requirement.

HELICOPTER

(Above and below) Two views of the Kamov Ka-25 "Hormone" the latter with flotation bags on the undercarriage.

KAMOV KA-25 (HORMONE)

Country of Origin: Soviet Union.
Type: (Hormone-A) Shipboard anti-submarine warfare and (Hormone-B) over-the-horizon missile targeting helicopter.
Power Plant: Two 900 shp Glushenkov GTD-3 turboshafts.
Performance: (Estimated) Max speed, 130 mph (209 km/h); normal cruise, 120 mph (193 km/h); max range, 400 mls (644 km); service ceiling, 11,000 ft (3 353 m).
Weights: (Estimated) Empty, 10,500 lb (4 765 kg); max take-off, 16,500 lb (7 484 kg).
Dimensions: Rotor diameter (each), 51 ft 7½ in (15,74 m); fuselage length (estimated), 32 ft 0 in (9,75 m).
Armament: (Hormone-A) Nuclear depth charges, ASW torpedoes and other stores in weapons bay.
Accommodation: Crew of two on flight deck with ASW systems operators in main cabin which has sufficient capacity to accommodate up to 12 passengers on folding seats.
Status: Flown in prototype form in 1967, the Ka-25 entered Soviet Navy service in 1969–70, and 400–500 had been built by the time production was phased out in 1975. The Ka-25 has been exported in small numbers to India, Syria and Yugoslavia, and some 250 remained in Soviet service at the beginning of 1982.
Notes: Standard Soviet Navy shipboard helicopter equipment, the Ka-25 serves aboard the *Kirov*, *Kara* and *Kresta* classes of cruisers, and the *Sovremennii* and *Udaloi* classes of destroyer in Hormone-A form, and in a mixed complement (with Hormone-B) aboard the *Kiev* class carriers and *Moskva* class anti-submarine cruisers. The *Hormone-B* provides over-the-horizon targeting information for the 340-mile (550-km) range SS-N-12 Sandbox anti-shipping missile. A utility transport version of the Ka-25, Hormone-C, is also in service, and new "fire-and-forget" air-to-surface missiles were being applied to the Ka-25 in 1982.

KAMOV KA-32 (HELIX)

Country of Origin: Soviet Union.
Type: Shipboard anti-submarine warfare helicopter.
Power Plant: Two (approx) 1,500–1,700 shp turboshafts.
Performance: (Estimated) Max speed, 150 mph (241 km/h) at sea level; normal cruising, 130 mph (209 km/h); max range, 600 mls (965 km).
Weights: (Estimated) Normal loaded, 20,000–21,000 lb (9 070–9 525 kg).
Dimensions: (Estimated) Rotor diameter (each), 55 ft (16,75 m); fuselage length, 36 ft 4½ in (12,00 m).
Armament: ASW torpedoes, nuclear depth charges and other stores in weapons bay.
Accommodation: Flight crew of two and two–three systems operators. The main cabin is believed to have sufficient capacity to accommodate up to 18–20 troops.
Status: Prototypes believed to have flown 1979–80, with initial deployment by Soviet Naval Air Force in 1981.
Notes: Retaining the pod-and-boom fuselage configuration and a similar superimposed coaxial rotor arrangement to the Ka-25 Hormone (see page 238), Helix was first seen by western observers during the Zapad-81 exercises held by WarPac forces in the Baltic in September 1981. During that exercise, two Helix-type helicopters operated from the new guided missile destroyer *Udaloi*. Compatible with the lifts of the *Moskva*- and *Kiev*-class vessels, Helix is substantially larger and more powerful than Hormone which it is evidently intended to supplant in Soviet Naval Air Force service. Its appreciably greater internal capacity suggests that it is intended for alternative missions to ASW, such as that of troop transport for operation from *Berezina*-class replenishment ships. Helix is also likely to replace Hormone-B for over-the-horizon targeting.

(Above and below) "Helix" ASW helicopters operating from the Udaloi guided missile destroyer during exercise Zapad-81.

MBB BO 105

Country of Origin: Federal Germany.
Type: Light observation and armed anti-tank helicopters.
Power Plant: Two 429 shp Allison 250-C20B turboshafts.
Performance: (BO 105 CB) Max permissible speed, 167 mph (270 km/h); max cruising speed, 152 mph (245 km/h); normal cruising speed, 144 mph (232 km/h); initial rate of climb, 1,773 ft/min (9,0 m/sec); operating ceiling, 17,000 ft (5 180 m); hovering ceiling, IGE, 9,514 ft (2 900 m); hovering ceiling, OGE, 6,500 ft (1 980 m); range with max payload, 408 mls (656 km) at 5,000 ft (1 525 m); ferry range, 690 mls (1 110 km).
Weights: Empty equipped, 2,820 lb (1 279 kg); max take-off, 5,290 lb (2 400 kg).
Dimensions: Main rotor diameter, 32 ft 3½ in (9,84 m); fuselage length, 28 ft 1 in (8,56 m); height, 9 ft 10 in (3,0 m).
Armament: (BO 105P/PAH-1) Fuselage-side outriggers carry six Euromissile HOT wire-guided anti-tank weapons.
Accommodation: Two pilots side-by-side; provision in cabin for three passengers or two stretchers according to rôle.
Status: First BO 105 prototype flown on 16 February 1967 and second on 20 December 1967; first pre-production BO 105 flown on 1 May 1969; first production BO 105A flown on 11 April 1970; prototype BO 105C first flown 11 January 1971. Production/sales include 30 BO 105C for Dutch Army, 20 BO 105CB for Nigeria, 60 BO 105 CB for Spanish Army (assembled by CASA), BO 105CB for Philippine Air Force and Navy (assembled by PADS), 16 NBO 105 for Indonesian Air Force and others for Indonesian Army and Navy (assembled by Nurtanio), 10 NBO 105 for Royal Malaysian Air Force; 100 BO 105M/VBH and 212 BO 105P/PAH-1 for Federal German Army.
Notes: The BO 105 originated as a product of the Bölkow company before its merger into Messerschmitt-Bölkow-Blohm.

(Above) An MBB BO 105 carrying HOT anti-tank missiles; (below) the BO 105 "Giraffe" with mast-mounted sight.

(Above) A Mil Mi-2 with anti-tank missiles on outriggers; (below) an Mi-2 "Hoplite" of the Polish Air Force.

Country of Origin: Soviet Union (Poland).
Type: Light utility transport and anti-armour helicopter.
Power Plant: Two 400 or 450 shp Isotov GTD-350P turboshafts.
Performance: Max speed, 130 mph (210 km/h); max cruise, 124 mph (200 km/h); econ cruise, 118 mph (190 km/h); range (max payload), 105 mls (170 km), (max fuel), 360 mls (580 km); max initial climb, 885 ft/min (4,5 m/sec); hovering ceiling (in ground effect), 6,550 ft (2 000 m), (out of ground effect), 3,275 ft (1 000 m).
Weights: Empty, 5,213 lb (2 365 kg); max loaded, 7,826 lb (3 550 kg).
Dimensions: Rotor diameter, 47 ft 6¾ in (14,50 m); fuselage length, 38 ft 10 in (11,86 m); height, 12 ft 3½ in (3,75 m).
Armament: (Anti-armour role) Four AT-3 Sagger wire-guided missiles on lateral pylons, or UB-16-57U rocket pods.
Accommodation: Normal accommodation for pilot only on flight deck and up to eight troops in main cabin. Max payload, 1,763 lb (800 kg).
Status: First flown as a prototype in September 1961, the production of the Mi-2 was assigned to the Polish aircraft industry under an agreement signed in January 1964, the first Polish-built example flying on 4 November 1965. Between 5,000 and 6,000 Mi-2s have since been manufactured, primarily for military roles, and production was continuing at the beginning of 1982, when it was planned to phase out manufacture in 1985–86.
Notes: The Mi-2 is the standard liaison and light utility helicopter of the Warsaw Pact forces, and variants include a dual-control pilot training model and an aeromedical model, the latter accommodating four casualty stretchers and a medical attendant. The Mi-2 also fulfils the light observation helicopter role with the Soviet, Czech, Polish and Romanian air forces.

(Above) The radar-equipped anti-submarine "Hound B" version of the Mil Mi-4; (below) an Mi-4 troop transport of the Indian Air Force.

Country of Origin: Soviet Union.
Type: (Hound-A) General-purpose transport, (Hound-B) anti-submarine warfare and (Hound-C) electronic countermeasures helicopter.
Power Plant: One 1,700 shp Shvetsov ASh-82V eighteen-cylinder radial air-cooled engine.
Performance: Max speed, 130 mph (210 km/h) at 4,920 ft (1 500 m); econ cruise, 99 mph (160 km/h); range (with max troop load), 155 mls (350 km); max range, 370 mls (595 km); service ceiling (at 16,204 lb/7 350 kg), 13,780 ft (4 200 m).
Weights: Empty, 11,650 lb (5 268 kg); max loaded, 17,200 lb (7 800 kg).
Dimensions: Rotor diameter, 68 ft 11 in (21,00 m); fuselage length, 55 ft 1 in (16,80 m); height, 17 ft 0 in (5,18 m).
Accommodation: (Hound-A) Flight crew of three and up to 14 fully-equipped troops or 3,525 lb (1 600 kg) of freight.
Status: First flown in 1951, the Mi-4 entered production in 1952, and was phased out of production in the Soviet Union in 1969 after some 3,500 had been built. Licence manufacture was continued in China at Harbin as the H-5 until 1979, the first Chinese-built example having been completed early 1958, and more than 1,000 having been built by the time production terminated, some examples having been converted for the Pratt & Whitney PT6T-6 Turbo Twin Pac turboshaft.
Notes: Although the Mi-4 has now been largely supplanted by turboshaft-powered helicopters in the first line inventory of the Soviet Air Force and in those of other WarPac air forces, it remains in service in some numbers in secondary roles, and with the air forces of many of the 25 countries to which it was exported. The ASW (Hound-B) version remained with the Baltic Fleet AF at the beginning of the 'eighties.

MIL MI-6 (HOOK)

Country of Origin: Soviet Union.
Type: Heavy-lift transport helicopter.
Power Plant: Two 5,500 shp Soloviev D-25V turboshafts.
Performance: Max speed, 186 mph (300 km/h); max cruise, 155 mph (250 km/h); range (with 13,228 lb/6 000 kg internal payload), 404 mls (650 km), (with 9,480 lb/4 300 kg payload and external auxiliary tanks), 652 mls (1 050 km); max ferry range, 900 mls (1 450 km).
Weights: Empty, 60,055 lb (27 240 kg); max take-off, 93,700 lb (42 500 kg).
Dimensions: Rotor diameter, 114 ft 10 in (35,00 m); fuselage length, 108 ft 10½ in (33,18 m); height, 32 ft 4 in (9,86 m); span of auxiliary wings, 50 ft 2 in (15,30 m).
Armament: One 23-mm cannon in extreme nose.
Accommodation: Flight crew of five comprising two pilots, navigator, flight engineer and radio operator, and up to 90 troops or 41 stretcher casualties plus medical attendants. Max internal payload of 26,450 lb (12 000 kg), or max slung load of 19,840 lb (9 000 kg).
Status: Flown for the first time early in 1957, five prototypes were used for flight development, large-scale series production following a pre-series of 30, with a total of some 850 built when manufacture phased out in the early 'seventies. Some 350–400 remain in service with the Soviet Air Force, and the Mi-6 also serves with the armed forces of Bulgaria, Egypt, Iraq, Peru, Syria and Vietnam.
Notes: A key element in the Soviet battlefield mobility concept, the Mi-6 was, at the time of its debut, the world's largest helicopter. It is assumed that the Mi-6 will begin to give place to the Mi-26 from mid-decade. Flying crane derivatives of the Mi-6 are the Mi-10 and Mi-10K.

(Above and below) A production example of the Mil Mi-6 in civil markings for demonstration purposes.

MIL MI-8 (HIP)

Country of Origin: Soviet Union.
Type: Assault transport, (Hip-D) electronic warfare and (Hip-E and F) anti-armour helicopter.
Power Plant: Two 1,700 shp Isotov TV2-117A turboshafts.
Performance: Max speed, 161 mph (260 km/h) at 3,280 ft (1 000 m), 155 mph (250 km/h) at sea level; max cruise, 140 mph (225 km/h); range (standard fuel), 290 mls (465 km); hovering ceiling (in ground effect), 6,233 ft (1 900 m), (out of ground effect), 2,625 ft (800 m).
Weights: (Hip-C) Empty, 14,603 lb (6 624 kg); normal loaded, 24,470 lb (11 100 kg); max, 26,455 lb (12 000 kg).
Dimensions: Rotor diameter, 69 ft 10¼ in (21,29 m); fuselage length, 60 ft 0¾ in (18,31 m); height, 18 ft 6½ in (5,65 m).
Armament: (Hip-E) Four AT-2 Swatter anti-armour missiles, or (Hip-F) six AT-3 Sagger anti-armour missiles and up to six pods each containing 32 57-mm rockets, plus one 12,7-mm gun in the nose.
Accommodation: (Hip-C) Flight crew of three and 24 fully-equipped troops, or 12 casualty stretchers and medical attendant. Max payload, 8,820 lb (4 000 kg).
Status: Original (single-engined) prototype flown in 1961, with second (twin-engined) prototype following on 17 September 1962. The total since produced exceeded 6,000 by the beginning of 1982, when manufacture was continuing at a rate of some 60 monthly.
Notes: Numerically the most important Soviet helicopter and widely exported, the Mi-8 in its Hip-C form is the standard equipment of Soviet tactical helicopter regiments and can be fitted with 128 57-mm rockets in four packs. The Hip-E is allegedly the world's most powerfully-armed helicopter, the Hip-F being an export equivalent with downgraded armament.

(Above) An early version of the Mil Mi-8 operated by the Czech Air Force; (below) the armed anti-tank "Hip C" version of the Mi-8.

HELICOPTER

(Above and below) Two views of the Mil Mi-14 "Haze" shore-based anti-submarine helicopter.

Country of Origin: Soviet Union.
Type: Amphibious anti-submarine warfare helicopter.
Power Plant: Two 1,700 shp Isotov TV2-117 or 1,900 shp TV3-117 turboshafts.
Performance: (Estimated with TV3 turboshafts) Max speed, 150 mph (241 km/h); max cruise, 145 mph (233 km/h); tactical radius, 125 mls (200 km); range, 300 mls (483 km); service ceiling (at normal loaded weight), 16,405 ft (5 000 m).
Weights: (Estimated) Max take-off, 29,000 lb (13 155 kg).
Dimensions: Rotor diameter, 69 ft $10\frac{1}{4}$ in (21,29 m); fuselage length, 59 ft 7 in (18,15 m).
Armament: Nuclear depth charges, ASW torpedoes and other stores in weapons bay.
Accommodation: Crew of five comprising two pilots, flight engineer, navigator and systems operator, and provision for up to 26 troops in secondary assault transport role.
Status: The Mi-14 was under test in 1973–74, entering Soviet naval service late 1975. Approximately 80–100 were believed to be in service with the Soviet Naval Air Force at the beginning of 1982, when production rate was two per month. A small number have reportedly been supplied to Bulgaria
Notes: The Mi-14 is an amphibious ASW helicopter utilising the power plant and dynamic components of the Mi-8. Featuring a boat-type hull with lateral sponsons, which, in addition to providing stability on the water, house the retractable twin-wheel main undercarriage members. The Mi-14 equips shore-based ASW helicopter elements of the Soviet Navy and current production models are believed to employ power plant and dynamic component commonality with the Mi-17 derivative of the Mi-8. A search radar installation is mounted beneath the nose and a sonar "bird" beneath the tailboom root.

HELICOPTER

(Above) The "Hind-A" version of the Mil Mi-24 with four rocket pods; (below) the "Hind-D" showing the nose gun turret.

Country of Origin: Soviet Union.
Type: (Hind-A) Armed assault and (Hind-D and E) attack helicopter.
Power Plant: Two 1,900 shp (2,200 shp short-period emergency) Isotov TV3-117M turboshafts.
Performance: (Hind-D estimated) Max speed, 200 mph (320 km/h); max continuous cruise, 160 mph (260 km/h); max inclined climb rate, 3,000 ft/min (15,24 m/sec); radius of action (max pay-load), 40 mls (65 km), (with auxiliary fuel), 185 mls (300 km).
Weights: (Hind-D estimated) Empty, 15,430 lb (7 000 kg); normal loaded, 23,150 lb (10 500 kg); max, 26,455 lb (12 000 kg).
Dimensions: (Estimated) Rotor diameter, 55 ft 0 in (16,76 m); fuselage length, 55 ft 6 in (16,90 m); height, 18 ft 0 in (5,50 m).
Armament: (Hind-A) One 12,7-mm machine gun and four pods each containing 32 57-mm rockets, or four AT-2 Swatter anti-armour missiles. Armament of Hind-D similar apart from replacement of single-barrel nose gun with four-barrel 12,7-mm rotary gun in turret, while Hind-E replaces the Swatter missiles with tube-launched AT-6 Spiral missiles.
Accommodation: (Hind-A) Crew of four and provision for eight troops, or (Hind-D and E) weapons operator and pilot in tandem.
Status: First flown in 1969–70, the Mi-24 attained initial operational capability in 1973, more than 1,000 having been delivered by the beginning of 1982 (all versions), when production was reportedly 15 monthly.
Notes: The Mi-24 has been exported (primarily in the Hind-A version) to several countries, including Afghanistan, Algeria, Cuba, Iraq, Libya and South Yemen. Most WarPac countries are now operating the Hind-D version for the anti-armour mission, the Hind-E being operated exclusively by the Soviet Union.

MIL MI-26 (HALO)

Country of Origin: Soviet Union.
Type: Heavy-lift transport helicopter.
Power Plant: Two 11,400 shp Lotarev D-136 turboshafts.
Performance: Max speed, 183 mph (295 km/h); normal cruise, 158 mph (255 km/h); range with 5 per cent reserves (at 109,127 lb/49 500 kg), 310 mls (500 km), (at 123,457 lb/ 56 000 kg), 497 mls (800 km); hovering ceiling (in ground effect), 14,765 ft (4 500 m), (out of ground effect), 5,905 ft (1 800 m).
Weights: Empty, 62,169 lb (28 200 kg); normal loaded, 109,127 lb (49 500 kg); max loaded, 123,457 lb (56 000 kg).
Dimensions: Rotor diameter, 104 ft 11⅞ in (32,00 m); length (nose to tail rotor), 110 ft 7¾ in (33,73 m); height (to rotor hub), 26 ft 5⅛ in (8,05 m).
Accommodation: Flight crew of five comprising two pilots, flight engineer, navigator/radio operator and loadmaster, and at least 90 combat-equipped troops or 40 casualty stretchers. Max internal payload, 44,090 lb (20 000 kg).
Status: The first prototype Mi-26 made its initial (hover) flight on 14 December 1977, the first forward flight following on 21 February 1978. Production of pre-series commenced 1980, with preparations for full-scale production being initiated in 1981.
Notes: The heaviest and most powerful – although not dimensionally the largest – helicopter yet flown, the Mi-26 is obviously intended as a successor to the Mi-6, and although intended to fulfil some civil roles, its primary mission is obviously military and it is anticipated that the Soviet Air Force will achieve initial operational capability with the series version in 1984–85. The Mi-26 possesses a larger freight hold than the fixed-wing An-12 transport, and wheeled or tracked vehicles may be driven straight into the hold via the rear-loading ramp and clamshell-type rear doors.

(Above and below) Air and ground views of an early example of the Mil Mi-26 "Halo".

SIKORSKY S-55/WHIRLWIND

Country of Origin: USA (and United Kingdom).
Type: General purpose helicopter.
Power Plant: One 800 hp Wright R-1300-3 piston radial engine.
Performance: Max speed, 112 mph (180 km/h) at sea level, cruising speed, 91 mph (148 km/h); inclined rate of climb, 1,020 ft/min (5,2 m/sec); hovering ceiling, IGE, 5,800 ft (1 770 m), hovering ceiling, OGE, 2,300 ft (700 m); normal range, 360 mls (578 km).
Weights: Empty, 5,250 lb (2 381 kg); max take-off, 7,900 lb (3 583 kg).
Dimensions: Rotor diameter, 53 ft 0 in (16,16 m); fuselage length, 42 ft 3 in (12,88 m); height, 13 ft 4 in (4,07 m).
Armament: None.
Accommodation: Crew of two and up to 10 fully armed troops or six stretchers plus one attendant.
Status: Sikorsky S-55 first flown on 10 November 1949; first Westland-built Whirlwind HAR Mk 1 flown 15 August 1953; first HAR Mk 5 flown 28 August 1955; first HAS Mk 7 flown 17 October 1956. Production totals, 1,267 by Sikorsky, 485 by Westland, 71 by Mitsubishi and five by Sud-Aviation.
Notes: The S-55 was the first Sikorsky helicopter to reach four-figure production and was widely used by the US armed services (as the H-19, USAF and Army, HRS Marine Corps and HO4S, US Navy). Many were supplied to other nations and some are still operating in the general utility rôle outside of the USA. In Britain, the S-55 was built as the Whirlwind for the RAF and Royal Navy, and was developed in exclusive UK variants with the Alvis Leonides piston engine and, later, the 1,050 shp Gnome turboshaft. A few of the latter, as Whirlwind 10s, were still in RAF service in 1982, principally in Cyprus to support UN operations. S-55s were also built by Mitsubishi in Japan.

(Above) A Sikorsky S-55 (H-19) operational with the Republic of Korea Air Force; (below) Westland Whirlwind 10 serving in Cyprus.

HELICOPTER

(Above) A Sikorsky S-58 with original piston engine; (below) A Sikorsky S-58T turbine-engined conversion of the Royal Thai Air Force.

SIKORSKY S-58 AND S-58T

Country of Origin: USA.

Type: General utility and transport helicopter.

Power Plant: One (S-58) 1,525 hp Wright R-1820-84 piston engine or (S-58T) one 1,800 shp PT6T-3 Twin-Pac turboshaft.

Performance: (S-58) Max speed, 123 mph (198 km/h) at sea level; cruising speed, 98 mph (158 km/h); initial rate of climb, 1,100 ft/min (5,6 m/sec); service ceiling, 9,000 ft (2 740 m); hovering ceiling, IGE, 4,900 ft (1 490 m); hovering ceiling, OGE, 2,400 ft (730 m); range, 280 mls (450 km).

Performance: (S-58T) Max speed, 138 mph (227 km/h) at sea level; cruising speed, 127 mph (204 km/h); hovering ceiling, OGE, 1,433 m (4 700 ft); range 300 mls (483 km).

Weights: Empty (SH-34J), 8 275 lb (3 754 kg); max take-off weight, (S-58), 14,000 lb (6 350 kg), (S-58T) 13,000 lb (5 896 kg).

Dimensions: Main rotor diameter, 56 ft 0 in (17,07 m); fuselage length (S-58), 46 ft 9 in (14,25 m), (S-58T), 47 ft 3 in (14,4 m); height, 14 ft 3½ in (4,36 m).

Accommodation: Two pilots side-by-side in cockpit; up to 18 troops in cabin, or eight stretchers plus one attendant.

Armament: None.

Status: Prototype S-58 (XHSS-1) first flown 8 March 1954; first production S-58 flown 20 September 1954; first S-58T flown 19 August 1970. Production total, 1,821 by Sikorsky, completed January 1970; 171 built by Sud-Aviation in France and 20 assembled by Mitsubishi in Japan.

Notes: Production of the S-58 included HSS-1 (later SH-34) for Navy, HUS (later UH-34) for Marine Corps and H-34 (later CH-34) for USAF and Army, named Seabat, Seahorse and Choctaw respectively. The S-58T was a conversion programme only, launched in 1971, and a few examples were in military service in 1981, notably with the Royal Thai Air Force.

HELICOPTER

(Above) A Sikorsky SH-3H Sea King of US Navy Helicopter Anti-submarine Squadron HS-4; (below) an Agusta-built SH-3D for Peru.

SIKORSKY SH-3 SEA KING

Country of Origin: USA.

Type: Anti-submarine helicopter (and, S-61A) troop transport.

Power Plant: Two (SH-3A) 1,050 shp General Electric T58-GE-6 or 1,250 shp T58-GE-8B or (SH-3D, 3G, 3H) 1,400 shp T58-GE-10 turboshafts.

Performance: (SH-3H) Max speed, 158 mph (254 km/h) at sea level; 143 mph (230 km/h) at 1,500 ft (1 525 m) with two torpedoes; initial rate of climb, 2,400 ft/min (12,2 m/sec) clean at max power, 1,700 ft/min (8,6 m/sec) with two torpedoes at max power; service ceiling, 15,850 ft (4 831 m); hovering ceiling, OGE, 5,900 ft (1 798 m); mission radius, two torpedoes, 186 mls (300 km); ferry range, 745 mls (1 198 km) at 114 mph (183 km/h).

Weights: (SH-3H) Empty equipped, 13,918 lb (6 313 kg); basic mission operating weight empty, 14,809 lb (6 717 kg); max take-off, 21,000 lb (9 526 kg).

Dimensions: Main rotor diameter, 62 ft 0 in (18,89 m); length (blades folded), 47 ft 3 in (14,40 m); height, 15 ft 4 in (4,67 m).

Armament: Fixed launching points (two sponsons, two on fuselage) for two Mk 46 homing torpedoes (ASW missions).

Accommodation: Operational crew of four; space provision for 15 troops in cabin; (S-61A-4) 31 troops in cabin.

Status: YHSS-2 prototype first flown 11 March 1959; first deliveries May 1961. Production: YSH-3A (YHSS-2), 10; SH-3A (HSS-2), 245; CH-3A, eight; SH-3D, 73 for US Navy plus 10 for Spanish Navy; S-61D, four for Argentine Navy, four for Brazilian Navy and four for United Kingdom; SH-3A (CHSS-2, later CH-124), 41 for Canadian Navy/CAF; S-61A-4, 38 for Royal Malaysian Air Force; Mitsubishi in Japan produced 101 HSS-2 (S-61B) ASR and 10 S-61A SAR helicopters for JMSDF. In Italy, Agusta built 10 SH-3D for Iran, 24 SH-3D for the Italian Navy, six S-61A for Iraq, two S-61A for Saudi Arabia and four SH-3D for Peru.

SIKORSKY CH-3 JOLLY GREEN GIANT

Country of Origin: USA.

Type: Troop and supply transport helicopter.

Power Plant: Two (CH-3C) 1,300 shp General Electric T58-GE-1 or (CH-3E, HH-3E, HH-3F) 1,500 shp T58-GE-5 turboshaft.

Performance: (CH-3E) Max speed, 165 mph (266 km/h) at sea level; speed for best range, 131 mph (211 km/h) at 5,000 ft (1 525 m); initial rate of climb, 2,030 ft/min (10,3 m/sec); service ceiling, 20,000 ft (6 100 m); time to 10,000 ft (3 050 m), 16,2 min; basic mission range, 315 mls (508 km); long-range cargo mission, 786 mls (1 265 km); ferry range, 852 mls (1 370 km).

Weights: (CH-3E) Empty equipped, 13,134 lb (5 958 kg); max take-off, 22 050 lb (10 000 kg).

Dimensions: Main rotor diameter, 62 ft 0 in (18,90 m); fuselage length, 57 ft 3 in (17,45 m); height, 16 ft 1 in (4,90 m).

Armament: (CH-3) Provison for one or two 7·62-mm minigun sideways-firing from cabin.

Accommodation: Normal crew of two pilots and one flight engineer, provision for up to 25 troops or 15 stretchers plus two attendants.

Status: CH-3B (HSS-2) evaluation by USAF April 1962; CH-3C first flown 17 June 1963; first HH-3E delivery 5 November 1965; first HH-3F flown October 1967. Production: CH-3B, three; CH-3C, 75; CH-3E, 45; HH-3E, eight (plus 42 CH-3E conversions); HH-3F, 40. Agusta in Italy built 20 HH-3Fs for the Italian Air Force.

Notes: The CH-3 was developed from the SH-3 (separately described) to meet a USAF requirement for a long-range transport helicopter, with a rear-loading ramp and redesigned sponsons without tip floats. Further developed into the HH-3E with protective armour and defensive armament, this helicopter served with distinction in Vietnam, earning the name Jolly Green Giant. The amphibious HH-3F for US Coast Guard was named Pelican.

(Above) A Sikorsky HH-3E demonstrating air-to-air refuelling; (below) an Agusta-built HH-3F.

SIKORSKY CH-54 TARHE

Country of Origin: USA.

Type: Heavy flying-crane helicopter.

Power Plant: (CH-54A) 4,500 shp Pratt & Whitney T37-P-1 or (CH-54B) 4,800 shp T37-P-700 turboshafts.

Performance: (CH-54A at 38,000 lb/17 237 kg) Max speed, 127 mph (204 km/h) at sea level; max cruise, 109 mph (175 km/h); initial rate of climb, 1,330 ft/min (6,75 m/sec); hovering ceiling, IGE, 10,600 ft (3 230 m), hovering ceiling, OGE, 6,900 ft (2 100 m); range 230 mls (370 km).

Weights: (CH-54A) Empty, 19,234 lb (8 724 kg); max take-off (CH-54A), 42,000 lb (19 050 kg), (CH-54B), 47,000 lb (21 320 kg).

Dimensions: Rotor diameter, 72 ft 0 in (21,95 m); fuselage length, 70 ft 3 in (21,41 m); height, 25 ft 5 in (7,75 m).

Armament: None.

Accommodation: Two pilots side-by-side and aft-facing winch-operator in cockpit. Two optional crew/passenger seats can be fitted in cabin.

Status: First of three S-64 prototypes flown 9 May 1962; first YCH-54A delivery to US Army late-1964; first CH-54B flown 30 June 1969. Production totals, YCH-54A, six; CH-54A, 54; CH-54B, 37 (plus commercial S-64A, S-64E and S-64F).

Notes: The heavy-lift S-64 flying crane helicopter was developed primarily to meet a Federal German Defence Ministry requirement and two of the three prototypes were evaluated in Germany. The only production orders were placed by the US Army, however, which adopted the S-64 primarily for service in Vietnam. A detachable pod/fuselage could be fitted, allowing the CH-54 to carry up to 87 troops, as demonstrated in 1965. By 1981, most Army CH-54s had been transferred to the National Guard, which had about 70 in service.

(Above and below) two aspects of CH-54B Tarhe helicopters in service with the US Army.

HELICOPTER

SIKORSKY S-65 (CH-53,HH-53) SEA STALLION

(Above) A CH-53D Sea Stallion of Marine Medium Helicopter Squadron HMM-261; (below) a CH-53G operated by the Federal German Army.

Country of Origin: USA.

Type: Medium lift and search and rescue helicopter.

Power Plant: Two (CH-53A) 2,850 shp General Electric T64-GE-6 or 3,080 shp GE-3 or 3,435 shp GE-16 or (CH-53D) 3,925 shp T64-GE-413 or (HH-53B) 3,080 shp T64-GE-3 or (HH-53C,CH-53G) 3,925 shp T64-GE-7 turboshafts.

Performance: (CH-53D) Max speed, 196 mph (315 km/h) at sea level; cruising speed, 173 mph (278km/h); initial rate of climb, 2,180 ft/min (11,1 m/sec); service ceiling, 21,000 ft (6 400 m); hovering ceiling, IGE, 13,400 ft (4 080 m); hovering ceiling, OGE, 6,500 ft (1 980 m); range, 257 mls (413 km).

Weights: Empty, 23,485 lb (10 653 kg); max take-off weight, 42,000 lb (19 050 kg).

Dimensions: Rotor diameter, 72 ft 3 in (22,02 m); fuselage length, 67 ft 2 in (20,47 m); height, 24 ft 11 in (7,60 m).

Accommodation: Flight crew of three and up to 55 troops, or 24 stretchers and four attendants.

Status: First YCH-53A prototype flown 14 October 1964; first HH-53B flown 16 March 1967; first RH-53D flown 27 October 1972; first CH-53D delivered 3 March 1969. Production totals: YCH-53A, two; CH-53A, 139 (15 converted to RH-53A); CH-53C, 20; CH-53D, 126 (two converted to VH-53D); HH-53B, eight; HH-53C, 44 (eight converted to HH-53H); CH-53G, 112 (including 110 built by VFW-Fokker); S-65-Oe (Austria), two; S-65 (CH-53D Israel), about 25; RH-53D (Iranian Navy), six.

Notes: CH-53A Sea Stallion was first developed as an assault transport for US Marine Corps; CH-53G is similar version adopted by Federal German Army. RH-53A and RH-53D are mine countermeasures variants for US Navy. HH-53B and HH-53C Super Jolly are USAF search and rescue versions, and the HH-53Hs have added equipment for night and all-weather operations.

HELICOPTER

SIKORSKY CH-53E SUPER STALLION

(Above) A production prototype of the CH-53E in US Navy markings; (below) the first production CH-53E Super Stallion in Marine Corps markings.

Country of Origin: USA.

Type: Heavy lift multi-purpose helicopter.

Power Plant: Three 4,380 shp (10-minute rating) General Electric T64-GE-415 turboshafts.

Performance: (At 56,000 lb/25 400 kg take-off weight) Max speed, 196 mph (315 km/h) at sea level; cruising speed, 173 mph (278 km/h) at sea level; initial rate of climb, 2,750 ft/min (14 m/sec); service ceiling, 18,500 ft (5 643 m); hovering ceiling, IGE, 11,550 ft (3 523 m); hovering ceiling, OGE, 9,500 ft (2 895 m); max range, 1,290 mls (2 075 km).

Weights: Empty, 32,878 lb (14 910 kg); max internal payload, 30,000 lb (13 607 kg) for 115-ml (185-km) radius; basic mission payload (external), 32,000 lb (14 512 kg) for 57-ml (92,5-km) radius; max take-off weight, 73,500 lb (33 339 kg) with external loads, 69,750 lb (31 638 kg) with internal loads.

Dimensions: Main rotor diameter, 79 ft 0 in (24,08 m); fuselage length, 73 ft 4 in (22,35 m).

Accommodation: Flight crew of three and up to 55 troops.

Status: Two YCH-53E prototypes, first flown 1 March 1974 and April 1974; two pre-production CH-53Es, first flown 8 December 1975 and February 1976. First production CH-53E flown 13 December 1980. Production programme, two YCH-53E and 51 CH-53E (including two pre-production aircraft).

Notes: The CH-53E is a substantially modified and updated version of the original Sikorsky S-65 (CH-53) design, (separately described). Adding a third engine and uprating the transmission allowed Sikorsky to double the lift capability of the CH-53D to meet the Marine Corps and Navy requirements. Deliveries began early in 1981 against initial Marine Corps procurement of 33 and Navy purchase of 19; further purchases were planned, including MH-53E airborne mine countermeasures variant.

SIKORSKY UH-60 BLACK HAWK

Country of Origin: USA.
Type: Utility tactical transport helicopter.
Power Plant: Two 1,560 shp General Electric T700-GE-700 turboshafts.
Performance: Max permissible speed, 224 mph (361 km/h); max operational speed, 182 mph (293 km/h) at sea level; max cruising speed, 167 mph (269 km/h) at 4,000 ft (1 220 m); initial rate of climb, 2,460 ft/min (12,5 m/sec); service ceiling, 19,000 ft (5 790 m); hovering ceiling, IGE, 9,500 ft (2 895 m); hovering ceiling, OGE, 10,400 ft (3 170 m); range at max take-off weight, 373 mls (600 km); endurance, 2 hrs 18 mins.
Weights: Empty, 10,624 lb (4 818 kg); mission take-off weight, 16,260 lb (7 374 kg); max take-off weight, 20,250 lb (9 183 kg).
Dimensions: Main rotor diameter, 53 ft 8 in (16,36 m); fuselage length, 50 ft 0¾ in (15,26 m); height, 16 ft 10 in (5,13 m).
Armament: Provision for one or two 7.62-mm M-60 side-firing machine guns mounted in cabin.
Accommodation: Two pilots side-by-side and 11 fully-equipped troops or four stretchers with attendants.
Status: Three YUH-60A prototypes first flown on 17 October 1974, 21 January 1975 and 28 February 1975 respectively; fourth prototype (Sikorsky S-70) flown on 23 May 1975. First production UH-60A first flown 17 October 1978; first delivery to US Army on 19 June 1979; YEH-60B flown 6 February 1981; YEH-60A flown 24 September 1981. Production/orders: YUH-60A, five; UH-60A, 337 ordered by beginning of 1982; YEH-60B, five.
Notes: The Sikorsky S-70 was winner of a US Army design contest for a Utility Tactical Transport Aircraft System (UTTAS) at the end of 1976. The EH-60A is a special electronics mission aircraft, and the EH-60B is equipped as a Stand-Off Target Acquisition System (SOTAS).

(Above) A Sikorsky UH-60A Black Hawk carrying an Army vehicle; (below) the prototype YEH-60A "Quick Fix" helicopter.

SIKORSKY SH-60 SEAHAWK

Country of Origin: USA.
Type: Anti-submarine and anti-shipping helicopter.
Power Plant: Two 1,690 shp General Electric T700-GE-401 turboshafts.
Performance: Max dash speed, 167 mph (269 km/h); max cruising speed, 155 mph (249 km/h) at 5,000 ft (1825 m); vertical rate of climb, 1,192 ft/min (6,1 m/sec).
Weights: Empty equipped, 13,648 lb (6 191 kg); mission gross weight, 20,244 lb (9 183 kg); max take-off weight, 21,884 lb (9 924 kg).
Dimensions: Main rotor diameter, 53 ft 8 in (16,36 m); fuselage length, 50 ft 0¾ in (15,26 m); height, 17 ft 2 in (5,23 m).
Armament: Fuselage-side hardpoints for two Mk 46 homing torpedoes, or air-to-surface missiles, depth bombs, etc.
Accommodation: Two pilots and one operator in cockpit and sensor operator in cabin.
Status: Five YSH-60B prototypes flown on 12 December 1979 and 11 February, 17 March, 26 April and 14 July 1980 respectively. Production/orders: YSH-60B, five; SH-60B, 18 ordered by mid-1981 against total US Navy requirement for 204, for deliveries starting 1983, plus 195 simplified SH.60Cs.
Notes: The Sikorsky S-70L, based upon the design of the S-70 (US Army UH-60A Black Hawk, separately described) was selected by the US Navy in September 1977 to meet its requirement for an improved Light Airborne Multi Purpose System, known as LAMPS Mk III. As the SH-60B Seahawk, the LAMPS Mk III combines an airframe by Sikorsky with avionics developed in an integrated system by IBM and a DAF Indal recovery, assist, securing and traversing (RAST) system to permit safe operation to and from very small helipads on the hangar decks aft of the superstructure on destroyers, frigates and cruisers.

(Above and below) Two aspects of the SH-60B Seahawk anti-submarine helicopter version of the Sikorsky S-70.

HELICOPTER

(Above and below) Examples of the Westland Wessex HC Mk 2 in service with the Royal Air Force.

WESTLAND WESSEX

Country of Origin: United Kingdom.
Type: General purpose, search and rescue and training helicopter.
Power Plant: Two (HC Mk 2) 1,350 shp Rolls-Royce Bristol Gnome 110/111 or (HU Mk 5) Gnome 112/113 or (HAS Mk 3) one 1,600 shp Napier Gazelle 165 or (HAS Mk 31) 1,540 shp Gazelle 162 turboshaft.
Performance: (HC Mk 2) Max speed, 132 mph (212 km/h) at sea level; max cruising speed, 121 mph (195 km/h); initial rate of climb, 1,650 ft/min (8,4 m/sec); hovering ceiling, OGE, 4,000 ft (1 220 m); range, 478 mls (770 km).
Weights: Basic operating (HC Mk 2), 8,304 lb (3 767 kg); max take-off, 13,500 lb (6 120 kg).
Dimensions: Rotor diameter, 56 ft 0 in (17,07 m); length, 48 ft 4½ in (14,74 m); overall height, 16 ft 2 in (4,93 m).
Accommodation: Two pilots and up to 16 troops in cabin.
Status: Imported Sikorsky S-58 (HSS-1) with Gazelle engine first flown 17 May 1957; first pre-production Wessex HAS Mk 1 flown 20 June 1958; HC Mk 2 first flown 18 January 1962; pre-production HC Mk 2 flown 5 October 1962; first new-build HAS Mk 3 flown 3 November 1964; prototype HU Mk 5 flown 31 May 1963; first production Mk 5 flown 17 November 1963; HCC Mk 4s flown on 17 March and 13 May 1969. Production totals: Pre-production, three; HAS Mk 1, 137; HC Mk 2, one prototype and 72 production; HAS Mk 3, three and Mk 1 conversions; HCC Mk 4, two; HU Mk 5, one prototype and 100; HAS Mk 31, 27 for RAN; Mk 52, 12 for Iraqi Air Force; Mk 53, three for Ghana Air Force; Mk 54, one for Brunei.
Notes: Wessex was a re-engined and Anglicized version of Sikorsky S-58 (separately described), built for the Royal Navy. The HC Mk 2 troop transport continues in RAF service, together with HAR Mk 2s converted for search and rescue duty.

HELICOPTER

(Above) A Westland Scout AH Mk 1 operated by the Royal Marines; (below) the Wasp as operated by the South African Navy.

WESTLAND WASP (AND SCOUT)

Country of Origin: United Kingdom.
Type: General-purpose and anti-submarine warfare helicopter.
Power Plant: One (Wasp) 710 shp Rolls-Royce Bristol Nimbus 503 or (Scout) 685 shp Nimbus 101 or 102 turboshaft.
Performance: (Wasp) Max speed, 120 mph (193 km/h) at sea level; max cruise, 110 mph (177 km/h); initial rate of climb, 1,440 ft/min (7,4 m/sec); hovering ceiling, IGE, 12,500 ft (3 810 m), hovering ceiling, OGE, 8,800 ft (2 682 m); max range with standard fuel, 303 mls (488 km).
Weights: (Wasp) Empty, 4,452 lb (1 566 kg); max take-off, 5,500 lb (2 495 kg).
Dimensions: Rotor diameter, 32 ft 3 in (9,83 m); fuselage length, 30 ft 4 in (9,24 m); height, 11 ft 8 in (3,56 m).
Armament: (Wasp) Two Mk 44 torpedoes or (Scout) provision for up to four SS.11 anti-tank missiles or machine gun or cannon installations.
Accommodation: Operational crew of two and provision for (Scout) three passengers or (Wasp) up to four passengers.
Status: First Saro P531 prototype flown 20 July 1958; first P531 (Nimbus engine) flown on 9 August 1959; first prototype Wasp flown 28 October 1962; first pre-production Scout flown 4 August 1960; first production Scout AH Mk 1 flown 6 March 1961. Production, P531 prototypes, 2; P531 pre-production, 2; Wasp prototype, 2; Wasp HAS Mk 1, 96; Scout AH Mk 1, 150; export Wasp, 17 for South Africa, 6 for New Zealand, 12 for Netherlands and nine for Brazil; export Scout, 2 for Australia, 1 for Uganda.
Notes: The Royal Navy Wasp, operating from frigates and destroyers, had been almost wholly replaced by the Lynx by 1981 in the Royal Navy, Netherlands Navy and Brazil; four of the Dutch aircraft have been re-sold to Indonesia, and some of those supplied to Brazil and New Zealand were from RN stocks.

WESTLAND SEA KING

HELICOPTER

Country of Origin: United Kingdom.
Type: Anti-submarine and search and rescue helicopter.
Power Plant: Two (HAS Mk 1) 1,500shp (2½-min rating) Rolls-Royce Bristol Gnome 1400 or (later marks) 1,660 shp (2½-min rating) Gnome 1400-1 turboshafts.
Performance: (HAS Mk 5) Max cruising speed, 129 mph (208 km/h) at sea level; initial rate of climb, 2,020 ft/min (10,3 m/sec); hovering ceiling, IGE, 5,000 ft (1 525 m); hovering ceiling, OGE, 3,200 ft (975 m); normal range, 764 mls (1 230 km).
Weights: Operating weight empty, 14,051 lb (6 313 kg); mission equipped weight (three torpedoes), 16,341 lb (7 412 kg); normal take-off, 21,000 lb (9 525 kg); overload, 21,400 lb (9 707 kg).
Dimensions: Main rotor diameter, 62 ft 0 in (18,90 m); fuselage length, 55 ft 9¾ in (17,01 m); height, 16 ft 10 in (5,13 m).
Armament: Up to four homing torpedoes or depth charges.
Accommodation: Two pilots, radar operator and sonar/LAPADS operator for ASW rôle; two pilots, winchman, winch operator and up to 19 survivors in search-and-rescue rôle.
Status: First flight of imported SH-3D with Gnome engines, 8 September 1967; first Westland-built Sea King HAS Mk 1 flown 7 May 1969; first HAS Mk 2 flown 18 June 1976; first HAR Mk 3 flown 6 September 1977; first HAS Mk 5 flown 1 August 1980. Production: Mk 1, 56; Mk 2, 21 (plus converted Mk 1s); Mk 3, 16; Mk 5, 17 (plus 53 Mk 2 conversions); Mk 41 (Germany), 23; Mk 42 (India) 12, Mk 42A, 3 and Mk 42B, 3; Mk 43 (Norway) 12; Mk 45 (Pakistan), 6; Mk 47 (Egypt), 6; Mk 48 (Belgium), 5; Mk 50 (Australia), 10.
Notes: Mks 1, 2 and 5 for Royal Navy and Mks 42, 45, 47 and 50 for export are anti-submarine; five Mk 45 converted for anti-shipping rôle carry Exocet missiles. Mk 3 for RAF and Mk 41, 43, and 48 for export are for search and rescue.

(Above) A Westland-built Sea King Mk 42 for service with the Indian Navy; (below) the Sea King HAS Mk 5.

WESTLAND COMMANDO

HELICOPTER

Country of Origin: United Kingdom.
Type: Tactical transport helicopter.
Power Plant: Two 1,660 shp (2½-min rating ISA) Rolls-Royce Gnome H.1400-1 or 1,465 shp (2½-min rating ISA + 30 deg C) Gnome H.1400-1T.
Performance: (Commando 2 at 21,000 lb/9 526 kg gross weight, ISA) Max permissible speed, 140 mph (225 km/h) at sea level; normal operating speed, 129 mph (207 km/h) at sea level; initial rate of climb, 2,020 ft/min (10,3 m/sec); hovering ceiling, IGE, 5,000 ft (1 525 m); hovering ceiling, OGE, 3,200 ft (975 m); range with max payload (28 troops), 276 mls (445 km).
Weights: Basic equipped weight, 11,174 lb (5 069 kg); operating weight, VIP version, 13,576 lb (6 158 kg); max take-off, 21,000 lb (9 526 kg).
Dimensions: Rotor diameter, 62 ft 0 in (18,90 m); fuselage length, 55 ft 9¾in (17,01 m); height, 16 ft 10 in (5,13 m).
Armament: Fuselage-side strongpoints or (Commando 3) sponsons to carry air-to-ground missiles, gun pods or rocket pods.
Accommodation: Crew of two on flight deck and up to 28 troops.
Status: Commando 1 first flown 12 September 1973; Commando 2 first flown 16 January 1975, Commando 2B first flown 13 March 1975; Commando 2A first flown 9 August 1975; Commando 2C first flown 9 October 1975; Sea King HC Mk 4 first flown 26 September 1979. Production totals: Commando 1 five; Commando 2/2A/2B/2C, 17/three/two/one; Sea King HC Mk 4, 15.
Notes: The interim Commando 1 had minimum changes from the Sea King; definitive Mk 2 (Egypt), Mk 2A (Qatar) and Sea King HC Mk 4 for RN Commando squadrons are similar and Mk 2B/2C are VIP versions. Commando 3 has sponsons and retractable undercarriage plus increased armament provision.

(Above) The Westland Commando 2A for Qatar; (below) a Sea King HC Mk 4 Commando transport.

249

HELICOPTER

(Above) A Westland Lynx HAS Mk 1 carrying four Sea Skua anti-shipping missiles; (below) A Lynx Mk 23 for Argentina.

WESTLAND NAVAL LYNX

Country of Origin: United Kingdom.
Type: Shipboard anti-submarine and SAR helicopter.
Power Plant: Two (HAS Mk 2) 900shp (2½-min contingency) Rolls-Royce Gem 2 or (HAS Mk 3 and 4) 1,120 shp (2½-min contingency) Gem 41-1 turboshafts.
Performance: (Lynx HAS Mk 2) Continuous cruising speed, 144 mph (232 km/h); initial rate of climb, 2,170 ft/min (11,0 m/sec); hovering ceiling, OGE, 8,450 ft (2 575 m); time on station (two torpedoes), 2 hrs 29 min at 58 mls (93 km) from base; max range, 368 mls (593 km); max ferry range with auxiliary tanks, 650 mls (1 046 km).
Weights; Operating weight empty (ASW), 7,370 lb (3 343 kg); operating weight empty (SAR), 7,531 lb (3 416 kg); max take-off, 10,500 lb (4 763 kg).
Dimensions: Rotor diameter, 42 ft 0 in (12,80 m); fuselage length, 39 ft 1¼ in (11,92 m); height, 11 ft 9¾ in (3,60 m).
Armament: Fuselage-side pylons with hardpoints to carry four Sea Skua anti-shipping missiles or two Mk 44 or Mk 46 homing torpedoes or four AS 12 wire-guided missiles or other weapons.
Accommodation: Pilot and co-pilot side-by-side in cockpit and observer/sonar operator in cabin.
Status: First of five development Lynx prototypes flown 21 March 1971; first HAS Mk 2 prototype flown 25 May 1972; first HAS Mk 2 (FN) prototype flown 6 July 1973; first production HAS Mk 2 flown 10 February 1976. Production/sales: prototypes, 5; development aircraft (naval configuration), six; HAS Mk 2, 80; HAS Mk 2 (FN), 26; HAS Mk 4 (FN) 14; Mk 23 (Argentine Navy), 10; Mk 21 (Brazilian Navy), 9; Mk 25 (Netherlands Navy UH-14A), 6; Mk 27 (Netherlands Navy SH-14B), 10; Mk 81 (Netherlands Navy SH-14C), 8; Mk 80 (Danish Air Force), 8; Mk 86 (Norwegian Air Force), 6; Mk 88 (Federal German Navy), 12; Nigerian Navy, 6.

HELICOPTER

(Above) A British Army Lynx AH Mk 1 with HOT missile launchers; (below) Lynx AH Mk 1s carrying TOW missiles.

WESTLAND UTILITY LYNX

Country of Origin: United Kingdom.
Type: General purpose and utility helicopter.
Power Plant: Two 900 shp (2½-min rating) Rolls-Royce Gem 2 turboshafts.
Performance: (Lynx AH Mk 1) Max continuous cruising speed, 161 mph (259 km/h); max endurance speed, 81 mph (130 km/h); initial rate of climb, 2,480 ft/min (12,6 m/sec); hovering ceiling, OGE, 10,600 ft (3 230 m); typical range, 336 mls (540 km); max ferry range, with auxiliary tanks, 834 mls (1 342 km).
Weights: Operating weight empty, 6,144 lb (2 787 kg); max take-off weight, 10,000 lb (4 535 kg).
Dimensions: Main rotor diameter, 42 ft 0 in (12,80 m); fuselage length, 39 ft 7 in (12,06 m); height, 12 ft 0 in (3,66 m).
Armament: Unarmed in troop transport rôle; as armed escort and scout, has provision for one 7,62 mm pintle mounted machine gun or 20-mm cannon in cabin; or two 7,62-mm miniguns or gun pods or turret-mounted gun under cabin; fuselage-side mountings for 68-mm, 80-mm or 2,75-mm (7-cm) rocket pods; or up to six AS.11 or up to eight HOT or TOW wire-guided missiles.
Accommodation: Crew of two and up to 10 armed troops.
Status: First of five development Lynx prototypes flown 21 March 1971; first AH Mk 1 prototype flown 12 April 1972; first production AH Mk 1 flown 11 February 1977. Production/sales: prototypes, five; development aircraft (general utility configuration), two; Lynx AH Mk 1, 114; Mk 28 (Qatar), 1; Mk 84 (Qatar Army) two.
Notes: The utility Lynx, together with the naval Lynx (separately described) is part of the 1967 Anglo-French agreement covering production of three types of helicopters. It is in production and service primarily for the British Army, and up to early 1982 had been ordered also only by Qatar, for the Police and Air Force.

WESTLAND WG 30

Country of Origin: United Kingdom.
Type: General purpose and utility helicopter.
Power Plant: Two 1,120 shp (max contingency) Rolls-Royce Gem 41-1 turboshafts.
Performance: Max speed, 150 mph (241 km/h) at sea level; hovering ceiling, IGE, 6,300 ft (1 920 m); hovering ceiling, OGE, 3,900 ft (1 190 m); range 4,000 lb (1 815 kg) internal payload, 142 mls (228 km); max ferry range, 403 mls (648 km).
Weights: Bare weight, minimum equipment, 6,680 lb (3 030 kg); typical operating weight, tactical troop transport, two crew IFR, 7,412 lb (3 362 kg); max take-off weight, 12,000 lb (5 443 kg).
Dimensions: Main rotor diameter, 43 ft 8 in (13,31 m); length (rotors folded), 47 ft 5¼in (14,46 m); height, 14 ft 5 in (4,39 m).
Armament: Normally unarmed; provision for 7,62-mm machine gun or 20-mm cannon to be pintle-mounted in cabin to fire through the doorway.
Accommodation: Two pilots side-by-side in cockpit; up to 14 fully equipped troops or 22 personnel without equipment.
Status: First of two prototypes flown 10 April 1979.
Notes: The WG 30 was evolved by Westland, initially as a company-funded venture, to take advantage of the dynamic system already proven for the Lynx (separately described) and the higher power becoming available from later variants of the Rolls-Royce Gem engine. A completely new fuselage was designed, incorporating a retractable undercarriage, and the diameter of the main and tail rotors was increased to absorb the extra power. Although initial orders (up to the end of 1981, when the first customer aircraft became available) were for commercial versions of the WG30, the design was conceived with military rôles in view, and in particular the new helicopter is offered in the air mobility rôle, carrying a complete squad.

(Above and below) Two aspects of the prototype Westland WG 30 tactical troop transport.

ACKNOWLEDGEMENTS

The authors wish to thank the following individuals and organisations for the use of their copyright photographs in this edition:

Air Portraits; Anglie Aeropics; Aviation Photo News; "Knario" Azaola; D Balaguer; Dr Alan Beaumont; Dave Becker; Peter J Bish; Austin J Brown; Consultair (Capt K E Sissons); P J Cooper; T Coxall; FlugRevue; G D Fraser; John Fricker; Federico Alberto Giro; J M G Gradidge; P H T Green; W Gysin-Aegerter; Takaeki Hoshina; J-C H Hoste; David Hughes; Israir Aviation Press Services; Paul A Jackson; Michael C Klaver; Hans Konig; Howard Levy; MAP; Larry J MacDougal; Godfrey Mangion; Andrew March; Peter R March. MoD (PE)/RAE Bedford (Peter Hudson); David Oliver; Lindsay Peacock; Stephen P Peltz; Photair Press; RAF/MoD (Crown Copyright); John D R Rawlings; Hans Redemann; A Reinhard; Herbert Rittmeyer; M Rostaing; Javier Saez; Jose Luis Gonzalez Serrano; Donald Sims; Swedish Air Force; M Takeda; Tass; Norman J Taylor; USAF and USN/DoD; John Visanich; L J Vosloo; Mick West.

INDEX

A-3, Douglas Skywarrior 99
A-4, McDonnell Douglas Skyhawk 29
A-5, Nancheng Kiang 5 41
A-6, Grumman Intruder 22
A-7, Vought Corsair II 58
A-10, Fairchild Thunderbolt II 18
A-37, Cessna Dragonfly 183
A 109 Agusta 229
A 129, Agusta Mangusta 229
AB-204, Agusta 232
AB-205, Agusta 233
AB-212, Agusta 233
AB-412, Agusta 233
AC-47, Douglas 122
AC-119, Fairchild 126
AC-130, Lockheed Hercules 151
Academe, Grumman TC-4 205
Aeritalia-Aermacchi AM.3C Bosbok 88
Aeritalia-Aermacchi-EMBRAER AMX 220
Aeritalia F-104S Starfighter 27
Aeritalia G.91 7
Aeritalia G.222 104
Aermacchi AL.60 Trojan 154
Aermacchi AM.3C Bosbok 88
Aermacchi MB-326 175
Aermacchi MB-326K 8
Aermacchi MB-339 176
Aermacchi MB-339L Veltro 2 8
Aero L 29 Delfin 195
Aero L 39 Albatros 177
Aerospace CT/4 Airtrainer 195
Aérospatiale Alouette II 225
Aérospatiale Alouette III 225
Aérospatiale CM 170 Magister 190
Aérospatiale Dauphin 228
Aérospatiale Ecureuil 228
Aérospatiale Gazelle 227
Aérospatiale Lama 226
Aérospatiale N262 Fregate 105
Aérospatiale Puma 227
Aérospatiale Super Frelon 226
Aérospatiale TB 30 Epsilon 196
Aerotec T-17 Tangará 196
Aerotec T-23 Uirapuru 196
Agusta A 109 229
Agusta A 129 Mangusta 229
AH-1G/Q/S, Bell 209 Hueycobra 230
AH-1J/T, Bell 209 Seacobra 231
AH-64, Hughes Apache 237
AIDC PL-1B Chienshou 212
AIDC T-CH-1 197
AIDC XC-2 220
Airtrainer, Aerospace CT/4 195
AJ 37, Saab Viggen 48
Ajeet, HAL 25
AL.60, Lockheed Trojan 154
Albatros, Aero L 39 177
Albatross, Grumman HU-16 165
Albatross, Piaggio P.166 143
Alize, Breguet 76
Alouette II, Aérospatiale 225
Alouette III, Aérospatiale 225
Alpha Jet, Dassault-Breguet/Dornier 184
AM.3C Bosbok, Aeritalia-Aermacchi 88
Amit (IAI Magister) 190
AMX, AEritalia-Aermacchi-EMBRAER 220
Andover, British Aerospace HS.748 113
Antonov An-2 Colt 153
Antonov An-12 Cub 106
Antonov An-22 Cock 107
Antonov An-24 Coke 108
Antonov An-26 Curl 108

Antonov An-32 Cline 108
Antonov An-72 Coaler 221
Antonov An-3 153
Apache, Hughes AH-64 237
Arava IAI-201 132
Arrow, Piper PA-24 213
AS 202, FFA Bravo 203
AS 350, Aérospatiale Ecureuil 228
AS 365/366, Aérospatiale Dauphin 228
Astar (Aérospatiale Ecureuil) 228
AT-28D, North American 188
AT-33A, Lockheed 187
Atlantic, Dassault-Breguet 77
Atlas Kudu 154
AU-23A, Fairchild Turbo-Porter 170
Aurora, Lockheed CP-140 83
AV-8A, Hawker Siddeley (BAe) Harrier 10
AV-8B, McDonnell Douglas Harrier II 33
Aviocar, CASA 212 115
Aviojet, CASA C-101 182
Avro Shackleton 73
AWACS (Boeing E-3 Sentry) 97
Azor, CASA 207 114
Aztec, Piper U-11 172

B-1, Rockwell 69
B-5 (Ilyushin Il-28) 67
B-52, Boeing Stratofortress 62
B-57, Martin (Canberra) 64
BAC Canberra 64
BAC Jet Provost 179
BAC Lightning 9
BAC One-Eleven 109
BAC (Percival) Pembroke 142
BAC Strikemaster 179
BAC VC 10 149
Backfire, Tupolev 72
Badger, Tupolev Tu-16 70
Bandeirante, EMBRAER 125
Beagle, Ilyushin Il-28 67
Bear, Tupolev Tu-142 87
Beaver, de Havilland Canada DHC-2 161
Beech 18 110
Beechcraft 33 Bonanza 198
Beechcraft 45 Mentor 197
Beechcraft Baron 199
Beechcraft VC-6 156
Beechcraft C-12 Huron 111
Beechcraft King Air 156
Beechcraft Musketeer 198
Beechcraft Queen Air 155
Beechcraft Sundowner 198
Beechcraft Super King Air 111
Beechcraft T-34 Mentor 197
Beechcraft T-34C 178
Beechcraft T-42 Cochise 199
Beechcraft T-44 156
Beechcraft U-21 Ute 156
Beechcraft U-8 Twin Bonanza 155
Bell 47 (Sioux) 230
Bell 204 Iroquois 232
Bell 205 Iroquois 233
Bell 206 Jet Ranger 232
Bell 206 Kiowa 231
Bell 206L Texas Ranger 232
Bell 209 Hueycobra 230
Bell 209 Seacobra 231
Bell 212 233
Bell 214 Huey Plus 234
Bell 406 231
Bell 412 233
Beriev Be-12 Mail 75

Bird Dog, Cessna O-1 90
Bison, Myasishchev M-4 85
Black Bird (Lockheed SR-71) 93
Black Hawk, Sikorsky UH-60 247
Blinder, Tupolev Tu-22 71
Blue Canoe (Cessna U-3) 159
BO 105, MBB 239
Boeing 707 148
Boeing 737 112
Boeing 747 98
Boeing B-52 Stratofortress 62
Boeing E-3 Sentry 97
Boeing E-4 98
Boeing EC-135 89
Boeing KC-135 Stratotanker 148
Boeing RC-135 89
Boeing T-43 112
Boeing Vertol 107 234
Boeing Vertol CH-46 Sea Knight 234
Boeing Vertol CH-47 Chinook 235
Bonanza, Beechcraft 33 198
Bosbok, Aeritalia-Aermacchi AM.3C 88
Bravo, FFA AS 202 203
Breguet Alizé 76
Breguet Atlantic 77
Brewer, Yakovlev Yak-28 60
British Aerospace (BAC) One Eleven 109
British Aerospace Bulldog 199
British Aerospace Harrier 10
British Aerospace Hawk 180
British Aerospace HS.125 206
British Aerospace (HSA) Buccaneer 66
British Aerospace (HSA) HS.748 Andover 113
British Aerospace Jetstream 200
British Aerospace Jet Provost 179
British Aerospace Nimrod AEW 96
British Aerospace Nimrod MR 74
British Aerospace Sea Harrier 11
British Aerospace Strikemaster 179
British Aerospace VC 10 149
Britten Norman Islander/Defender 171
Bronco, Rockwell OV-10 95
BT-6, Shenyang 215
Bu 131, Bücker (CASA) Jungmann 200
Buccaneer, Hawker Siddeley 66
Bucker Bu 131 Jungmann 200
Buckeye, Rockwell T-2 191
Buffalo, de Havilland Canada DHC-5 119
Bulldog, British Aerospace 199

C-1, Grumman Trader 80
C-1A, Kawasaki 134
C-2, Grumman Greyhound 131
C-5, Lockheed Galaxy 138
C-6, Beechcraft 156
C-7, de Havilland Canada DHC-4 Caribou 118
C-9, McDonnell Douglas Nightingale/Skytrain II 139
C-12, Beechcraft Huron 111
C 22J, Caproni Vizzola 221
C-42, Neiva Regente 168
C-47, Douglas Skytrain 122
C-54, Douglas Skymaster 123
C-95, EMBRAER Bandeirante 125
C-101, CASA Aviojet 182
C-117, Douglas 122
C-118, Douglas Liftmaster 124
C-119, Fairchild Packet 126
C-123, Fairchild Provider 127
C-130, Lockheed Hercules 135

C-131, Convair 116
C-135, Boeing Stratotanker 148
C-137, Boeing 148
C-140, Lockheed Jetstar 136
C-141, Lockheed Starlifter 137
C-160, Transall 147
C-207 CASA Azor 114
C-212 CASA Aviocar 115
C-3605, EKW 164
Canadair CC-109 Cosmopolitan 116
Canadair CF-104 Starfighter 27
Canadair CL-30 Silver Star 187
Canadair CL-41 Tutor 181
Canadair CL-215 157
Canberra, English Electric 64
Candid, Ilyushin Il-76 133
CAP 10, Mudry 210
CAP 20, Mudry 210
Caproni Vizzola C/22J 221
Caribou, de Havilland Canada DHC-4 118
CASA 1.131E Jungmann 200
CASA 207 Azor 114
CASA 212 Aviocar 115
CASA C-101 Aviojet 182
CASA C-127 (Dornier Do 27) 163
CASA (MBB) 223 Flamingo 208
Cayuse, Hughes OH-6 236
CC-108, de Havilland Canada DHC-4
    Caribou 118
CC-109, Canadair Cosmopolitan 116
CC-115, de Havilland Canada Buffalo 119
CC-138, de Havilland Canada Twin Otter
    120
CE-14 (Dassault Breguet Mirage F) 16
Centurion, Cessna 158
Cessna O-1 Bird Dog 90
Cessna O-2 91
Cessna 172 201
Cessna 310 159
Cessna 402 160
Cessna 411 160
Cessna 421 160
Cessna A-37 Dragonfly 183
Cessna Centurion 158
Cessna Skywagon 158
Cessna T-37 183
Cessna T-41 Mescalero 201
Cessna Turbo Stationair 158
Cessna U-3 159
Cessna U-17 158
CF-18, McDonnell Douglas Hornet 32
CF-101, McDonnell Voodoo 28
CF-104, Canadair Starfighter 27
CH-3, Sikorsky Jolly Green Giant 245
CH-34, Sikorsky S-58 244
CH-46, Boeing Vertol Sea Knight 234
CH-47, Boeing Vertol Chinook 235
CH-53, Sikorsky Sea Stallion 246
CH-53E, Sikorsky Super Stallion 246
CH-54, Sikorsky Tarhe 245
CH-118, Bell 205 233
CH-124, Sikorsky Sea King 244
CH-136, Bell 206 231
CH-139, Bell 206 232
Cheetah, HAL (Aérospatiale Lama) 226
Cherokee, Piper PA-28 213
Chetak, HAL (Aérospatiale Alouette III) 225
Cheyenne, Piper PA-31T 173
Chienshou, AIDC PL-1B 212
Chincul 213
Chinook, Boeing Vertol CH-47 235
Chipmunk, de Havilland 202
Chiricahua, Pilatus UV-20A (Turbo-Porter)
    170
Choctaw, Sikorsky S-58 244
CIAR IAR-93 Orao 51
CL-41, Canadair Tutor 181
CL-215, Canadair 157
Cline, Antonov An-32 108
CM 170, Potez Magister 190
CM 175, Potez Zephyr 190

Coaler, Antonov An-72 221
Coastguarder, British Aerospace HS.748
    113
Cochise, Beechcraft T-42 199
Cock, Antonov An-22 107
Coke, Antonov An-24 108
Colt, Antonov An-2 153
Comanche, Piper PA-24 213
Commando, Westland 249
Convair C-131 116
Convair F-106 Delta Dart 12
Convair FB-111 65
Coot, Ilyushin Il-18 81
Corsair II, Vought A-7 58
Cosmopolitan, Canadair CC-109 116
CP-121, Grumman (DHC) Tracker 80
CP-140, Lockheed Aurora 83
Crusader, Vought F-8 59
CS-102 (MiG-15 UTI) 208
CSR-123 (de Havilland Canada Otter) 162
CT/4, Aerospace Airtrainer 195
CT-39, Rockwell Sabreliner 144
CT-134, Beechcraft Musketeer/Sandowner
    198
Cub, Antonov An-12 106
CUH-1, Bell 205 233
Curl, Antonov An-26 108

D.12 (CASA Aviocar) 115
Dagger, IAI 15
Dakota, Douglas 122
Dassault-Breguet Atlantic 77
Dassault-Breguet/Dornier Alpha Jet 184
Dassault-Breguet Etendard 13
Dassault-Breguet HU-25 Guardian 78
Dassault-Breguet Mirage III 14
Dassault-Breguet Mirage 5 15
Dassault-Breguet Mirage 50 15
Dassault-Breguet Mirage 2000 17
Dassault-Breguet Mirage F 16
Dassault-Breguet Mystère 10 MER 201
Dassault-Breguet Super Etendard 13
Dassault-Breguet Super Mirage 4000 222
Dassault Mirage IVA 63
Dauphin, Aérospatiale 228
DC-4 (Douglas C-54) 123
DC-6, Douglas 124
DC-7, Douglas 124
DC-10, McDonnell Douglas 152
DC-130, Lockheed Hercules 151
Defender, Hughes 500 237
Defender, Pilatus Britten-Norman 171
De Havilland D.H.115 Vampire 202
De Havilland DHC-1 Chipmunk 202
De Havilland Canada DHC-2 Beaver 161
De Havilland Canada DHC-3 Otter 162
De Havilland Canada DHC-4 Caribou 118
De Havilland Canada DHC-5 Buffalo 119
De Havilland Canada DHC-6 Twin Otter
    120
De Havilland Devon 117
De Havilland Dove 117
Delfin, Aero L 29 195
Delfin (FMA IA 58 Pucara) 19
Delta Dart, Convair F-106 12
Devon, de Havilland 117
D.H.115, de Havilland Vampire 202
DHC-1, de Havilland Chipmunk 202
DHC-2, de Havilland Canada Beaver 161
DHC-3, de Havilland Canada Otter 162
DHC-4, de Havilland Canada Caribou 118
DHC-5, de Havilland Canada Buffalo 119
DHC-6, de Havilland Canada Twin Otter
    120
Do 27, Dornier 163
Do 28D, Dornier Skyservant 121
Do 128, Dornier Skyservant 121
Dolphin, Aérospatiale HH-65 228
Dominie, Hawker Siddeley HS.125 206
Dornier 128 Skyservant 121
Dornier Do 27 163

Dornier Do 28D Skyservant 121
Douglas A-3 Skywarrior 99
Douglas C-47 Skytrain 122
Douglas C-54 Skymaster 123
Douglas C-118 Liftmaster 124
Douglas Dakota 122
Douglas DC-6 124
Douglas DC-7 124
Dove, de Havilland 117
Dragonfly, Cessna A-37 183
Draken, Saab 35 47

E-2, Grumman Hawkeye 101
E-3, Boeing Sentry 97
E-3B (CASA 1.131E) 200
E-4, Boeing 98
E.16 (North American T-6) 211
E.17 (Beechcraft T-34 Mentor) 197
E.19 (Piper Turbo Aztec) 172
E.22 (Beechcraft King Air) 156
E.24 (Beechcraft Bonanza) 198
E.25 (CASA Aviojet) 182
E.30 (Piper PA-24) 213
E.31 (Piper Twin Comanche) 172
EA-3B, Douglas Skywarrior 99
EA-6, Grumman Prowler 102
Eagle, McDonnell Douglas F-15 31
EC-47, Douglas 122
EC-95, EMBRAER Bandeirante 125
EC-130, Lockheed Hercules 151
EC-135, Boeing 89
Ecureuil, Aérospatiale AS 350 228
EF-111, Grumman (GD) 100
EH-60, Sikorsky 247
EH Industries EH-101 235
EKA-3B, Douglas Skywarrior 99
EKW C-3605 164
EMB-111, EMBRAER 79
EMB-121, EMBRAER Xingu 203
EMB-326, EMBRAER Xavante 175
EMBRAER EMB-110 Bandeirante 125
EMBRAER EMB-111 79
EMBRAER EMB-121 Xingu 203
EMBRAER EMB-312 185
EMBRAER EMB-326 Xavante 175
EMBRAER T-27 Tucano 185
EMBRAER U-7 (Piper Seneca) 172
English Electric Canberra 64
English Electric Lightning 9
EP-3, Lockheed Orion 83
Epsilon, Aérospatiale TB 30 196
Esquilo (Ecureuil), Helibras 228
Etendard, Dassault 13
EV-1, Grumman Mohawk 92
Expeditor (Beech 18) 110

F-1, Mitsubishi 40
F 4, McDonnell Douglas Phantom II 30
F-5 (MiG-17) 34
F-5, Northrop Tiger II 43
F-5G, Northrop Tigershark 44
F-6 (MiG-19) 35
F-7 (MiG-21) 36
F-8, Vought Crusader 59
F-14, Grumman Tomcat 23
F-15, McDonnell Douglas Eagle 31
F-16, General Dynamics Fighting Falcon 20
F-18, McDonnell Douglas Hornet 32
F27, Fokker Troopship/Maritime 128
F 35 Draken 47
F-100, North American Super Sabre 42
F-101, McDonnell Voodoo 28
F-104, Lockheed Starfighter 27
F-105, Republic Thunderchief 46
F-106, Convair Delta Dart 12
F-111, General Dynamics 21
Fairchild A-10 Thunderbolt II 18
Fairchild C-119 Flying Boxcar/Packet 126
Fairchild C-123 Provider 127
Fairchild Swearingen Merlin III 146

INDEX

Fairchild Swearingen Merlin IV 146
Fairchild Turbo-Porter 170
Falcon 10, Dassault-Breguet 201
Falcon 20, Dassault-Breguet 78
Fantan-A, Nancheng Kiang 5 41
Farmer, MiG-19 35
FB-111, General Dynamics 65
Fencer, Sukhoi Su-24 56
Fennec (North American T-28) 188
FFA AS 202 Bravo 203
Fiat G.91 7
Fiddler, Tupolev Tu-128 57
Fighting Falcon, general Dynamics F-16 20
Firebar, Yakovlev Yak-28 60
Firecracker, NDN Aircraft 224
Fishbed, MiG-21 36
Fishpot, Sukhoi Su-11 53
Fitter, Sukhoi Su-7 52
Fitter, Sikhoi Su-17, Su-20, Su-22 55
Flagon, Sukhoi Su-15 54
Flamingo, MBB (CASA) 323 208
Flogger, MiG-23 37
Flogger, MiG-27 39
Flying Boxcar, Fairchild C-119 126
FMA IA 50 GII 129
FMA IA 58 Pucara 19
FMA IA 63 222
Fokker F27 Maritime & Troopship 128
Folland Gnat 25
Forger, Yakovlev Yak-36 61
Fouga CM 170 Magister 190
Foxbat, MiG-25 38
Fregate, N262 105
Fresco, MiG-17 34
FT-2, Shenyang 208
FT-5, Shenyang 216
FT-6, Shenyang 216
Fuji T1 204
Fuji T3 204

G2-A, SOKO Galeb 194
GII, FMA IA 50 129
G.91 (Aeritalia) 7
G.222, Aeritalia 104
GAF N22 Nomad 130
Galaxy, Lockheed C-5 138
Galeb, SOKO G2-A 194
Gardian, Dassault-Breguet 78
Gaviao (Lama), Helibras 226
Gazelle, Aérospatiale SA 341/342 227
General Dynamics F-16 Fighting Falcon 20
General Dynamics F-106 12
General Dynamics F-111 21
General Dynamics FB-111 65
General Dynamics (Grumman) EF-111 100
Genet (SIAI Marchetti Warrior) 192
Gnat, HAL 25
Greyhound, Grumman C-2 131
Grumman A-6 Intruder 22
Grumman C-2 Greyhound 131
Grumman E-2 Hawkeye 101
Grumman EA-6 Prowler 102
Grumman F-14 Tomcat 23
Grumman HU-16 Albatross 165
Grumman OV-1 Mohawk 92
Grumman S-2 Tracker 80
Grumman TC-4 Academe 205
Grumman (GD) EF-111 100
Guarani (FMA IA 50) 129
Guardian, Dassault-Breguet HU-25 78
Gulfstream I, Grumman 205
Gulfstream American peregrine 600 223

HA-200, Hispano Saeta 207
HA-220, Hispano Super Saeta 207
HAL Ajeet 25
HAL Cheetah (Lama) 226
HAL Chetak (Alouette III) 225
HAL Gnat 25
HAL HJT-16 Kiran 186
HAL HPT-32 206

Halo, Mil Mi-26 243
Handley Page Victor 150
Hansa, MBB HFB 320 166
Harrier, British Aerospace 10
Harrier II, McDonnell Douglas AV-8B 33
Harrier GR Mk 5, McDonnell Douglas/BAe 33
Hawk, British Aerospace 180
Hawker Hunter 24
Hawker Siddeley Buccaneer 66
Hawker Siddeley Gnat 25
Hawker Siddeley Harrier 10
Hawker Siddeley Hawk 180
Hawker Siddeley HS.125 Dominie 206
Hawker Siddeley Nimrod MR 74
Hawker Siddeley Shackleton 76
Hawkeye, Grumman E-2 101
Haze, Mil Mi-14 242
HC-130, Lockheed Hercules 151
HC-131A, Convair 116
HE.20 (Hughes TH-55) 236
Helix, Kamov 239
Hercules, Lockheed C-130 135
Hercules, Lockheed KC-130 151
HFB 320 Hansa 166
HH-1, Bell Iroquois 232
HH-3, Sikorsky Jolly Green Giant 245
HH-53, Sikorsky Super Jolly 246
HH-65, Aérospatiale Dolphin 228
Hind, Mil Mi-24 242
Hip, Mil Mi-8 241
Hispano HA-200 Saeta 207
Hispano HA-220 Super Saeta 207
HJT-16, HAL Kiran 186
HKP-4, Boeing Vertol/Kawasaki 234
Hook, Mil Mi-6 241
Hoplite, Mil Mi-2 240
Hormone, Kamov Ka-25 238
Hound, Mil Mi-4 240
HPT-32, HAL 206
HS.125, Hawker Siddeley Dominie 206
HS.748, British Aerospace Andover 113
HU-16, Grumman Albatross 165
HU-25, Dassault-Breguet Guardian 78
Hueycobra, Bell 209 230
Huey, Bell 204/205 232
Hughes 300 236
Hughes 369 236
Hughes 500 Defender 237
Hughes AH-64 Apache 237
Hughes OH-6 Cayuse 236
Hughes Th-55 Osage 236
Hunter, Hawker 24
Huron, Beechcraft C-12 111

IA 50, FMA 129
IA 58, FMA Pucara 19
IA 63, FMA 222
IAI-101, Arava 132
IAI-201, Arava 132
IAI-202, Arava 132
IAI Arava 132
IAI Dagger 15
IAI Kfir 26
IAI Nesher 15, 26
IAR-93, CIAR Orao 51
Ilyushin Il-28 *Beagle* 67
Ilyushin Il-38 *May* 81
Ilyushin Il-76 *Candid* 133
Intruder, Grumman A-6 22
Iroquois, Bell 204 232
Iroquois, Bell 205 233
Iskra, PZL-Mielec TS-11 217
Islander, Pilatus Britten-Norman 171
Israel Aircraft Industries Arava 132
Israel Aircraft Industries Dagger 15
Israel Aircraft Industries Kfir 26
Israel Aircraft Industries Nesher 15, 26

J-1, SOKO Jastreb 50
J 35 Draken 47

JA 37, Saab Viggen 48
Jaguar Sepecat 49
Jaktviggen, Saab JA 37 48
Jastreb, SOKO J-1 50
JC-130, Lockheed Hercules 151
Jet Provost, British Aerospace 179
Jetranger, Bell 206 232
Jetstar, Lockheed C-140 136
Jetstream, British Aerospace 200
Jolly Green Giant, Sikorsky 245
Jungmann, Bücker (CASA) 200

KA-6, Grumman Intruder 22
Kaman SH-2 Seasprite 238
Kamov *Helix* 239
Kamov Ka-25 *Hormone* 238
Kawasaki C-1A 134
Kawasaki KV-107 234
Kawasaki P-2J 82
KC-10, McDonnell Douglas 152
KC-130, Lockheed Hercules 151
KC-135, Boeing Stratotanker 148
Kfir, IAI 26
Kiang 5, Nancheng 41
King Air, Beechcraft 156
Kiran, Hal JHT-16 186
Kiowa, Bell 206 231
KM-2, Fuji 204
Kudu, Aermacchi 154
KV-107, Kawasaki 234

L-19, Cessna Bird Dog 90
L 29, Aero Delfin 195
L 39, Aero Albatros 177
L-42, Neiva Regente 168
L-70, Miltrainer 217
L-70, Valmet Miltrainer 217
L-100, Lockheed Hercules 135
Lama, Aérospatiale 226
LAMPS Mk III (Sikorsky SH-60) 247
LASA-60, Lockheed Azcarate 154
LC-47, Douglas 124
Liftmaster, Douglas C-118 124
Lightning, BAC 9
Lipnur LT-200 212
Lisunov Li-2 122
LM-1, Fuji 204
Lockheed AL.60 154
Lockheed C-5 Galaxy 138
Lockheed C-130 Hercules 135
Lockheed C-140 Jetstar 136
Lockheed C-141 Starlifter 137
Lockheed CP-140 Aurora 83
Lockheed F-104 Starfighter 27
Lockheed KC-130 Hercules 151
Lockheed P-2 Neptune 82
Lockheed P-3 Orion 83
Lockheed S-3 Viking 84
Lockheed SR-71 93
Lockheed T-33A Shooting Star 187
Lockheed TR-1 94
Lockheed U-2 94
LR-1, Mitsubishi 167
LRCA (Rockwell B-1) 69
Lynx (Reims FTMA Milirole) 91
Lynx, Westland 250

McDonnell Douglas A-4 Skyhawk 29
McDonnell Douglas AV-8B Harrier II 33
McDonnell Douglas C-9 Nightingale/Skytrain II 139
McDonnell Douglas DC-10 152
McDonnell Douglas F-4 Phantom II 30
McDonnell Douglas F-15 Eagle 31
McDonnell Douglas F-18 Hornet 32
McDonnell Douglas F-101 Voodoo 28
McDonnell Douglas TA-4J Skyhawk 207
McDonnell Douglas KC-10 Extender 152
Magister, Potez CM 170 190
Mail, Beriev Be-12 75
Mancro C-123T 127

Mangusta, Agusta A 129 229
Maritime, Fokker F27 128
Matador (British Aerospace AV-8A) 10
Max, Yakovlev Yak-18 218
May, Ilyushin Il-38 81
MB-326, Aermacchi 175
MB-326K, Aermacchi 8
MB-339, Aermacchi 176
MB-339L, Aermacchi Veltro 2 8
MBB BO 105 239
MBB 223 Flamingo 208
MBB HFB 320 Hansa 166
Mentor, Beechcraft T-34 197
Merlin III, Fairchild Swearingen 146
Merlin IV, Fairchild Swearingen 146
Mescalero, Cessna T-41 201
Messerschmitt Bölkow Blohm, See MBB
Metro, Fairchild Swearingen 146
MFI-15, Saab Safari 215
MFI-17, Saab Safari 215
MH-53E, Sikorsky Super Stallion 246
Microjet 200, Microturbo 223
Microturbo Microjet 200 223
Midget (MiG-15UTI) 208
MiG-15UTI *Midget* 208
MiG-17 *Fresco* 34
MiG-19 *Farmer* 35
MiG-19UTI 216
MiG-21 *Fishbed* 36
MiG-23 *Flogger* 37
MiG-25 *Foxbat* 38
MiG-27 *Flagger* 39
Mikoyan-Gurevich, See MiG
Mil Mi-2 *Hoplite* 240
Mil Mi-4 *Mound* 240
Mil Mi-6 *Hook* 241
Mil Mi-8 *Hip* 241
Mil Mi-14 *Haze* 242
Mil Mi-24 *Hind* 242
Mil Mi-26 *Halo* 243
Milan, Dassault-Breguet 15
Milirole, Reims FTMA 91
Miltrainer, Valmet L-70 217
Mirage III, Dassault-Breguet 14
Mirage IVA, Dassault 63
Mirage 5, Dassault-Breguet 15
Mirage 50, Dassault-Breguet 15
Mirage 2000, Dassault-Breguet 17
Mirage 4000, Dassault-Breguet 222
Mirage F, Dassault-Breguet 16
Missionmaster, GAF N22 130
Mitsubishi F-1 40
Mitsubishi LR-1 167
Mitsubishi MU-2 167
Mitsubishi T-2 209
Mohawk, Grumman OV-1 92
Morane-Saulnier MS-760 Paris 209
Moss, Tupolev Tu-126 103
MRCA (Panavia Tornado) 68
MS-760, Morane-Saulnier Paris 209
MU-2, Mitsubishi 167
Mudry CAP 10 210
Mudry CAP 20 210
Mushak (Saab MFI-15) 215
Musketeer, Beechcraft 198
Myasishchev M-4 *Bison* 85
Mystère 10, Dassault-Breguet 201
Mystère 20, Dassault-Breguet 78

N22, GAF Nomad 130
N262 Nord Fregate 105
N.2501, Nord Noratlas 141
NAMC YS-11, Nihon 140
Nancheng Kiang 5 41
Navajo Chieftain, Piper PA-31 173
NBO 105, MBB (Nurtanio) 239
NDN Aircraft Firecracker 224
Neiva C-42/L-42 Regente 168
Neiva T-25 Universal 210
Neptune, Lockheed P-2 82
Nesher, IAI 15, 26

Nightingale, McDonnell Douglas C-9 139
Nihon (NAMC) YS-11 140
Nikko, Fuji LM-1 204
Nimrod AEW, British Aerospace 96
Nimrod MR, British Aerospace 74
Nomad, GAF N22 130
Noratlas, Nord N.2501 141
Nord N.2501 Noratlas 141
Nord N262 Fregate 105
North American F-100 Super Sabre 42
North American OV-10 Bronco 95
North American T-2 Buckeye 191
North American T-6 Texan 211
North American T-28 Trojan 188
North American T-39 Sabreliner 144
Northrop F-5 Tiger II 43
Northrop F-5G Tigershark 44
Northrop T-38 Talon 211

O-1, Cessna Bird Dog 90
O-2, Cessna 91
O2-337, Summit Sentry 91
OH-6, Hughes Cayuse 236
One-Eleven, BAC 109
Orao, SOKO 51
Orion, Lockheed P-3 83
Osage, Hughes TH-55 236
Otter, de Havilland Canada 162
OV-1, Grumman Mohawk 92
OV-10, Rockwell Bronco 95
P-2/P-2J, Lockheed/Kawasaki 82
P-3, Lockheed Orion 83
P.3, Pilatus 213
P-95, EMBRAER EMB-111 79
P.149, Piaggio 212
P.166, Piaggio 143
PA-24, Piper Comanche 213
PA-28, Piper Cherokee 213
PA-28R-300XBT, Piper Pillan 214
PA-31, Piper Navajo & Cheyenne 173
Packet, Fairchild C-119 126
PAH-1, MBB BO 106 239
Panavia Tornado F Mk 2 45
Panavia Tornado GR Mk 1 68
Paris, Morane-Saulnier MS-760 209
Pazmany PL-1B Chienshou 212
Pazmany PL-2 212
PC-6, Pilatus Turbo-Porter 170
PC-7, Pilatus Turbo-Trainer 189
PD.808, Piaggio 169
Pembroke, Percival 142
Percival Pembroke 142
Peregrine 600, Gulfstream American 223
Phantom, McDonnell Douglas F-4 30
Piaggio P.149 212
Piaggio P.166 143
Piaggio PD-808
Pilatus Britten-Norman Islander/Defender
  171
Pilatus P.3 213
Pilatus PC-7 Turbo-Trainer 189
Pilatus Turbo-Porter 170
Pillan, Piper PA-28R-300XBT 214
Piper PA-23 Aztec 172
Piper PA-24 Comanche 213
Piper PA-28R-300XBT Pillan 214
Piper PA-28 Cherokee 213
Piper PA-31 Navajo Chieftain 173
Piper PA-31T Cheyenne 173
Piper Seneca 172
PL-1B, Pazmany Chienchou 212
PL-2, Pazmany 212
Potez CM 170 Magister 190
Provider, Fairchild C-123 127
Prowler, Grumman EA-6 102
PS-1, Shin Meiwa 86
Pucara, FMA IA 58 19
Puma, Aérospatiale 227
PZL-Mielec TS-11 Iskra 217

QF-100, North American Super Sabre 42
Queen Air, Beechcraft 155

RC-95, EMBRAER Bandeirante 125
RC-130, Lockheed Hercules 151
RC-135, Boeing 89
Reims FTMA Milirole 91
Republic F-105 Thunderchief 46
Regente, Neiva C-42/L-42 168
RF-4, McDonnell Douglas Phantom II 30
RF-8, Vought Crusader 59
RF 35, Saab Draken 47
RF-101, McDonnell Voodoo 28
RH-53D, Sikorsky Sea Stallion 246
RJ-1, SOKO Jastreb 50
Rockwell B-1 69
Rockwell OV-10 Bronco 95
Rockwell T-2 Buckeye 191
Rockwell T-39 Sabreliner 144
RU-21, Beechcraft 156
RU-21J, Beechcraft Super King Air 111
RV-1, Grumman Mohawk 92

S-2, Grumman Tracker 80
S-3, Lockheed Viking 84
S-55, Sikorsky 243
S-58, Sikorsky 244
S-61, Sikorsky 245
S-61A, Sikorsky 244
S-64, Sikorsky 245
S-70, Sikorsky 247
S.211, SIAI Marchetti 224
SA 315, Aérospatiale Lama 226
SA 316, Aérospatiale Alouette III 225
SA 318, Aérospatiale Alouette II 225
SA 319, Aérospatiale Alouette Astazou 225
SA 321, Aérospatiale Super Frelon 226
SA 330, Aérospatiale Puma 227
SA 341/342, Aérospatiale Gazelle 227
Saab 35 Draken 47
Saab 37 Viggen 48
Saab 91 Safir 214
Saab 105 193
Saab MFI-15 Safari 215
Saab MFI-17 Safari 215
Sabre 144
Saeta, Hispano HA-200 207
Safari, Saab MFI-15 215
Safir, Saab 91 214
SBLim-1 (MiG-15UTI) 208
SC-7, Short Skyvan 145
Scottish Aviation Bulldog 199
Scottish Aviation Jetstream 200
Scout, Westland 248
Seabat, Sikorsky S-58 244
Seacobra, Bell 209 231
Sea Devon, de Havilland 117
Sea Harrier, British Aerospace 11
Seahawk, Sikorsky SH-60 247
Seahorse, Sikorsky S-58 244
Sea King, Sikorsky 244
Sea King, Westland 249
Sea Ranger, Bell TH-57 232
Searchmaster, GAF N22 130
Seasprite, Kaman SH-2 238
Sea Stallion, Sikorsky CH-53 246
Sea Warrior, Siai Marchetti 192
Seneca, Piper 172
Sentry, Boeing E-3 97
Sepecat, Jaguar 49
SF 37, Saab Viggen 48
SF.260, Siai Marchetti 192
SH-2, Kaman Seasprite 238
SH-3, Sikorsky Sea King 244
SH-34, Sikorsky S-58 244
SH 37, Saab Viggen 48
Shackleton, Avro 73
Shenyang BT-6 215
Shenyang FT-5 216
Shenyang FT-6 216
Shin Meiwa PS-1 86

INDEX

Shin Meiwa SS-2 86
Shin Meiwa US-1 86
Shooting Star, Lockheed T-33A 187
Short SC-7 Skyvan 145
Siai Marchetti S.211 224
Siai Marchetti Sea Warrior 192
Siai Marchetti SF-260 192
Siai Marchetti Sm 1019 90
Siai Marchetti Warrior 192
Sikorsky CH-3 Jolly Green Giant 245
Sikorsky CH-54 Tarhe 245
Sikorsky S-55 243
Sikorsky S-58 244
Sikorsky S-61 245
Sikorsky S-64 245
Sikorsky S-65 246
Sikorsky S-70 247
Sikorsky SH-3 Sea King 244
Sikorsky SH-60 Seahawk 247
Sikorsky UH-60 Black Hawk 247
Silver Star (Lockheed T-33A) 187
Sioux, Bell 47 230
SK 60, Saab 193
Skyhawk, McDonnell Douglas 29
Skyhawk, McDonnell Douglas TA-4J 207
Skymaster, Douglas C-54 123
Skyservant, Dornier Do 28D 121
Skytrain, Douglas C-47 122
Skytrain II, McDonnell Douglas C-9 139
Skyvan, Short SC-7 145
Skywagon, Cessna 158
Skywarrior, Douglas A-3 99
SM 1019, Siai Marchetti 90
SOKO G2-A Galeb 194
SOKO J-1 Jastreb 50
SOKO Orao 51
Squirrel (Aérospatiale Ecureuil) 228
SR-71, Lockheed 93
SS-2, Shin Meiwa 86
Starfighter, Lockheed F-104 27
Starlifter, Lockheed C-141 137
Stratofortress, Boeing B-52 62
Strike Eagle (McDonnell Douglas F-15) 31
Strikemaster, British Aerospace 179
Sukhoi Su-7 *Fitter* 52
Sukhoi Su-11 *Fishpot* 53
Sukhoi Su-15 *Flagon* 54
Sukhoi Su-17 *Fitter* 55
Sukhoi Su-20 *Fitter* 55
Sikhoi Su-22 *Fitter* 55
Sukhoi Su-24 *Fencer* 56
Summit Sentry, Cessna 91
Sundowner, Beechcraft 198
Super Etendard, Dassault-Breguet 13
Super Frelon, Aéorspatiale 226
Super Jolly, Sikorsky HH-53 246
Super Mirage 4000, Dassault-Breguet 222
Super Sabre, North American F-100 42
Super Saeta, Hispano HA-220 207
Super Skymaster, Cessna 337 91
Super Stallion, Sikorsky CH-53E 246
Supporter, Saab MFI-17 215
Swearingen Merlin III 146
Swearingen Merlin IV 146

T1, Fuji 204
T-2, Mitsubishi 208
T-2, Rockwell Buckeye 191
T3, Fuji 204
T-6, North American Texan 211
T-7 (CASA Azor) 114
T.9 (de Havilland Canada DHC-4 Caribou) 118
T.12 (CASA Aviocar) 115
T-17, Aerotec Tangará 196
T-23, Aerotec Uirapuru 196

T-25, Neiva Universal 210
T-27, EMBRAER Tucano 185
T-28, North American Trojan 188
T-33A, Lockheed Shooting Star 187
T-34C, Beechcraft 178
T-34, Beechcraft Mentor 197
T-37, Cessna 183
T-38, Northrop Talon 211
T-39, Rockwell Sabreliner 144
T-41, Cessna Mescalero 201
T-42, Beechcraft Cochise 199
T-43, Boeing 112
T-44, Beechcraft 156
TA-4J, McDonnell Douglas Skyhawk 207
TA-7, Vought Corsair II 58
Talon, Northrop T-38 211
Tangará, Aerotec T-17 196
Tarhe, Sikorsky CH.54 245
TAV-8A, British Aerospace Harrier 10
TB 30, Aérospatiale Epsilon 196
TC-4, Grumman Academe 205
T-CH-1, AIDC 197
TE-2, Grumman Hawkeye 101
Tebuan (Canadair CI-41G) 181
Texan, North American T-6 211
Texas Ranger, Bell 206L 232
TF-18, McDonnell Douglas Hornet 32
TF 35 Saab Draken 47
TF-101, McDonnell Voodoo 28
TH-1, Bell Iroquois 232
TH-55, Hughes Osage 236
TH-57, Bell SeaRanger 232
Thunderbolt II, Fairchild A-10 18
Thunderchief, Republic F-105 46
Tiger II, Northrop F-5 43
Tigershark, Northrop F-5G 44
TJ-1, SOKO Jastreb 50
TN-1, Fuji 204
Tomcat, Grumman F-14 23
Tornado ADV, Panavia 45
Tornado F Mk 2, Panavia 45
Tornado GR Mk 1, Panavia 68
Tornado IDS 68
Tp 86 (Rockwell Sabre 40A) 144
TR-1, Lockheed 94
Tracker, Grumman S-2 80
Trader, Grumman 80
Transall C-160 147
Trojan, Lockheed AL.60 154
Trojan, North American T-28 188
Troopship, Fokker F27 128
TS-11, PZL-Mielec Iskra 217
Tucano, EMBRAER T-27 185
Tupolev *Backfire* 72
Tupolev Tu-16 *Badger* 70
Tupolev Tu-22 *Blinder* 71
Tupolev Tu-126 *Moss* 103
Tupolev Tu-128 *Fiddler* 57
Tupolev Tu-142 *Bear* 87
Turbine Mentor, Beechcraft T-34C 178
Turbo-Porter, Pilatus 170
Turbo Stationair, Cessna 158
Turbo-Trainer, Pilatus PC-7 189
Tutor, Canadair CL-41 181
Twin Otter, de Havilland Canada DHC-6 120
U-1A Otter, de Havilland Canada 162
U-2, Lockheed 94
U-3, Cessna 159
U-6, de Havilland Canada Beaver 161
U-7 (Piper Seneca) 172
U-8, Beechcraft Twin Bonanza 155
U.9 (CASA C-127) 163
U-11, Piper Aztec 172
U-17, Cessna 158
U-21, Beechcraft Ute 156

UC-12, Beechcraft Huron 111
UD.13 (Canadair CL-215) 157
UH-1B/K/L Bell 204 Iroquois 232
UH-1D/H Bell 205 Iroquois 233
UH-1N, Bell 212 233
UH-34, Sikorsky S-58 244
UH-46, Boeing Vertol Sea King 234
Uirapuru, Aerotec T-23 196
Universal, Neiva T-25 210
US-1, Shin Meiwa 86
US-3, Lockheed Viking 84
UTVA-60 174
UTVA-66 174
UV-18, de Havilland Canada Twin Otter 120
UV-20A, Pilatus Chiricahua 170

Valmet L-70 Miltrainer 217
Vampire, de Havilland 202
VC-131H, Convair 116
VC-135B, Boeing 148
Veltro, Aermacchi MB-339L 8
Vickers VC 10 149
Victor, Handley Page 150
Viggen, Saab 37 48
Viking, Lockheed S-3 84
Vinka, Valmet L-70 217
Volpar Turbo-Beaver 161
Voodoo, McDonnell F-101 28
Vought A-7 Corsair II 58
Vought F-8 Crusader 59
VC-4, Grumman 205
VC-6, Beechcraft 156
VC-9, McDonnell Douglas Nightingale 139
VC-10, British Aerospace 149
VP-3, Lockheed Orion 83
VU-9 (EMBRAER Xingu) 203

Warrior, SIAI Marchetti 192
Wasp, Westland 248
Wessex, Westland 248
Westland (Aérospatiale) Gazelle 227
Westland (Aérospatiale) Puma 227
Westland Commando 249
Westland Lynx (Naval) 250
Westland Lynx (Utility) 250
Westland Sea King 249
Westland Scout 248
Westland Wasp 248
Westland Wessex 248
Westland WG 30 251
Westland WG 34 (EH-101) 235
Westland Whirlwind 243
WG 30, Westland 251
WG 34, Westland (EH-101) 235
Whirlwind, Westland 243
WP-3, Lockheed Orion 83
WU-2, Lockheed 94

Xavante, EMBRAER EMB-326 175
XC-2, AIDC 220
Xingu, EMBRAER EMB-121 203
XT-CH-1, AIDC 197

Yakovlev Yak-18 *Max* 218
Yakovlev Yak-28 *Firebar* 60
Yakovlev Yak-36 *Forger* 61
Yakovlev Yak-52 218
YAV-8B, McDonnell Douglas Harrier II 33
YS-11, NAMC 140

Z.14 (Bell AH-1G) 230
Z.18 (Bell 212) 233
Zephyr, Potez CM 175 190
Zlin 526 219
Zlin 42M 219
Zlin 43 219